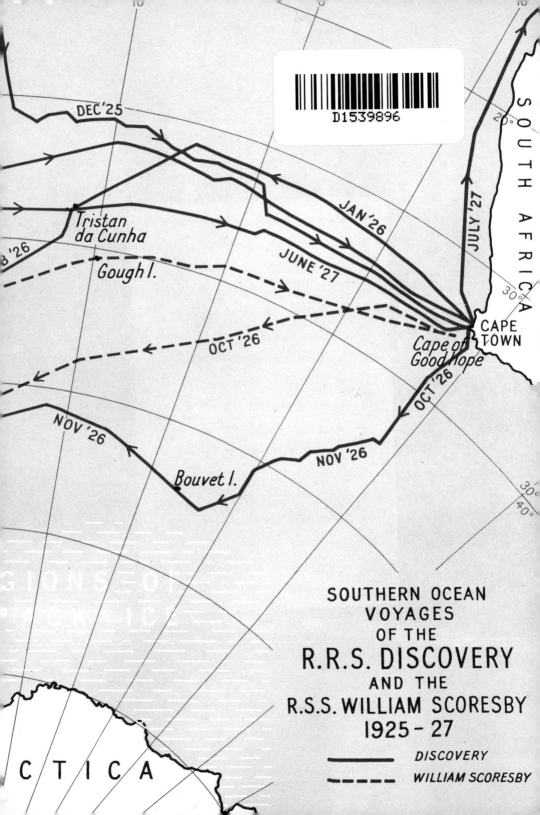

DEC '25

Tristan
da Cunha

Gough I.

'26

JAN '26

JUNE '27

OCT '26

Cape of
Good Hope

CAPE
TOWN

SOUTH AFRICA

20°

30°

JULY '27

OCT '26

NOV '26

Bouvet I.

NOV '26

30°
40°

GIONS OF
PACK ICE

CTICA

SOUTHERN OCEAN
VOYAGES
OF THE
R.R.S. DISCOVERY
AND THE
R.S.S. WILLIAM SCORESBY
1925 - 27

————— DISCOVERY

- - - - - WILLIAM SCORESBY

GREAT WATERS

The Royal Research Ship *Discovery*, 1925

GREAT WATERS

A Voyage of Natural History to Study Whales,
Plankton and the Waters of the Southern Ocean

BY

SIR ALISTER *Clavering* HARDY

Harper & Row, Publishers
New York and Evanston

They that . . . do business in great waters;
These see the works of the Lord,
And His wonders in the deep.

Psalm 107: 23,24

FIRST U.S. EDITION

LIBRARY OF CONGRESS CATALOG CARD NUMBER: 67-26583

TO THE MEMORY OF

Dr. Stanley Kemp, F.R.S.

*Leader of the 1925-27 'Discovery' and the 1929-31
'Discovery II' Expeditions and Director of Research for
the 'Discovery Investigations' 1924-36.*

AND OF

Comdr. J. R. Stenhouse, D.S.O., O.B.E., D.S.C., R.N.R.

Captain of the R.R.S. Discovery 1923-28

CONTENTS

CONTENTS

PLATES

All the photographs in the plates are the author's except those for which he gratefully acknowledges kind permission to reproduce as follows: Frontispiece: Russell & Sons of Southsea; Plate 1, upper group: Russell & Sons of Southsea; lower group: Dr. E. H. Marshall; Plate 13, upper photograph: Dr. S. Kemp; Plate 14, lower photograph: Dr. N. A. Mackintosh; Plate 17, Dr. N. A. Mackintosh; Plate 19: Mr. A. Saunders; Plate 25: Dr. S. Kemp; plate 38, lower photograph: Dr. S. Kemp.

PREFACE

Although this book is about a scientific expedition, it is not a work of science in the technical sense. The complete results of this voyage of the old Royal Research Ship *Discovery*, and of those of the R.R.Ss. *William Scoresby*[1] and *Discovery II* which followed her to the south, are to be found in the long series of *Discovery Reports* published by the Cambridge University Press; it is to these that the students of zoology and oceanography should turn for the full facts of their subject.

My book, which has a background of travel, aims at giving a non-technical account of ocean natural history, both tropical and polar, and the scientific results achieved. Whilst my narrative deals with the old expedition as a thread of personal experience, we shall, as I go along, see how the later researches have developed from these early beginnings. In this way, I hope to bring the work up to date, to introduce the general reader to the Discovery Investigations as a whole and perhaps help the student to find his way about in these great *Discovery Reports* which now total over 13,000 pages. It would certainly be late if this was just a record of an expedition which returned in 1927, but that is not my main purpose; not until the autumn of 1962 could this account be completed in the way I wished, by linking the early results with those of the later voyages. Only then (November, 1962) had the late Dr. James Marr's huge volume on 'The Natural History and Geography of the Antarctic Krill' (*Discovery Reports*, vol. XXXII, pp. 33-464) appeared, bringing together all the work on the whale food, the krill, carried out by the many later expeditions; this tremendous task, based on over 12,000 plankton samples, had taken many years to complete. It is only through these results, and much other work on the plankton in general, which I have briefly described in chapter 21, that the findings of our first expedition can properly be related to the whole Antarctic scene; and the same applies to the important new evidence of whale migrations which I give in chapter 20. As my story of the voyage proceeds I shall break it from

[1]The *William Scoresby*'s title was Research Steamship (R.S.S.) in her first commission, but in 1929 His Majesty gave her the title of Royal Research Ship at the same time as he conferred that honour on the new *Discovery II*.

time to time [within square brackets] to describe many discoveries which are still quite unknown to the general public because up to now they have been hidden within the thirty-four volumes of the *Reports* which are usually only to be found in rather specialist libraries.

No apology, I feel, is needed for blending in such a book the impressions of a traveller with the findings of research. Even the most ardent scientist may have another side to him which sees a different world from that revealed by the analytical approach, one which delights in viewing nature as a whole. The first glimpse of some little-known island, the play of light and shade on fields of ice, or the changing hues of the tropical seas, all make contributions, together with those from science, to the picture I want to put before the reader.

Apart from two short articles by our leader Dr. Stanley Kemp in *Nature* (vol. 118, p. 628, 1926; and vol. 121, p. 795, 1928) and the lecture which I gave in 1928 before the Royal Geographical Society on our return and which was published in *The Geographical Journal* (vol. LXXII, pp. 209-34, 1928), no general account of this voyage has hitherto appeared. This may seem somewhat extraordinary in view of the magnitude and scope of the undertaking. No one, I think, will dispute the statement made by the late Sir Sidney Harmer, K.B.E., F.R.S., then Director of the British Museum (Natural History) when he spoke after the lecture to which I have just referred; I quote from the account of the discussion (*loc. cit.*, p. 229) where, after referring to the work of the expedition, he said: 'Then I should like to emphasise the fact that the *Discovery* Expedition is the largest and most important scientific expedition that has left our shores since the time of the *Challenger*. I think I am right in saying that there has been no other large British expedition devoted exclusively to a study of the whole science of oceanography.'

Although the old *Discovery* did not cover as much ocean as did the *Challenger* it is perhaps worth recording that she in two years and the smaller *William Scoresby* in one together during 1925-7 worked 435 stations[1] as compared with the *Challenger*'s 362 in her three and a half years' voyage. (The *Discovery* did 299 and the *Scoresby* 136.) Since the old *Discovery*'s voyage there have been six expeditions by the *Discovery II* of equal or greater magnitude.

I have given one of the reasons for delaying the account, but there were others. Being appointed a professor at the new University (or University College as it was then) of Hull, I was heavily engaged in

---

[1] The word station, as used here, is the technical term for the position taken up by a research ship when stopping in her voyage to take samples and observations with her nets, dredges and other equipment.

preparing lectures, as well as developing an entirely new department. In addition, I felt I must finish off my share of the working up of the expedition's data, before thinking of a more general account; this took longer than expected and by then I had a new research school to build up. Whilst I hoped one day to publish my journal as the personal experiences of a naturalist, I felt no responsibility to do more; would not Dr. Kemp himself write a combined official history of this and the subsequent expeditions of the *Discovery II*? Alas, it was not to be—but I am going a little too fast, there are some other factors to recall.

The old *Discovery*, splendid for working in the ice, was soon found to have neither the power nor speed for the later expeditions which must extend our initial findings. On our return Dr. Kemp planned the R.R.S. *Discovery II*, and the old ship, after being lent to Sir Douglas Mawson for his B.A.N.Z. Antarctic Research Expedition of 1929, was presented to the nation as a memorial to Captain Scott and now rides on the Thames in the heart of London at the Temple Embankment. The new ship sailed for the South in 1929, and other expeditions followed in 1931, '33, '35, '37 and '50. In 1936 Dr. Kemp gave up the Directorship of the *Discovery* Investigations to become Director of the Plymouth Laboratory and Dr. N. A. Mackintosh succeeded him.

Then came the war. Rolfe Gunther, who had worked with me on the plankton throughout the 1925-7 expedition and subsequently in the writing up of the results, had taken a commission in the Territorial Army to prepare for the hostilities he felt sure would come; tragically he was accidentally killed in 1940. In the aerial bombardment of Plymouth Dr. Kemp suffered a severe strain in saving the laboratory from destruction by fire while incendiaries destroyed his own house with all his precious personal belongings, including his as yet un-published research material; few can doubt that this was largely responsible for bringing on the illness from which he died in 1945. I then realised that writing the account of the first expedition must surely rest with me, for Dr. Mackintosh had in the early days been in charge of the Marine Laboratory at South Georgia and was only for a short time on the old ship. By this time, however, I was committed to write *The Open Sea*, a natural history of the seas round Britain, for the *New Naturalist* Series, and this, as it turned out, had to be a work of two volumes instead of one; having now gone to the Linacre Chair at Oxford, with much administration, they took me, with all the illustrations to draw from living animals, over a dozen years to complete.

It was not until 1961 that I was able to begin work on this account. Is it now *too* late? I think not, for the reason I have explained; it is only with the publication of some of the more recent *Discovery Reports*, that we can see the natural history of the Southern Ocean as a whole and its importance for the future of mankind. Whilst drawing on some of their results I am not in any way writing a history of these later voyages. Short accounts of these have appeared in *The Geographical Journal* as lectures given after the ship's return (Stanley Kemp, vol. LXXIX, pp. 168-85, 1932; D. Dilwyn John, vol. LXXXIII, pp. 381-98, 1934; N. A. Mackintosh, vol. LXXXVIII, pp. 304-21, 1936; G. E. R. Deacon, vol. XCIII, pp. 185-209, 1939 and N. A. Mackintosh, vol. XCVII, pp. 201-16, 1941); and Dr. Mackintosh delivered a lecture to the Royal Society in 1950 on the general organisation of the work, which was published in their *Proceedings*[1]. Then F. D. Ommanney in his book *South Latitude* (Longmans, 1938) gave us a delightful and more personal account of his experiences on one of these expeditions. And Coleman-Cooke has recently published a short general account: *Discovery II in the Antarctic* (Odhams, 1963). The last Antarctic voyage of the *Discovery II* was in 1950-1; since then the work of the *Discovery* Investigations (as the organisation was called) has been merged into that of the new National Institute of Oceanography. Since then yet another R.R.S. *Discovery* has been built to replace the now ageing *Discovery II*, and it was my privilege to be present at her launching on 3rd July, 1962.

In using my original journal I have extensively revised the writing without I hope in any way altering the original sense or depriving it of its freshness. It was written day by day and often under conditions hardly conducive to the composition of well-regulated prose; sometimes it was written in a great hurry, or when very tired after a long day's work, or more frequently on a heaving sea in a ship which rolled excessively. I shall make clear the parts that are taken from the diary, as each will be introduced by the date of the original entry. In addition to my own journal I have kindly been allowed by the Council of the National Institute of Oceanography to consult the official ship's log of the expedition, as well as to quote from Cruise Reports and the naturalists' Note and Sketch Book to which we all contributed notes or drawings during the voyage. I have made acknowledgments wherever I have quoted from these sources.

The colour plates and black-and-white illustrations in the text, apart from charts and diagrams, are from my own drawings; the water-colours of scenery and sea are untouched since they were done on the spot, but many of the pen-and-ink sketches have been redrawn either from ones in colour (too costly to reproduce as such) or from

[1] *Proc. Ross. Soc.*, Series A. vol. 202, pp. 1-16, 1950.

very rough pencil notes or are new ones made with the aid of photographs to bring back the details of the original scenes. All the photographs, except for a few which are acknowledged on p. 11, I took with a quarter-plate Enfield Press Camera with a Zeiss Tessar f.4 lens.

Regarding the graphs and maps I must first thank the Council of the National Institute of Oceanography for kindly allowing me to reproduce many of those in the various *Discovery Reports* to which I have referred (usually giving the volume reference with the abbreviation *D. R.*) and the Council of the Royal Geographical Society for the charts which illustrated my paper in their *Journal* in 1928; and then I wish to express my appreciation of the care and skill with which Mr. J. F. Trotter has redrawn many other such charts for reproduction, particularly mentioning the attractive map which forms the end-papers of the book.

I am most grateful to former fellow members of the *Discovery* Expeditions who have kindly read the chapters specially concerned with their work and made valuable suggestions for their improvement: Dr. N. A. Mackintosh, c.b.e. and Dr. F. C. Fraser, c.b.e., f.r.s. for those dealing with whales, Dr. G. E. R. Deacon, c.b.e., f.r.s. with physical oceanography and the late Dr. J. W. S. Marr with the chapter on krill.

Finally I wish to thank my publishers for all the trouble they have taken over this rather complicated volume to make it a unified whole, and for the patience with which they have tolerated my various foibles and whims.

Aboard the *Discovery*, looking for'ard to the bridge.

CHAPTER I

GENESIS IN WHALING HISTORY

On 24th September, 1925, the Royal Research Ship *Discovery*, famous as Scott's first Antarctic vessel, sailed again for the South. Her purpose now was not to discover or explore new land, or indeed, except for the mapping of uncharted coasts, to be concerned with the land at all; she went on a voyage of natural history to study the Antarctic seas and all within them that might have a bearing on the lives of the great whales which there formed the object of so rich a fishery.

The expedition was under the leadership of Dr. Stanley Kemp (later elected F.R.S.) who had been Superintendent of the Zoological Survey of India; and the Captain of the ship was Commander J. R. Stenhouse, D.S.O., O.B.E., D.S.C., R.N.R., who had previously seen service in the Antarctic as Captain of Shackleton's ship *Aurora* and in the Arctic with the North Russian expeditionary force of 1918. It was my great good fortune to have the honour of being appointed Chief Zoologist on this unusual venture of biological exploration.

The *Discovery* was built by the Dundee Shipbuilding Company specially for Scott's 1901-03 expedition and was designed on the lines of an earlier *Discovery*: a real Dundee whaler. This older ship had been called the *Bloodhound* in her whaling days, but was then renamed when she was taken over by the Admiralty to join the *Alert* in the Government Arctic Expedition of 1875. Scott, referring to this earlier venture in the first volume of his *The Voyage of the 'Discovery'* (1905) writes:

The contrast between these two ships for ice-work was remarkable. The *Alert* had a bluff straight bow, whilst the *Discovery* had the more recently designed overhanging stem, and as a result the *Discovery* had often to be sent ahead to force a passage in order that the *Alert* might follow.

The lines of the *Discovery* represented the experience gained in the whaling trade . . . she probably reached the best form for such a vessel.

So it was that Scott's historic ship, the one we were to sail in, was built at Dundee on these same lines. She was, indeed, the very last

The strengthened stem of the
R.R.S. *Discovery*.

of a long line of Dundee whalers and now, on her new voyage, she was actually sailing after whales. She was not, however, going to hunt them for destruction, but the very reverse; she was setting out to find the facts that might help in their conservation.

As a boy I had been thrilled by Frank Bullen's enchanting story *The Cruise of the Cachalot*; in it, I always remembered, he had written, 'To this day I can conceive of no more delightful journey for a naturalist than a voyage in a southern whaler especially if he were allowed to examine at his leisure such creatures as were caught.'

Was such an adventure still possible in the world of to-day, I had wondered; and now, as if by a miracle, we were about to experience it. Not only were we going to be *allowed* to examine such creatures as were caught, but were being provided with every device of modern science to assist in their capture. It was perhaps the last opportunity for such an experience that might ever occur, for from the fast whaling ships of to-day a naturalist can see little except the whales that are caught. Indeed a full-powered research vessel, such as the *Discovery II* which succeeded our old ship for the later voyages, although much more efficient for oceanography, is not nearly such a rewarding ship for the general zoologist as was the old one; by that I mean for the naturalist who delights in the unexpected creatures which may continually come to his notice as his ship is almost becalmed in the tropics or pushes slowly through the ice. Whether we were always able to examine the creatures *at our leisure* is another matter; such pressure as there was, however, was entirely due to the abundance of material our equipment showered upon us. But I am anticipating what is to come. I must begin by explaining the origin of our expedition and to do this I must recall the past fortunes, or more particularly the misfortunes, of the whale fisheries, for our venture was a new chapter in their history. Then to appreciate what happened we must in turn have some idea of the different kinds of whale that have been hunted;

and I must also say a little about whales in general for those who are not zoologists.

Although by tradition we speak of the whale *fisheries*, we know, of course, that whales are not really fish, but are just as much warm-blooded red-fleshed mammals, which suckle their young, as are elephants and cows. Whale steak, as we found in the war, is not so very different from beef, certainly more like it than say pork or venison. But how came these mammals to live now like fish? When the fossil record tells us that all the land beasts were originally derived from fish-like ancestors of long, long ago, is it not curious that the whales should have returned to the sea? The answer is to be found in over-population and an excessive competition for the limited supply of food on the land; it is this which has driven not only the forerunners of the whales, but race after race of terrestrial animals, back into the water for a living. The seals and their kin only come ashore to breed, and we can see how such a trend began in the way polar bears have to take to the water for their food.

The whales are more perfectly adapted to an aquatic life than any other mammals. Their fore limbs have become modified into 'flippers' which are not paddles like the limbs of a turtle but used as elevating or depressing planes and for general stability control; their hind limbs have disappeared except for the tiny vestigial bones to be found deep within their bodies. In shape they are as streamlined as a fish, and like the fish their tail is the main propulsive organ, but here is an interesting difference: the fish's tail fin is vertical and drives the fish forward by side-to-side strokes, whereas the tail of the whale, with its wide-spread 'flukes,' is horizontal and beats up and down.

Whilst all the whales, dolphins and porpoises are classed together in one major division, the order Cetacea (Gk. *Ketos*, a whale), they can be separated into two well-defined groups. There are the so-called whalebone whales which lack teeth,[1] of the suborder Mystacoceti[2] (from the Greek *mystax*, a moustache), and there are the toothed whales, of the suborder Odontoceti (from the Greek *odons, odontos*, a tooth).

Instead of teeth, the whalebone whales have a long series of thin strips of horn, the so-called 'whalebone' or baleen plates, projecting downwards on each side from the lower surface of their upper jaws; these are frayed out at their inner margins to form a fringe of very fine fibres like a vast internal moustache (hence the name of the suborder which we have just noted). The very largest whales, which are indeed the largest animals that have ever lived—far more massive

[1]Little vestigial teeth appear in early development but are soon lost.
[2]Some authors use a different form of the name: Mysticeti.

than the great dinosaurs of the past—belong to this group and have enormous mouths; yet strange to say they feed upon the little shrimp-like crustaceans of the plankton. When I say their mouths are enormous I do not just mean that they are so because the whale itself is big; I mean that they are actually huge out of all proportion to the rest of the body. Such a whale takes in a vast mouthful of sea as it swims forwards and then squirts it out again through the 'moustache' at the sides so that all the little shrimps in the water are strained out of it; only so large a mouth could collect sufficient of this scattered food, which is now wiped off the moustache by the tongue and swallowed. The size of the mouth in relation to the rest of the body can be seen from the sketch of a skeleton of a North Atlantic right whale which shows the enormous jaw bones required to make a frame for so great a cavity; it also shows the arrangement of the baleen plates.

There are three main types of whalebone whales: the so-called right whales (family Balaenidae), the rorquals, together with the related humpback whale (Balaenopteridae), and one very unusual kind, the grey whale of the Pacific, which zoologically is given a family name all to itself (Rachianectidae).

Among the toothed whales only the sperm whale or cachalot reaches a really large size and has been hunted extensively. The bottlenosed and pilot whales have at times been sought after but have never been important commercially; other examples of toothed whales are the narwhal, the killer, the much smaller dolphins and the porpoise.

The first fisheries were concerned only with the right whales which were slower and more docile than the others; when attacked in the early days, they had no experience of such danger and allowed themselves to be quite easily approached and hand-harpooned from open boats. Whaling, at least by the white man,[1] began with the hunting of the North Atlantic right whale (*Balaena glacialis*), sometimes known by its Dutch name of *nordkaper*; it is a species which on our side of

---

[1] I have so qualified this statement because we do not know when the red-skins of the Pacific coast of North America first began their whaling. There are a number of accounts (see for example J. G. Swan's 'The Indians of Cape Flattery' *Smithsonian Contributions to Knowledge*, no. 220, 1868 or the article by A. B. Reagan on 'Whaling of the Olympic Peninsula Indians' in *Natural History*, vol. 25, pp. 25-32, 1925, New York) and their methods are illustrated by an excellent exhibit which I saw recently in the anthropological section of the Provincial Museum at Victoria B.C. They hunted mainly the Pacific grey whale which they speared with a bone-headed harpoon from a canoe; the wooden shaft was then withdrawn leaving in place the barbed head which, being fastened by a hide lanyard to a number of seal-skin (or seal stomach) floats, kept the whale on the surface until it could be lanced to death by repeated thrusts. Then, of course, the Eskimos spear the narwhal in the Arctic.

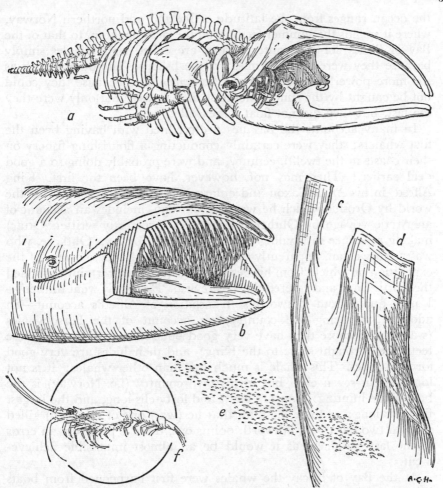

Sketches illustrating the feeding of a 'whalebone' whale: *a*, the skeleton of an Atlantic right whale drawn from the right front to show, in relation to *b*, the huge jaw bones which provide the frame for the capacious mouth; *b*, model of the mouth of the same whale with the right side of the lower jaw cut away to show the tongue and baleen plates of which some from the right side have been removed to show the full set opposite; *c* and *d*, single baleen plates of a right whale and a rorqual respectively, with *e*, a swarm of krill (their food) drawn to scale, and *f*, one greatly enlarged on that scale, but actually life-size. From the author's *The Open Sea*, Part II.

the ocean ranges from the latitude of Iceland and northern Norway, where it spends the summer feeding on the rich plankton, to that of the Bay of Biscay for the winter. They are called right whales simply because they were the *right* ones for the fishery. The others, such as the more powerful rorquals, were the *wrong* ones because they could not be caught by the simple methods then in use; not only were they too fast, but they did not float when killed.

In many accounts the Basques are credited with having been the first whalers; they were certainly conducting a flourishing fishery on their coasts in the twelfth century, and were probably doing so a good deal earlier.[1] They may not, however, have been the first. King Alfred, in his Anglo-Saxon and enlarged version of the history of the world by Orosius, which he wrote about 890, includes an account of an Arctic voyage by Ohthere (sometimes incorrectly written Ottar) making reference to whaling off the coasts of Norway. Ohthere, who was a Norwegian, apparently visited King Alfred and told him of the expedition on which, from his description, he almost certainly rounded the North Cape and entered the White Sea. 'He chiefly went thither'— I now quote from Bosworth's[2] translation of Alfred's account—'in addition to seeing the country, on account of the horse-whales (walruses) because they have very good bone in their teeth: of these teeth they brought some to the King; and their hides are very good for ship-ropes. This whale is much less than other whales: it is not longer than seven ells; but in his own country (i.e. Norway) is the best whale hunting: they are eight and forty ells long, and the largest fifty ells long: of these, he said, that he (was) one of six (who) killed sixty in two days.' As Bosworth points out, there is probably an error in the last statement as it would be an almost impossible achievement.

At the Bay of Biscay the whales were first harpooned from boats launched from the shore, but later they were hunted farther from the coast by ships which carried and lowered the smaller harpooner's boats. With the increasing activity the whales were steadily reduced and by the eighteenth century the fishery was over. In the meantime, however, reports of large numbers of the same species off Newfoundland began to attract vessels from many nations; the first whaler from Britain, the *Grace* of Bristol, sailed there in 1594. But before long, both

---

[1]William Scoresby in a history of whaling in vol. II of his *An Account of the Arctic Regions* (1820) refers to a work dated 875 entitled *Translation et des Miracles de Saint Vaast* in which mention is said to be made of a whale-fishery on the French coast.

[2]*King Alfred's Anglo-Saxon version of the compendious History of the World by Orosius*, ed. Rev. J. Bosworth, London, 1859.

this fishery and another which had developed off Iceland came to an end through the inevitable destruction of the stock.

The Basques, now pushing farther north, came across the Greenland right whale (*Balaena mysticetus*), a larger species producing more oil and having much larger whalebone plates. It was just at this time, in 1607, that Hudson, acting for the English Muscovy Company of Merchant Adventurers, made the first of his memorable Arctic voyages on which he discovered the north of Greenland and Spitsbergen, and, on his return course, the island of Jan Mayen. From this, and another voyage to Spitsbergen, in the following year, he brought back news of enormous numbers of these larger Greenland whales, with the result that the Muscovy Company sent the first whaling

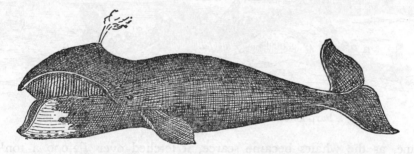

A Greenland right whale, 53 feet long, redrawn from an engraving in Scoresby's *Arctic Regions*.

expedition to Spitsbergen in 1611. Very soon other nations followed, leading to rivalry and conflict; and in 1618 the coastline was, by agreement, divided between the English, Dutch, Danes and Biscayans to give each a separate bay to work in. The Dutch also hunted round Jan Mayen and soon, of course, both areas were fished out. The scene now moved to Greenland itself.

The Dutch in 1719 first sent whalers into the Davis Straits and were quickly followed by the British. Hull, and to a lesser extent Whitby, in England, and Dundee and Peterhead in Scotland, became the more important of our ports sending vessels to the Greenland fishery. In 1750 only some twenty vessels were taking part, but by 1788 there were no less than 253 ships engaged; and consequently, the whales were again fished out. The last northern whaling ship from Hull, the *Truelove*, sailed in 1868; from Dundee a few vessels continued to the end of the century. In those days the 'whalebone' was in such demand to make the corsets worn by every lady of fashion that at one

Lancing a harpooned whale; a sketch made from an old Dutch print.

time, as the whales became scarce, it fetched over £2,000 a ton[1]. One of these large Greenland whales might produce a ton and a half of whalebone, in addition to nearly 30 tons of oil; since the expeditions on small sailing ships cost little to finance it was no wonder that the

[1]This figure is from Sir Sidney Harmer's 'History of Whaling' in the *Proceedings of the Linnean Society of London*, Session 140, 1928. In the early days when whales were more numerous whalebone fetched only some £80 a ton as recorded by William Scoresby who gives so much interesting information regarding the fishery at the beginning of the nineteenth century in his *Account of the Arctic Regions* 1820 (also referred to by Sir Sidney). I give the following extract from Scoresby (vol. II, p. 120):

'From the year 1810 to 1818 inclusive, 824 ships sailed from England to the whale-fisheries of Greenland and Davis Straits and 361 from Scotland. In the four years ending with 1817, 392 vessels sailed from England to these northern fisheries, the amount of whose cargo was 3348 whales, besides seals, narwhales, bears and seahorses [= walruses], and the produce 35,824 tons of oil and about 1806 tons of whalebone, together with a quantity of skins. The average quantity of oil produced *per* ship on each voyage was 91.4 tons and about 4 tons 12 cwt. of whalebone. . . . The British whale-fishery of 1814 was uncommonly prosperous, especially at Greenland; 76 ships in this fishery having produced 1437 whales, besides seals etc., the produce of which in oil only was 12,132 tons, being an average of $18\frac{9}{10}$ fish or 159.6 tons of oil *per* ship! The average fishery of Davis Straits the same season was about one third less *per* ship. The gross value of the freights of the British Greenland and Davis Straits fleets (bounties included) estimating the oil at 32 £ a ton, which was about the average price, and the whalebone at 80 £ per ton, exceeds in this one year 700,000 £.'

whales were relentlessly followed to the remotest corners of the Arctic—hunted till no more could be found. This almost complete extermination[1] of the species was helped in the last days of the fishery by many vessels combining sealing with hunting the whale.

I should just mention that another stock of Greenland whales to the north of the Pacific, near the Bering Straits, was fished by the Americans who called it the bowhead whale, but I need hardly repeat the story: high success, with a maximum of 292 vessels by the middle of the century (1846), was followed by the same characteristic decline to complete failure.

I have been stressing the massacre in order to emphasise the folly of overfishing, but I should not pass on without a word or two of praise for the skill, courage and endurance of those daring and hardy sailors who made this early history. Not only did they despatch the whales with hand harpoons and lances from open boats with the risk of being tossed into freezing seas; at times they suffered terrible hardship when their vessels were caught and crushed in the ice, and many never returned. There was the disastrous year of 1830 when nineteen British ships were lost, but few years went past without their casualties.

A remarkable document, which, as a record of endurance, deserves to be better known, is the diary kept by a surgeon, Charles Edward Smith, who sailed with the Hull whale-ship *Diana* on a voyage to Greenland in 1866; it was edited and published years later by his son with the title *From the Deep of the Sea* (London, A. and C. Black, 1922). Early in the book he records the loss of the *Sarah and Elizabeth* of Hull in 1857 when some eight miles from the *Diana*:

She was laid in the pack when a strong gale sprang up and forced the ice upon her, stoving in her quarters. . . . The first intimation Captain Gravill, senior, received of the loss of his son's ship was the sudden appearance of two of her crew alongside of the *Diana*. The crew of the *Sarah and Elizabeth* travelled over the pack to the *Diana*, leaving their bags on the ice by their wrecked ship. The three following days were thick, with heavy falls of snow. When the weather cleared up, the crew of the *Sarah and Elizabeth*, together with a number of the *Diana's* men, travelled to the wreck to get their clothes, etc., the ice being horribly soft and rotten, and a strong gale blowing at the time. They found that the ship had

[1]The smaller Atlantic right whale, which at one time was thought to be extinct, has now turned up in moderate numbers and recently there have been records of the Greenland whale being seen again; C. D. H. Clarke writing in the *Canadian Field Naturalist* (vol. 58, p. 102) in 1944 says 'this species is increasing in the Beaufort Sea and schools are occasionally reported.'

The Hull whaler *Diana* locked in the ice, December 1866; sketched from a contemporary painting in the Hull Museum of Fisheries.

sunk, but was held up by the main yard catching upon the ice. Whilst busy securing their bags, etc., a heavy swell set in and the pack started to break up.

A terrible scene ensued, seventy or eighty men springing from one fragment of ice to another, struggling for dear life to get to the *Diana*, the pack breaking up and spreading more and more every minute. . . . A number of the men were saved by being dragged and forced along by their companions . . . ; others staggering along, weak, exhausted, and benumbed by the terrible cold and exposure to intense frost whilst wet through.

The *Diana* was to leeward of the pack . . . , she was able barely to hold her own and keep near the edge of the pack whilst her boats picked up the men off the fragments of ice.

They saved every man on that occasion, but tragedy came on the last voyage. The *Diana* herself was held in heavy pack and abandoned for a time when it was thought she would be crushed; her crew who had camped on the ice rejoined her but were forced to winter in the Arctic. The captain and twelve others, many of whom were Shetlanders, died of cold and scurvy. It is too long a story to tell here; it must be read in the original. I will only quote an extract from the newspaper *The Scotsman* which describes the arrival of the crippled *Diana* at the Shetlands on the morning of 11th April, 1867:

The sight which met the eyes of the people from the shore who first boarded her cannot well be told in prose. Dante might have related it in the 'Inferno'. Coleridge's 'Ancient Mariner' might have sailed in such a ghastly ship—battered and ice-crushed, sails and cordage blown away, boats and spars cut up for fuel in the awful Arctic winter, the main deck a charnel-house not to be described. The miserable, scurvy-stricken, dysentery-worn men who looked over her bulwarks were a spectacle, once seen, never to be forgotten.

. . . Most pitiable sights of all were the ship's boys, with their young faces wearing a strange aged look not easily to be described.

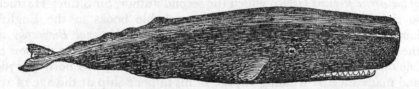

A sixty foot sperm whale drawn from a cast in the British Museum (Natural History).

Returning to our history, I must now refer to the sperm whale fisheries, for they occupy a unique position in that they link one fishery with another. The sperm whale, as we have already noted, is one of the toothed whales, and a creature of a very different appearance. It feeds upon fish or, more especially, on squids—those oceanic relatives of the cuttlefish—and its smaller mouth, with teeth only in its narrow lower jaw[1], is on the underside of a great square-fronted head which holds a vast store of liquid spermaceti. These New Bedford and Nantucket fisheries, made for ever famous by Herman Melville's *Moby Dick*, are perhaps the most romantic of them all; they developed from the hunting of the right whales off the coasts of New England before that early fishery collapsed. The whalers going farther afield in search of their quarry came upon the sperm whales and so began this new venture which extended right round the world, but mainly in tropical waters.[2]

[1] There are small stevigial teeth in the upper jaw, but they rarely come through the gums.
[2] They failed eventually not through overfishing, but because the sperm oil, so different

Now this sperm fishery was in turn to give rise to yet another right whale fishery, but one at the other end of the world. The whalers, going south, eventually came across large numbers of whales very similar to those which they had first hunted in the north. These are generally regarded as belonging to a distinct but very closely related species (*Balaena australis*); they were found around Cape Horn, the Falkland Islands, South Africa, Kerguelen, Australia and New Zealand. Between the years 1804 and 1817 it has been estimated that something like 190,000 of these whales were taken by the Americans. The hunting to depletion was again enacted.

Whilst there are many accounts of these old whaling days, there are two above all others which I should mention for those who would go farther into this history, and these again have many references to other works; they are those already quoted in the footnote on p. 26. Both are by authors who are outstanding in the science of our subject. The first is that classic of whaling literature by William Scoresby *An Account of the Arctic Regions* (1820) which the second author, Sir Sidney Harmer, so rightly calls 'one of the most remarkable books in the English language'; it is described in the *Dictionary of National Biography* as the foundation-stone of Arctic science. Scoresby, who was the son of one of the most noted whaling captains of his time, was born in 1789 and made his first whaling voyage in his father's ship at the age of 10. After returning to school he proceeded to Edinburgh University to qualify in physics, chemistry and anatomy, and then in 1810, at the age of 21, became captain of his father's whaling ship *Resolution*. As a scientific whaler he gave us splendid accounts of the meteorology, water and ice conditions of the Arctic as well as of the natural history of the Greenland whale; he was the first to observe the Arctic plankton, figuring various kinds in a plate in his work. More than a hundred years before us he was pioneering in the north the kind of observations we were now setting out to make in the south. It was indeed fitting that the little ship which was later to join us in our voyaging should be named the *William Scoresby*. I will quote from Sir Sidney again:

He was not content with finding plankton and ascertaining that it

---

from that of the right whales or the rorquals, could not compete with the mineral and vegetable oils which came in due course to be obtained at a lower cost. Whilst the American fishery has gone, sperm whales are still fished to-day by the same heroic methods of hand harpoons and open boats at the Azores as so well described by Robert Clarke (*Discovery Reports*, vol. xxvi, pp. 281-354, 1954). And indeed some of the large modern whaling ships will still capture sperm whales as a side line when waiting for the rorqual season to open, particularly off the coasts of Peru and Chile; more recently a flourishing sperm fishery by Japanese and Russian whalers has grown up in the North Pacific.

was the food of the larger animals at sea, but he invented what is known to modern hydrographers as a water-bottle which he sent down to the depths of the sea for the purpose of bringing up water and taking its temperature. He also examined what we now speak of as the salinity of the water, estimating the quantity of salt present, in exactly the same way that a modern hydrographer does.[1]

In 1823 Scoresby gave up whaling and entered Queens' College, Cambridge, to read theology; he was elected a Fellow of the Royal Society in 1824 and was ordained a year later. In 1839 he became a D.D. of Cambridge and then, at the age of 67, in 1856, a year before he died, made a voyage to Australia and back to carry out magnetic observations, he was certainly a man of many parts. In addition to his science he gave us a first rate account of the whale fisheries.

The second history of whaling I want to mention formed Sir Sidney Harmer's Presidential Address to the Linnean Society in 1928 (see footnote to p. 26); this is particularly valuable for all his facts and figures relating to the industry since Scoresby's account of 1820. I have drawn extensively on both for my information. Sir Sidney added much to our knowledge of whales by organising a system for the reporting by coast guards of all stranded whales in Great Britain and so leading to their examination by himself and other experts. As we shall see he had much to do with the launching of our expedition.

We come now to the more modern period with the gigantic rorquals under fire. These are the whales which are too fast and powerful to be hunted by the old methods; they are those we are concerned with in this book. Just when the right whale fisheries were nearing their end, a Norwegian, Svend Foyn, in 1865, invented his new and deadly gun—a stout little cannon which fires a large harpoon with an explosive head. It is mounted on the bows of a small but fast steamship, called a whale-catcher, and can be swivelled to point in any direction. The harpoon it fires is fastened to a great length of cable which can run out or be hauled in by a steam winch so that the leviathans can now be caught and pulled in like a fish on a line. This method also overcame the further obstacle which, as already mentioned, had prevented them from being fished before: the fact that a rorqual, unlike the right or sperm whale, sinks when dead. The new harpoon, having great steel barbs which open out under the blubber, is strong enough to hold the whale and pull it to the surface against the ship where compressed air is pumped into it until it floats.

In the northern hemisphere there are four species of these rorquals,

[1] *The Geographical Journal*, vol. LXXII, p. 229, 1928.

all much faster and more finely streamlined than the right whales; and they all have a small triangular fin, about two-thirds of the way down their backs, which the right whales lack. The largest is the blue-grey, blue whale (*Balaenoptera musculus*) which measures up to 100 feet in length, although 85 feet is more usual. Next in size is the fin whale or common rorqual (*B. physalus*) which may reach up to 80 feet but is more usually about 70; it is a very dark grey above and white below. The sei whale (*B. borealis*) is smaller again, growing to not more than 60 feet, and is grey all over but darker on the top than underneath. The lesser rorqual, mincke or pike whale (*B. acutorostrata*) is the smallest and never

1. *Above.* The officers, scientists and cadets on the *Discovery* just before sailing in 1925. Top row: (left to right): E. H. Marshall (Surgeon), W. A. Horton (Chief Engineer), D. D. John (zoologist)*, J. E. Hamilton (zoologist), J. M. Chaplin (Second, and later Chief Officer, also Naval Hydrographic Surveyor), T. W. Goodchild (Third and later Second Officer), A. N. Porteous (Second Engineer) Middle row: H. F. P. Herdman (hydrologist), J. R. Stenhouse (Captain), Stanley Kemp (Director of Research and leader of the expedition), W. H. O'Connor (Chief Officer), A. C. Hardy (zoologist) In the front: J. Bentley (cadet), E. R. Gunther (zoologist), W. P. O'Connor (cadet), F Pease (cadet)

*came out later on the R.R.S. *William Scoresby*

Below: Personnel of the *Discovery*, the *William Scoresby* and the Marine Biological Station at South Georgia, photographed on board the *Discovery* at Grytviken, South Georgia, Christmas 1926 Seated from left to right: A. Irving (Chief Officer, *Scoresby*), W. A. Horton (Chief Engineer, *Discovery*), G. M. Mercer (Captain of *Scoresby*), Stanley Kemp (Director of Research and leader of the expedition), J. R. Stenhouse (Captain of *Discovery*), A.C. Hardy (zoologist), J. M. Chaplin (Chief Officer, *Discovery*), J. W. Riley (Chief Engineer, *Scores-by*), A. J. Clowes (hydrologist) and, unfortunately just out of picture (but shown in the group above), E. R. Gunther, (zoologist) Standing immediately behind those seated: H. F P Herdman (hydrologist), F. C. Fraser (zoologist), J. F. G. Wheeler (zoologist), J. E. Hamilton (zoologist), L. H. Matthews (zoologist), M. C. Lester (Second Officer, *Scoresby*), N. A. Mackintosh (zoologist), G. Brabender (Second Engineer, *Scoresby*), A. N. Porteus (Second Engineer, *Discovery*), C. Sanderson (Third officer, *Discovery*), T. W. Goodchild (Second Officer, *Discovery*), E. C. Cunliffe (Wireless Operator, *Discovery*), D. S. Sherrington (steward, *Discovery*), F. E. Hollands (steward, Marine Station) and unfortunately just out of the picture, but shown in group above, D. D. John (zoologist) Seated in front are the three cadets: J. Bentley, W. P. O'Connor and F Pease

Photograph taken by E. H. Marshall (Surgeon, *Discovery*) who is in the group above.

2. On the way out. *Left*, fishing for bonito and albacore. *Below*, dolphins swimming in formation in front of the ship

The Svend Foyn whale gun.

exceeds 30 feet; it is coloured much like the fin whale except that it has a most characteristic white patch on the outside of each flipper as if it were wearing a white armband. All four species have a number of parallel grooves on the throat and chest. Related to the rorquals, but somewhat different in form, is the humpback whale (*Megaptera novaeangliae*); it has a shorter, rather more robust body which tapers markedly towards the tail and is particularly characterised by the long, slightly curved and curiously 'knobbly' flippers; it is black above and white below.

Whaling stations, with all the equipment for boiling down the blubber for oil, were set up at various points on the coasts of Norway, Iceland, Labrador, the Faroes, and later at Shetland, the Hebrides and on the west of Ireland; also in the north Pacific where hunting took place from British Columbia, Japan and Korea. Each shore station was served by a small fleet of steam whale-catchers which hunted the whales in the vicinity and towed the carcasses back to the wooden flensing plane: a gently sloping platform up which the whales are drawn by a steam winch and cable to be flensed, i.e., stripped of their coating of blubber. The blubber, from which most of the oil comes, is a layer of fatty tissue—up to ten or eleven inches thick in a large whale—completely covering the body underneath quite a thin smooth skin, except for the dorsal fin, flippers and tail flukes. The oil from the rorquals is the most valued of all, and is extensively used in the manufacture of soap and margarine. The whalebone plates, although more numerous, are much shorter than those of the right whales and

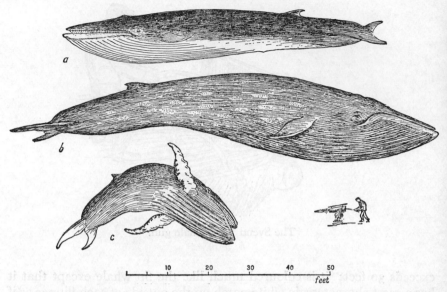

10   20   30   40   50
feet

Fin, blue and humpback whales (*a*, *b*, and *c*, respectively) drawn to the same scale as the gunner sketched on the right.

are of no value; indeed, with plastic substitutes, there is to-day no demand for whalebone, and the ladies' corsets, which formerly took so much, are now all but things of the past.

The larger and more valuable blue whales were sought after most, but the fin whales, sei whales and humpbacks were also hunted and came to be taken in increasing numbers as the blue whales declined in abundance. Again, in each area, the story was the same as it had always been; great success to begin with—a period of fabulous profits—followed by the inevitable decline to final failure. Throughout this sketch I have not spared the reader the repetition of this story because my purpose has been to emphasise the folly of such thoughtless hunting. This, however, was to be for the last time in the northern hemisphere. There was only one important stock of these rorquals left, and as it turned out the greatest of them all, that in the far south. By the time of the First World War the fishery there was developing fast. Could this remaining stock be saved? To answer that question was the object of our voyage.

At the turn of the century, when this last northern fishery was waning, came news from various expeditions of large numbers of rorquals in the waters at the other end of the world. In 1892 four vessels of the

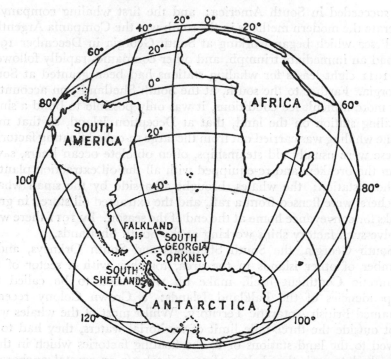

A sketch of the world looked at from below the south pole to
show the positions of the Falkland Islands and the three centres
where the great southern whale fisheries began: South Georgia,
the South Shetlands and the South Orkneys, and where the main
work of our expedition was carried out.

Dundee whaling fleet visited the regions of South Georgia and the
South Shetlands; on one of these, the *Balaena*, as a naturalist, was
Dr. W. S. Bruce, who later led the Scottish National Antarctic
Expedition in the *Scotia*. In the same year Captain C. A. Larsen, a
famous Norwegian whaling captain, went south in the *Jason*, and again
in 1893; none of these vessels, however, were equipped for hunting
rorquals. In 1901 Larsen came south once more but this time as
captain of the *Antarctica*, the ship of the Swedish scientific expedition
led by Dr. Otto Nordenskjöld. Crushed in the ice of the Weddell Sea,
the ship sank, but the party safely reached some islands off the east
coast of Graham Land and, after wintering there, were rescued by the
Argentine ship *Uruguay*. Captain Larsen returned from this expedition
convinced that rorqual hunting in the south must be a great success.

Having failed to raise the money in Europe to support his venture, he succeeded in South America; and the first whaling company to operate the modern methods in the south was the Compania Argentina de Pesca which began working at South Georgia in December 1904. It had an immediate triumph, and other companies rapidly followed; by 1911 eight leases for whaling stations had been granted at South Georgia. Farther to the south, at the South Shetlands, on account of the more difficult ice conditions, it was only possible to build a single whaling station on the land, that at Deception Island, so that most of the whaling was carried out from the large so-called floating factories. These were usually old steamships, often obsolete ocean liners, saved from the breakers and re-equipped with all the oil extraction plant of a shore station; the whales, brought alongside by the small whale-catchers, were flensed from a raft, and the extracted oil stored in great tanks for conveyance home at the end of the season. By 1911 there were twelve such factory ships working at the South Shetlands.

South Georgia, the South Shetlands and South Orkneys, and a number of other islands in the area, together with a sector of the Antarctic Continent itself, make up what used to be called the Dependencies of the Falkland Islands: a Crown Colony recently renamed British Antarctic Territory. Whilst most of the whales were shot outside the three-mile limit of territorial waters, they had to be towed to the land stations or to the floating factories which in those days had to seek the shelter of some harbour or coastal anchorage. The Colonial Government, seeing what had happened in the past, realised the danger to the stock and began to exercise control over the industry. It limited the number of whale-catchers that could be used, prohibited the shooting of young whales or of mother whales accompanied by their calves, and insisted that all of the whale's body should be used so that there should be no waste.

The Government also levied a tax on the oil taken so that money should be available to finance scientific investigations in order that any further restrictive legislation which became necessary could be based upon sound knowledge. That was how the money was raised for our expedition and those of the R.R.S. *Discovery II* which followed it; they have been a direct charge on the industry itself and have cost the taxpayer at home nothing. Surely it was a splendid and enlightened policy; from the whales killed money was provided for a proper investigation to prevent overfishing and the destruction of the stock.

Then came the First World War, and nitro-glycerine, which was a by-product of the industry, was badly needed for the manufacture of explosives. The restrictions for a time were relaxed and the number of whales killed in a single season at South Georgia rose in 1915-16 to 11,792. The war also delayed the planning of the investigations; in the meantime, however, the funds from taxation were accumulating to make possible a full-scale attack on the problem when the opportunity came. The first plans developed, as we shall see in the next chapter, from the deliberations of a very unusual Government Committee: an Inter-departmental Committee which published its report in 1920; and the actual formation of this Committee sprang from the imaginative vision of the late Mr. Roland Darnley of the Colonial Office. His more personal views on the possibilities of such a venture can be found in an article he wrote entitled 'A New Antarctic Expedition' published in the *Nineteenth Century Review* for May 1923. It was that article that first drew my attention to the possibilities of going south; I still have my tattered copy and find it good to look back on, so recapturing the excitement it gave me long ago.

CHAPTER 2

PURPOSE, PLANS AND PREPARATIONS

The report of the Committee which set the whole thing going was one
of those forbidding-looking foolscap volumes published by the
Stationery Office; seldom, however, can a more exciting 'blue-book'
have appeared. I fear it is almost forgotten, so let me give it its full
title:

REPORT
OF THE
INTER-DEPARTMENTAL COMMITTEE
ON
RESEARCH AND DEVELOPMENT
IN THE DEPENDENCIES OF THE
FALKLAND ISLANDS

with appendices, maps, etc.

Presented to Parliament by Command of His Majesty
April 1920

The report itself occupies only 31 pages, but the Appendices, written
by various experts and full of fascinating information on the region
in question, fill 130 pages more.

So important was this document for our work and all that has sprung
from it that I must include some account of the laying of these plans.
I will give an abridged version of its opening paragraphs:

In 1917 attention was drawn to the question of the development
of the Dependencies of the Falkland Islands by Mr. E. R. Darnley,
of the Colonial Office, and in the same year the Secretary of State
for the Colonies addressed the Lords Commissioners of the
Admiralty on the subject, with special reference to the preservation of the whaling industry. Copies of the letter were sent to
various Departments likely to be interested, including the Natural
History Departments of the British Museum.

38

The proposals met with a cordial response and Mr. Secretary Long constituted a Committee for the Dependencies of the Falkland Islands, to advise him on the subject, with the following members:

Mr. J. O. Borley, o.b.e., of the Board of Agriculture and Fisheries.

Mr. E. R. Darnley, of the Colonial Office.

Dr. S. F. Harmer, sc.d., f.r.s., of the British Museum (Natural History).

Mr. P. C. Lyon, c.s.i., of the Department of Scientific and Industrial Research.

Captain C. V. Smith, c.b.e., r.n., of the Admiralty with Mr. H. T. Allen, of the Colonial Office, as Secretary.

The terms of reference to the Committee . . . were:

'To consider what can now be done to facilitate prompt action at the conclusion of the War in regard to the preservation of the whaling industry and to the development of other industries in the Dependencies of the Falkland Islands; and to consider not only the economic questions above referred to, and the scheme for the employment of a research vessel, but also what purely scientific investigations are most required in connexion with these regions, and whether any preliminary inquiries by experts in this country should be instituted.'

That was the beginning. The committee met on twenty-one occasions and its final report is dated 27th August, 1919. It had clearly begun to meet early in 1918, if not before; is it not good to remember that the planning of such a quest of peace and science was contemplated and undertaken by a nation still struggling with a great war? Its conclusions and recommendations were set out in the fullest detail. To appreciate them, however, we must first see how marine science had been developing, particularly in relation to the true fisheries, i.e., those for fish!

This science of the sea was still relatively young when these preparations began; indeed it was not yet 50 years since the *Challenger* made her famous voyage which many regard as the real birth of oceanography. An earlier beginning had of course been made, as we have seen, in the work of Scoresby; and Vaughan Thompson had started his pioneer observations on the plankton in 1829, to be followed a little later by Edward Forbes dredging up the life from the sea floor.

The nineteenth century also saw a great development of the fishing industry leading to some concern over the possible effects of the

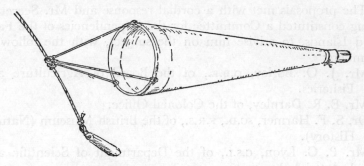

A very simple tow-net of silk gauze tapering to a collecting jar at
its end.

increased trawling upon the exploited stocks; it began to be realised
that worthwhile regulations must be based on better knowledge.
Several governments began scientific investigations and in 1899 King
Oscar II of Sweden called together a conference at Stockholm, which
led, in 1901, to the foundation of the International Council for the
Exploration of the Sea: a then unique example of international
co-operation. The different nations agreed to appoint scientists and to
equip research ships to study different areas of the sea and particular
problems. Ever since, except for a temporary suspension during the
two World Wars, representatives have met each year to discuss progress
and to plan for the future.

This Council has been the greatest stimulus to marine research.
The fishery naturalists are not simply confining their attention to the
fish themselves, their migrations, feeding habits, spawning grounds and
so on, but are studying all the factors which may influence their lives.
As we shall be following their lead, although in relation to whales, let
us look at their field of work.

While conditions in the sea differ widely from those on land, the same
fundamental laws of nature apply, of course, to both. We know that
all animal life—worm, crab, whelk or fish—must depend ultimately
upon plant life; one kind of animal may prey upon another kind,
which may in turn prey upon yet another, but however long the
chain, its first link must be an animal feeding upon some green plant
or the product of its decay. Plants alone have the power of using the
energy of sunlight to build up from the simpler chemicals the more
complex substances which animals require as food. But where are the
plants to support the vast quantities of fish that are drawn from the
sea? The seaweeds form but an insignificant fringe along the coasts,

for they can only live a few fathoms from the surface where there is sufficient light for them to grow. The tow-net has given us the answer.

This device, the tow-net which we shall so often be using, is a conical bag net, something like a butterfly net but made of silk gauze; in its simplest form it has bridles attached in front for towing it through the water, and a small collecting jar at its other end. If it is made of the very finest gauze and drawn through the sea near the surface in spring or summer, the little jar may soon be found to contain a thick green sediment; under the microscope this becomes a glistening galaxy of beautiful green and yellow shapes. The plants of the open sea are individually invisible to the unaided eye, but what they lack in size they make up in number, and may often give the sea a greenish tinge. The reason why they are so small is because they absorb their required phosphates, nitrates, etc., through their surfaces, and the smaller a body is, the *larger* is its surface *in proportion to its mass*: when, as often happens, there is a shortage of these substances, only the smaller forms can get sufficient to survive. The sea is a vast culture medium of the substances that plants require, including oxygen and carbon-dioxide dissolved into it from the atmosphere; just as these ideal conditions are spread through the water, so is the plant life itself, spread as a fine

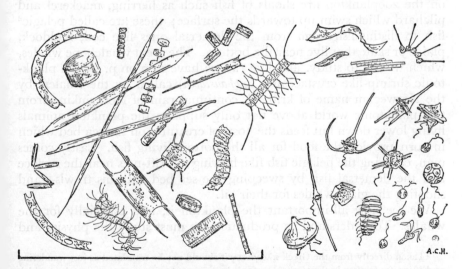

A.C.H.

The small plants of the plankton (*phytoplankton*) as seen through a microscope (× 50). Flagellates (supported by whip-like processes called *flagella*) are seen in the group on the right; all the rest are diatoms. The line below the diatoms represents $\frac{1}{20}$ of an inch. Reproduced from the author's *The Open Sea*, Part II.

aquatic dust of living specks, but *only* for as deep as there is sufficient light penetrating from above.

Upon this diffuse vegetation feed hosts of tiny animals of many different kinds, also scattered in their millions through the water. Small shrimp-like crustaceans predominate, many of them smaller than a pin's head, swarming in the sea as insects do on land, but in addition there are tiny jellyfish, little worm-like forms, miniature snails which keep themselves up by beating wing-like fins, and hordes of other exquisite and fantastic creatures familiar only to the specialist. Not all of these feed directly on the plants, some are carnivorous and prey upon the vegetarians. So numerous may these little animals be that a tow-net in only five or ten minutes may yield a catch of many thousands. I show some of them opposite.

All these little creatures of the open sea are part of the *plankton*. This is a collective term[1], applying to the whole category of this small drifting life, both plant and animal. The little plants make up the *phytoplankton* (Gk. *phuton*, a plant) and the animals, the *zoöplankton* (Gk. *zoös*, an animal).

To explain the natural economy of the sea in simple terms I shall draw the little sketch (p. 44) that I first used in my lecture to the Royal Geographic Society on our return from our expedition. Feeding on the zoöplankton are shoals of fish such as herring, mackerel and pilchard which swim up towards the surface; these are called pelagic[2] fish to distinguish them from the demersal ones like cod, haddock, plaice or skate that live near the bottom. The great whalebone whales, which we are to study, also live (as we have seen on p. 23) on plank-tonic shrimp-like crustaceans (*Euphausiacea*) called by the whalers by the Norwegian name of krill. A continual rain of food sinking from this planktonic world above not only supports the plankton animals living lower down but feeds the hosts of creatures on the sea bed which in turn provide the food for all the bottom-living fish. Lastly comes man, catching the pelagic fish like herring in drift-nets near the surface and the demersal fish by sweeping the sea bed with his trawls—and shooting the giant whales for their oil.

We see how all-important the plankton is, and especially for the whales. To understand its production we must study the physics and

---

[1]Taken directly from the Greek πλαγκτογ it should not be translated as just wandering or drifting (as so often in the textbooks), for it has a more *passive* sense, meaning those which are *made* to wander; it is applied to all those organisms which are powerless to prevent themselves being carried at the mercy of the moving waters.

[2]The adjective 'pelagic' is a useful one to denote animals or activities of the open sea; ours was indeed a *pelagic* expedition essentially setting out to investigate *pelagic* life.

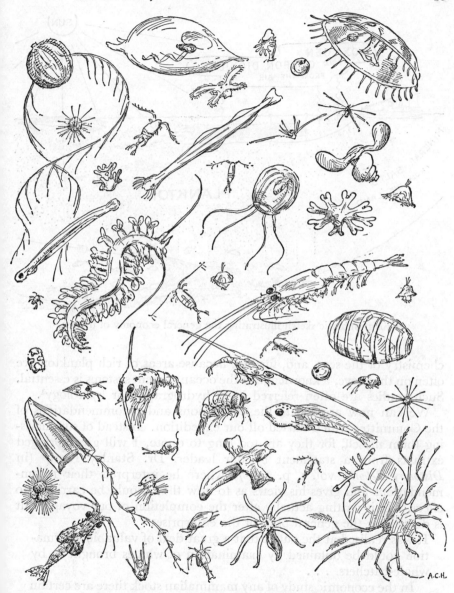

A selection of the animals of the plankton (*zooplankton*) magnified variously from 2 to 8 times, to show the variety of form ranging from protozoa to young fish. The typical whale food, one of the euphausian shrimps, the krill, is seen half-way up the figure on the right-hand side, and opposite it, to the left, is the large transparent worm *Tomopteris*. Also reproduced from *The Open Sea*, Part II.

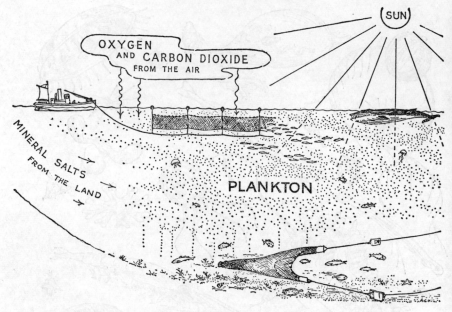

A diagrammatic sketch illustrating the general economy of the sea.

chemistry of the sea; and, further, because areas of rich plankton are often on the move, a knowledge of the ocean current systems is essential. Such studies are often referred to as hydrography or hydrology[1].

We can now appreciate the conclusions and recommendations of the Committee which started off our expedition. Instead of summarising them myself, for they are too long to quote, I will give abridged extracts from a statement by our leader, Dr. Stanley Kemp (in *Discovery Reports*, vol. I, p. 144-7) where he interprets their recommendations and gives his views as to how they should be carried into effect. He is writing actually after the completion of our voyage, but is describing the general plan of the enterprise:

It was realised at the outset that a great deal of valuable information could be obtained by examination of whales brought in by whale-catchers. . . .

In the economic study of any mammalian stock there are certain elementary facts which must be thoroughly understood before progress can be made. Among the more important are the rate of growth, the age at sexual maturity, the time of pairing, the period

[1]The latter is preferable, for the term 'hydrography' was first used (and still is) to denote the charting of the seas.

of gestation, the number at a birth, the length of the suckling period and the nature of the food. In whales most of these facts are less easily ascertained than in other mammals and the information already available was very deficient. By special anatomical investigation it is, however, possible to obtain results which will throw much light on such questions, and the Committee consequently decided to build a laboratory at South Georgia. . . .

But work on shore . . . can only give solutions to some of the problems which are involved. It requires to be supplemented by observations at sea, and the principal reason for such research is the necessity for a thorough study of the environment of southern whales. Experience has shown that the hydrological and planktonic methods employed by the International Council for the Exploration of the Sea have been productive of valuable results [in relation to fish] in the north-east Atlantic and it could not be doubted that equally good results would follow their application in the south. Whaling, like most fisheries, fluctuates greatly from season to season, and the causes of these fluctuations are to be sought in changes in the environment. The food of southern rorquals is now known to consist exclusively, or almost exclusively, of large Euphausian crustaceans, which themselves feed mainly on diatoms. . . . The phytoplankton in its turn is dependent on the physical and chemical constitution of the water, and it is to hydrological, and ultimately perhaps to meteorological conditions, that the fluctuations in the whaling industry are to be ascribed.

So much could be inferred from the scientific work which had been done in the north, but much special investigation was needed before theory and fact were brought into accord. . . .

It was accordingly decided to equip a vessel for oceanographic research in southern waters.

In drawing up a programme the Committee recognised the immensity of the area in which observations were required and the numerous directions along which research might profitably be undertaken. But practical considerations made it necessary to set some limit to the scope of the work, and in the plan which was finally adopted preference was given to investigations holding the most early promise of useful economic results.

To examine the conditions existing on the whaling grounds of the Dependencies was evidently of first importance and an intensive survey of the waters in the neighbourhood of South Georgia was planned. . . .

Such intensive surveys would not, however, yield all the

information desired. . . . It was thus necessary to supplement the survey of the South Georgia grounds by other investigations— necessarily less intensive—spread over a wider field. The region enclosed by lines connecting the Falkland Islands, South Georgia, the South Orkneys, the South Shetlands and Cape Horn was considered the most important, but observations were to be made whenever practicable in other parts of the southern ocean. . . .

The Committee foresaw that the work was likely to be more than a single square-rigged vessel (the *Discovery*) could undertake and that certain other lines of research were beyond her power.

Whales are well known to be migratory animals. . . . In an economic study . . . it is of the utmost importance that we should have a fuller and more accurate knowledge of these migrations. . . .

In tracing the migrations of fish the method most generally adopted is that of marking. Fish are caught, suitable marks bearing a reference number are attached to them, and they are then liberated. A proportion of these marked fish are recaptured in the course of commercial operations, and the offer of a reward increases the chance that the mark, together with the necessary data, will be returned to the fishery authority. By this means valuable information on the migrations of fish has been obtained, and some years ago it was suggested that a similar method might usefully be employed with whales. It is, for obvious reasons, more difficult to mark whales than fish, but as a result of experiments made before the *Discovery* sailed on her first commission, a practicable method was discovered. . . .

In considering the design of a second ship . . . , the Committee attached great importance to this question of whale-marking. A vessel of comparatively high speed was necessary, built generally on the lines of a whale-catcher, but it was recognised that she would also be required to assist in routine work on plankton and hydrology, and it was also considered desirable that she should carry a full-sized otter trawl for the exploration of certain areas in the Dependencies which might prove commercially profitable.

These varied requirements have been successfully met in the Research Steamship *William Scoresby*. . . .

We see then that our work in the south is to be essentially of the same general kind as that of the fishery scientists of the European seas but dealing mainly with the biology of whales.

It also seemed likely that occasions would arise when oceanographic work might be undertaken quite apart from that directly concerned with the biology of whales; and such opportunities should not be missed. It was thus decided to equip the ship with the gear to send large nets to the great depths of the ocean to capture the strange creatures of those dark abysmal regions. There would be times, too, when stormy weather would prevent work being done on the more open whaling grounds and it might then be possible with trawl and dredge to study the life of the sea bed in the more sheltered waters near the coasts.

Let me now come to our preparations. To organise and plan the expedition a new committee was set up which, following the decision to use the *Discovery*, thus became known as the *Discovery* Committee and its campaign as the *Discovery* Investigations. It had as members, in addition to Darnley, Sir Sidney Harmer, Allen and Borley who had already served on the earlier Committee (see p. 39), Rear-Admiral H. P. Douglas, c.b., c.m.g. (Admiralty), Sir J. Fortescue Flannery, Bt., m.i.c.e. (Consulting Naval Architect), H. G. Maurice, c.b. (Ministry of Agriculture and Fisheries) and J. M. Wordie, m.a. (Royal Geographical Society).

The *Discovery* at the completion of Scott's 1901-3 expedition had been bought by the Hudson Bay Company and converted for use in the Arctic fur trade. Scott had wished to get her back for his second expedition of 1912, but was unsuccessful and sailed in the *Terra Nova* instead. Until 1923, when she came on the market again and was acquired for our work, she had remained in the Arctic service. Before purchase, a detailed examination of the ship was made in dry dock in January 1923 and this revealed a much greater deterioration than had been anticipated; nevertheless it was easier to replace such affected timber, than to build entirely anew. On this point it is interesting to quote again from Scott's 1905 volume:

> The art of building wooden ships is now almost lost to the United Kingdom; probably in twenty or thirty years' time a new *Discovery* will give more trouble and cost more money than a moderate-sized war-ship. . . . It must become increasingly difficult to find the contractors who will undertake to build a wooden ship, or the seasoned wood and the skilled workmen necessary for its construction.

The extensive repairs and replacements necessary meant that all hope of being ready in the autumn of 1924 must be abandoned[1]. My first view of the ship, in dry dock at Portsmouth, was something of a shock; she was a mere skeleton, reminding one of the dug-up remains of some

---

[1]Those who are specially interested in the extent to which she was rebuilt will find the information in vol. 1 of the *Discovery Reports*, p. 155, 1929.

ancient viking galleon. Could she be ready even in time to sail in 1925, we wondered?

In the spring of 1924, Dr. Stanley Kemp was appointed Director of Research and Leader of the Expedition; and at the same time I had the honour of becoming his first member of staff. What an exciting day that was. After the decision of the Committee I met Kemp at his hotel and we talked of plans and of our ideas for the work until far into the night. I shall never forget that evening, the first of so many happy nights (and days) of eager planning and discussions; the first meeting with so great a friend. 'Dr. Kemp was tall and finely built with a quiet but most powerful manner; this was combined with a sense of humour and a gift of genuine friendship. No finer leader and no better companion for a long and lonely voyage in sub-Antarctic waters could be imagined.' I have quoted from the obituary notice in *The Times* (18th May, 1945); I never knew for certain who wrote it but it is a perfect description of him.

Here at the outset will perhaps be the best place for me to try and give some impression of Kemp the man and what he meant to us. At his untimely death in 1945 I wrote of his life and work in *The Journal of the Marine Biological Association*[1]. I will quote it because I find it difficult to put into other words what I then wrote and now feel as keenly as then. Having recorded how he was beloved by so many and by all who served under him, and stressed the very wide feeling of the loss of a great leader, not only in marine science but in zoology generally, I wrote as follows.

Future generations might wonder what was the secret of his outstanding position: his scientific publications were in the main in a somewhat restricted field of zoology, he was not a writer of books and he always shunned publicity. We, his contemporaries, and particularly those who served under him, know what it was: it was not an autocratic power but an exceptional capacity for a most energetic devotion to the task in hand, the example of which compelled all his followers to action. There was no parade of this unselfish devotion, no Dedication to Duty atmosphere; he just went full steam ahead carrying everyone with him: as someone aptly said, 'he put through the big and difficult jobs without any fuss or heroics'. Kemp's lasting monument will be the great series of *Discovery Reports*; the foundation of this work and so much of its achievement is due to his energetic planning and leadership, yet characteristically his name as author (and each time as joint author) appears on only three of the *Reports* so far issued. He was

[1] Vol. 26, pp. 219-34, 1946.

the spirit behind it all, filling his time with making perfect the many sides of the organisation and so willing to give the kudos of authorship to all his staff. How in his modesty he would hate to hear all this said! I can almost hear him now replying to a speech I made in his praise at a dinner when he left the *Discovery* Directorship to become Director at Plymouth; instead of the thanks I had expected for my words, with a pretence at scorn but with a twinkle in his eye for my benefit, he dismissed them as: 'This nauseating eulogy.'

After our first few meetings and our discussions as to which were the more urgent matters to start on, we parted for some three months. He had to return to India almost at once as he had much to see to before handing over his Superintendentship of the Zoological Survey of India to his successor. I too had work to finish off before I could leave my post as a naturalist on the staff of the Fishery Laboratory of the Ministry of Agriculture and Fisheries at Lowestoft. Kemp was unable to be free from India until June; I, however, was able to start in May.

An urgent matter was the designing of the laboratory and residence for the shore party who were going to do mainly anatomical and embryological research on the whales themselves at the whaling station at Grytriken, South Georgia. This building was to be shipped out in sections in the autumn and erected ready for the party in the following January (1925). I made sketches of what I thought the laboratory should look like: perspective views of all the fittings—benches, shelving, sinks, etc.—imagining myself working in the laboratory. The architect, Mr. C. H. Rose, who was splendidly co-operative, converted my ideas into plans and elevations. It was pleasant to see, when we came out, how like the finished building was to what I had envisaged; and it was a considerable satisfaction to know that the design turned out so well. 'The plan of the laboratories has been found very convenient' wrote Dr. Mackintosh in his description of the building (*Discovery Reports*, vol. I, p. 225).

As indicated by Kemp, the scientific work fell naturally into two main divisions: that at the shore station concerned with a study of the whales caught, and that on the ship concerned with the conditions in the sea which may govern their movements and habits. The shore party consisted of three zoologists, a hydrologist and a technician; they sailed ahead of us in the autumn (of 1924) to make a start in the coming whaling season and to be well established by the time we arrived. The zoologists were Dr. N. A. Mackintosh (now C.B.E.), leader of the party and later to follow Kemp as Director of Research, Dr. J. F. G. Wheeler who until recently has been Director of Fisheries Research in East Africa and Dr. L. Harrison Matthews, later F.R.S.

who is now Scientific Director of the Zoological Society of London. The hydrologist was the late Dr. A. J. Clowes who after the expedition joined the South African Fishery Service. Mr. A. Saunders was laboratory technician and photographer; he later served on the *Discovery II*.

The ship's scientific party, in addition to Kemp and myself, consisted of the late Dr. J. E. Hamilton who had come from Port Stanley, temporarily seconded for work with the expedition from his post as naturalist to the Falkland Islands Government (investigating the seal

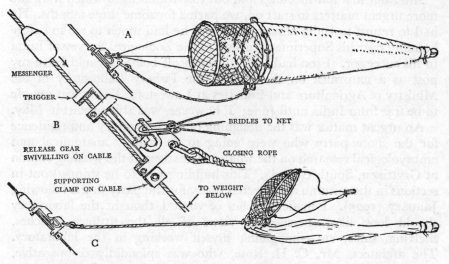

A tow-net designed to be closed at the end of its tow at some particular depth so that it will not catch plankton from other levels as it is hauled up to the surface. A, the rig of the net when towed; B, enlarged view of the release gear about to be struck by the messenger weight sent down from above; C, the towing bridles released and the net closed by the throttling rope.

populations), the late E. Rolfe Gunther, zoologist, then fresh from Cambridge, who alas, as recorded in the Preface (p. 15) was so tragically killed in the last war, and Dr. H. F. P. Herdman, hydrologist, from Belfast University. These will be our scientific companions throughout the greater part of the coming voyage. The ship's officers and crew we shall meet later. Hamilton had arrived from the Falklands, and Gunther and Herdman had been appointed by the time Kemp returned from India. All five of us now worked at separate tables in just one room, which was none too large, at the top of the Colonial Office; charts of the ocean, plans of the ship, and samples of all kinds of gear filled it to overflowing. There we worked out every detail of the ship's scientific equipment and laboratories. From all this which might have been confusion, Kemp with his admirably blended qualities of tact, understanding and firmness, distilled an ordered progress. While we each had our different jobs to do, he supervised and discussed every smallest detail.

The many new devices of plankton net design, the various mechanisms for opening and closing nets at different depths below the surface (to ensure that they only took samples from the required levels and not on the way up or down), and numerous other gadgets, including depth gauges and my continuous plankton recorder, were all invented in that room. Each was drawn to scale on squared paper, discussed, redesigned and redrawn perhaps several times before finally being passed for construction. Then during their manufacture, there were many visits to be made to the various engineering firms carrying our ideas into effect. The fittings of the ship's laboratories, the arrangements of winches, davits, wires for lowering water sampling bottles and stouter steel cables for sending nets to the great depths all had to be worked out. All the different kinds of log books with their various headings and columns for the entry of hydrological and plankton data, also the many kinds of labels to go in the specimen jars, were evolved after much deliberation and the testing of various label papers in sea water. Nothing was left to chance. It was this attention to small but vital points that contributed so much to the subsequent success in the field.

A study of the migrations of whales, as already pointed out, was clearly most important, and, as we have seen, the successful marking of fish raised the hope that somewhat similar measures might be employed; the firing of numbered darts into them naturally suggested itself. There was already evidence that such might prove successful, for harpoons of North American origin had been found in blue whales killed by Norwegian whalers in the Barents Sea in 1888 and 1898, providing the first direct evidence of extensive whale migrations[1].

The mark we evolved was like a large drawing-pin mounted on a wooden shaft fitted with felt wads and fired from a 12-bore sporting gun; the stout pin, which was $2\frac{1}{2}$ inches long and bore three strong barbs, entered the blubber but the disc remained visible on the outside while the wooden shaft flew off on the shock of impact. The disc head of the mark bore a number and an inscription saying 'Reward for return to *Discovery* Committee, Colonial Office, London.' A sketch of this mark and shaft is shown overleaf.

Another device for whale-marking was also tried and should be

[1]Murray and Hjort, *The Depths of the Ocean*, p. 714. London, MacMillan, 1912.

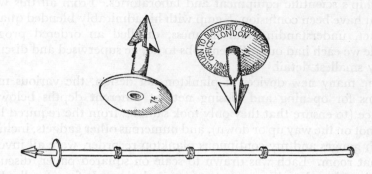

The whale mark as first used in 1924; it is shown in the lower figure as fitted to the wooden shaft for firing from a 12 bore gun. The improved type introduced in 1932 is show on p. 447.

recorded. Sir Sidney Harmer, then Director of the British Museum (of Natural History) and a member of our Committee, was keenly interested in our experiments but believed it might be an advantage to have a silent weapon; he thought the gun might scare the whale so that if we made a bad shot it might swim off at speed and not allow us a second chance. He therefore got his friend Professor C. V. Boys, the famous Cambridge physicist, to design us a large crossbow to shoot our marks like arrows with almost the same velocity as our gun. This bow was a somewhat terrifying instrument mounted on a stand; its 'string' was a steel wire drawn back by a jack and ratchet against two powerful springs. If the wire snapped and whipped back, the archer must surely be cut in two, we thought! I well recall, not without a little amusement I'm afraid, the scenes at target practice behind the Natural History Museum, exactly where now stands the great Whale Gallery. A large oil-cloth dummy whale had been prepared as a target and as I wound back the spring for the first shot everyone stood back, almost taking cover. It had the flavour of an old Victorian print, with Sir Sidney directing operations in the frock coat which he always wore on duty.

Then came the practice with both gun and crossbow on a dead whale stranded near Ventnor in the Isle of Wight. The results were encouraging, for the marks held firmly in position in the blubber; we brought a large piece of blubber back to London to use as a target for further practice. I well remember driving down Piccadilly on our way from Waterloo Station to deliver the blubber at the Bond Street shop of Messrs. Holland & Holland who had made the guns for us and at whose range in North London we practised; we wondered what kind of hunters people thought we were, with a large piece of highly odorous blubber sticking out of a barrel tied to the back of the taxi and the large cross-bow on the roof!

Now quite independently Professor Johan Hjort, the great Norwegian oceanographer and fishery scientist, was initiating similar experiments in Norway. He invited me to join him in the *Michael Sars* on the first whale-marking expedition ever made so that we could compare our two methods. He had planned a considerable investigation in relation to the whale stocks of the north and so we decided to make our plankton nets to the same design as his in order that there might be strictly comparable data from the two poles[1]. Thus there was another reason for my going: to bring back detailed notes of the *Michael Sars* equipment. I met Hjort in Oslo and travelled with him to join the ship at Trondhjeim and then made a three-weeks' cruise sampling plankton and hunting whale off the north-west of Norway, round the Faroe Islands and off Iceland.

It was an invaluable experience to see all the equipment and methods of working on the ship made famous by the Atlantic voyage described in that classic *The Depths of the Ocean*. One important reason, among others, for the fame of that *Michael Sars* cruise was Hjort's use, at different depths, of large tow-nets which could be closed at the end of their tow *before* being hauled up; they gave accurate information on the life in the different water layers because they did not also catch animals from other levels on the way up to the surface. In this way he was able to correlate the various adaptations of the fish and other animals with differences of depth. Kemp and I admired Hjort's work enormously and we were resolved, with our own large nets, to follow his lead and add to the knowledge of this deep water life.

I could write so much on the delights and interest of that cruise with Hjort; but, as it is hardly part of my theme, I must be brief. With Hjort was Professor H. H. Gran, the great authority on phytoplankton, and I learnt much from him too. For my benefit, they and other scientists and officers insisted on speaking English always in my presence and gave me the utmost help in all the notes and sketches I made of their equipment and methods of working. In the matter of whale marking, we had successful hunting off the Faroes, and again near the Westmann Islands off the south coast of Iceland, where we came across many fin whales. Hjort's method was to fire a barbed mark, a good deal larger and heavier than ours, from a shoulder

[1]Actually, as it turned out later, he was not able to go on with the project so that the planned comparative study of the distribution of whale food (the krill) at the two ends of the world never materialised.

harpoon gun. His mark was mounted on a metal shaft (which went down the barrel of the gun as our wooden one did), but was also attached to a length of line coiled up in a special container below the barrel of the gun; on making a hit the shaft was released from the head and pulled back on the line, to give the firer news of success, whereas, if he failed to score a hit, the head came back to be used again. A number of successful shots were made by each, but I felt that ours had the advantage of being a lighter gun which could be more quickly reloaded for a second shot; and it was not usually difficult to see if our mark had hit the whale.

With the cross-bow I never succeeded in despatching an arrow at all, for it was much too cumbersome; the whale never came up in just the right place and by the time I had got the bow on its tripod mounting into position the whale was well below the surface again! Our practice also showed that a silent weapon was unnecessary, for with our guns we succeeded in putting several marks into one whale without it taking fright. Sir Sidney Harmer had had two cross-bows made, one of which I took with me on the *Michael Sars* and had instructions to present it to Hjort. After the way he laughed when he first saw it I found it a little difficult to break the news that I had brought it specially for him; however, we both saw the funny side of it and when I left I expect it was quietly dropped over the side!

Back in London the work went on. I must not, however, dwell much longer on all we had to do; too many details become tedious. In truth we ourselves were beginning to weary of them and longed to be off. Our work at the office, however, was relieved not only by visits to the different firms making our gear but sometimes by a trip on the Thames, when we chartered a tug to test the rope tensions with various large tow-net frames we had specially made of stream-lined section to reduce the towing strain. And from time to time we visited Portsmouth to see the progress on the *Discovery* herself and to fix the position of winches, davits and so on.

The ship's reconstruction took much longer than anyone had supposed and in the end it was being dreadfully hurried in an attempt to reach the South for the opening of the 1925-6 whaling season at the end of November. This led to a false start which was very frustrating. We sailed from Portsmouth in July intending to carry out tests off the Bay of Biscay with the new deep-water echo-sounding gear then in its infancy, and to return to let the technical experts land in Falmouth before finally heading south. It proved to be a test of more than the echo gear; by good fortune, as it turned out, we struck a summer gale of unexpected violence in the Bay. The hurried work on many of the fittings and hatchways was found to be faulty as heavy green seas thundered on the decks and at times sent cascades of water into the cabins below. But for this gale we might not have had such a trial till we were in the 'roaring forties' of the Southern Ocean.

We returned to lie in the River Dart for two months while she was made perfect at the yards of Messrs. Phillips & Co. Now we saw a Dr. Kemp we had not seen before: Kemp the craftsman, the cabinet maker. In the former hurry to get the ship to sea so many of the laboratory details which we had carefully specified had not materialised: the little table racks for tubes and bottles to prevent breakage in a rolling ship, shelves and brackets to hold this and that upon the walls, a frame for whale-marking guns and many other such things. Under Kemp's guidance we all became workers in teak. His products, beautifully dovetailed and fitting to perfection, might have come from the hands of Chippendale; they were superb. Mine, I always maintained, had a certain rustic charm about them: a certain artistic (if unintended) asymmetry!

Here at Dartmouth we were joined by our two new zoologists who were to follow us out on the *William Scoresby* in a year's time: D. Dilwyn John, who is now C.B.E. and Director of the National Museum of Wales, and F. C. Fraser, who is now C.B.E., F.R.S. and Keeper of Zoology at the British Museum (Natural History).

At last, after so many delays, the great day was at hand; we were ready to sail once more.

CHAPTER 3

OFF AT LAST: AN INTRODUCTION TO OCEAN LIFE

Thursday, 24th September, 1925. It is seven o'clock as we steam slowly down the Dart in the fading evening light. The false start of two months ago and the long period of waiting had tended to deaden the feeling of excitement; but now, however much some of us may try to hide it, I am sure we are all experiencing the same almost physical sensation of satisfaction.

[This and the chapters which follow are taken in the main from my day-to-day journal written on the voyage, but to some extent revised and expanded as explained in the preface. Some new material has been incorporated in places and such passages will be placed in square brackets. These additions may be of several kinds: more mature comments on what was originally written, notes of more recent research bearing on the subject discussed, or simply a fuller explanation of some phenomenon or perhaps a bit of earlier history relating to the events recorded.]

In true English fashion I should, no doubt, hide my inner self; yet, if my journal is to recall the real feelings of the day, I must set down the thoughts that run continually through my head—and I am sure through others' too. At last the day has come. We are sailing south, through the tropics with all its wealth of unfamiliar ocean life, to the expanses of the 'roaring forties,' the home of the wandering albatross; and then on to the world of ice, peopled by penguins, seals and whales. The leviathan is our special quest. After a call at the Canaries we shall make for Cape Town and so go sailing into Table Bay; we shall then go south-west to South Georgia and then south again from there. It is a schoolboy's dream come true. We are sailing in a square-rigged ship—with only auxiliary steam. I recall again Frank Bullen's remark from *The Voyage of the Cachalot*: 'I can conceive of no more delightful journey for a naturalist than a voyage in a southern whaler . . .'. We grip the rail to make sure that it is really true, and see the banks of the Dart go sliding past. The setting refuses any longer to be ignored:

56

Sailing south—a sketch from the bridge.

surely this is one of the fairest spots in all England from which to say good-bye. I am thankful that my personal farewells were over a day or two ago, so that I am freer than some others to enjoy the spectacle; for in its own small way it *is* something of a public show.

On either side of the river, as we pass through Dartmouth, little crowds of people have gathered to cheer us and to shout 'good luck.' From windows all about the town handkerchiefs are waving—and even flags. Engine and steamer whistles hoot. The captain waves good-bye to his wife and children who are up a lane on the hillside where they can get a last view of us; we pass round a bend, out of sight of the town, and out into the open sea. Astern of us the sun has set leaving a lemon-yellow sky behind the velvety-black of the coast-line; ahead, the sky is a deepening blue with a brilliant crescent moon sending across the water a path of gold into which we turn our bows.

While we have yet to make certain tests with the new deep-water echo-sounding apparatus and then to return our guests, the Admiralty experts on the machine, to Penzance, I cannot help regarding this as the real start. *'We are off at last!'* Who is not repeating it to himself with a wild joy?

Sunday, 27th September. The first day out, Friday, was cold and rough with a freshening sou'westerly wind against which we made little headway; and in the afternoon we ran back for shelter to the Cornish coast anchoring in the mouth of Helford River, thick with mist and rain. In the night, after blowing hard, the wind shifted round to the north so that we were off at seven in the morning with lower top-sails set—sailing and steaming down the coast in brilliant sunshine. All yesterday and to-day we have been sailing to the south-west, adding more canvas bit by bit until by this afternoon we had a dozen or more sails set. Both with the sun by day and with the moon at night she is a superb sight.

No one, who has not experienced it, can appreciate the full attraction of seeing—and *hearing*—square-rig sails set. Gradually, one after another, they are unfurled and the yards raised; they are raised to the chorus of some old sea-shanty—'Blow the Man Down,' 'Whiskey Johnnie,' or 'Roll the Cotton Home'—as all hands heave on the long rope stretching away aft. We all give a hand at it, or, in the case of the lighter fore-top-gallant sail, we run aft with the rope. A number of our crew have been specially selected for their experience in square-rig; and old 'Sails' himself (Sailmaker Jimmy Forbes) in his younger days, had made a number of voyages in the old Dundee whalers. To any one who has only heard sea-shanties sung in drawing-rooms, or from the concert platform, it is indeed impressive to hear them used *functionally*: to lighten the labour of heaving and to keep all hands pulling together.

Here it may be well to give a few particulars of the ship herself. She is rigged as a barque and her masts, yards and rigging are well shown in the photograph in Plate 37 (p. 448).[1] She has an overall length of 198 feet (or on the waterline, stem to rudder post, 172), an extreme breadth of 34 and a draught of 16 feet. Her bows are sharp, at an angle like an advancing sword, and heavily strengthened, all for cutting through the ice; to this end the stem is reinforced with

---

[1]During the reconstruction her masts, spars, sails and rigging were entirely renewed so that it was possible to carry into effect some of the suggestions made by Captain Scott for the improvement of her sailing qualities; to this end the centre of effort was advanced by placing the fore and main masts farther forward than in the original design. There was also a slight increase made in her sail area, and, to facilitate handling, the original single top-gallant sails were replaced by upper and lower ones on both fore and main masts.

The R.R.S. *Discovery* sailing south, sketched from a photograph (not the author's) taken from the tip of the bowsprit.

heavy oak timbers to a thickness of 8 feet at the head and 10 feet at the foot, and its outer cutting edge is sharpened by galvanised steel plates. She will advance upon an ice floe, ride up it as the inclined bows make contact, and then, with the great weight of her strengthened stem, begin to slice down like a cake-knife cutting the icing of a cake. Apart from this she is of wood throughout with a framing of English oak made as far as possible from naturally-grown curving timber; her planking is Canadian elm below the waterline and pitch pine above, with an outer sheathing of green-heart. A stronger vessel could hardly be imagined. Her displacement is about 1,600 tons, and her auxiliary steam (triple expansion) engine is of 450 h.p.

Let us take a look round and begin by mounting to the forecastle head. From here are the most glorious views of the sea imaginable; we have a feeling of soaring up over the waves like a bird, whilst behind us are the great towers of sails, filled with the breeze and brilliant in the sun, like outstretched wings. But it is the equipment I want to explain. I am indenting this descriptive section so that those who may find the details too technical can skip to the end of it on p. 63.

Each item mentioned will be followed by a number referring to the sketch plan opposite, so that the reader by glancing at this will, I hope, get a good idea of the general arrangement. On the centre line forward is the wide swinging anchor davit (1) which not only lifts the anchor over the side but also serves for working the deep-water sampling bottles; for this latter purpose a fine-stranded steel wire runs round blocks to the davit from a small steam-winch (4) carrying $3\frac{1}{2}$ miles (3,500 fathoms) of it. Also on the centre line is the capstan (2), geared to a steam windlass on the deck below, and farther aft still is a powerful searchlight (3) which, when we get south, will be invaluable for navigating among icebergs at night. On either side of the forecastle, jutting out beyond the rail are small platforms (5) from which a sounding with the lead can be taken in shallow water; and, against that on the port side, is the Lucas steam sounding machine (6), capable of plumbing the greatest depths with its fine piano wire.

Coming down from the forecastle to the upper deck (the main deck being that of the cabins below) and proceeding aft we pass the companion-ways (7) leading down to the galley and the crew's quarters and come to the bridge (8). This is most spacious for it covers a large deck house which contains a number of cabins. These include the chart room (9) facing for'ard and spanning the whole width of the house, with a survey store (10) and the wire-

Outline plan of the upper deck and forecastle of the
R.R.S. *Discovery*

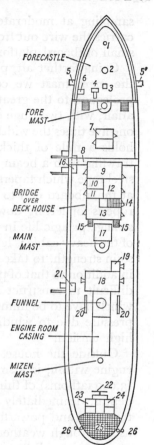

FORECASTLE

FORE
MAST

BRIDGE
OVER
DECK HOUSE

MAIN
MAST

FUNNEL

ENGINE ROOM
CASING

MIZEN
MAST

1. Anchor davit
2. Capstan
3. Searchlight
4. Deepwater   hydro-
   graphic winch
5. 5′ Sounding plat-
   forms
6. Lucas sounding ma-
   chine
7. Companion ways to
   galley and crew's
   quarters
8 Wing of bridge (above
   deck house)
9. Chart room
10. Survey store
11. Wireless cabin
12. Deck cabin
13. Main laboratory
14. Companion way to
    ward room
15. Stairways up to
    bridge

16. Shallow water hydro-
    graphic and plank-
    ton winch (with out-
    board platforms)
17. Wardroom skylight
18. Main winch house
19. Auxiliary winch
    drum
20. Accumulator springs
    for use with towing
    warps
21. Deepwater plankton
    winch (with out-
    board platform)
22. Auxiliary steering
    wheel
23. Officers' lavatories
24. Armoury and lamp
    store
25. Grating platform
26. Stern fair-leads for
    the warps from the
    main winch

less cabin (11) on the port side, a spare cabin[1] (12) on the
starboard side, and, at the after end, the large main laboratory
(13); then between the last two items is the companion-way (14)
down to the ward room below. The laboratory we shall see in more
detail later on. The bridge, gained by two stairways (15) up
from the deck aft, is entirely open giving a view of all the rigging
and sails; at its forward end it spans the full beam of the ship
so that the officer of the watch can look out from either side and
see the whole length of the vessel's flank from stem to stern.

Opposite the chart room on the port side is a small steam
engine (16) driving two winch drums, each holding 1,000 fathoms
of stranded wire; they are for vertical plankton nets and water

[1] This can be used as a sick bay if needs be.

sampling at moderate depths, and against each a short boom carries the wire out from the side of the ship, where there are also small outboard platforms for working the gear.

Going farther aft, past the skylights of the wardroom (17) and the main mast we come to the steel house (18) which gives protection to the great steam winch[1]. This is a truly magnificent affair, with two huge drums like the winch of a trawler, but with one five times the width of the other. The smaller, on the port side, holds a mile of thick steel rope ($1\frac{5}{8}$ inches circumference) for trawling with a beam trawl; the other carries 5 miles of a special steel rope which tapers in thickness from $1\frac{3}{4}$ inches circumference at the inboard end to $1\frac{1}{2}$ inches at the outboard end. This latter rope is for letting down and towing very big nets to fish for the strange pelagic life in the great ocean depths; as more and more of the heavy cable is let out, it gradually increases in thickness, and so in strength, to take the strain of its gradually increasing weight in addition to that of pulling the net. Such a tapering warp is very difficult to construct and so very costly. The drums of such a winch have to be immensely strong to withstand the accumulating pressure due to winding on such a great length of cable under high tension.

Outside the house, on the starboard side, but geared to the engine within, is a smaller auxiliary drum (19) carrying 3 miles (3,000 fathoms) of thinner cable for pulling plankton nets at lesser depths. Immediately behind the winch house, on either side, are two long and powerful springs (20); these, when large nets are used in rough weather, are linked by clamps to the cables so that any uneven pull due to the ship's pitching may be damped down by their expansion and contraction and so reduce oscillations in the forward motion of the net.

Slightly abaft the winch house on the port side is yet another small steam engine and winch drum (21) for operating the deep-water vertical plankton nets; this unit is equipped with a similar outward platform and boom to that of the 'shallow-water' unit farther forward, but here the winch drum carries 3,500 fathoms of fine stranded wire. When we come to work a full scale plankton

---

[1]The position of the main winch in front of the engine room casing was far from ideal because the ropes coming out from the house forward had to pass round two right-angles, i.e., round bollards, to pass aft to the towing leads at the stern and also because the man working the winch had not a direct view of what was happening as the nets were coming in aft. A better position would have been abaft the engine-room facing the stern, but this, on account of the mizzen mast, was impossible to arrange.

and hydrographic station over deep water we shall be using all four small winches on the port side at the same time: water-sampling bottles and nets will be sent to the great depths by the two winches farthest apart (to avoid entangling the wires) while at the same time samples will be taken from the lesser depths by the double unit amidships. Above the engine room casing are the lifeboats, and abaft the mizzen mast are two small houses, one on either side (23, 24), containing an armoury, a lamp store and officers' lavatories. Then at the very stern is a slightly raised platform, a wooden grating (25), on which the large tow-nets will be received as they are pulled in over the port or starboard quarters; here in the rail are placed the 'fairleads' (26) for the cables running aft from the main winch. It is on this platform that we may expect some of our great moments; here we shall eagerly watch the large nets come in to see what they may have caught after being towed for several hours in the dark depths of some two miles down. Massive wooden bulwarks, breast high, limit our domain on either side, but here and there, both port and starboard, are lengths of step enabling us to jump up and lean over the side; these will be much used, we hope, in the tropics when beautiful jellyfish go drifting by and the ship may be slowed down to allow us to catch them with hand nets and other devices. Let that now suffice for our survey of the upper deck; too much description is tedious.

The sun-fish, *Mola mola.*

During the day two large sunfish (*Mola*) were seen; they are grotesque creatures with their stout oval bodies and large upper and lower fins, of which the former showed from time to time above the surface. Later a dolphin was seen and then our first large whale— a fin whale. We rushed to get a marking gun in readiness, but were unable to get close enough and soon lost him.

Tuesday, 29th September. Late on Sunday night, in some 600 fathoms of water, the first trials were made with the deep-water echo-sounding apparatus and the following morning it was again tried in much deeper water when a sounding of 2,210 fathoms was recorded. It worked well and the result was checked by the normal method of sounding by wire from the Lucas machine. This is quite a triumph for the Admiralty men, for it is the first time the machine has actually been tested over deep water under ordinary working conditions. The instrument itself is very complicated; behind the large recording dial the uninitiated will find an apparent tangle of wires, switches, electrically-controlled tuning forks, compensating clocks and what not; but the principle upon which it is based is very simple. A sharp sound, that of a hammer striking a metal drum, is made below the surface of the sea and its echo, sent back from the ocean floor, is picked up by a microphone placed in the bottom of the ship; by timing this echo exactly by electrical means, and knowing the speed of sound in sea water, the depth can be measured and recorded to the nearest foot. This is indeed a valuable invention which will enable us to chart the configuration of the ocean bed, thousands of fathoms below us, with an enormous saving of time; the normal method, that of lowering and raising a sounding lead on thousands of feet of wire, is a time-consuming occupation.

The sounding with the Lucas machine produced almost the same result, although giving a slightly higher reading, no doubt on account of the drift of the wire. This is another advantage of the echo apparatus, for one can never be sure to what extent the sounding wire is carried one way or another from the vertical by the various ocean currents flowing at different depths below the ship. [And to-day we are realising how much more considerable may be the speed of deep-water currents than was originally supposed; water masses two miles down in the Atlantic have recently been shown, by using deep-water radio marker buoys, to be travelling at speeds of one or two knots.] Attached to the sounding lead from the Lucas machine was a small tube which penetrated the ooze of the sea floor and so brought back a little of it for examination; now this is something that the echo-sounder can never do for us. As expected, this part of the ocean gave a typical

3. *Above*, sunset in the North East Trades. *Below*, a remarkable phosphorescent display of *Pyrosoma* in the wake of the 'Discovery' on Nov. 11, 1925 (at 1°06'S; 13°05'W) not far from Ascension Island

sample of what is known as Globigerina ooze. I had seen examples when I was an undergraduate at Oxford where we had some microscope slides of it from the great *Challenger* Expedition, but there is something very different about seeing it actually brought up from the depths; looking at it at once under the microscope, one almost feels the excitement that the early naturalists must have experienced when they first saw it.

This ooze is given its name because it contains large numbers of the

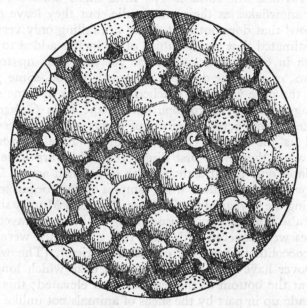

Globigerina oose seen under a microscope, (× 50).

beautiful little clusters of spherical shells formed by a tiny protozoan animal *Globigerina*, each about a twentieth of an inch across. It was first discovered, in the middle of last century, by J. M. Brook, a midshipman in the U.S. Navy, who hit on the idea of attaching a quill to the sounding lead to bring up a small sample of the ooze it penetrated. When the little shells were first found they created quite a stir. Were they formed by animals on the sea floor or were they the sunken shells of animals which lived near the surface? It is amusing to recall that those who held the latter and correct view did so for the wrong reason; they thought it was impossible for life to exist under the great pressure of the depths. By the late 1860's, however, many delicate animals had been dredged up from deep water and it came to be realised that they

C

would not suffer any inconvenience, provided that their bodies did not hold matter in the gaseous state. Liquids being almost incompressible, there can be no appreciable decrease in volume under high pressure, and the fluids within the body, if the body wall is flexible, will take up the same state of pressure as the water outside; with the pressures so balanced, inside and out, a deep-sea animal may move a delicate tentacle or limb with as much ease as one near the surface.

In the meantime, however, the tow-net showed that *Globigerina* actually lives near the surface. The little shells fall from the upper layers like snowflakes as their owners die, but they leave on the sea floor a 'snow' that does not melt. They are falling only very sparsely, and it is estimated that about a third of an inch is added to the depth of the ooze in every thousand years; yet this adds up to a foot in 36,000 years, or since the days of the Jurassic period, some 75,000,000 years ago, the ooze will have reached a thickness of some 2,000 feet.

Searching with the microscope among the little *Globigerina* shells in our ooze I came across numbers of much smaller objects which I recognised as the famous coccoliths which had also excited much attention when they were first discovered. They are little oval calcareous plates only about a thousandth of an inch across. They were found all over the ocean floor when samples of ooze began to be taken. Later, during the voyage of the *Challenger*, Sir John Murray showed that they came also from small organisms living in the upper layers; because their bodies were covered with these tiny plates they were given the name of coccolithophores (the coccolith carriers). [The white chalk cliffs of Dover have been formed from an ooze which long ago was deposited at the bottom of the sea and then elevated; this particular chalk is made up in part by the shells of animals not unlike *Globigerina* and in a larger part by immense accumulations of these minute coccoliths. I show a coccolithophore, *Coccosphæra* in my sketch opposite.]

To-night we are steaming back to Falmouth in a thick fog. We have decided to land our echo-sounding experts there rather than at Penzance so that we can replace an engine condenser pipe which has developed a leak. It may mean a delay of a day or two. The phosphorescence in the water to-night is unusually brilliant; a band of white fire surrounds the ship, whilst every few moments sudden sparks flash out in the waves alongside and occasionally some larger continuously-glowing bodies go drifting by. All such phosphorescence is now known to be due to living organisms.

The finer brilliance, forming this constant margin of 'flame' around the ship is due to the disturbance of myriads of tiny flagellates in the water. These are little single-celled organisms supporting themselves

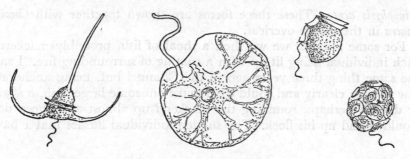

Flagellates of the plankton sketched through a microscope: from left to right, *Ceratium tripos* (× 150) *Noctiluca miliaris* (× 60) both highly luminous, *Dinophysis acuta* (× 200) and *Coeccosphaera atlantica* (× 1000).

in the water by beating little whip-like processes, called flagella, which act much as do the rotor blades of a helicopter. I have just referred to the little cocolithophores; they are also members of this class of tiny beings. Some flagellates contain green pigments and live like plants, but others are animal in nature and feed on solid particles; at this low level of life animals and plants are not far separated and indeed some of these little creatures live by both methods at once. Some have only one flagellum, others have two. Particularly common in the sea are the dinoflagellates which have one flagellum working in a girdle-like groove to make them spin round (hence the name from the Greek *dinos* meaning whirling round) and another driving them forward; actually the whole rotating body acts like a propeller. It is the dinoflagellates which are so particularly luminous.

On this occasion the luminescence round the ship was due to the little dinoflagellate *Ceratium tripos* which was present in millions in the water as we found by lowering a net of fine mesh silk into the sea and examining the sample obtained with the microscope. They are far too small to be seen individually by the unaided eye. They may occur, however, as here, in such large numbers that, when they are agitated and produce their light, the very water itself appears to be afire; so it is that any object thrust through the water, like the oar of a boat, appears as if surrounded by a flame. On some nights, as many readers will have noticed, every wave breaks on the beach with a flash of light, particularly in autumn when these little dinoflagellates are very abundant. Another of these little flagellates, commonly the cause of such phosphorescence, is *Noctiluca miliaris*. In our sample, with *Ceratium*, we also found another allied form, the beautiful little

Dinophysis acuta. These three forms are shown together with *Coccos-phaera* in the sketch overleaf.

For some minutes we watched a shoal of fish, probably mackerel, each individual being lit up with a coating of surrounding fire. I saw the same thing three years ago in the Channel but, being anchored, saw it more clearly and could then make out some larger fish, a shark or dogfish perhaps, rounding the mackerel up almost as a sheep dog would round up his flock. The sudden individual flashes that I have

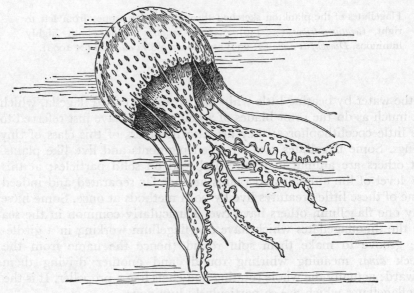

The luminous jelly-fish *Pelagia noctiluca* ($\times \frac{3}{4}$).

mentioned might be caused by various plankton animals, perhaps some of the small crustacea, and the larger continuously-glowing bodies would be the discs of luminous jelly fish, probably *Pelagia*.

Taken at the same time as the luminescent flagellates were a number of those other tiny single-celled plants called diatoms, of many different kinds. It is these that make up the main pastures of the sea. Under the microscope they glistened like jewels as their glass-like body-walls (of silicon) and their green and yellow plant pigments sparkled in the light reflected from the mirror below the slide. As we have already seen (p. 41) all the plants of the open sea are extremely small. Most of these planktonic diatoms have special shapes which give them a greater surface area in relation to their mass: some are flat and paper-like, others are drawn out into long needle-like forms and yet others are provided with fine hair-like spines, like thistledown, to give them parachute support. Some, however, are round just like pill-boxes but these have little oil globules to give them buoyancy. They reproduce by just dividing into two, and often the two daughter cells may remain attached to one another for a time; in this way, by repeated divisions, the long chains of diatoms so familiar to the student of the plankton may be formed. Examples of some of these different kinds are sketched on p. 41.

Yesterday afternoon we passed a most melancholy object: a broken lifeboat floating empty, derelict upon a flat calm sea. We steamed slowly close beside it, but there was no name or other sign upon it to give a clue as to whence it came.

Tuesday, 6th October. We reached Falmouth on Thursday morning

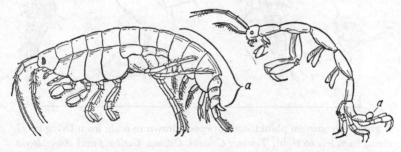

A typical amphipod (*Gammarus*) and the remarkable *Caprella*. The 'abdomen' *a* of the former is represented by just a little 'button' in the latter.

and anchored close beside the beautiful *Cutty Sark* [which is now, like the *Discovery*, preserved in London, but at Greenwich.] Here we remained until last night; having fitted the new condenser pipe, taken on more coal and engaged a new stoker, we slipped away just as it was dark. We are now steaming south as hard as we can; actually we are not doing much more than 6 knots and this is attributed to the thick coating of 'weed' which grew on the ship's bottom during our two months at Dartmouth—green seaweeds, hydroids and barnacles. The rope, on which was lowered the 'striker' for the echo-sounding instrument, on being pulled up was found to be covered with those remarkable crustaceans, caprellid amphipods, which had evidently come from the 'weed' as it brushed the hull. This was later shown to be so when we scraped off some of it at Falmouth and found it to be alive with these grotesque little creatures. They look so comical,

when compared with their more typical shrimp-like relatives, because
the whole of the hind part of the body, the abdomen, which normally
is made up of six segments, each provided with a pair of swimming
limbs, is here reduced to a tiny vestigial button—as seen in the drawing
overleaf. Instead of swimming, these little caprellids have taken to
feeding on weeds, or more usually upon the little hydroids, which look
like plants but are really animals[1]; to such climbing and browsing
creatures an abdomen would be an unnecessary encumbrance, so that
by natural selection it has been gradually reduced as those varieties
in which it was smaller climbed and fed the better. It will be interesting

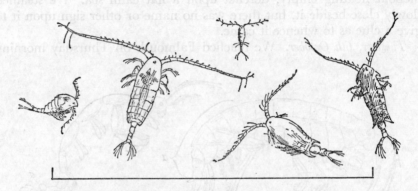

A group of common planktonic copepods drawn to scale from living specimens, from left to right, *Temora*, *Calanus*, *Oithona*, *Candacia* and *Anomalocera*.
The line below the drawing represents one half-inch.

to see how far into the tropics these Dartmouth specimens will survive.
   This morning there were many porpoises playing round the ship and
this afternoon a pair of chaffinches, a great tit and a pied wag-tail
have flown on board. This evening we put out another tow-net for
sampling the plankton. We have not yet started serious work, but are
just trying out our different pieces of equipment as we go along. We
must hurry south, with the least possible delay. The net we have just
used was a 1-metre diameter net, of coarser mesh than that used
before, intended to capture the larger plankton animals. Here we took
some of their most typical representatives; although actually different
species, they are of the same general kinds that will be playing an
important part in our studies on the whaling grounds south; in fact
we shall be meeting these main types all along, so let me here introduce
them with sketches as the principal actors on the planktonic stage. The

[1]Described on p. 73.

few group names are ones we shall be using frequently, so that it is well to get to know them.

Let us begin with four different kinds of shrimp-like animals (crustaceans). First there are the COPEPODA,[1] or copepods as we shall call them, the most numerous of animals of the sea; they teem in untold billions and range in size from a pin's head to that of a grain of rice. *Calanus*, one of the largest, is the principal food of fish like the herring and mackerel. The sketches I give will save much verbal description.

Next there are the AMPHIPODA[2], or amphipods, somewhat larger.

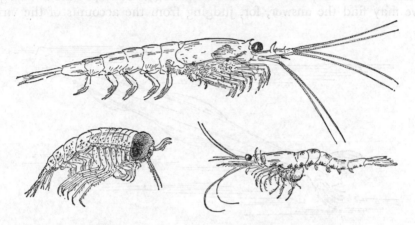

Three of the main kinds of larger planktonic crustacea: *above*, the euphausiacean (krill) *Meganyctiphanes norvegica; below left*, the hyperiid amphipod *Themisto gracilipes;* and *right* the mysid *Praunus flexuosus*. (All × 1½).

Those that live in the plankton, such as *Themisto* which we took here, have very large compound eyes; compare the drawing given here with that of a more typical bottom-living amphipod which is shown on p. 69 against the unusual *Caprella*.

Then there are a few mysids (MYSIDACEA) often called opossum shrimps because they carry their young in a pouch; most members of this group live near the bottom, but some are truly planktonic. They are more truly shrimp-like. In this same haul we were lucky to get one specimen of a euphausian (EUPHAUSIACEA). I say lucky, because the species we took (*Meganythiphanes norvegica*), while having a wide range of distribution, is much commoner farther north, where it forms an important food of the large whales; it is the counterpart of the krill

[1]Meaning oar-footed, Gk. *Kope*, oar.
[2]With two kinds of feet.

in the south which we are so much to be concerned with. A euphausian looks rather like a mysid, but may be distinguished, along with other characters, by a series of well-developed light-producing organs— reddish spots—on the underside of its body: hence the name of the group, from the Greek: *eu*, true; *phausis*, shining light. Perhaps some of the bright flashes of light we saw the other night were due to these animals. Each such organ is like a little bull's-eye lantern, complete with a lens in front and a reflector behind its source of light. What is the real function of their light? We do not know; it is still one of the present unsolved problems of marine biology. Perhaps on our voyage we may find the answer, for, judging from the accounts of the vast

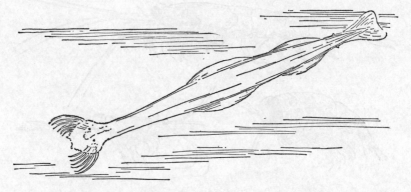

The arrow-worm *Sagitta* which is as transparent as glass and about an inch in length.

quantities of krill which feed the stocks of whales in the south, we may see more of these animals than any biologist has ever seen before.

In the same catch there were also many of the beautiful arrow-worms *Sagitta*. So transparent are they that they are all but invisible as they hang motionless in a bowl of water; then with a rapid vibration of their fish-like tails (but which are horizontal instead of vertical) they shoot forward like an arrow to seize some hapless prey, perhaps some small crustacean, in their powerful jaws. They are among the most voracious carnivores of the plankton.

Friday, 9th October. The last three days have been glorious, with sunshine and an intense blue sea. We have now crossed the Bay and are out over the really deep water. Yesterday and to-day a stiff north-easterly wind has filled our sails; it is on our port quarter so that with all canvas set we are flying along. If it were not for the weed on our hull we should be doing an almost record speed, the captain says, but as it is we are only making some 8½ or 9 knots. The light and shade on the curving, swelling sails by day is beautiful enough, but at night the lantern on the foremast casts a mellow glow into the fore top-sail producing a magical effect against the starlit sky.

Each day we have tried out a few more plankton nets and each time our zoological education has been enlarged. Yesterday we used a large 2-metre diameter one which caught many delicate little members of that strange group of animals called siphonophores; *Muggiaea* was their name and it was the first time I had ever seen them alive. How satisfying it is to see, actively swimming, the animals one has only read about or at best seen as a poor contracted specimen in a jar of spirit. I shall try to let the general reader share some of this pleasure by describing the more unusual creatures in as simple terms as possible. I want, as we go along, to give an account of the natural history of the ocean, both of the large creatures and the very small; the small are often more surprising than the large and just as exciting if you know something of their nature. The siphonophores are those curious composite animals which have aroused much interest because they pose quite a problem concerning individuality. They have a great variety of form and, as we are certain to meet with many different kinds, it will be well to discuss their general make-up now. To explain them, however, to those who are not zoologists, I must first describe their more simple relatives, the hydroids.

The very simplest hydroid is the little freshwater polyp *Hydra* of our ponds and ditches. It is somewhat like a bottle and round its mouth at the top is a crown of long tentacles: these capture prey— small waterfleas—by means of special paralysing stinging cells, and convey them to the mouth, to be passed into the large digestive cavity, the interior of the 'bottle.' Actually it doesn't just stand like a bottle; by a sticky secretion it can cling at any angle, and bend its body this way and that. In addition to reproducing by eggs, *Hydra* can bud off new individuals from its side; when these get large enough they break away and so start a new independent existence. In the sea there are many similar little animals which we call hydroids; most of them differ, however, from *Hydra*, in that the new individuals formed by buds remain attached and in turn bud again and again, and so build up branching colonies of many polyps. After a time, instead of budding off more polyps, they bud off tiny jellyfish, little bell-like medusae, which break off and float away; these carry the sexual cells, the eggs and sperm, to be scattered in the water and so give rise eventually to a new generation of the little branching colonies of polyps. The medusae spread the species far and wide as they are carried in the

C2

currents of the sea. There is in fact an alternation of generations: mobile sexual individuals (medusae) alternating with the sedentary budding polyp forms[1]. Now let us return to our siphonophores.

A siphonophore is like a hydroid colony, being made up of many polyps joined together by a common stem, and it also has medusae, which, however, are not set free but remain as part of it. It is a colony which hangs in the water, either just floating or being propelled by some medusoid persons which act as swimming organs, and is beautifully adapted for life in the great waters. We see a remarkable differentiation of persons; some are concerned with feeding, some with just

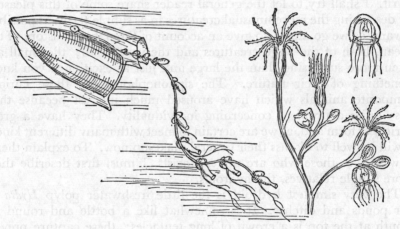

The siphonophore *Muggiaea*, ×3 (left) compared with a typical hydroid colony (*Bougainvillea*).

capturing food, others with propulsion, or with protection, and some with reproduction. Not only is there a division of labour between the persons composing the 'colony,' but there is a striking co-ordination of activity among them; indeed when we see them in action as a whole we are tempted to say that surely here is a higher plane of individuality made up by the fusion of many lesser beings. Should we be right? Which really is the individual now—the co-operating member or the whole complex? It is not easy to say.

At the 'head' of a *Muggiaea* 'colony' is a powerful swimming bell, a modified medusa, and from this trails a long stem along which at intervals are little groups of 'persons' each consisting of a similar set of

[1]There are some exceptions which do not free their medusae but retain them as eggs and sperm-producing sacs.

units: a feeding polyp with a long dangling tentacle for capturing prey, a reproductive medusa which produces eggs or sperm but is not itself set free from the group[1], and a protective 'bract' covering them like an umbrella (probably derived from a medusoid person). The swimming bell, the spearhead of the whole concern, has a constricted opening so that when it sharply contracts, the water filling it is shot out in a powerful stream backwards, shooting it through the water; its elastic sides cause it to fill again, and again it contracts, so that, by a continuous pulsation, it is jet propelled. It draws the long trailing 'colony' behind it as a locomotive draws a train. It is indeed very like a train and from the line of 'carriages' hang fishing lines which every now and again violently contract to jerk some struggling prey, perhaps a small crustacean, to the 'fishermen' sitting in each 'compartment.' They are fascinating to watch in an aquarium; the 'locomotive' is almost invisible because of its glass-like transparency, but the long trailing stem, shown up by the partly digested food in the polyp 'persons,' is seen to be thrown into gentle undulations so that it traces a wavy path through the water.

In the same haul as the *Muggiaea* were some of those curious oceanic animals called salps which look at first sight as if they too might be some kind of jellyfish, but are really very different; they are in fact very primitive relations of the vertebrate animals. They are so characteristic of the open ocean, and we shall meet with them so often, that it will be well now to find out how they live. Unlike the siphonophores which capture the more active animal members of the plankton, the salps specialise in feeding upon the very smallest elements of the floating world, particularly the tiny plants. The species we have caught is *Salpa zonaria*[2], but there are many other kinds similar in general form. They are another example of creatures originally descended from animals living on the sea-bed, but now specially modified for pelagic life, although in quite a different way. To explain them I will again refer to their more typical kindred: to the so-called sea-squirts or ascidians which we may sometimes find on rocks exposed by a very low tide. These have a sack-like body but with two openings at the top instead of one; if you try to pull one off a rock, two jets of water will shoot out, each like that from a water-pistol—hence the name of sea-squirt. Let us examine one.

Let us look at *Ciona*, one of the commonest ascidians. A sketch of

[1]Actually in some forms the main stem may break up and each little group of persons then go drifting along independently; an improved means of distributing the next generation as widely as possible.

[2]It is now called *Iasis zonaria* by some authorities.

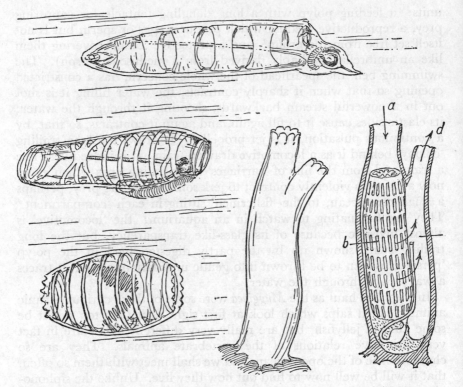

The salps *Salpa zonaria* (at top) and *S. fusiformis* (middle left) with *Doliolum* (bottom left) compared with the sea-squirt *Ciona* (shown whole and in diagrammatic section). All natural size, except *Doliolum* ×5. For further explanation see text.

the whole animal is shown above, together with a diagrammatic section. Water is drawn in at the opening *a* into a large basket-like cavity *b*, which has a vast number of little slits in its sides; through these it passes to another cavity *c*, surrounding the first like a jacket and from this it goes to the outside again through the aperture *d*. The water is propelled through the system by what are technically called *cilia* which are microscopic, hair-like processes projecting into the water from cells lining the little slits; they beat rhythmically and so drive the water forward[1]. This form of motive power is much used by aquatic animals; very small ones may actually swim by such means, but many larger ones, like our *Ciona*, use the method as a kind of pumping system to draw currents of water to them bringing finely

[1]Each cilium is not unlike the flagellum of the little flagellates which we discussed on p 67.

scattered food or dissolved oxygen for respiration. As the water is driven through the little openings in *Ciona*, thin strands of sticky slime (mucus) are secreted and passed across them (by other cilia) like a fine moving network to catch the tiny planktonic food which the water contains; these streams of mucus meet one another at the opposite side to form one banding of slime, like a moving conveyor belt, carrying its meal to its stomach. Let us now return to our salp.

Instead of having the two openings together at one end of its body, the salp has one at each end so that it is more like a barrel with open ends than like a sack; and its body is almost entirely transparent, except for the food showing in its stomach. The opening at what we call the front end leads into the first cavity and this, by quite a large aperture at each side (instead of many little slits as in the sea-squirt) connects with the second cavity, which has its exit at the back. There are muscles in the sea-squirt which can make its body contract; in the salp these are very well developed for locomotion and arranged in transverse bands. When they contract they drive the water out through the rear opening and so propel the 'barrel' forwards; the rear opening now closes and the front one opens so that water again enters as the elastic walls of the body take up their original shape. Now the front opening closes and once more the muscle-bands contract so that the water is again ejected backwards. So the salp swims forwards and as it goes, it sieves food from the water which flows through it. In an allied planktonic animal, *Doliolum*, the body is even more barrel-like with the muscle bands forming complete hoops, as shown in the sketch, and it has a number of small slits, like those of the sea-squirt.

To-day, using a small torpedo-shaped plankton-collecting device which can be used at full speed, we obtained some beautiful little pteropods of the genus *Clio*; these are little snail-like molluscs, adapted to a planktonic life by having wide wing-like fins which they flap and are hence often called sea-butterflies. Some have little spiral shells like typical snails, but others, like our *Clio*, have finely pointed ones. Several such pteropods are sketched on p. 113.

Now with the *Clio* were large numbers of living *Globigerina*, the little animals whose shells, when they die, sink to form the great deposits of ooze, a sample of which we saw last week (p. 65). But how different the living creatures look! In place of the little cluster of smooth spherical shells is a group of bodies each radiating thousands of extremely fine needle-like spines; and instead of being white they are a deep rose colour. It is the living protoplasm that has this striking hue, and this, of course, is lost at death; and then the fine spines break off at the slightest touch and no doubt dissolve away as the dead shells

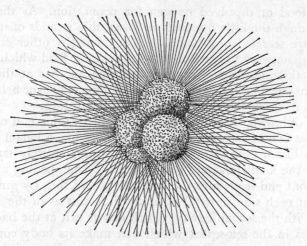

A living specimen of *Globigerina* (× 50).

make their long journey sinking to the ocean floor. The little *Globigerina* animal, apart from its shell, is almost as simple as the famous *Amoeba*— a mass of protoplasm of no fixed shape. Instead, however, of sending one or two blunt processes flowing out to capture food as does the *Amoeba*, it sends out vast numbers of much finer streams of protoplasm which branch and run together repeatedly to form a living network spreading out like a spider's web through the surrounding water.

More chaffinches and wagtails, as well as a goldfinch and a turtle dove have come on board in the last day or two; I fear some of them were taken by our kittens, almost young cats now, which are continuously on the prowl. Around the ship shearwaters circle and glide over the waves in sweeping curves.

Sunday, 11th October. The brilliant sunny days go on; the breeze, filling our full complement of sails, carries us forward over a gentle swell on the deepest of blue seas. The shapes that the curving sails take, brilliant and majestic by day, dark and fantastic by night, continue to delight the eye. Night after night, before turning in, we have stood by the rail to watch the fireworks of the sea: the countless sparks of luminescence flashing past the ship.

Yesterday we had the very exciting zoological experience of sending one of our 2-metre diameter tow-nets for the first time down to a depth of about 500 fathoms (or half a mile) by letting it out on the full length of the 1,000 fathom cable from the main winch. Here for the first time we saw examples of many of the deep-water animals. Here were the famous scarlet crustaceans, of many different groups, all looking as if they had been boiled like lobsters. Here too were jet-black fish of many kinds, and deep-red and plum-coloured jellyfish . . . [Now, however, I shall postpone further description of these animals from the depths because many more and better samples are to be met with later in the book, particularly in chapter 9.]

One animal, however, which came from this haul, I will mention now because it is not really a specially deep-water form and must have been caught in the net as it neared the surface. This is *Phronima sedentaria*. It is a perfectly transparent crustacean, a planktonic amphipod with enormous eyes, which fashions a barrel-shaped house (also quite transparent) by attacking and biting away the unwanted

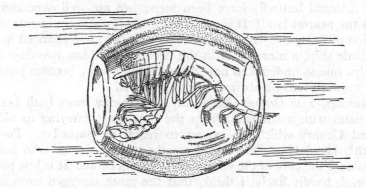

Phronima inside its transparent 'barrel' ($\times 1\frac{1}{2}$).

parts of the gelatinous bodies of certain planktonic animals such as *Doliolum* and *Pyrosoma* (related to the salps). Here we see *Phronimia* going through all his amusing antics with his barrel swimming in an aquarium. The females use the barrel as a protection for their developing young. Sometimes they ride inside it propelling themselves along by the swimming action of their limbs forcing a current of water out at the back; at other times they grip the barrel with a pair of clawed limbs and swim behind it pushing it forward like a perambulator; and sometimes as if for sheer *joie-de-vivre* they twirl it round and somersault with it through the water.

To-day a young merlin came on board; and this evening it caught one of our chaffinch visitors, flying with it to the water where it lost it and nearly lost its own life too.

Tuesday, 13th October. It is now getting much hotter. This morning my sea-water bath, instead of being a cold one, was quite warm.

Yesterday we stopped and took water samples and temperatures from depths of 2,000 metres upwards. The temperatures near the surface registered over 21°C. A strong warm south-easterly wind has been blowing and bringing hot air from the Sahara. To-day it has increased in force with—between the hot spells—heavy bursts of tropical rain and an occasional flash of lightning. Birds of all sorts continue to alight on the ship, but many of them, even though fed and cared for by the doctor (!), soon die; they seem to have reached a state of weariness from which they are unable to recover. Our merlin died this morning in spite of our efforts to feed him with meat. More interesting than the birds (to me at least) are the insects which arrive on board. To-day a beautiful Spurge Hawk moth or closely allied species, and a Silver-'Y' moth were caught and other moths and a Red Admiral butterfly have been seen; we are well over 200 miles from the nearest land! It is remarkable what distances insects may be carried alive by the wind, and what a number have chanced to reach our little ship, a mere speck in the ocean, in the last two days alone; it helps one to understand how distant islands may become populated with animals and plants from the continents.

Thursday, 15th October. Yesterday and to-day have both been hot and calm with a fair wind from the north-east carrying us along to Grand Canary which we expect to reach on Saturday. To-day a Death's Head Hawk moth was caught by the doctor who has now taken over the care of the entomological collections. It is just possible, although hardly likely, I think, that the moth emerged from a pupa packed with the potatoes which we shipped at Dartmouth; I doubt whether a pupa could survive being mixed loose with potatoes and tossed in a sack on to the ship.

We are still carrying along quantities of the caprellid amphipods (p. 69) from Dartmouth in the weed on our hull in spite of the high temperature of the water—now close on 22°C; we know this as we frequently catch one or two in the tow-nets as they are pulled in over the side and when we stop we can see them swimming (or rather kicking) in the water round the weed. We must have dropped a continuous line of them across the ocean. This is another example of the forces acting in the distribution of animals and plants across the sea. It is likely that ships have considerably extended the range of many species.

Friday, 16th October. To-day we made further tests with the Lucas sounding machine recording a depth of 3,100 metres and bringing up another rich sample of *Globigerina* ooze. We also made more trials with the deep-water hydrographic winch which before had not been working satisfactorily. Again it was found not to have sufficient power to lift the water-sampling bottles from the great depth required. This will require the introduction of new gears which must be fitted at Cape Town: a disappointment as we had specified most carefully what was needed. The deep-water plankton winch is the same and must be equally deficient, although we have not yet been able to test it with really deep nets.

This evening we let down a 2-metre diameter net on the full 1,000 fathom warp, reaching we suppose a depth of some 900 metres and kept it out for two hours. In addition to a wonderful selection of deep-water plankton animals [which I will not describe now] there was a very lively example of the pilot fish *Naucrates ductor*, evidently caught just below the ship on the way up. This striking fish, with the broad vertical bands of deep blue, is noted for its curious habit of swimming

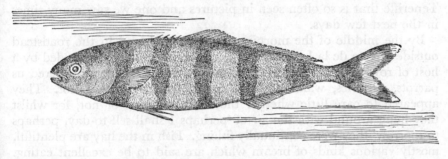

The pilot fish *Naucrates ductor*.

alongside or below whales and large sharks and even ships. Sailors believe that it has sharper eyesight than the sharks and so guides them to their prey and then gets scraps of food as the shark tears its victim to pieces. The latter part of this story may well be correct but the first part is most unlikely; they probably follow ships as seagulls do, to pick up scraps thrown overboard. In the old days it was not uncommon for several pilot fish to accompany the old sailing ships into Plymouth and Falmouth harbours. Actually on examining its stomach contents we found it had been feeding mainly on pteropods and planktonic amphipods.

Tuesday, 20th October. The last four days have been full of colour. On Saturday morning I had asked to be called a little before sunrise and on coming on to the bridge got my first view of Grand Canary: a massive purple mountain rising out of the sea ahead of us. Like the band round the planet Saturn hung a white belt of cloud about its slopes. In another moment the sun jumped over the horizon, over a sea of sparkling emerald and gold; astern, we looked down on a deeper green and orange surface across which waved ribbons of vivid crimson: reflections of the brilliant filmy clouds above. The mountain tops were now tinged with rose and, little by little, like watching the development of a photographic plate, the irregular ridges down their sides stood out and took shape. Over on the western horizon the base of Teneriffe could be seen rising into the clouds which hid the peak itself; presently, as the sun rose higher, the vapour screens slowly dispersed, like gauze curtains drawn aside in a pantomime transformation scene, revealing the whole mountain against the now pale blue morning sky. Later still, when I came on deck again, the curtain had once more rolled across her slopes; this time, however, it was her base which was hidden, veiled by a deep blue haze below the thick white band of cloud, whilst her summit stood out sharp and clear above. This is the view of Teneriffe that is so often seen in pictures and one we saw many times in the next few days.

By the middle of the morning we were anchored in the roadstead outside Puerto de la Luz, the harbour of Las Palmas, surrounded by a host of rowing boats whose occupants, swarthy Spaniards, offered us parrots, canaries, walking sticks, cigars, fruit and what not. They appeared to care little whether they sold anything or not, for whilst they hung around with the air of 'perhaps I shall sell to-day, perhaps to-morrow' they were continually fishing. Fish in the bay are plentiful, mostly various kinds of bream which are said to be excellent eating. La Luz lies on a narrow isthmus, only a few hundred yards in width, which connects the little peaked Isleta to the mainland; Las Palmas itself is some three miles along the coast to the south.

One is struck at first by the aridity of the place. I had somehow imagined that the 'Islands of the Blest' would be rich in luxuriant vegetation; plantations, however, will only flourish if carefully irrigated. The whole atmosphere is almost Eastern: blue sky, brilliant sunshine, sand, flat-topped houses and date palms. A parched and very dusty road connects La Luz with Las Palmas; along it run noisy trams [the date is 1925] and very small motor buses which are old Fords with bodies modelled on the lines of the little horse carriages peculiar to the islands. Taxis there are too, but their fares are exorbitant. Here and there along the road are hotels and villas with irrigated gardens: each a paradise of flowers presenting a strange mixture of European and more exotic blooms; particularly conspicuous were the red hibiscus flowers, crimson and magenta bougainvillaeas and the pale blue plumbago. It is the end of the dry season and in the city the view from the lower bridge, looking up the completely dry and stony bed of the river, was particularly colourful because of the sheets of the scarlet poinsettias which lined one side of it, and the cascades of pink ivy-leaved geraniums that tumbled over the walls. Very pleasing too was the little square, shaded by palms and magnolia trees, where we sat and drank beer or Canary wine; little green porcelain frogs spouted fine jets of water from their mouths into long rectangular blue-tiled basins in which swam gold-fish and terrapins.

On Sunday, making up a party in three motor cars, we journeyed up into the Monte district above Las Palmas. As we climbed higher and higher up the twisting roads the vegetation became more luxuriant; we passed from the more arid region of date palms and irrigated banana plantations with trees heavily laden with fruit, to the level of the vineyards when the road became lined on either side with tall and very graceful eucalyptus trees. Higher up still the vines gave way to little fields of ripening maize—patches of vivid orange in the strong sunlight; and the eucalyptus trees were now replaced by poplars and Spanish chestnuts. Above San Mateo (2,680 feet) the trees became scarce and the steeper mountain-slopes were covered with a stunted bracken. We went as far as Laquenetas (3,700 feet). At the end of the dry season the wild flowers were few; most conspicuous were the various species of *Euphorbia* of which there are a great many, some peculiar to the Canaries. The gardens of villas, however, were a blaze of colour; particularly fine was that of the hotel at Santa Brigida where we lunched in the open air on the way down. It was an Eden of tropical flowers and trees; in addition to those already mentioned as being common in the island there were deep red and pale carnation-pink oleanders, scarlet snapdragon trees, the great white drooping blossoms of *Datura*, deep blue clematis, honeysuckle, roses and white plumbago.

In the gardens and up the roads there were many canaries, not so yellow as the cage variety, but noticeably splashed with colour. Was it fancy that their song, heard amongst their native branches, seemed sweeter than when heard in some dim back parlour? Wagtails and finches were also numerous. A red-brown kestrel-like hawk was frequently seen hovering or sweeping across the road in front of us, and high up above the valley running down to Las Palmas, circled a great grey vulture, sweeping round in circles, gliding and soaring, without a flap of the wings. Insect life was disappointing; we saw few butterflies; the commonest being whites similar to those at home and a variety of Red Admiral whose red band on the upper wings was enlarged and spotted somewhat after the manner of the Painted Lady.

Of all the memories I shall carry away from this brief excursion,

The peak of Teneriffe seen above the clouds from the Bay of La Luz, Grand Canary.
Redrawn from a watercolour.

foremost will be that of the scenic effects: the rich reds and yellows
of the rocks and soil contrasting with the green plantations, the play
of light and shade in the countless little valleys and the brilliance of the
sun on the groups of white and yellow houses. Beyond this mountain
panorama lay the blue of the sea, with, far below, the promontory of
Isleta, jutting out on its thin finger-like isthmus. The sea we looked
down upon merged into a band of cloud and reappeared again above
it as the distant blue horizon; this cloud was the encircling belt which
we had seen from the ship as we approached, and it was now below us.
Far away along the horizon, the islands of Fuerteventura and Lanzarote
looked like enchanted fairy-story lands floating in the sky. Teneriffe
was hidden behind the range of mountains to the left.

Pages could be filled with the memories of these four full days: of
the crowds that collected round me as I sketched in the city, of the
charming little covered balconies, of the good Canary wines, of the
markets and the snail sellers. I will give only one other impression—
of the western bay of La Luz beyond the isthmus leading to Isleta.
This is semicircular and looks straight out towards the floating peak

of Teneriffe high above the clouds; it has a wide sandy beach and, drawn across it, is a submerged reef upon which the Atlantic breakers fall in a line of white foam leaving a calm blue lagoon within. Pink, white and yellow colour-washed houses line the shore, while here and there stand tall Canary pines. Here we came to swim, once in the evening as the sun set beyond Teneriffe in a sky of gold and once in the blazing heat of midday. Swimming to the reef, and looking down through the clear water, we found the rocks to be covered with black sea urchins with long needle-like spines; these must be avoided like the plague for their spines are barbed and poisonous.

This evening we said good-bye and slipped away in the dark, heading south again.

CHAPTER 4

THROUGH TROPICAL SEAS

Friday, 23rd October. We are now running on only one boiler, partly because of the heat in our very confined stokehole in the tropics and also to conserve our limited supply of coal for the long voyage to the Cape. We have not, however, decreased speed, for we have entered the North-East Trades—those winds which perpetually blow towards the equator—and with all sails set we are bounding along over a big ocean swell at some $6\frac{1}{2}$ to 7 knots. We are anxious to make the passage as quickly as possible, so we have not used nets in the past few days— except for the brief incident about to be recorded. We are taking every advantage of the wind.

On Wednesday, however, we captured our first Portuguese man-o'-war, as that fantastic jellyfish-like animal *Physalia* is popularly called; it had been seen glistening in the sunlight ahead of us and, by manœuvring and slowing down the ship for a moment, we ran alongside it and with a hand-net plucked it out of the water without stopping. It was a magnificent specimen, having a float some eight or nine inches long. Few more exquisite creatures can be imagined, yet, like so many that are beautiful, how deadly. It is another member of that curious group of animals, the siphonophores, which we discussed on p. 74 when we described the much smaller example, *Muggiaea*; they are those strange composite organisms made up of a large number of persons (some polyp-like and some medusa-like) yet so closely co-ordinated as to act as a single whole. *Muggiaea* was a fast moving, active swimmer; *Physalia* is the exact opposite: an entirely passive floating type. It is well named a man-o'-war, for it is indeed like a stately galleon in full sail. The blue and iridescent float—blown up like a balloon—rides on the very surface of the ocean and is driven forwards by the wind; along its under surface, as if from an inverted crowded deck, hang hundreds of polyp persons 'head' downwards in the water. Some of these are feeding 'individuals' with mouths that can be enormously distended. [I have put the word individuals in inverted commas for the reason we discussed in the last chapter (p. 74), and in a moment we shall see that we have still more reason to doubt their individuality.] Others are 'fishermen,' who capture the food for mouths to eat; each is provided with an immensely long and elastic tentacle which, when fully extended, reaches for 30 feet or more through the water as a fishing line and is heavily charged with the most powerful stinging cells. As the galleon sails forwards, these tentacles, which are of a deep and intense blue when contracted, trail behind as thin ribbons and then appear the same colour as their ocean background; invisible, they stick to any unfortunate fish which touches them. As such a victim twists to free itself, it gets more and more encoiled. The tentacles stick to it because each of their thousands of stinging cells have discharged into it a barbed thread like a tiny, microscopic harpoon; each is hollow and acts at the same time as a hypodermic needle injecting a paralysing poison.

The tentacles now contract and draw the stunned fish upwards towards their bladder 'ship' riding at the surface; and it may be a fish almost as big as the float itself. [Now a remarkable thing occurs: a thing I did not know at the time of writing my journal, but which I have seen since and which is beautifully described and illustrated by Dr. D. P. Wilson[1] of the Plymouth Laboratory. All the feeding 'individuals' act together by distending their mouths; and each mouth spreads out to cover one or two square inches of the fish's surface. The tentacles holding the fish relax and release themselves as the mouths take charge; eventually, as all the lips of the neighbouring mouths meet to form a mosaic over its surface, the fish's body is completely enclosed in a vast composite stomach formed by the widely everted cavities of all the feeding polyps. The fish, so active a little time ago, hangs limp in a great bag; slowly it is broken down by the combined digestive juices of the many units and is then communally absorbed. Are all these polyps really individuals, or has the whole colony, which now appears to act as one, obtained a higher individuality? We shall ask ourselves this question yet again when we see some more examples of these remarkable composite animals, and we will find it equally difficult to give an answer.]

In addition to these fishing and feeding persons which crowd the underside of *Physalia*, there are also vast numbers of reproductive bodies: little stems bearing clusters of small globular medusoid persons looking like bunches of tiny grapes—and purple too—and protected by small overhanging leaf-like processes which give the whole a very vegetable-like appearance.[2] It is the vivid colouring of the animal that

[1] *Jur. Marin Biol. Ass. U.K.* vol. 27, pp. 139-72, 1947.
[2] There has recently appeared in vol. xxx of the *Discovery Reports* a magnificent monograph

makes it such a striking object. Above the water-line the bladder turns from pale blue to peacock green and bears a rose-pink crest which is sometimes touched with orange; below is the mass of purple generative organs and the long trailing tentacles of almost gentian blue. My painting of *Physalia* in Plate 4 (p. 96) was made on a later voyage of the R.R.S. *Discovery II*.

For a naturalist this first view of a living *Physalia*—and we were able to view it closely in a glass aquarium on deck—made a day to be remembered; wonders continue, however, for at sunset on the same day we saw the 'green flash,' or 'green ray' as it is sometimes called. It was very brilliant and the few who had seen it before said it was a good example of this rare phenomenon. It occurs over the sea under conditions of exceptional clarity. It showed itself again this evening and knowing what to expect I was able to examine it more closely through field glasses[1]. It all takes place in barely a second of time. As the last thin arc or 'limb' of the sun falls behind the horizon, its two pointed sides become a brilliant prismatic green closing together across the top in a bright green flash as the thin remaining arc drops from view. Some people have tried to maintain that this is not really an objective phenomenon at all, but merely a subjective effect like the seeing of green after one has stared at a bright red object for a time and then looked away at a white surface. The green flash, however, does not occur when the sun is red at sunset, but only when it is particularly bright and yellow. The effect is certainly real and has, I understand, been examined with the spectroscope[2]; it is due to a difference in the refraction of the light in the red and green parts of the spectrum.

---

entitled 'Studies on *Physalia physalis* (L)'; it is in two parts: one dealing with the animal's natural history and morphology by A. K. Totton, and the other with its behaviour and histology by G. O. Mackie. Here the zoologist will find a fascinating account of all its complicated structure and its life history from the simple, very early, stages; as well there are first hand observations on the animal's behaviour made by the authors who went specially to the Canary Islands to study them alive. Totton points out that there is actually no evidence that the little female medusoid gonophores are ever set free as was at one time supposed.

[1] There have been rare instances of its being seen in mountain situations, I believe, when the atmosphere is particularly clear. We never saw it again during the whole of the two years' voyage; conditions have to be exactly right. Many years later, in 1954, I saw it once more, again on two consecutive nights, on passage from Colombo to Bombay.

[2] It has now been recorded by colour photography. See the fine article by D. J. K. O'Connell, s.j., in the *Scientific American* for January 1960 showing photographs taken at the Vatican Observatory.

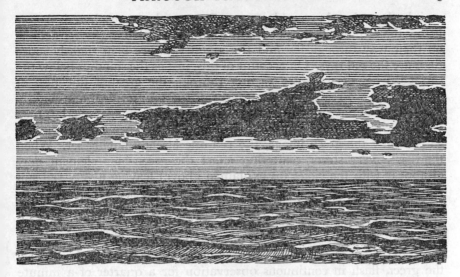

An impression of the rare green flash at sunset: like a momentary flat globule of prismatic green light. Redrawn from a watercolour made at the time.

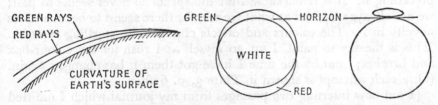

Under exceptional atmospheric conditions against the ocean surface the green rays of the setting sun are bent rather more than the red rays so that green and red images of the sun are slightly displaced as in the centre diagram; then like a mirage the green part may for a moment be detached above the horizon before finally disappearing from view. The curvature of the rays on the right is exaggerated.

[I confess that at the time I wrote this I did not fully understand the effect; but it appears to be very simple. The account I now give is based on the lucid description by Professor Minnaert of Utrecht in his excellent book *Light and Colour in the Open Air*, translated and published in London (Bell & Sons) in 1940. When the sun is low its rays have a long way to travel through the atmosphere so that a great part of its yellow and orange light is absorbed by the water vapour present. The violet light is considerably reduced by scattering so that we have left mainly the red and green-blue rays. Because the atmosphere is denser below than above, the rays of light are bent in a curve (by refraction) on their way through it; and the green rays are bent slightly more than are the red rays. On account of this, just as the sun dips below the surface, when its rays are passing through the greatest thickness of atmosphere, we really see two images of the sun, a green one slightly above the red one; now where the red and green images overlap they give the white light, but just on the top edge of the sun as it disappears we see only the green image, the red one already having set. When there is a very strong scattering effect the green-blue element may disappear with the violet (as explained above) leaving a very red sun and that is why we never get a green flash when the sunset is red. I am told that if, on board ship, one runs quickly up a ladder from one deck to another, one can see the green flash for a second or even a third time at the one sunset; in fact if one could be hauled up in a 'bo'sun's chair' to the mast head at just the correct speed one could no doubt view the green flash in continuous observation for a quarter of a minute or more.]

We are to-day in the tropics proper and night after night there are vivid sunset scenes; each evening's display seems better than the one before it and each instant seems to surpass in glory the moment preceding it. It is remarkable that the spectacle never seems to pall; we are always surprised at what we see, for there seems to be an endless novelty in it. The colours and effects change with startling rapidity. 'This is the sky to paint' I say to myself as I rush for my colour-box and brushes; but by the time I have got them it has changed again. (One such attempt is shown in Plate 3, p. 65.)

[I am now inserting two passages from my journal which I omitted under the entries of just over a week ago, 15th and 16th October, before we reached Grand Canary. I left them out partly because I felt the reader had then had a surfeit of plankton and also because the animals were typically tropical forms, so characteristic of the plankton we are now continually seeing.]

Yesterday (14th October) we took hauls with the 1-metre diameter and the 75-cm. diameter nets at 9 o'clock in the morning and another haul with the metre net at 6 o'clock in the evening, each at the surface. The 75-cm. net, of finer mesh, produced a rich catch of great variety, remarkable for the number of brightly coloured animals; it is hardly an exaggeration to say that the glass dish of specimens, so transparent and refractive beneath the low power of the microscope, presented the appearance of a bowl of sparkling precious stones. There were exquisitely delicate molluscs (heteropods) of the genus *Atlanta* with

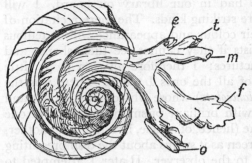

The planktonic snail *Atlanta* with its beautiful translucent lavender shell: *e*, eyes; *f*, expandible swimming 'foot'; *m*, mouth; *o*, operculum (a door to close the entrance to the shell when the head and foot have been drawn in for safety against attack), ×5.

thin spiral shells of pale translucent lavender[1]; there were 'long-tailed' salps (*Salpa mucronata*) whose glass-like bodies were picked out here and there with points of blue; and there were pale blue mysids or opossum shrimps, one of which bore a cluster of brilliant sky-blue eggs. All these contrasted with the hosts of little red, orange and yellow copepod crustaceans.

The number of different kinds of copepod present was such that it would have taken many hours to have identified them all with certainty; they were all new to us, but could be hunted down in the

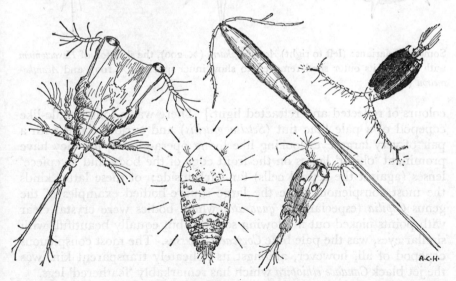

Some striking copepods of the tropical plankton, from left to right: *Copilia quadrata*, *Sapphirina ovatolanceolata* (with a flashing iridescence), *Setella gracilis* (above), *Corycaeus obtusus* (below) and the black *Candace ethiopica*. (Magnified approx. × 10).

[1]The heteropods are planktonic snails like pteropods but belonging to a different group.

large monographs which we had in our library on board. I will mention only some of the more striking kinds. The mere recitation of their names with notes on their colour and appearance will be tedious to those who are not zoologists if they cannot see their shapes and appreciate their delicate structures; I therefore give on p. 91 little sketches in black and white of all the ones I name. There was the celebrated *Sapphirina* (*S. ovatolanceolata*) whose whole body, as flat and thin as a fish's scale, flashes with brilliant prismatic colours; at one moment a vivid sapphirine blue (hence, of course, its name), at another, orange, fiery red or emerald green as it swims about the dish presenting first one angle, then another to the observer. [Later I attempted to paint this range of colour, but pigments can never record the *flashing*

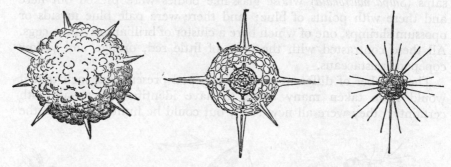

Some radiolarians: (left to right) *Acanthasphaera* (× 200), the skeleton of *Hexactonium* with part of its outer shell removed to show inner spheres (× 100), and *Acantho-metron* (× 50).

colours of reflected and refracted light.] There was a long needle-like copepod of a pale lilac tint (*Setella gracilis*) and curious forms with a pair of very large eyes looking like living opera-glasses, for they have prominent 'object' lenses on the front edge of the body and 'eyepiece' lenses (against the retinal cells) far back inside; of these latter kinds the most conspicuous were the large square-bodied examples of the genus *Copilia* (especially *C. quadrata*) whose bodies were crystal clear with points picked out in glowing scarlet; but equally beautiful, with similar eyes, was the pale blue *Corycaeus obtessus*. The most conspicuous copepod of all, however, amongst its delicately transparent kin, was the jet black *Candace ethiopica* which has remarkably 'feathered' legs.

In writing of the wealth of tropical planktonic life I must explain that it is a richness of quality rather than of quantity. There are a great many different species but not an immense number of each kind. In the polar or temperate seas we may get much larger plankton samples, but they are made up of a smaller number of species with many of them occurring in vast hordes; there we see hundreds of the same kind, whilst here in the tropics every one looks different. It is the same in the tropical forests where both animals and plants present an extraordinary number of species; it is as if species formation occurred much faster in the equatorial regions. Another feature makes the tropical plankton appear more striking than that of cooler latitudes: the creatures are drawn out into more fantastic shapes and more covered with slender spines and furnished with more feathery limbs. This is not just the expression of mere exuberance, but the result of a

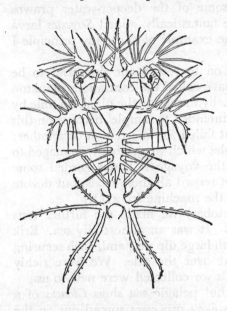

One of the remarkably spiny larvae of the prawn *Sergestes vigilax* redrawn from a drawing by R. Gurney of a *Discovery* specimen ✕ 20.

very simple physical fact: warmer water is more fluid (less viscous) than cooler water because its molecules have more motion and flow over one another more easily. On account of this the same object would sink twice as fast in the tropics as in the polar seas; if, however, it had a larger surface area to offer more resistance to the water, it would not sink so quickly. Thus evolution has continually tended to select the plankton animals of the tropics which are more spiny or feathery, or flat as paper or thin and needle-like to help them keep up in the water with less expenditure of energy.

This same sample of plankton was also rich in Radiolaria: protozoan animals of a different order from the *Globigerina* we have hitherto met, and having glass-like skeletons of silicon instead of ones of lime. The radiolarians do not send out a net of protoplasmic streams as does *Globigerina* but a radiating system of long thin spikes of protoplasm supported by fine axial rays. Particularly common was the beautiful *Acanthometron pellucidum*. *Globigerina* itself was represented by a particularly large species.

In the metre nets, of rather coarser mesh, we caught many more examples of those curious planktonic snails, the pteropods, one of which, *Clio*, we had met in the last chapter (p. 77). Here they were represented by *Limacina*, *Creseis*, and *Cavolinia* with shells and *Clione* with no shell at all; they are sketched on p. 113. Among the crustaceans were a number of the young stages of some of the deeper-water prawns including a superb example of the fantastically spined *Sergestes* larva which I have drawn as an extreme example of the spiny principle I have just referred to.

[My journal at this point goes on to record the first trial to be made with an apparatus which I have called the continuous plankton recorder, and is intended automatically to sample the plankton mile by mile as the ship goes along. I said 'intended to sample' because on this first and several subsequent trials it failed for one reason or another; these, however, were teething troubles which we gradually managed to overcome so that by the end of the voyage it had recorded some 2,300 miles of plankton. I shall not record all these trials, but devote a section to them where I describe the machine (p. 415).]

On the following day (16th October) we made the further tests with the Lucas sounding machine. It was an almost oily sea. Erik Hamilton and I armed ourselves with large dip nets and, each securing ourselves with a bowline, hung far over the side. We were richly rewarded, for nearly all the animals we collected were new to us.

There were many of the beautiful pelagic sea slugs *Glaucus* of a deep metallic blue and with long spikey processes spread out on the surface of the water like the wings of a butterfly or perhaps more like branching limbs. All that we took were floating with half the body exposed to the atmosphere and heat of the sun; they were indeed crawling upon the surface of the now stagnant ocean. They were upside-down so that it was their underside that projected through the water while their feathery 'limbs' held them up, apparently adhering by surface-tension to the underside of the surface film itself along which they stretched; the larger the specimens, the more feathery and extended were their limbs to give them greater support.

> *Yea, slimy things did crawl with legs*
> *Upon the slimy sea.*

What I have called limbs are not actually moved like legs in locomotion; these slugs crawl as do the water-snails we may see hanging from underneath the surface of a stagnant pond.

[I had indeed wondered how Coleridge could have put so many vivid descriptions of ocean life into his 'Rime of the Ancient Mariner,' given with all the appearance of first-hand knowledge, when the only voyage he had ever made, apart from the trip across the channel, was

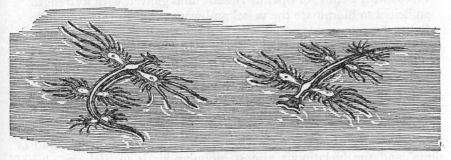

'Yea, slimy things did crawl' the sea-slugs *Glaucus* on the surface of a tropical sea.

from Italy to Malta. The answer has been given us in that remarkable study, almost a detective story, *The Road to Xanadu*, by John Livingston Lowes, first published (by Constable, London) in 1927 (second edition 1951); he calls it, as a sub-title, 'A Study in the Ways of Imagination.' With the insight of a Sherlock Holmes he traces the source of nearly all these descriptive passages. By consulting the old records of the Bristol Library, he was actually able to find out the books borrowed by Coleridge at the very time he was writing 'The Ancient Mariner' and showed that he had read the accounts of many of the voyages of the time, either in separate books or in some of the descriptions given in the *Philosophical Transactions of the Royal Society*.

> *But where the ship's huge shadow lay,*
> *The charmed water burnt alway*
> *A still and awful red.*

Lowes (on his p. 46) shows us from where, most likely, Coleridge got the idea of the red glow: 'from the 257th page of the second volume of the narrative of Cook's last voyage.' The *Resolution* is off Sir Francis Drake's 'New Albion,' out a little distance from what is now the coast of Oregon:

> *During a calm*, on the morning of the 2d, some parts of the sea seemed *covered with a kind of slime*; and some small sea animals were *swimming about*. The most conspicuous of which, were of the gelatinous . . . kind, almost globular; and another sort smaller,

that had a white, or shining appearance, and were very numerous. Some of these last were taken up, and put into a glass cup, with some salt water.... When they began to swim about, which they did, with equal ease, upon their back, sides, or belly, they emitted the brightest colours of the most precious gems.... Sometimes they ... assum[ed] various tints of *blue* ... which were frequently mixed with a ruby, or opaline *redness*; and glowed with a strength sufficient to illuminate the vessel and water.... But, with candle light, the colour was, chiefly, a beautiful, pale *green,* tinged with *a burnished gloss*; and, in the dark, it had a faint appearance of *glowing fire.* They proved to be ... probably, an animal which has a share in producing some sorts of *that lucid appearance, often observed near ships at sea, in the night.*

Although Professor Lowes does not realise it, the description he has quoted from Cook is undoubtedly of the little copepod *Sapphirina,* which we have observed a few pages back (p. 92), and the 'kind of slime' and the 'gelatinous almost globular kinds of life' are almost certainly salps; indeed we shall see later in this voyage (p. 132) how at times the sea is discoloured by great concentrations of salps which

4. Some of the blue and transparent animals at and near the surface of the tropical ocean. A key to the various kinds illustrated is given below.

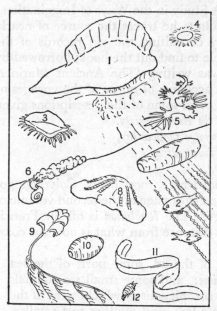

1. The 'portuguese man-of-war', *Physalia physalis.*
2. The fish *Nomeus gronovii,* which associates with *Physalia,* seen against the long trailing tentacles of the latter.
3. *Velella velella* or 'Jack sail-by-the wind'.
4. *Porpita sp.* (*umbella?*)
5. The pelagic sea-slug *Glaucus atlanticus.*
6. The snail *Ianthina janthina* with its bubble float.
7. The salp *Salpa fusiformis.*
8. The ctenophore *Deiopea.*
9. The siphonophore *Hippopodius hippopus.*
10. The pelagic tunicate *Doliolum.*
11. 'Venus's girdle', the ctenophore *Cestus veneris.*
12. The amphipod *Brachyscelus rapax.*

are accompanied by large numbers of *Sapphirina*; the latter being seen to be parasitic upon the former.

Let me give one more example:

> Beyond the shadow of the ship,
> I watched the water-snakes:
> They moved in tracks of shining white,
> And when they rear'd, the elfish light
> Fell off in hoary flakes.

And quote again from Lowes (his p. 44):

Our initial certainty (and on this point the evidence of the Note Book is irrefragable) is this: Coleridge read both Priestley's chapter in the *Opticks* on 'Light from Putrescent Substances,' and Father Bourzes's letter in the *Philosophical Transactions* on 'Luminous Appearances in the Wakes of Ships.' Moreover, his reading of the letter was due to his interest in those portions of it which he had already seen in Priestley—an interest which was keen enough to send him directly to Priestley's source of information. He came to the letter, then, not casually, but with an alert and receptive mind. And he read, for the second time, the statements which had stirred his curiosity. This time, however, they were detailed in a remarkably interesting record (touched with an engaging personal charm) of first-hand observations in distant seas. And here are a few of the sentences which Coleridge read— repeated, in part, for us as for him:

'In my Voyage to the Indies . . . when the ship ran apace, we often observed a great Light in the Wake of the Ship. . . . The Wake seemed then like a River of Milk. . . . Particularly, on the 12th of June, the Wake of the Vessel was full of large Vortices of Light. . . . When our Ship sailed slowly, the Vortices appeared and disappeared again immediately like *Flashes of Lightning*. Not only the Wake of a Ship produces this Light, but Fishes also in swimming leave behind 'em *a luminous Track*. . . . I have sometimes seen a great many Fishes *playing in the Sea*, which have made *a kind of artificial Fire in the Water*, that was very pleasant to look on.'

In this delightful account of the phosphorescence of the sea we are reminded of the fish we saw outlined on the night of 29th September (p. 68) and 'the great light in the wake of the ship . . . full of large vortices of light' is a splendid description of a ship passing through quantities of *Pyrosoma* as we ourselves shall presently see in our entry for 12th November (p. 120). Actually Lowes does not seem to have run across the original source of Coleridge's 'slimy things did crawl

D

with legs,' but I am sure he must somewhere have seen some voyager's description of the sea slug, *Glaucus*, which prompted me to make this digression.]

Also on the very surface were several specimens of that remarkable pelagic snail, *Ianthina*, each with its raft of eggs. The little snail itself is deep purple but forms a shell of the most vivid blue and buoys up its pale mauve egg clusters by a long floating raft of bubbles many times its own size. The commonest animals at the surface, however, were radiolarians, but very different from those met with yesterday; they were examples of *Colozoum*, one of the so-called colonial forms, i.e., many individuals held together in a common gelatinous mass, sometimes three-quarters of an inch across.

Among the more beautiful of all the surface animals we saw were further examples of the siphonophores. Here for the first time we came across the famous *Velella* or Jack-sail-by-the-wind as the sailors call it. This is one of the entirely passive drifting kinds again, like *Physalia* provided with a float, but much smaller, being at most only some 3 inches in length, and also provided with a sail. Here the float is made up of little air chambers formed of a thin, horny substance, and diagonally across its top, supported by the same horny skeleton, is a triangular sail set to catch the wind and send it, like a miniature yacht, sailing across the sea. On its underside, hanging down as in *Physalia*, are the tentacles, and the feeding and reproductive bodies[1]. *Velella*, *Ianthina* (but a different species from that just described), *Glaucus* and *Porpita* (which is about to be mentioned) are all shown in colour in Plate 4.

Porpita is built on the same general plan as *Velella* but is circular and has no sail. *Velella* is blue-green and violet; the disc of *Porpita* is a most intense blue so that when we look down on it from above it perfectly matches the deep blue of the tropical ocean and all that you can make out, as it drifts by, is the circle of fine tentacles looking like the delicate down of a dandelion seed head[2]. We collected more than a dozen *Porpita* in our hand nets, but the prize of the day was a true siphonophore *Athorybia ocellata*, again one of the passive drifting kind,

[1]Since this was written the true nature of these extraordinary animals has been revealed in 1946 by a remarkable paper in the *Quarterly Journal of Microscopical Science*, vol. 87, pp. 103-93, 1946, by my father-in-law, the late Professor Walter Garstang, and written when in his eightieth year. He has shown that *Velella*, and related forms such as *Porpita*, about to be mentioned, are really quite different in their nature from the rest of the siphonophores, different even from *Physalia*. He has shown them to be very large single polyps adapted to a floating life. I have given an account of this in my book *The Open Sea*, Vol. 1, p. 112.

[2] In the Indian Ocean and the Pacific only the young forms appear to be bright blue, the older ones becoming a dull grey.

The siphonophore *Athorybia ocellata*, redrawn from Haeckel ($\times \frac{1}{2}$.)

but with quite a small float. It looked like some exotic water lily, I have sketched it here. The float is rose red and, like the centre of a flower, it is surrounded by large petal-like bracts transparent towards the outside but splashed with orange nearer the centre; peeping out between the bracts were numerous rose-pink tentacle-like structures (the so-called palpons[1]) and down below hung five large pink feeding polyps each provided with a very long tentacle having numerous side branches armed with batteries of stinging cells: fishing lines for gathering food.

[These last few passages were taken, as explained, on p. 90, from the journal of over a week ago; let us now return to the true sequence of events.]

[1]Supposed by Haeckel to be concerned with tasting.

Sunday, 25th October. Each day brings its novelty. Yesterday a large flying fish flew on board and all day to-day shoals of smaller ones have been flinging themselves from the water and skimming the great waves in all directions from the ship. The sea is too rough and broken for good observation, but it seems certain that the wings do not flap to propel the fish through the air; they appear to act as the planes of a glider. The initial speed must be obtained by a swift rush through the water before taking off aided in the final launching by the lower blade of the tail, still below the surface, acting as a powerful propeller. [This is now well established by high speed photography.]

Yesterday afternoon the largest school of dolphins that I, or most

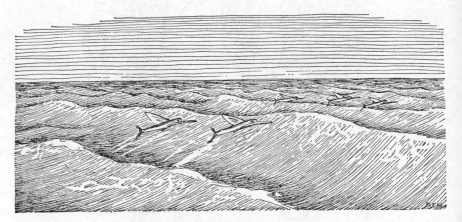

Flying fish (*Exocoetus*) in a tropic breeze.

of the ship's officers, had ever seen, approached and played round the ship. There were certainly no less than a hundred and some estimated that there were at least two hundred. Many of them kept leaping completely clear of the water. They did not stay with us long, however, and Hamilton, who was ready to try his harpoon, was frustrated. Who can doubt that they are leaping in play for the sheer joy of it? Well, yes, there are some who believe that they are doing this to rid themselves of lice; but they give every appearance of sporting in the waves [and there is abundant recent evidence of their capacity for play, as witness their games in the Oceanaria at Miami and elsewhere]. Was not Herman Melville right in *Moby Dick* to give the dolphin the name of Huzza Porpoise?

The name is of my own bestowal; for there are more than one sort of porpoises, and something must be done to distinguish them.

I call him thus, because he always swims in hilarious shoals, which upon the broad sea keep tossing themselves to heaven like caps in a Fourth of July crowd. Their appearance is generally hailed with delight by the mariner. Full of fine spirits, they invariably come from the breezy billows to windward. They are the lads that always live before the wind. They are accounted a lucky omen. If you yourself can withstand three cheers at beholding these vivacious fish, then heaven help ye; the spirit of godly gamesomeness is not in ye.

Making another trial with my continuous plankton recorder we caught two specimens of the remarkable little *Leptocephalus*; this was

Part of a large school of common dolphins—drawn from a diorama in the whale gallery of the British Museum (Natural History) and with help from photographs.

at first thought to be a distinct species of pelagic fish until it was observed by the Italian naturalists Grassi and Calandruccio in 1896 to turn into an elver, the young stage of the freshwater eel. Anything less eel-like than the *Leptocephalus* can hardly be imagined; it is quite flat and transparent, has the shape of a willow leaf and is about two inches long. Whether our specimens are actually the larvae of the common freshwater eel, whose typical *Leptocephalus* is shown in the sketch overleaf I am not certain, for they are too damaged by the rollers of my machine for definite identification [a fault now largely remedied]. The marine eels also have a similar larva; but our specimens may indeed be the young of the fresh-water eel which occurs in the streams of the Canary Islands. The life history of the common freshwater eel, with its larvae carried by the ocean currents from the breeding grounds in the depths of the Sargasso Sea more than two

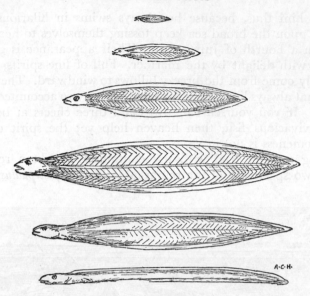

Sketches showing the development of the young freshwater eel, or elver, from its earlier stages as a flat
transparent *Leptocephalus* larva in the Atlantic plankton.
From the author's *The Open Sea*, Part ii.

thousand miles away, is certainly one of the most extraordinary in the
whole of zoology, but it is too well known to be repeated here.

Saturday night is a special one for the sailorman at sea, for then
his abstinence during the week is broken by the toasts of 'sweethearts
and wives.' The crew for'ard get a rum ration and we in the ward-
room pass round the port and drink first to the King. Being a royal
ship we toast His Majesty in naval fashion, remaining seated; this
custom, I believe, was started by William IV who, when at dinner
aboard a warship, noticed that some of the officers in the low-ceilinged
ward-room either bumped their heads or had to stoop on rising, and
so decreed that in future the Sovereign's health should be drunk
without rising to the feet. In addition to port some of us may share a
bottle of wine, a welcome change from the water and orange juice of
the week. After dinner we have a festive time; often, as on this
Saturday, we gather round the piano to sing old sea-shanties, working
our way through most of a book of them until we are hoarse. Sometimes
Dr. Kemp regales us with some of the old favourites from Gilbert and
Sullivan or our incomparable Scots comedian, Andrew Porteous

(Second Engineer) gives us 'I belong to Glasgow'. It is the breezy Chief—Chief Engineer Horton—who is the tireless pianist on these occasions; and with what gusto he plays!

To-day when experimenting with the new Ekmann full-speed water-sampling bottle we found in the water taken some beautiful radiolarians and, strange to relate, a single specimen of that rare and extraordinary copepod, *Calocalanus plumulosus*, with one of its tail plumes of the most enormous length. Other species of the genus, such as *C. parvo* which is shown here with it in the same sketch, also have

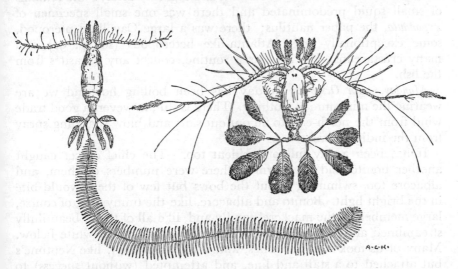

Two remarkable plume-bearing copepods of the tropical plankton: *Calocalanus plumulosus* and *C. pavo* (×8).

large feathery appendages, most likely to give increased support; but it is only *plumulosus* that has just *one* of the tail plumes so extravagantly lengthened, brightly coloured and shot with flashing gold. So far the male of this rare species has not yet been discovered. It seems likely that this strange structure may be a sexual device carried only by the lady. Now to explain the possible significance of this I must relate that the copepods, in mating, bring about an internal fertilisation of their eggs in a most original way. The male secrets a graceful plastic flask (called a spermatophore) round the sperm cells he has produced, and then, swimming up to the female, he attaches it—in some species using a remarkable forceps-like limb—to a cavity on the underside of her abdomen; in this cavity the sperms are stored ready to fertilise the eggs as they are laid. It would not surprise me if this long tail plume of the female *plumulosus* were shown to be a guide line for the male: first attracting his attention with its brightness and then providing a gilded staircase up which he can run to present his precious casket to his spouse.

Just as it was getting dark this evening several bonito appeared round our bows and the chief officer caught one with a line baited with a rubber eel. A good 10 pound fish it was, and, cooked for supper, proved to be excellent eating. Before passing it to the galley we examined its stomach for food and found a great variety: the remains of small squid predominated and there was one small specimen of *Argonauta*, the paper nautilus; there was a large Cavolinid pteropod, some exceptionally large Atlanta-like heteropods (see p. 91) and many crustaceans. We also, as a routine, collect any parasites from the fish.

Monday, 26th October. To-day has been boiling hot and we are wearing the minimum of clothing. There is still, however, a good trade wind from the north-east to fill out our sails and blow sparkling spray from the indigo waves.

It has been a day full of incident too. The chief officer caught another bonito and all morning there were numbers of them, and albacore too, swimming about the bows but few of them would bite in the bright light. Bonito and albacore, like the tunny, are, of course, large members of the mackerel family and, like all of them, beautifully streamlined and coloured ocean blue above and silver-white below. Many of us took rods and lines, and I took a trident, like Neptune's but attached to a staff and line, and attempted (without success) to harpoon them from the stay cables below the jib boom. It is most exhilarating to stand here, or to lie in the net which stretches out and up beneath the jib boom, and, looking back, watch the bow, rising and falling, cut through the waves, and, from a new angle, see the dazzling white canvas towering above it; or to look directly down into that indescribable blue where the bonitos flash, sometimes a dozen or so darting in different directions, reflecting the sun's rays with an iridescent sheen. Some, for a fraction of a second, flash red, like huge goldfish. I saw what I thought was a bright yellow and blue shark [but I now think it must have been the highly coloured *Coryphaena*, or sailor's 'dolphin,' which we shall meet later]. At times beautiful Portuguese men-o'-war (*Physalia*) went sailing by, and later in a hand net we caught a small specimen somewhat different from the one we caught before; it has only one long tentacle, and has a deeply-coloured spot of blue upon the float and much green about it. I suffered the

5. Crossing the line. *Above*, the first initiate in the hands of the barber—Dr. Kemp.
Below, another victim going over

6. At Ascension Island. *Above*, fish, mainly black file-fish, being tossed in the rollers along the shore. *Below*, Wideawake Fair, the great breeding colony of wideawake or sooty terns (*Sterna fuscata*) all facing into the wind

unpleasant experience of being stung in transmitting it from the net into a jar; and a sharp burning pain it was as the long tentacle fell across and fixed itself upon my wrist.

For lunch we again had bonito steaks and the table was decorated with large green water melons (from the Canaries) cut like huge lotus flowers to display their red interiors and jet black seeds: a delicious and exotic meal.

Directly after lunch a patch of 'discoloured' water was observed from the bridge and was thought possibly to be an uncharted shoal. The ship was swung about and we passed over it again. It was only some 15 yards in breadth, but, running in a N.N.E.—S.S.W. direction, stretched in an unbroken line as far as we could see in either direction.

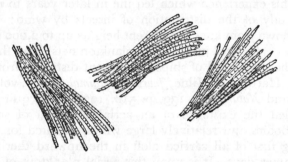

Typical bundles of the filamentous alga *Trichodesmium* causing a discolouration of the sea (× 20).

It was more or less in the direction of the current and parallel to the coast line (Cape Verde bearing 180°, approx. 95 miles). Water drawn from the surface with a bucket as we passed through it contained countless little white specks which when examined with a hand-lens looked like little chips of wood; under the compound microscope each of these was seen to be a bundle of closely adhering strands of a filamentous alga called *Trichodesmium*. Such discoloured water, often in a long belt, has been noted in many parts of the world and sailors have given it the descriptive name of 'sea sawdust.' Darwin records such a patch during his voyage in the *Beagle* and the Red Sea is said to have got its name from a discolouration due to the same organism. As we crossed the belt we quickly took four bucketfuls of water: one just before reaching it, two in it and one just after passing it. Taking a litre of water from each and counting the number of 'bundles' of algae contained therein, we found that there were 2, 84, 53 and 19 per litre respectively; and the average number of filaments per bundle, examining ten at random, was found to be 25·8.

More insects have come on board to-day than ever before; several butterflies, numbers of moths and beetles, and countless grasshoppers, locusts and flying bugs. The latter were a perfect pest, appearing everywhere, and the doctor, who has taken charge of the insect collections, has had a busy day with a constant stream of people arriving at his cabin with small tubes, match boxes, hats and clasped fists bearing entomological offerings. Rolfe Gunther who climbed to the barrel at the top of the main mast saw numbers of locusts flying overhead and the sea was covered with their dead and struggling forms. We are some 130 miles from the African coast. The waste of life in nature is prodigious.

[It was this experience which led me in later years to make a considerable study of the distribution of insects by wind: first by the use of nets flown from kites at different heights up to 2,000 feet (opened and closed at each level just like our plankton nets), and then by flying nets from the mast-head of ships at different distances from the coast. The results (Hardy and Milne, *Journal of Animal Ecology*, vol. 7, pp. 199-229, 1938 and *Nature*, vol. 139, p. 510, 1937) were quite surprising; they revealed the existence of an aerial plankton of small insects, with light bodies and relatively large wings, adapted for dispersal by wind, being first of all carried aloft in the upward thermal currents on hot summer days. It is upon this aerial plankton, of course, that the swifts and swallows feed.]

Tuesday, 27th October. As we went to bed last night the heat was very oppressive and lightning flashed at frequent intervals from many points on the horizon. At four in the morning I was awakened by the ship rolling heavily; a sudden storm had arisen and the wind changed completely round from being a helping N.E. trade to a strong head-wind from the south. After breakfast it blew for a short period at hurricane force and in an hour or two had died away to lead on to as peaceful an evening as the one before it with the old helpful trade-wind speeding us along again. It is surprising how quickly these tropical disturbances come and go, without any reasonable warning on the barometer. Luckily the captain read the signs—the lightning, the gathering clouds and other effects—and he quickly ordered all sails to be furled or we might have been caught by the sudden onslaught of the storm.

In the morning, when the wind was at its highest, a school of so-called black fish (really small whales, *Globicephala melaena*) came near the ship, close on twenty of them, continually breaking surface and sometimes leaping completely clear of the water; they are a little like miniature sperm whales with their blunt heads, although not so square. The thrill of the day, however, occurred later in the afternoon when we were visited by another school of dolphins even larger than the one before. We were called from tea by shouts and a commotion on deck. O'Connor, the chief officer, had successfully harpooned one of them and as we came on deck all hands were heaving on the line; looking over the rail we saw the unfortunate cetacean, writhing and plunging, staining the surrounding water crimson with his blood. He was soon, however, hauled to the ship's side and despatched by a lance driven to his heart; and now a noose lowered over his tail flukes hauled him on board. He is a big fellow close on eleven feet from snout to tail and beautifully marked; in the main he is a leaden grey above and white beneath but blotched with white spots at the sides and having the grey and white dappling meeting across his breast which in front is tinged with a delicate rose colour. There are many species of dolphin, some of them differing only in minor characters. This one appears to be the rough-toothed dolphin, *Steno bredanensis*.

Below the bows of the ship his brothers and sisters still cross and recross in their numbers, and often arrange themselves in lines like platoons of soldiers carrying out manœuvres on parade. For a long time eight or nine swim in perfect line immediately below the bows, as if carrying out some ceremonial drill to do honour to their dead comrade on the ship. I trust this was only fancy, for whilst so doing they offered an excellent target, and, since we wanted a second specimen for the British Museum, we were able to pick out just which one we would like. O'Connor, climbing into the jib-boom stays, sent another harpoon flying to its mark. Round and away to starboard rushed the victim, but so well placed was the harpoon that it died almost immediately. Unfortunately they both turn out to be males; we had hoped to secure one of each sex, but they are very difficult to distinguish except by close examination. Careful measurements and notes are taken, their alimentary tracts are examined for food and parasites and then the body of one is to be preserved whole in salt in a special tank and the other prepared as a skeleton. The food in each case was shown by many beaks and eyes to be squid; the numbers of squid in the sea must be legion, but how difficult they are to catch with our nets and other devices. The parasites were mainly cestodes (i.e. tapeworms) or nematodes (round worms); the latter in one stomach occurred not in hundreds but in thousands.

More interesting than the internal parasites, however, were those on their outside, particularly the whale-lice, curiously flattened little crab-like crustaceans (actually much modified amphipods) which appear to have no free swimming stage and are thought to be transmitted from one whale to another during pairing or from mother to calf in suckling. We may speak of them by the general name of *Cyamus*[1]; different species are to be found on whales both large and small, occurring in patches on their skin and eating into the flesh to form unpleasant looking wounds which must indeed be a source of irritation to their hosts. In addition to the lice were a number of the stalked barnacle *Conchoderma auritum*[2] which is peculiar to whales. [A further note on *Cyamus* may be of interest for it certainly presents

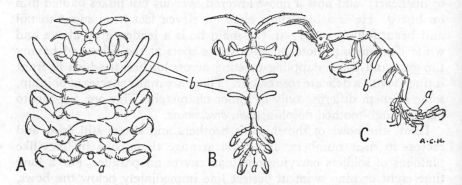

The whale louse *Cyamus* (A) compared with the amphipod *Caprella* (B and C): *a*, greatly reduced abdomen; *b*, gill-like respiratory organs replacing limbs, ×2.

zoologists with a problem. I have already said that it is really an amphipod, but strange as it may seem it is actually a close relative of *Caprella* (p. 69) which we found to be swarming amongst the 'weed' on the hull of our ship and is adapted for climbing and feeding on hydroids. If you look at them closely, comparing the sketches of each, you will see that they are identical in the arrangement of their bodies, but of quite different proportions; they both have the same comically reduced abdomen and their limbs are exactly the same in number and design except that those of *Cyamus* are more hooked for clinging to its host. *Cyamus* is a much flattened and shortened version, as if the slender *Caprella* was seen through some

[1]Nowadays two other closely allied genera are recognised: *Paracyamus* and *Isocyamus*, with their various species characteristic of particular kinds of whales. Actually the specimens here obtained have been shown by Dr. K. H. Barnard in his fine monograph on the amphipod of our exhibition (*Discovery Reports*, vol. v, pp. 1-136, 1932) to belong to the last named genus.

[2]See drawing on p. 204.

distorting lens. Now in my book *The Open Sea*, part II, *Fish and Fisheries*, 1959, I have suggested a solution to the problem of the strange distribution of these two branches of the Caprellid family. Let me quote what I then wrote:

How is it possible that the members of this one family of very aberrant crustacea should have become specialised to live upon two such very different organisms as the delicate little sedentary hydroids of our coasts and shallow seas, and the great fast-moving monarchs of the open ocean? Did ancestral whales, perhaps slower than those of to-day, once carry fringes of hydroids growing upon them as well as barnacles? It is a mystery whose solution may well be buried for ever in the past; the one I have just suggested, however, seems to me the most feasible. It is not difficult to imagine that the original hydroid browsers changed their habits when they found by chance that their usual diet was growing not on stones, but upon a bed of food as rich as butter.

The amusing point is that when I wrote that a few years ago I had quite forgotten the extent to which *Caprella* can live among the hydroids and weeds on the surface of a moving ship; surely this lends support to my hypothesis. I had forgotten my own journal of more than thirty years ago!]

Thursday, 29th October. Yesterday was a day long waited for: that on which we should first try out our largest tow-net. Our long conical nets have openings in front supported by metal hoops ranging in diameter from 50 cms. through 75 cms., 1 metre and 2 metres to 4½ metres, the last being the largest tow-net ever to be fished—nearly 15 feet across—with a heavy steel frame of streamlined cross section. It was sent out to the fullest extent of our 1,000 fathom warp reaching a depth of some 900 metres; later on it will be sent much deeper on our main 5,000-fathom cable. We kept it down for 4 hours, towing at 4 knots. The great moment comes when it reaches the surface again. What has it caught? Has it worked at all? At last we see the frame appearing and then the whole net. From the mouth downwards the net is festooned with strange creatures; fish clinging by their long teeth, scarlet shrimps and prawns, and pieces of jellyfish. As we undo the large bucket at the end of the net and peer in, we see indeed that the catch has surpassed our wildest dreams. It is poured into a shallow bath on deck: a mass of bizarre fish, squids of most unusual shapes, crimson and purple jelly-fish, patterned like turkey carpets, siphonophores and literally thousands of red crustacea of so many different kinds. Part of such a sample is shown in Plate 20 (p. 224). [But now I must say no more here of these treasures which will be fully described

in chapter 9. I just give an indication of the thrill of such deep-sea
sampling with a really outsize net; there were many of these occasions
as we went along.]

Last night we had a dolphin steak for dinner, and very good it was
with potatoes and leeks, although it would have been improved by
hanging a little; its liver for breakfast this morning was excellent,
and so was the curried dolphin we had for lunch. We have also had
more of the delicious bonito steaks; it is good to dine so much off
fresh ocean produce.

This afternoon we passed numbers of cuttlefish 'bones' floating on
the surface. It is remarkable that these objects should occur in such
quantity; and it sets one wondering what kind of cataclysm could
possibly have overwhelmed these creatures at one time and place
to set so many of their skeletons floating together on the ocean. There
must have been thousands of them for they went drifting by in one
and twos continuously for two or three hours and most likely they
stretched as far on one side as on the other. We picked one up as it
drifted by, and, as we expected, it was a little raft of life. Such floating
objects are nearly always interesting in having their own fauna. This
particular cuttlebone carried at least four different kinds of passenger,
each from a very different group of the animal kingdom; and some
others may well have escaped as it was lifted from the water in the net.
Most prominent of all were the stalked barnacles (*Lepas*, the ship's
barnacle) in all stages of growth from the little 'cypris' larval stages
just settled to the adult animal; next in number were some little
bristle-worms (polychaetes), very beautiful with green and yellow
'limbs' (parapodia), walking over the surface for all the world like the
caterpillars of the small tortoise-shell butterfly so commonly seen on
nettles at home. Then there were some half-dozen small snails and,
last, but not least, an exquisite little fish caught swimming beneath
the cuttlebone; he was a *Polyprion* of sorts, belonging to the group of
wreck-fish which accompany floating objects, logs, spars from wrecked
ships, etc., which are covered with barnacles. I should not wonder if
such fish are mainly feeding on the countless offspring continually
being sent out into the water by the barnacles.

Saturday, 31st October. Yesterday in making further trials with the
2-metre net we caught some specimens of the celebrated *Pyrosoma*,
the species being *P. atlanticum*. It is indeed well named (Gk. *pyro*,
pyros, fire; *soma*, body) for to-night it occurred in great numbers at
the surface attracting our attention by its brilliant luminescence as it
was swept along the side of the ship. We captured a number of them
and as they were lifted up in the hand-net they glowed like incan-

descent gas mantles and indeed approached them in size. [I am here comparing them to the old-fashioned long variety of mantle.] Their phosphorescence, however, did not remain for long. We caught them just before dinner and we produced them at table to entertain the company by showing examples of nature's fireworks; we were disappointed, however, to find, on extinguishing the lights, that they had ceased to function. [It has since been shown that light production in many luminous animals is inhibited by their being exposed to light and that they will not flash again until they have been some twenty minutes in the dark. If we had kept the *Pyrosoma* in a darkened jar and then uncovered them after we had turned out the lights, no doubt we could have got a good display]

Pyrosoma is a colony of a vast number of individuals held together

The brilliantly luminous *Pyrosoma atlanticum* ($\times \frac{1}{2}$).

embedded in a common gelatinous mass which has the form of a cylinder. Each little unit is like one of the 'sea squirts' described on p. 76; they are present, however, in thousands and have been produced by a simple budding, one from another. While the whole colony, I have said, is a cylinder, it is one which is closed at one end like a thimble. Each individual draws in water from outside and, after passing it through the feeding chamber (as already described for the sea-squirt), passes it out by an opening leading into the *inside* of the cylinder; water is thus continually being pushed out of the open end of the thimble so that it is slowly propelled through the water with the closed end pointing forward as shown in the sketch above.

I have noticed, apart from the bright flashes produced by jellyfish, *Pyrosoma*, etc., that as we have got into the more tropical waters, the diffused and more general luminescence, due to small dinoflagellates like *Ceratium*, which was so prominent each night after leaving England, has gradually diminished.

Sunday, 1st November. We are now in the doldrums. To-day has been one of 'boiling' heat, with hardly a movement in the atmosphere.

We are steaming slowly along over an 'oily' calm sea: calm save for a long gentle swell. The morning was overcast but in the afternoon the sun blazed down from a clear sky. Expecting a host of surface life we slung a bo'sun's chair (a board supported by ropes on each side like a swing) close to the water below the 'dolphin striker'[1]: that is right in front of the bows themselves. Here Kemp and I took turns with a hand-net and bucket. For sheer pleasure it was ideal: swinging in mid-air and gently rising and falling with the swell over the deep blue surface which occasionally rose to bathe and cool one's legs; one advanced like a gliding and soaring bird with nothing in front of one but the virgin ocean, as yet quite undisturbed by the bows behind. Delightful as an experience it certainly was, but zoologically it was most disappointing; we saw and caught nothing but a very young *Physalia*.

Tuesday, 3rd November. Yesterday morning I awoke to hear shouts and people running on the desk above; on tumbling out to join the throng I found that three very large *Physalia* were floating alongside and the ship had been slowed down to pick them up. Sheltering beneath each was a group of small fish. In catching the first *Physalia* we missed the fish which at once swam off to join their fellows below the next floating man-o'-war; with the other two we managed to collect no fewer than nine of these remarkable little associates which go by the name of *Nomeus gronovii*. They are remarkable for two reasons. Firstly they are silver but banded with exactly the same intense blue as that of *Physalia*'s tentacles so that they possess a perfect camouflage (see Plate 4): the silver mirrors the tones of the surrounding water just as it is seen through the hanging tentacles. Secondly there is the puzzle of how the fish themselves avoid being stung by the paralysing threads amongst which they seek protection from hungry predators; do they always move so deftly that they completely avoid the deadly bands of blue which they so closely resemble (that seems hardly possible) or have they become by some genetical freak mutation completely resistant to the poison darts of their overlord. Here in this extraordinary association is a fascinating subject of study for some future naturalist who is not forced to hurry on to other fields of explorations[2]. Another

---

[1]The downwardly pointing iron strut to which the stay ropes below the bow sprit are attached.

[2]In the monograph to which I referred in the footnote on p. 87 Totton remarks upon this association of *Nomeus* with *Physalia* as follows:

'. . . Garman (1896) reported partially digested *Nomeus* attached to the tentacles, and an 18 cm. long specimen of a male *Physalia* taken by *Discovery II* on 29 December 1929, . . . is accompanied by a label in the handwriting of Dr. Stanley Kemp, recording that "twenty

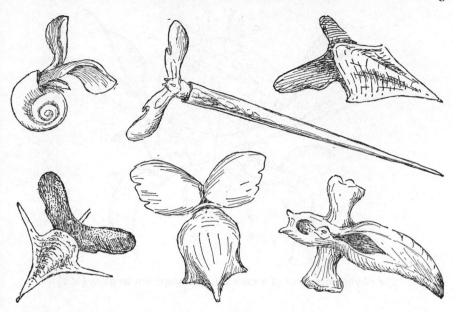

A group of pteropods, the so-called 'sea-butterflies'. Top row, left to right: *Limacina*, *Creseis*, *Clio pyramidata;* bottom row *Clio cuspidata*, *Cavolinia* and *Clione*.

unusual feature of these fish is their greatly enlarged pelvic fins which can be spread out like a dark skirt and folded in and out of clefts like an opening and closing fan.

It is extraordinary how on some days, for instance last Sunday afternoon, the surface is so devoid of life and on others, as on this, the following day, so rich. I now repeated the performance of Sunday and rode again in the bo'sun's chair beneath the bows; this time I rode in triumph, fishing out treasure after treasure as they came floating towards me on the very gentle undulating swell. An experience never to be forgotten. There were many *Glaucus* and also *Porpita*, with discs as large as half-crowns, and, new to us, some beautiful blue, and some blue and pink, flat-worms (polyclad Turbellaria) swimming on the surface.

---

or more small *Nomeus* were seen swimming below the *Physalia* and in one dip the latter was caught as well as several of the fish. In the net the fish came into contact with the tentacles of the siphonophore and were immediately killed." Kojiro Kato (1933) observed that *Nomeus* vigorously attacked *Physalia* from below, eating parts of it, including the tentacles. On opening the stomach of one fish as a check, he found unmistakable *Physalia* issues inside.' Thus it is still a puzzle.

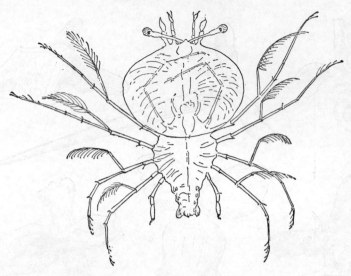

The phyllosoma larva of a crawfish, as transparent as glass ($\times 2\frac{1}{2}$).

Friday, 6th November. We are all getting a little disappointed at the progress made; we had expected to be well across the line by now, but we are still some three hundred miles to the north of it and making only sixty miles a day. We have not sufficient coal to use more than one boiler and with the wind against us, as it has been these last few days, our speed is barely 3 knots. The weather had become very sultry and oppressive, and on Wednesday afternoon we had a very heavy tropical rain storm. I have rarely seen such a deluge; the sea all round was blotted out for several hours. We were glad to get this extra supply of water, for our supply of fresh water is strictly limited to a gallon per man per day, and this has to be divided to allow so much for cooking, so much for drinking and so much for washing. We all set to to collect it in baths, jars, bottles, indeed anything which could contain it that we could lay our hands on as it poured from the bridge and boat-decks in thick streams. We bathed in the rain; we washed our clothes in it. It was a comical sight to see figures, some just in shorts, some in bathing costumes and some in nature's garb all busy on the deck with soap, scrubbing at shirts, shorts, socks and what not in the torrential downpour. It was by no means cold, but very invigorating after the sultry hot days which had preceded it.

Sunday, 8th November. To-night there was a good display of *Pyrosoma*: gruops of half a dozen or more at a time being swept along the side of

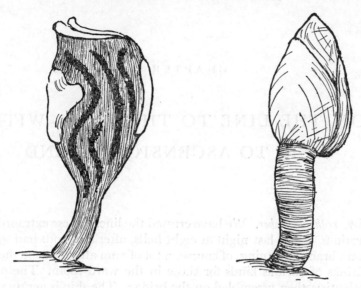

The zebra barnacle *Conchoderma virgata* (left) and the common ship's barnacle *Lepas anatifera*.

the ship. We caught two very fine specimens in a hand-net together with some large *Phyllosoma* larvae; these are the remarkably flattened and transparent young stages of sea crayfish (Palinuridae). Also in the hand-nets, scraped from the ship's sides, were several barnacles: *Lepas* the ordinary ship's barnacle and another more striking form *Conchoder a virgata*. The latter is curiously modified; the plates of the shell are reduced to mere vestiges so that the animal has a fleshy appearance unusual in a barnacle, and it has a beautiful lavender colour heavily barred with black, giving rise to its more popular name of the zebra barnacle.

To-morrow night we should reach the equator.

CHAPTER 5

FROM THE LINE TO THE CAPE—WITH A VISIT TO ASCENSION ISLAND

Tuesday, 10th November. We have crossed the line. These extraordinary celebrations began last night at eight bells, after all hands had 'spliced the main brace,' meaning, of course, a tot of rum all round for the crew and drinks of various kinds for those in the ward-room. The officers and scientists then assembled on the bridge. The ship is gently rolling to a slight swell. With all sails furled, as there is still a breeze against us on the starboard bow, the masts and spars stand out darkly and sweep slowly to and fro across a brilliant star-speckled sky.

Bang! A flash, a crash and a streak of fire—a rocket soars above the swaying rigging. As soon as it had burst, a sound of deep voices—as of a crowd off-stage—is heard away in the darkness for'ard, as if coming from the sea itself. What fine theatre it is: a sudden beam of light now reveals none other than Father Neptune in his scarlet robes and crown, with Amphitrite and their courtiers standing on the bows.

'What ship is this?' calls the gruff voice of King Neptune through a megaphone.

'The Royal Research Ship *Discovery*,' replies the captain from the bridge.

'Welcome to my kingdom,' cries Neptune. 'I hear you have on board a very fine captain, officers and crew; but I believe you have a goodly number of greenhorns who have never before entered my domain?'

(Growls and shouts from the courtiers.)

'Yes, that is so,' calls the captain.

(Renewed and louder shouts and growls.)

'Very well, I will board the ship to-morrow accompanied by my staff and teach them the wonders of the deep!'

After more such repartee the party descend from the forecastle and march round the ship to the beating of drums and to the stirring chant of 'Roll the chariot along!'

'We'll roll, we'll roll, the chariot along,
And, if the devil's in the way, we will roll it over him . . .'
Tramp, tramp, tramp, along the deck in the dark. The voices grow fainter, then louder, as the procession passes round the deck-houses aft and comes back to the bridge to be personally welcomed by the captain and officers. Then we all, all the ship's company, settle on the deck for a sing-song and smoke. 'Sally Brown,' 'Roll the Cotton Down,' and many more of the old favourites are sung with great gusto, and interspersed with solos and recitations. The singing in the lamp light, the flash of a match or the glow of a pipe in the shadows, and the black outline of the gently swinging rigging, made up a scene not easily forgotten.

At last another rocket heralded Father Neptune's temporary departure and the party were escorted to the bows with song. The main act, when we actually crossed the line, came to-day. I, of course, was one of the 'greenhorns' and so was initiated into the 'mysteries of the deep.' All morning 'Chips' (J. Jackson, the ship's carpenter) and old 'Sails' (Jimmy Forbes, the sailmaker), assisted by others, have been preparing for the great event. On the starboard side of the ship, on the wide deck between the forecastle and the bridge, they erected a square, sail bath nearly the size of a boxing ring and with sides as deep; the waterproof sailcloth of a huge mainsail, carefully folded and secured by lashing to a wooden frame, makes an admirable impromptu swimming bath. Immediately abaft of this and in front of the bridge, which serves as an officers' grandstand so to speak, is built a high wooden platform with steps leading up to it; this forms the ceremonial stage upon which are placed the thrones of King Neptune and his Queen Amphitrite, and in addition a stool, placed perilously near the water's edge, for their victims. It all looks very ominous, like the preparations for a public execution.

After lunch, punctually at 1.30, a loud voice from the bows calls 'Discovery, ahoy!'

'Hallo, who's there?' answers the captain.

'It is Father Neptune. Heave your ship to, I am going to board you!'

'Aye, aye!'

Father Neptune, Amphitrite, and their band stand forth in the brilliant sunshine.

Neptune, who is W. G. Chenoweth, the bo'sun's mate, is absolutely the part with a bright tin can cut into a painted crown, a scraggy beard, a cloak of scarlet, large trident and a megaphone. J. Flood, of Dundee, one of the oldest mariners, who has shaved off his big moustache specially for the occasion, is an amusing Amphitrite, in a big white wig and dressed in white calico with a large red rosette. She beams at us with obvious pride.

There are four 'policemen' in sou'westers and dark jackets (seamen J. Dale and M. Smith and Stokers J. C. Cook and W. B. Alsford). There is the barber (J. Cargill) with comic hat, wig and a wooden razor about two feet long, and J. D. Forsythe as his clerk with an equally large strop. The Doctor (D. Sherrington, our chief steward) is arrayed in a red top-hat, false nose and moustache, and a long black robe decorated with signs of the zodiac, skull and cross-bones, etc. 'Sparks' (the wireless operator, E. C. Cunliffe) is officially the band conductor but appears made up and dressed as a girl, and a very effective one too. Last, but not least, came the savage 'bears': the zoologist Erik Hamilton, Seaman W. Alexander, and two other sailors each naked but for bathing slips.

Down they came from the forecastle and ascend the platform.

'Produce your Articles, Captain,' calls Father Neptune, 'and give the names of those greenhorns who dare to cross my frontiers without first going through the ceremony of initiation!'

All the victims, officers and men alike, go through the same treatment with here and there a humorous little variation according to the individual. You are escorted to the scaffold by the policemen, brought before Neptune and made to sit on the stool, which, as I have already said, is poised on the very edge of the bath in which the 'bears' are now growling and leaping about ready to seize and duck you as soon as you are tipped over backwards into their watery den. After perhaps a little banter and cross talk Neptune calls in the Doctor (in red top-hat and long black robe) who feels your pulse and then pronounces some dreadful complaint. A large pill of some foul concoction is produced and pushed into your mouth and then a great bottle of some still more frightful coloured mixture is forced between your lips; the more you struggle the more you get. You cannot struggle much because each of your hands is now firmly held by two bears reaching up from the pool behind. Then, still more dreadful, comes the barber and the barber's clerk. The great razor is duly stropped and the soap and brush produced. The soap in a bucket looks like tar, but really it is a relatively harmless if very uncomfortable mixture of thick crude oil and soot with, I suspect, a dash of green paint to make it look more exciting; it is like a greenish black treacle, and the brush is an old whitewash brush. Slap, slap on it goes, all over your face; the more you move you try to avoid it, the thicker is the lather applied. All the time and are being asked questions as if by a talkative barber—absurd provocative questions, aimed as much for the amusement of the gallery, questions that you can hardly resist answering; if, however, you do answer, and nearly everyone does unwittingly at least once, as soon as your mouth opens to speak in goes the brush laden with green black oil to the great joy of the onlookers. For them it is superb slapstick fun, especially for those who have been through it and have now joined the spectators; I give two pictures in Plate 5.

'Shampoo, sir?' says the barber facetiously, after he has scraped little enough of the greasy mess from your face with the wooden razor; and before you could answer, he cries, 'Certainly, sir, certainly!' dabbing the oil brush across your hair and then applying a thick coating of flour. What a sight! Eyes blinking out through green black grease and powdery flour. Thus blinking, away you go backwards, heels over head in a somersault, down into the water to the waiting bears. Here you fight like mad and try to duck the bears themselves; but it is a one-sided contest, of course. After you have been ducked several times you are allowed to escape over the back of the bath, through a door under the forecastle and out of sight. Then you make a dash to strip off your wet and oily clothes (just shorts and an old vest), to scrape off as much of the filthy lather as possible (if you've been in the know, as I was, you will have obtained a large bottle of turpentine from the bo'sun beforehand!) and then back to a place in the 'grand stand' to watch the rest of the fun.

This the captain tells me has been a good example of a really old-fashioned sailing ship's crossing of the line, save that there was none of the bad horse-play which, one hears, sometimes marred these proceedings in the past when an unpopular man might be really hurt and when real tar was used and a rusty barrel hoop served as a razor.

Thursday, 12th November. In contrast to the day before, yesterday was Armistice Day. The ship's whistle announced the beginning and end of the two minutes' silence, and all hands stood silently wherever they happened to be or at whatever they were doing.

Every night since Monday we have witnessed displays of *Pyrosoma* (*P. atlanticum*) which, if the term remarkable has been used before, can now only be described as miraculous. I could not have believed it; nor have I seen anywhere described such brilliant luminescence as we have seen these last four nights. I resisted referring to it in my last entry so as not to confuse the description of crossing the line, but even as Father Neptune was making his first appearance over the bows, either side of the ship was brilliantly lit by the glowing of these organisms as they were swept along its side. They could only be seen by leaning over the rail, so they did not actually form part of the theatrical décor seen from the deck; on going to the stern, however, and looking aft, the full magnificence of the spectacle was seen. There were thousands and thousands of these bright glowing forms being thrown up to the surface by the churning of the ship's propeller. Outside the track of the ship there was only an occasional flash, but stretching away in our wake for hundreds of yards, at times it seemed for a full half-mile, was a wide band of bright greeny-blue phosphorescence; close at hand the individual colonies stood out as little oblongs of still brighter light—indeed, as I said last week, like large gas mantles fully lit.

We have caught samples each night and made some chemical experiments to extract the luminescent substances[1]. One night we caught 2,231 in just a few minutes' dip with a 2-metre net. As already explained (p. 111) each cylinder is really a colony of a vast number of little separate animals arranged in the jelly matrix; this being so it is interesting to note that the whole colony may be stimulated to luminescence if just one point is touched. First the point of contact will glow brightly and then a flash of light will pass over the whole surface of the colony. I know of no nervous connection between one member and the next; it seems that the light signal from one sets off the next, and so on as a chain reaction through the whole assemblage.

I did a water-colour of my impressions of the stream of luminescence as seen from the stern, taking notes and a pencil sketch at night and then working from them in daylight. It is certainly a difficult subject, but an amusing one to attempt. [I reproduce it in Plate 3.]

Yesterday one of the cadets, John Bentley, drew my attention to the condition of the ship's log line; this is a long towing rope connecting a vaned indicator, rotating in the water behind the ship, with the dial on the after rail which records the distance travelled. On examining the line I found it had a number of the same zebra barnacles as the one I described in last Sunday's note (p. 115), growing along it; they were of all ages. This is interesting for several reasons. For one thing is shows what remarkable powers these animals have, when in the free-swimming larval state, of attaching themselves to moving objects; this rope, in addition to being towed rapidly through the water is also

[1] In all such luminous marine animals as have been investigated the light is shown to be produced by the same general kind of chemical reaction. A substance called luciferin and oxygen are brought together in the presence of an enzyme called luciferase which facilitates the process: the luciferin gives off hydrogen which combines with the oxygen to form water and becomes itself the so-called oxyluciferin. The enzyme also excites a quantum of energy in the oxyluciferin which is thought to jump back to the enzyme molecule to be liberated as light.

7. Tristan da Cunha. *Above*, islanders coming out to us for stores and mail in their frail boats of oiled canvas stretched on a wooden frame. *Below*, typical Tristan cottages, reminiscent of those of Scottish crofters

8. Part of the Nordenskjold Glacier, which is over two miles wide, descending into East Cumberland Bay, South Georgia, from the Allardyce Range. The highest peak, Mount Paget, is 9,550 feet

continually spinning round as the log indicator turns, at a rate of several hundred revolutions a minute. It also gives us some idea of their hardihood, for the line has been hauled on board every day for checking and, whenever we have stopped for an observation, it has been kept coiled up on deck till the ship was under way again; yet in spite of this they continue to grow lustily. Further it shows how fast they must grow! Some are quite a good size and yet must have grown entirely since we left Grand Canary only twenty-three days ago, unless we are to suppose that they were hardy enough to withstand being dried up for four days in the hot sun on the deck whilst we were at anchor there, and that seems most unlikely. Their larvae have evidently a much greater power of attachment than have those of the ordinary ship's barnacle *Lepas*, for the latter is far and away the commonest form growing on the ship just now, yet not one of their kind was found on the log line. There can be little doubt, I think, that this line has been colonised by larvae swept back from the *Conchoderma* on the ship. The number which have been able to clutch this slender, fast moving and spinning rope must be only a very small proportion of those produced; the rest must be swept away to die in the wilderness of the ocean unless, by some happy chance, a few should find a floating log, a cuttlebone, or another ship just in the nick of time.

Saturday, 14th November. We are now heading for Ascension Island where we hope to get coal, for, being delayed by unfavourable winds, we have not sufficient left to carry us to the Cape. *Pyrosoma* is still occurring in large numbers although more in patches than before.

Friday, 20th November. We dropped anchor off Georgetown, the settlement of Ascension Island, early on Monday morning. After breakfast, whilst Dr. Kemp and the captain went ashore to make arrangements about coal, I made a sketch of the island from the ship. The colours are fantastic. The island, which is about $7\frac{1}{2}$ miles in length and 6 in breadth, consists of a large number of extinct volcanic cones and craters. The highest of these rises far above the others to a height of 2,280 feet, and, on account of the clouds which gather about it and give it rain, it alone supports a rich vegetation and is known as Green Mountain. The rest, which vary much in height, are arid cinder heaps; although barren they present a great variety of colour: raw sienna, reds, browns, dark and light greys and yellows, while some are almost crimson—all changing tone with the light and shade from passing clouds. The cones on the left, i.e., to the north (Georgetown being in the middle of the western coast) descend to a broken shelf of rocks which border the sea; those on the right slope more gradually to a beach of light yellow sand of dazzling brilliance. Above this beach is the settlement, of red and white bungalows. Behind all this is a deep blue sky with hard white cumulus clouds, and in front of it a still bluer sea streaked with purple shadows; it is a patchwork of colour not easily forgotten.

In the afternoon we made a dredge haul in the bay: the medium rectangular net being taken and dropped 450 yards from the ship by a launch and hauled slowly on board. It came up full of masses of the red calcareous alga *Lithothamnion*, which is often mistaken for a true coral, and a number of small brilliantly coloured fish: some all red, others blue and purple, and one brown with a bright canary-yellow tail. There were small octopuses and many sea-urchins and brittle-stars. The *Lithothamnion* itself, which we broke up with hammers, contained in its cavities a rich fauna of small crabs, prawns and amphipods, polychaete worms and other creatures (sipunculids, etc.).

The following morning we made a shore-collecting expedition to the rock pools along the coast. It was my first experience of such collecting in the tropics. The edges of the pools were encrusted with *Lithothamnion* and masses of worm tubes somewhat like those of *Pectinaria* at home or clusters of very fluted oyster-like bivalves; each pool was a little aquarium of brightly coloured fish, cut off from the sea by the out-going tide. There were the 'yellow tails' we had caught the previous afternoon, some canary yellow all over, some bright green with scarlet longitudinal stripes and others blue with five transverse bands of deeper indigo. Over the rocks scampered scores of grapsid crabs.

The waters round the island are infested with a fish known locally as blackfish; it is a species of *Balistes* generally known as file-fish on account of the strong first spine of the dorsal fin which is roughened in front like a file. They are about a foot in length and swarm along the edge of the shore and round the ship; as the waves come in to the beach with a big swell they are sometimes seen to be speckled with these fish as shown in my photograph on Plate 6. Any object thrown into the water from the ship instantly became the centre of perhaps a hundred or more of them. They are said to be unfit to eat; why I don't know; merely, I believe, because they are such scavengers. Both upper and lower jaws are provided with a row of most powerful chisel-like teeth with which they can break off pieces of corals on which they feed. During our stay here they have done us a great service, from the point of view of navigation, by completely stripping the ship's bottom of barnacles and weed; it all happened before we had time to find out if we had carried the caprellid amphipods (p. 69) as far as this. Swimming is prohibited on account of sharks; a twelve-foot one was seen cruising round the ship.

The island was discovered in 1501 by the Portuguese captain João da Nova on his way to India round the Cape[1]. It remained uninhabited until 1815 when a naval garrison was placed there after the arrival of Napoleon at St. Helena. For just over a hundred years it was held by the Admiralty, and then in 1922 it was transferred to Colonial Office administration under St. Helena. It has now become one of the most important cable relay stations of the Eastern Telegraph Company with a population of about 300. Practically all the officials of the E.T.C. rank as officers and many of them are young bachelors; they run a big mess and extended to us a wonderful hospitality. The servants and labourers of the island are St. Helena men.

In naval days 500 tons of coal were always kept on the island and in the current issue of *Sailing Directions* this was said to be still maintained. This, however, turned out to be no longer correct and we were disappointed to find that we could only obtain 50 tons which would have to be carried to the ship in small lighters and would take two days to put on board.

On Tuesday night a party of us stayed in a bungalow up on the top of Green Mountain where we were entertained by several of the E.T.C. officers taking leave there. Green Mountain lies towards the other end of the island and is approached by a rough and dusty road winding between the smaller cones and across the central plain. To the top it is a seven-mile walk and the last thousand feet rise very abruptly; the road zigzags up with sharp hairpin bends and precipitous sides. The scene had been likened by one of the officers to a lunar landscape on account of the number of extinct craters. This is particularly apt as you look down from the top of the mountain at the host of craters below, but even as you make the journey between them you feel as if you were marching across some other planet. The bare red volcanic ash shows no sign of life save the stunted acacia bushes and the patches of dried grass; the latter had appeared, we were told, after the abnormal rains of two years ago and as quickly died. The illusion of another world is heightened rather than diminished by the six gigantic steel masts, remnants of the abandoned naval wireless station, which stand in the middle of the plain like some infernal invention of Wellsian Martians. [In the last war the plain

[1] It is frequently said that he gave it its name because he discovered it on Ascension Day, and so I had written in my journal, following the account in the *Encyclopædia Britannica*; actually, however, he named it Conception Island because he sighted it on the Feast of the Annunciation (25th March) and it was renamed by another Portuguese mariner Alfonse d'Albuquerque who sighted it on Ascension Day in 1503—a fact that I learnt from Bernard Stonehouse's delightful book *Wideawake Island* (1960).

and some of the smaller craters were levelled to make a great air strip.]

As one ascends and begins to approach Green Mountain little patches of vegetation appear; there is a small plant called a Cape Daisy[1] (certainly no daisy and more like a rockrose) which, with its bright pink flowers makes here and there quite a gay display, and with it occurs a yellow poppy-like flower with prickly leaves.

It was in this region that we met the bands of wild donkeys, usually six or seven of them together; well set up animals they were, superior to any domestic ass that I have seen. They, like the wild goats and cats, have, of course, been introduced by man. Goats had been liberated soon after the island's discovery to provide a supply of meat for passing ships. After leaving the plain an attempt has been made to give the road some shade with a grove of coconut palms, but few of them are flourishing; and the same can be said for a row of aloes. It is not until we reached the last three or four hundred feet that we came to the vegetation proper and then we met it 'good and hearty' as the sailormen might say. Tall eucalyptus trees now lined the road, flowering shrubs, conifers and palms of many kinds appeared, and sheep grazed on slopes of grass in between patches of almost dense jungle. There is the same incongruous mixture of European, semi-tropical and tropical plants that we had seen in the Canary Islands; the homely English bramble is seen sprawling its stems through and across the shrubs of scarlet hibiscus.

There are several houses on the mountain top: the sanatorium where some of our party stayed and higher up two or three bungalows and a farm. It was at 'Bell's,' the highest villa, that I stayed, and from its veranda we obtained the most wonderful panorama of the island. It was dark by the time we reached it and it was not until next morning that we saw the spectacular view. At one moment the whole would be blotted out by thick damp cloud and at the next revealed in strong sunlight with all the craters—red, sienna, grey and yellow—standing out like a relief map modelled in coloured clay.

Behind the house the ground rises steeply by way of one or two smaller peaks to the highest point of all. At first the path thither lies over mountain grassland with sheep and goats grazing upon it, while over to the left lies the catchment, a little valley lined with concrete to collect the rain to supply water to Georgetown (or Garrison as it is still called) seven miles away. The view from here is the finest on the island, the blue of the horizon extends right round except where broken by the highest peak of all which lies a little beyond. The

[1] *Vinca rosea*, related to the periwinkle.

highest peak of all, surprising to relate, has no view at all, but this I must explain. After dropping down along a ridge we enter a belt of thicker vegetation. Through the ginger groves hung with white bell-like blooms with red centres, the path rose steeply and large screw pines (*Pandanus*) made their appearance. They are quite fantastic in that they send out roots from well up their main stem to strike the ground all round like extra supports to a decaying tree—and in fact that is what they are, for the main trunk has often rotted away. The vegetation becomes still more tropical as long trailing creepers hang in graceful curves from the branches. Naval officers in the past, we were told, vied with one another in the variety of exotic plants they introduced to Green Mountain from different parts of the world. Now we enter a jungle of bamboo and climb up and up through their tall damp stems, until suddenly we come upon a surprise: a circular basin, some fifteen feet in diameter, with beautiful blue water-lilies growing in it. Its edge is fringed with ferns and on all sides rise the tall bamboo stems; these rub against each other to produce an eerie sighing music as the wind ruffles their swaying tops high above us. Down by the pond the air is quite still and a heavy dampness hangs about it as moisture drips from the slender bamboo leaves. This dew pond, as it is called, is situated upon the uttermost peak of the island.

A few paces more through the closely growing stems and we emerge from the jungle upon a precipitous mountain side into an almost cold wind—the south-east trade—with nothing before us but the far away horizon of the sea; a greater contrast to the oppressive heat and shut-inness of the tropical vegetation could hardly be imagined. We now descended by a slippery zigzag path until we reached thicker vegetation again some hundred and fifty feet below. Here the track widens and we enter upon what is known as Elliot's path, cut in the mountain side, I believe in 1840 by the governing naval captain of that name; it leads back to the bungalow from which we started: at times hanging on the sheerest cliffs, or diving through forest or sometimes cutting deeply through the rock. Land-crabs (*Geocarcinus*) are common on the island and we obtained two specimens on this walk. They were not very large ones, not more than five or six inches across. After a short rest at the bungalow for refreshments we went in search of better specimens, conducted by our friend Mr. Stevens of the E.T.C., down into Breakneck Valley.

The approach to this valley of ominous name is by a tunnel over three hundred yards in length. We dropped down through the gardens of the bungalow and turned suddenly to one side into a hole of absolute blackness. There is no light ahead to show that there is a way out at all, for, in the middle, the tunnel makes a bend; you are guided by a wire which runs along its wall, and it is high enough to allow you to walk upright through nearly all of it. It was cut in the middle of last century to carry a water pipe, from a catchment on the other side, to join the aqueduct to Garrison. At the far end you emerge through the moss and fern-covered walls into a desolate curving valley which falls away between steep boulder-strewn grassy sides. Any entrance to the valley is hidden round the corner and behind you it ends in the wall-like side of the mountain through which the tunnel has broken. It is one of nature's cul-de-sacs, one of the secret places of the earth. Now you become aware of a horrible moaning sound, almost a squealing as from someone in acute pain. Again there was the feeling of being upon another planet. Then I realised how like this was to Butler's description of the outskirts of Erewhon; wasn't I hearing the wind blowing through the organ-pipe mouths of the terrible stone figures he had met when lost amongst the precipitous mountains? I looked for the idols above me, round to one side from whence the moaning came, and there I saw an ancient iron windmill. Quite by itself it stood, a structure of very simple design: six rusty iron plates on a wheel swung round to work a pump which filled a covered reservoir. The trade winds striking the mountain blow continuously up the valley; and day and night the blades swing ceaselessly round, crying pitifully to this remote wilderness.

Farther down the valley, as it curves steeply round, aloes and a group of pines stand on the slopes, and on either side of the path are what look like rabbit-holes; they are 'crabs' burrows' says my companion. We turn to the left and climb over the shoulder of ground that separates this valley from the next which I should indeed call the Valley of Crabs: it is smaller but similar to the one we have just left, and its sides are riddled with crabs' holes. Over the barren ground lay their parched remains: here a claw and there a broken piece of carapace, bleached by the sun. We were disappointed, however, in seeing so few active; we only secured two specimens. Mr. Stevens assured us that the last time he was here 'the ground was alive with them'; and judging by the number of their holes I could well believe it. What a strange place for crabs, some fifteen hundred feet above the sea. They are said to 'All go down to the sea in the breeding season'; I quote from Moseley's *Notes by a Naturalist*[1], but I know of no account of their migration and did not meet anyone who had actually seen them marching down to the shore.

During the afternoon I attempted a sketch of the 'crater land', from

[1]His account of observations on the *Challenger* Expedition which visited Ascension in 1876.

the path leading from 'Bell's' bungalow along the mountain side to the left. Through a frame of vegetation one looked out over the extraordinary panorama of the lunar country; in the foreground tall eucalyptus trees lined the mountain road as it dropped below in its zigzag descent, and far down one could follow its winding path across the plain towards Garrison. My sketch is redrawn here. In the distance over to the right the waves broke against the cliffs and it was sometimes

The 'lunar landscape' of Ascension Island seen from near the summit of Green Mountain, redrawn from a watercolour made on the spot.

difficult to distinguish what was surf from the dazzling white guano deposits of the sea bird colonies on the stacks (outlying rocks) and cliffs. Apart from the wideawake terns for which it is famed, Ascension Island is the breeding home of many other sea birds; these include two species of the beautiful tropic (or boatswain) birds (*Phaethon*) with their long trailing tails, three species of booby (*Sula*) which are tropical gannets, and the sinister black frigate birds (*Fregata*), of which we saw many along the coast near Garrison. When the island was discovered there were immense colonies of these birds on the cliff tops giving the rich deposits of guano; then cats were let loose and multiplied, and the birds, except the wideawakes, were driven to breeding only on the stacks and a small island, Boatswain Bird Island, off the north-east coast.

In the late afternoon we made our way back to Garrison racing the darkness; as we hurried across the plain the glow of sunset lit up the red craters to our right in violent contrast to the purple shadows on our left.

The next morning we started off early for Wideawake Fair. Ascension is particularly celebrated for its large breeding colonies of wideawake or sooty terns (*Sterna fusciata*), and such assemblies are known as fairs. We were lucky to arrive at the right season: [the season varies as we shall see]. The biggest fair lies some five or six miles to the south-west of Garrison, some of it pretty rough going over the 'clinker.' As you approach you see the birds circling round and hear their cries; then suddenly, over a ridge, you see the whole fair spread out before you. It is in a wide saucer-like hollow: an expanse of sand with raised edges of slag and ash. The air is thick with these graceful swallow-like sea-birds and all over the sand and clinker slopes they are sitting on their eggs, or with young (Plate 6). There are indeed millions of them, all sitting facing the same way, into the wind of course. As you walk between them some remain heroically upon their eggs, others rise squawking and screaming to reveal their spotted eggs, one to each bird, lying a yard or so apart. It is said that they normally lay only one egg each, but if that is taken from them they will lay another, and, if that is again taken, a third but not more; with each egg the number of spots decreases until the last is almost white. There were many young, some fairly advanced, but the majority newly-hatched. Here and there were little thickets of acacia concealing some of the old ones which would run out when disturbed.

[The wideawake tern is a very remarkable bird, in fact I believe it is unique, in regard to its breeding seasons. Over the greater part of its range it breeds, as one would expect, annually; at Ascension, however, it breeds at a shorter interval, every 9½ months, and at Christmas Island, and some other islands in the central Pacific, it is said to breed every 6 months. One of the main objects of the recent expedition to Ascension Island organised by the British Ornithological Union, under the leadership of Dr. Bernard Stonehouse, was to study the breeding cycles of the various seabirds there. Dr. Philip Ashmole was specially concerned with studying the wideawake tern. He confirmed a definite 9½ months period and showed that this appeared to be the shortest period in which the birds could carry out the full cycle of breeding in addition to the normal period of moult. This indicates that in this equatorial area, where there are no marked

9. *Above*, our first iceberg. *Below*, a glacier in West Cumberland Bay, South
Georgia

climatic seasons, there can be no significant changes in the marine food supply on which the birds depend; they must be able to get sufficient food for breeding at any time of the year since the 9½ months period brings the feeding of the young into every month in turn. It will be extremely interesting to find out what brings about the 6 months period in the Pacific; firstly whether a richer food supply enables them to breed more often and whether, as Dr. Ashmole suspects from the little information available, the moulting there is not confined to a period distinct from breeding, but spread out through it[1].]

We arrived back at Garrison just in time to return on board for a lunch given to members of the Telegraph Company. Considerable difficulty was experienced in getting our guests on and off the ship on account of the 'rollers' which had increased greatly during the morning; the difficulty is actually at the landing stage, a narrow flight of steps running down between the rocks. We had heard much of these rollers with which Ascension is frequently visited: large waves which run in and break with considerable force on the lee side of the island; they are due no doubt to the effect of an ocean swell (caused by a far away storm) being greatly exaggerated on suddenly reaching the shallow shelf on which the island stands. It is indeed a strange sight to see these great waves build themselves up out of what seems to be a perfectly calm sea and sweep forwards in a boiling line of foam.

We weighed anchor at six in the evening, and are now sailing south-south-west with a good wind on our port beam.

Monday, 23rd November. We are making good progress as the strong S.E. trade-wind continues and to-day saw our first Cape Horn pigeon (*Daption capensis*); actually it is a very prettily marked petrel: dark grey with white splashed on its wings. It is a long way north of its more usual range.

Friday, 27th November. To-night we have been followed by some large fish which could occasionally be made out by the light of the stern lamps. Hamilton, rigging a grains, a savage-looking barbed fork, and perching himself on the starboard boomkin, made an excellent shot at one as they swam alongside. It proved to be a splendid specimen of *Coryphaena*, known to all sailors as the dolphin. I was going to say 'incorrectly known,' but who is right in such a matter as an English name: the zoologist or the sailorman? Certainly *Coryphaena* is more like the heraldic dolphin (which has scales) than is the *Delphis delphis* of science, the small toothed whale which I call the true dolphin. *Coryphaena* is often described as the most beautiful fish in the sea; fresh

---

[1]Since this was written Dr. Ashmole has left on an expedition to Christmas Island to find out.   E

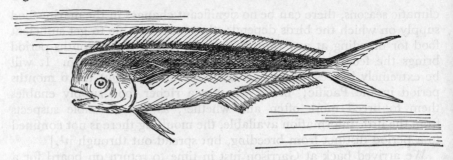

The sailors' 'dolphin': *Coryphaena*.

from the water he is a most brilliant ultramarine, yet shining too with
iridescent greens and gold. Strangely it is said to be more beautiful in
death. 'Wait till you see a dying dolphin' I have been told by old sailors
on more than one occasion; and it is indeed worth waiting for. The
body keeps changing colour, flushes of crimson and purple pass over it
and then gradually it becomes more and more golden, every scale
now appearing as if of burnished metal. It is said that such a display
was sometimes an entertainment offered by a Roman host to his guests
at a feast in Pompeii.

Yesterday we lost the trade-wind and have been making very slow
progress, running again on only one boiler. We have now left the
Tropic of Capricorn.

Sunday, 29th November. We have shut off the engines altogether to
save coal for emergencies, for we are now really short of it. All day
to-day we have been becalmed, floating idly under a brilliant sun
upon a glass-like azure sea, yet one whose surface very slightly rises and
falls in long curves as a gentle swell rocks the ship slowly to and fro.
The surface is rich with life; a number of beautiful *Physalia*, glistening
with iridescence, lie about the scene, becalmed like ourselves, and many
Porpita can be seen as we look down into the blue. Towards evening
the surface fauna became even richer and in a very short space of time
we caught many young flying fish, pteropods, *Glaucus, Ianthina*, some
beautiful ctenophores ('comb jellies'), various jellyfish and, most
remarkable of all, several amphipods of the most brilliant metallic
blue and green (*Brachyscelus rapax*, Claus). These last, one of which is
shown in Plate 4, shone like the glittering wingcases of those Indian
beetles which are sometimes used as jewellery.

I have not mentioned the comb-jellies before, members of the
Ctenophora, (Gk. *Kteis, Ktenos*, comb); I should give a brief description of them for they are important animals of the plankton which we

shall certainly be meeting again. Whilst much of their body has a jelly consistency, they do not swim like a jellyfish by pulsation and are really very different creatures. They are propelled by eight lines of comb-like plates (formed of fused cilia—see p. 76) which extend down their sides and beat rhythmically like rows of little paddles. Typically, as seen in the sketch, they have two very long contractile tentacles with side branches which are armed with vast numbers of extremely sticky adhesive cells; with these they capture all kinds of other plankton animals, including young fish, and convey them to a mouth which will suddenly open wide at the lower end of their bodies. Different kinds have all manner of beautiful shapes, and they are nearly

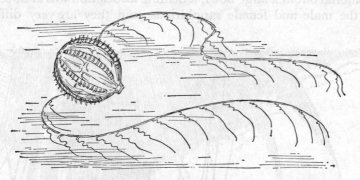

The common ctenophore: *Pleurbrachia pilus*, natural size.

all transparent; the comb-plates, however, act like little prisms and refract the light with all the colours of the rainbow: little waves of red, yellow, green, blue and violet flash in sequence down the lines of the plates as they swim and turn this way and that.

Sunday, 6th December. We have made but little progress during the week, having not yet struck the expected westerlies which would carry us quickly to the Cape. For the most part the wind has been either slight or against us. Three of four albatross have been with us all the week and a number of smaller petrels have been seen. The well-known powers of flight of the albatross are indeed remarkable; one can never tire of watching their gliding-soaring course over the waves without a beat of the wing—now rising, now falling, banking and sweeping round, riding both up and down wind with a baffling facility. Sometimes they approach within a few feet of us and it is then, and then only, that you can realise their tremendous span of wing: in some birds it must be ten feet at least.

Tuesday, 8th December. This morning I was called at a quarter to six by the chief officer to come and see some discoloration in the water. 'The thickest patches I have ever seen' he said. I hurried on deck and sure enough there were patches in no mistake, but small ones, of only a few yards across and of a deep muddy yellow appearance. I expected them to be due to the same algae as we had found in the last example, but no; on throwing over a bucket we pulled it up filled with a dense mass of very small salps (*Salpa democratica*) linked together in chains[1]. So thick was the sample that it seemed to be all salps and no water! A later count showed there to be some 26,000 in a litre. In among the salps were many of the beautiful copepod *Sapphirina* (*S. augusta*) which we had met before (p. 92). On separating some of the material out in a large bowl, a definite association was at once seen; both the male and female sapphirinas, and they are very different,

In the Westerlies at last, bound for the Cape.

[1]The salps we caught before (p. 75) were single ones, known as the solitary forms, and such produce a long line of buds which as they grow are set free as these chains, known as the aggregate forms; eventually they will separate to become the sexual individuals whose eggs will in turn grow into the solitary forms again. So the generations alternate; and this happens in all species of salps.

were spending most of their time riding on the chains of salps, hanging on tightly by their second antennae. At times one would leave a chain and flit madly round the vessel, flashing fiery colours as it went, to settle eventually upon another chain to continue its ride. Although close observation was made, feeding [on this occasion] could not be seen to be taking place, but some such relation is likely to exist because other species of the *Sapphirina* genus are said either to prey upon salps or to be parasitic inside them [and we shall in fact see it confirmed for this species within a few days]. The iridescence of the male *Sapphirina* is the most brilliant that I have yet observed, and I spent a good deal of time upon the almost hopeless task of trying to portray the changes of colour in water-colour. Violet, blue, green, gold and fiery red, they flash up and down the spectrum as their bodies alter their inclination to our eyes; there are other members of the genus which can only flash in ·a more limited range of colour, some, for example, at the violet and others at the red end. Such iridescent colouring is a *physical* effect quite distinct from that produced by a chemical pigment; this is the reason, of course, that it is impossible to reproduce it with pigments of paint. Such physical colours can be produced by several different systems; quite how it it produced in this particular case, whether by very fine striations on the outer plates causing diffraction effects, or whether by exceedingly thin overlying crystalline layers no thicker than the waves of light, causing inter- ference effects, I do not know. [I see that Dr. Colin Nicol in his *The Biology of Marine Animals* (1960) attributes it to guanine crystals in the integument.] I know of no iridescence in nature so brilliant as this. The female, strange to say, completely lacks this bright adorn- ment, yet is nevertheless very beautiful in a different more delicate and feminine way. Her body is transparent, but filled for its greater part with masses of eggs of a most exquisite lavender-blue; they not only fill the two flask-shaped egg-sacks which hang from her abdomen but fill the large ramifying ovaries which branch into almost every part of her anatomy. Her body, by the way, is of a more normal copepod shape; her spouse, as I have already said, is broad but extremely flat. *S. augusta* is the largest of all the *Sapphirina* species and our examples were a little larger than the measurements, 7·5 mm. long, given for the species.

Monday 14th December. We have continued to make very slow progress but to-night, at last, it seems we are coming into the westerly winds. We have still another 830 miles to go to Cape Town and only enough coal to last about four days steaming at a speed of some four or five knots; we thus want all the wind we can get to carry us there in time

Entering Table Bay. A sketch from a watercolour made as we rounded 'The Lion'
and saw Table Mountain behind opening out and taking its characteristic shape.

for Christmas and our expected mail. The south-west swell has been
increasing for the last two days until it reached a maximum in the
early hours of this morning when it caused the ship to roll sometimes
35° from the vertical as measured on our declinometer.

Last night two sperm whales were sighted and came within half a
mile of us, crossing our bows from port to starboard. Albatross and
small petrels remain with us and are a constant delight.

Sunday, 20th December. All this week we have been bounding along
with a good west wind behind us. We have passed several more
patches of discoloured water; one, on 15th December, was quite the
thickest and brownest I have yet seen. It was only about twenty to
fifteen yards across. As we shot through it we took samples with a
bucket and found it to be caused by *Salpa longichorda,* and *not S.
democraica* as was the previous patch. *Sapphirina* was again seen flashing
brilliantly within the patch, and in our sample a female was observed
through a lens to move freely in the main chamber of the salp, like a
bird flitting about a cage. At times it would settle upon the ciliated
band, which carries the salp's collected food in a stream towards its
gullet, and be seen to work its way along it feeding no doubt upon its
rich assortment of diatoms, dinoflagellates, etc.

I am sure that each one of us has certain things that he or she has always wanted to do. One of my dreams had been to go sailing into Table Bay. It has been accomplished, at least as good as; actually we steamed in, but we were sailing with plenty of white canvas up, well within sight of it. Here when we knew we had sufficient coal to carry us in, we were able to stop and make some further trials with the echo-sounding machine. This we did at midday.

Approaching Table Mountain as we did from the south we did not at first see its table-like appearance, we saw instead the line of jagged peaks called the Twelve Apostles. I started a sketch, but the arrangement altered so quickly as the ship changed position from moment to moment, that I could do no more than the most rapid outline. Now the Lion, both head and rump, a fine sandy-coloured prominence full of character, came to occupy the centre of the scene, whilst above it the real edge of the Table came into sight and grew and grew. I started another sketch: here was the view as I had always imagined it; the great side of the Table was now standing out in deep indigo shadow above and behind the sandy Lion which was in brilliant sunshine.

....

CHAPTER 6

SOUTH-WEST VIA TRISTAN DA CUNHA

Sunday, 17th January, 1926. We sailed from Cape Town this afternoon,
our stay being longer than expected owing to the Christmas and New
Year holidays interfering with work on the alterations to our winches.

[Any lengthy account of impressions of South Africa gained on so
brief a stay would be out of place. Let me just record that we carried
away so many pleasant memories: of hospitality, of Cape Town itself,
of a visit to the actual Cape of Good Hope, of climbs up Table
Mountain, and of surf bathing at Muizenberg; I shall always remember the magnificent view, from the top of Paarl Rock, across the Cape
Flats to a deep blue Table Mountain in the distance. The wild flowers,
particularly the gorgeous Proteas, are a vivid memory too, both as
seen growing in profusion on the mountain sides or so delightfully
displayed for sale on little stalls down the length of Adderley Street;
and the butterflies were exciting; especially the gaudy swallow-tails
and the lovely Table Mountain Beauty which is said to be found no
where else. To us zoologists, of course, the highlight of our stay was
finding—under the bark of rotting logs on the slopes of Table
Mountain—our first specimens of *Peripatus*, the most primitive of all
the arthropods (i.e., the insect-crab-centipede type of animals). It was
at the Cape that Professor Moseley, when on the *Challenger* Expedition,
first discovered their true nature by showing that they breathed by air
tubes like the tracheae of insects, only of a more primitive kind.
Lastly, while I must not discuss the colour question, I may say that
I found it deeply disturbing.]

Thursday, 21st January. We are steaming westward at a good
7 knots, carrying stores and mail to Tristan da Cunha: the first for
two and a half years. From there we shall go straight to South Georgia,
cutting out our originally planned visit to the Falkland Islands until
our return as we are already so late for the present whaling season.
We have a big deck cargo of extra coal to help us on our way for we
expect to be plugging into the westerly winds much of the voyage.

Both yesterday and to-day we have seen schools of male sperm whales; yesterday's were particularly large ones. At times we were very close to them but never quite near enough to mark them with our darts, although we had the guns in readiness. The presented a fine spectacle: sometimes displaying their huge heads as they rose, sometimes their great flukes as they plunged, throwing up walls of white foam over the bluest of blue seas.

Friday, 29th January. We have been most fortunate in not having encountered any strong head-winds. We should sight Tristan to-morrow having made the passage in very good time. Until yesterday, when a north-westerly wind freshened, we have had remarkably warm and calm weather.

On Tuesday there was an alarm. Water was found in one of the holds and it was thought that the ship was leaking. The hold, used as an extra bunker, had to be emptied as soon as possible for examination. We all worked until midnight shifting wet bags of coal along the deck, followed by the luxury of a hot bath in the engine-room. How the water got there remains a mystery; once the hold was empty no more water entered. It would have made a good study for a Brangwyn etching, figures heaving and hauling sacks of coal along the gently rolling deck with the lights catching, or throwing into silhouette, the energetic forms.

Sunday, 31st January. We sighted Tristan da Cunha early yesterday morning, twelve and a half days out from Cape Town, and dropped anchor off the settlement about 2 o'clock in the afternoon. The island is a great extinct volcano[1] practically circular in form; it arises abruptly from the sea with steep cliffs from one to two thousand feet in height, and then tapers more gradually to the crater at the peak, 7,640 feet[2] above sea level. The peak itself on our approach was hidden by cloud; later from our position at anchor this evening we had a clear view of it, and could see no snow on it. The cloud formations over the island are at times remarkable. To-day, above a low belt of irregular cloud the mountain emerged clearly for a space but then entered a second higher layer fitting closely over its peak almost like a cap of snow; in addition, high in the blue sky above, was a perfectly circular patch of delicate white cloud which hung like a halo directly over the top, but kept varying in size from a great disc, to the merest spot.

On the north-west coast of the island, below the wall-like cliffs, is

----

[1]The recent (1961) eruption and evacuation of the islanders will be fresh in everyone's memory.

[2]*Encyclopædia Britannica*, 14th edit., vol. 22, p. 486; but Martin Holgate in his recent book *Mountains in the Sea* (1938) gives the height as 6,760 ft.

Tristan da Cunha from the north-east: the settlement is on the spit of land on the extreme right. Note the calmer water near the shore; this lies inside a dense fringing line of kelp which surrounds the island. Redrawn from a watercolour made on the spot.

a small gently sloping grass-covered plateau raised some twenty to thirty feet above the sea. It is here that the settlement is built: a widely scattered group of little single-storied crofters' cottages of stone and thatch.

The island, with the smaller Inaccessible Island twenty miles to the south of it and Nightingale Island some ten miles from that, were discovered by the Portuguese admiral Tristao da Cunha, in 1506. It is sometimes described as the loneliest island in the world; lying almost in the middle of the South Atlantic it is nearly 1,500 miles from Cape Town, and a little more from South America. In 1810 three American whalers, Lambert, Williams and Currie, settled on the island and tried to farm it to provide vegetables, corn and pigs to whaling ships and passing merchantmen which frequently visited the Tristan group at that time; and they hoped to develop a small export trade in seal skins and seal oil. Their enterprise however, came to an end two years later when Lambert and Williams were drowned on a fishing expedition. The present settlement dates from 1816 when a small garrison was stationed there because it was thought that the island might be used as a base from which to assist Napoleon to escape from St. Helena. A year later when the contingent was withdrawn, Corporal William Glass of Kelso, with his wife and two children (he had married a coloured woman at the Cape), obtained permission to remain with two others from the relieving ship. They were joined later by other settlers (American sealers and whalers) and some ship-wrecked sailors who elected to remain; among the latter was a Dutch-man, Pieter Green, and, from a later wreck, two Italians, Andreas Repetto and Gaetano Lavarello, who decided to stay it was said because they would not again risk their lives upon the sea. Among the original settlers only Glass was married; five others, however, in 1826 persuaded a whaling captain on his next voyage to bring them half-caste wives from St. Helena. [About this incident I cannot resist quoting the story as told by Martin Holgate in his *Mountains in the Sea* (1958):

The five bachelors persuaded a Captain Amm, master of the sloop *Duke of Gloucester*, to fetch them wives from St. Helena on his next voyage. Captain Amm agreed to do so, but it is under-standable that he found few volunteers to go to marry an unknown man on an unknown island. The five that did consent to come were all more or less dark-skinned, and one was a widowed Negress with four children. The nearer Captain Amm got to Tristan, the less he fancied himself as a matrimonial agent, and, perhaps to avoid being left with unwelcome passengers for the whole voyage, when he arrived at the island he landed the women in the early dawn and put to sea. The five bachelors walked down to the beach and found their brides, lined them up in a row on the sand, and each picked his fancy.]

So it comes about that there is a considerable mixture of blood in the colony.

The Tristanites are famed throughout the world as remarkable boatmen. Their boats are of the most flimsy construction: mere shells of oiled canvas stretched upon a skeleton of wood. For the most part the wood used comes from the small trees, said to be apple trees, growing on the upper mountain slopes; but in addition all manner of pieces of drift-wood are used and nailed together with all sorts of nails both brass and iron. Many of their oars are built up of two or three pieces of wood. In these boats they will sometimes row fifteen miles out to a passing ship to barter sheep, eggs, skins, etc., in exchange for the cereals and clothing which are their principal needs. They also make journeys to the islands of Inaccessible and Nightingale for mollymauk eggs and birds; mollies, various petrels and greater shearwaters are important items of diet for them.

Two boats were alongside as soon as we had anchored. They surprised us greatly by calling out 'Good morning, Captain Stenhouse.' It turned out that a sailing-ship carrying timber had passed the island last September and her mate was a Mr. Letts who had originally been coming with us as chief officer, but had then resigned; he had given the news of our coming. This was quite a coincidence as only two or three ships a year pass the island now. One Robert Glass, a descendant of the founder of the settlement, acted as spokesman and made arrangements with the captain. They wore a great variety of clothing, all much the worse for wear; some had boots, some had their home-made moccasins, and one was just in socks with his toes protruding through large holes. They spoke in rather curious high-pitched voices. All afternoon until dark they made journeys backwards and forwards unloading their stores and mail. We carried the first mail to them for two years.

Dr. Marshall went ashore at once to start his medical work and observation, and the captain went ashore for a short time, but most of us remained on board until to-day. We had dredged in 40-50 metres before anchoring, and then set fish traps, fished with hand-lines and streamed out tow-nets in the current whilst at anchor. The dredge-hauls were disappointing, bring up quantities of small rounded stones encrusted with sponges, polyzoans and *Lithothamnion*, but little else. While the fish traps, which were probably continually being moved by the currents, came up empty, the hand-lines were most successful; altogether we caught well over a hundred fish during the afternoon and those which are not required for preservation will keep us in fresh fish for many days.

This morning several of us landed and spent a few hours ashore. The captain assembled all the population outside the little church and read a proclamation and message from the King. While many of the men we saw had fine features they did not appear a very robust lot, but then we did not see them all; we were seeing the older ones (and they appear to live to a great age) and the more infirm, because our visit unfortunately coincided with one of their biennial expeditions to Inaccessible Island, when twenty of their younger and more virile members go off in two boats to collect eggs and birds for food. The total population at the time of our visit was about 140.

We are as far as possible specialising on the marine fauna so did not spend more than a few hours ashore; we collected as many of the various land animals as we could find: insect, millipedes, woodlice, spiders, etc., and returned to the ship. During the afternoon we made some more dredge hauls from a boat inside the kelp near the shore, but again with only moderate success. There is a very thick belt of kelp, the giant *Macrocystis pyrifera*, which surrounds the islands and prevents ships from coming very near in or getting into the more sheltered water inside. The *Quest*, when she visited the island in 1922, was, I believe, one of the very few vessels to have come through the belt and anchored inside it. The stems of the *Macrocystis* attain a great length (up to 70 metres according to Skottsberg) and bear a large number of side branches on one side only, each having a little bladder and then a long flat lobe of leaf; the origin of these side branches is interesting, for they are seen to become split off from a large flat terminal leaf by the development towards its base of slits which increase in length till they meet the margin. The base of the stem forms an anchoring attachment by spreading out a large number of anastomosing root-like branches which, like fingers, clutch the stones and rocks of the bottom. [With some difficulty, I remember, we succeeded in hauling up some of these with their heavy load of stone and by cutting away the rootlets revealed, within the spaces inside, a rich fauna of small crustaceans and worms of many different kinds.]

Monday 1st February. To-day, at 10 o'clock in the morning, we weighed anchor and sailed for South Georgia. On leaving we decided to lower a heavy dredge in 100 fathoms of water, for at that depth, off Tristan, the *Challenger* Expedition had taken a large number of fine gorgonians (branching tree-like soft corals). The bottom drops away into the depths very steeply and it was with some difficulty that we found the 100 fathoms line. We were all hoping to see some of these beautiful forms, but no one, I think, could have expected the truly magnificent haul that we got. The dredge, which had evidently struck against some rock, had become very bent, but nevertheless was laden with masses of these exquisite gorgonians and, better still, antipatharians which are still more delicate tree-like colonies of polyps. It might have been dragged through some orchard in spring-time for the polyps looked like flowers; it came to the surface trailing branches, as if torn from trees, laden with blossom of many different colours: one species was a beautiful rose colour, another orange and yet another snowy white, and the branches were up to four feet in length. Then there was a superb yellow gorgonian (*Thouarella* or allied genus) reminding one of sprays of mimosa.[1] There were many other corals, some true calcareous corals and some beautiful sea-anemones, some clinging to a white coral skeleton. Zoologically perhaps the most interesting of them all was a colonial actinean, apparently one of the Zoanthidae, not unlike *Gerardia*. This is a sea-

[1] Some examples of the beautiful plant-like animals are shown in my sketches on p.373

anemone-like creature which buds off new individuals which remain together to form large colonies encrusting whatever they may be growing upon; here they were growing over the branches of the gorgonians (*Thouarella*), covering them like ivy smothering a tree. There were colonies in all stages of conquest from gorgonians just affected at one small point to others which were completely hidden (and killed) below the encrusting invader. From time to time we try to see if any of the animals we catch are phosphorescent. We were greatly rewarded on this occasion by taking one of these large *Gerardia*-like colonies into the dark-room; it was like a tree hung with a hundred blue-green fairy lights. What can possibly be the function of such luminescence in terms of advantage to its possessor? These animals, like all others of their kind, will no doubt have the powerful stinging cells which both help them to capture their food and protect them from possible enemies. Just as we so often see bright arresting colours associated with a sting or some other unpleasant quality— warning colours[1] as they are called, advertising their noxiousness— so perhaps such illumination may similarly serve as a warning of their unwholesomeness in the darkness of the depths.

[I must now relate a story which I have been greatly surprised not to find recorded in my narrative. It is one I vividly remember and I have often told it since; perhaps its nature may explain its omission from my journal. The reason why we had been fishing so enthusiastically with our lines, and using our fish traps too, was not entirely concerned with our culinary desires. There was a certain rare fish which we were especially anxious to obtain for the British Museum; we had been asked particularly to look out for it, for it occurs nowhere else in the whole world but around the Tristan da Cunha group. We had failed to catch a specimen in our fishing efforts on the Saturday and we tried again whenever possible on the Sunday (the yesterday of my journal); it was then in the late afternoon that we succeeded in obtaining a splendid specimen and laid it out with particular care, taking measurements and making colour notes, etc., prior to it being placed in one of the large tanks of spirit for preservation. We had also been very busy labelling and preserving our speciments from the dredge hauls and particularly from cutting open the kelp roots. We broke off from our labours for supper, and much enjoyed the fresh fish we had been catching, it was delicious. On returning to the deck we

---

[1] Such colours are produced by natural selection; the more brightly coloured noxious animals will have a better chance of survival since they are more readily recognised by the vertebrate (would be) predators which by experience learn to leave them alone. A few are sacrificed for the benefit of the race as a whole

opened one of the big spirit tanks in which to lay to rest our prize
specimen and then we went to pick it up. It was nowhere to be
found. We then realised the awful truth. It was indeed that specimen
which we had just found particularly palatable. We had a rule that
fish put outside the laboratory on the starboard side was for the galley,
whereas anything on the port side was for preservation and must on no
account be touched. We had taken on a new cook at Cape Town
and he had mistaken the instructions. We kept on fishing till we had
to sail but we never caught another, and we could wait no longer.
We were, I remember, very upset at this frightful blunder.

To set against this dreadful story I must now add that we did on
this day actually present the British Museum with a still rarer fish—

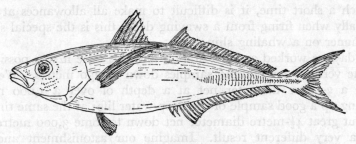

Our new species of fish from Tristan da Cunha: *Decapterus
lngimanus* (Norman).

a single fine specimen of a species entirely new to science. We did not
really know this till many years later when it was named by the
late Dr. J. R. Norman (of the Museum) *Decapterus longimanus* and
described by him in 1935 in the *Annals and Magazine of Natural History*,
vol. XVI, p. 258. In our dredging at Tristan we also discovered two new
crustaceans, amphipod 'shrimps,' *Paramoera tristanensis* and *Portogeneia
tristanensis*, described by Dr. H. K. Barnard in his big report on the
Amphipoda of the expedition in *Discovery Reports*, vol. V.]

Wednesday, 3rd February. To-day we took our first complete set of
water samples down to a depth of 3,000 metres, using the Nansen-
Pettersson apparatus for the shallow hauls and Ekmann reversing
bottles (see pp. 147-8) at the greater depths. We had previously made a
sounding obtaining a sample of *Globigerina* ooze from a depth of 3,200
metres.

Friday, 5th February. We have had our biggest storm so far, in fact
the only real gale since last July when on our trial run. The wind
blew from the SE., which is unusual in these latitudes, and it blew at

times with almost hurricane force, on top of a south-westerly swell, giving a very broken and angry cross sea: one of steep waves with their tops flying off. The ship has rolled heavily all day and we have had more water on the decks than ever before.

Monday, 8th February. To-day we took another series of water samples, again down to 3,000 metres, but the ship was rolling too heavily to allow us to use the vertical nets and we only towed the 1 metre and 2 metre diametre nets near the surface.

Thursday, 11th February. Yesterday afternoon two fin whales remained near the ship for a time, but only one came close enough for marking. I fired two shots but was unsuccessful; my first fell a yard or so short and my second went over its back. A strong wind was blowing, against me for the first, but with me for the second. A whale shows himself for such a short time, it is difficult to make all allowances at once, especially when firing from a swaying deck; this is the special skill of the gunner on a whaling ship.

To-day we worked another station and this time it was possible to use the vertical nets, taking samples down to 250 metres. We then towed a 2-metre diameter net at a depth of over a 1,000 metres bringing up a good sample of the deep-water life; at the same time we sent out great $4\frac{1}{2}$-metre diameter net down to some 3,000 metres but with a very different result. Imagine our astonishment and disappointment, after eagerly awaiting the catch from so great a depth, when we saw the huge frame break the surface with only the tattered remains of the front part of the net attached to it—the whole of the main bag had torn away. How can it be explained? Had the longitudinal strengthening ropes which took the main strain off the net become rotten? Was it the sheer magnitude of the catch which had caused too great a strain? Or was it, as the more imaginative were inclined to believe, some huge sea monster—a giant squid for instance—which, having got into the net, made its escape by going clean through it? We shall never know. The actual sounding had been over 4,000 metres; we could not have hit bottom.

It is getting perceptibly colder; the wind is biting and the surface water temperature has dropped 5° in the last week: it was 12·71 °c on the 3rd and 7·23 °c to-day.

Saturday, 13th February. To-day we worked another full station (Station 10) using vertical nets down to 500 metres, and water sampling bottles again down to 3,000 metres. Here we have made quite a discovery. Our sounding at this station gave us 4,402 metres. There have been relatively few soundings taken in this part of the ocean and the deposit which our 'snapper' lead brought up was not Globigerina

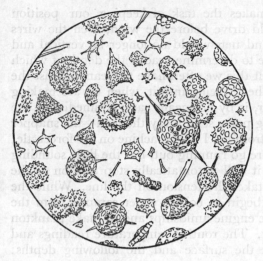

A typical example of Radiolarian ooze seen under a microscope (× 50): not actually the *Discovery* Atlantic sample, but one from the Pacific Ocean taken by the *Challenger* Expedition at their station 274 from a depth of 2750 fathoms.

ooze, as it had been at all other stations, but Radiolarian ooze. Our position is 46°11′30″S.; 22°27′30″W. It is likely to cause considerable surprise, for we believe this to be the first occasion on which such ooze has been recorded from the Atlantic; it is characteristic of many parts of the Indian and Pacific Oceans. The full beauty of the ooze is best seen after washing it in caustic potash; under the microscope one now sees the masses of delicate siliceous shells: some spherical, some helmet-shaped, perforated in honeycomb fashion and often set with slender spines. These shells have, of course, like those of *Globigerina*, sunk from the upper layers where their planktonic, protozoan owners once lived (see p. 66).

The snapper lead just mentioned is a sounding lead having jaws fitted below it so that they dip into the ooze; the impact releases a spring which causes its two jaws to snap together and bite out for us a bit of the ocean floor.

We shall from now onwards be making many of these 'standard vertical stations' as we call these takings of observations on a vertical line down into the depths; it will be well to describe just what happens, for we are now beginning our main work in earnest. As soon as we arrive on position the captain turns the head of the ship into the wind and endeavours to keep her stationary with an occasional use of the engine; it is, of course, impossible to anchor the ship in so great a depth of water. To-day there was a heavy south-westerly swell and a wind of 'force 4' which made working difficult. The heavy rigging of the *Discovery* offers almost as much resistance to the wind as if we still had some sail up, and so makes the task of keeping our position peculiarly hard. If we should drive before the wind, then the wires carrying our water bottles and nets would no longer be vertical and it would be next to impossible to determine exactly the depth at which we were sampling; to prevent this we often have to steam against the wind, but to keep the ship's head facing into it, when we are making no passage through the water, is by no means easy. Immediately the ship has stopped the sounding party send away the lead—the snapper lead—on the fine piano wire from the Lucas machine on the forecastle; the thousands of metres of wire go running out, but the little sounding machine is so designed that it will automatically stop as soon as the lead strikes the bottom and takes the tension off the line. While the sounding is being taken we begin to collect water samples from the shallower depths by using the engine amidships and to make plankton net hauls with the engine aft. The routine temperature readings and water samples are taken at the surface and the following depths: 5, 10, 20, 30, 40, 50, 75, 100, 200, 300, 400, 500, 1,000, 2,000 and 3,000 metres or as deep as the sounding will allow. The vertical plankton net hauls will usually be taken in six stages: from 50 metres to the surface, from 100 to 50 metres, from 250 to 100 metres, from 500 to 250, from 750 to 500, and from 1,000 to 750 metres, and sometimes even deeper; actually at to-day's station (as already noted) time is short and we only sampled down to 500 metres.

[I am now expanding my journal to give a fuller account of the procedure followed and the kind of apparatus used on such a standard station. I think perhaps the general reader may like to know just how we collected our data and how we spent so much of our time on these long sessions of fishing for knowledge in this deep-water world we cannot see; if, however, he should find too much detail for his liking, he can skip to the next entry—16th February (p. 153). This more technical section is indented.

The temperatures and water samples down to 100 metres are taken with the Nansen-Pettersson water-bottle which is very simple and quick to use. This is the joint invention of the great Swedish oceanographers Fridtjof Nansen (more famous still, of course, as the Arctic explorer) and Otto Pettersson. The bottle (shown in the sketch opposite) is made of metal and sent down suspended on a wire fixed to a clamp at the top of its frame; as it goes down its top and bottom are open so that the water passes through it. When it has reached the depth from which the sample is to be taken, a brass 'messenger' weight is slipped on to the wire and sent sliding down to close it; the top of the bottle acts

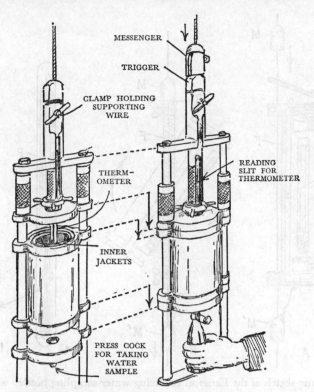

MESSENGER

TRIGGER

CLAMP HOLDING
SUPPORTING
WIRE

THERM—
OMETER

READING
SLIT FOR
THERMOMETER

INNER
JACKETS

PRESS COCK
FOR TAKING
WATER
SAMPLE

The Nansen-Pettersson water sampling bottle shown
open and closed.

like a trigger which releases springs to make the top and main
body of the bottle snap down on to the bottom and so tightly
enclose the sample of water. Now down the centre of the bottle is
a thermometer with its stem projecting up through the top into
a protective case which has a slit in it to allow a reading to be
taken when it comes up. There are actually three walls to the
bottle's cylindrical body, one inside the other with a little space
between them; these, when the top and bottom are closed, act as
insulating chambers preventing loss or gain of heat to the sample
as it is being hauled to the surface. As soon as it comes up the
temperature is read and the water sample run off, through a press
cock at the bottom, into one or more storage bottles for later
analysis; this is done by one of the staff, usually Dr. Herdman
our hydrologist, standing on the little platform outside the rail

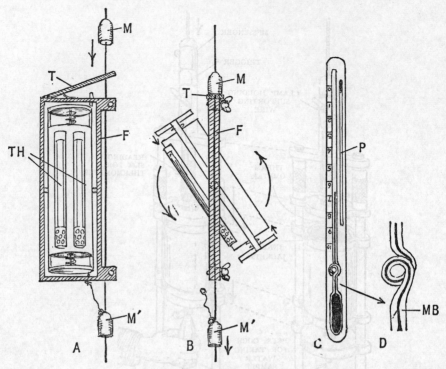

Diagrammatic sketch of the Ekmann reversing water sampling bottle. A, the bottle set open top and bottom in its frame F attached to the vertical wire. The messenger weight M, sent down the wire, hits the trigger T which allows the bottle, with its two thermometers TH attached to it, to rotate through 180° (by a spring mechanism). B is a side view showing the bottle beginning to turn and closing at its top and bottom as it does so; at the same time a lower messenger weight M is released to slide down the wire to operate another bottle at a greater depth. C, a reversing thermometer with its inverted scale and pilot thermometer P. D, detail of thermometer twist and the point at which the mercury column breaks MB.

of the ship. The messenger weight is now taken off, the bottle is opened, reset, and sent down again to the next depth. The wire running out passes over a recording sheave—a 'metre wheel' as we call it—which tells us on a set of little dials exactly how much line has gone out; this is watched closely by the person operating the little steam winch inboard.

The Nansen-Pettersson bottle, which is such a handy apparatus in that it can be sent down and brought up so quickly, can only be safely used down to depths of 100 metres; if used at deeper levels errors creep in both on account of it taking too long before the temperature can be read and also because the temperature of the sample is actually lowered slightly in consequence of the reduction of pressure as it comes up. For taking temperatures and samples from greater depths the 'reversing' bottle is used; it is so termed because it carries what are called reversing thermometers which have to be turned upside down to work. The bottle and thermometers (there are usually two to give check readings) are mounted, as seen in the drawing opposite, in a frame which rotates when a trigger is hit by a messenger weight sent down the wire; the bottle, which before was open, is closed as it swings over. The mercury tube of each thermometer, just above the bulb, has a loop and a kink in it, so that when it is swung rapidly upside down the thread of mercury breaks; as soon as this happens all the mercury that was *above* the kink runs to the opposite, and now *lower*, end of the tube. Now, when the bottle is brought up, the height of this *inverted* column of mercury is seen against a scale which can be read when the thermometer is upside down; this tells us the actual temperature that the thermometer was recording at the moment it turned over. A small pilot thermometer gives the temperature at the time of reading so that a correction can be made for the expansion of the main mercury colums on reaching the surface. These were the bottles we used for all depths below 100 metres and to save time we used a series of them, up to five at a time on the one vertical wire let out from the winch on the forecastle head as soon as the Lucas sounding line had come in. They are clamped to the wire, one above the other, at intervals of 100 or more metres apart, as the wire is let out over the side. When the lowest bottle has reached its proper depth, a messenger weight is sent down the wire to hit the trigger to reverse the first bottle which, as it turns, releases another messenger already threaded on the wire below it; this slides down to operate the second bottle, which in turn liberates a third messenger and so on to the bottom. In spite of this method of simultaneous working, the letting out and winding in of thousands of metres of wire may take five or six hours for the whole series.

In the meantime the plankton nets are being worked from the platform and winch aft. Our standard net for these vertical hauls is that of 70 cm. diameter modelled, as explained in chap. 2 (p. 53), on the lines of the one used by Professor Johan Hjort on his cruise in the North Atlantic with Sir John Murray on the *Michael Sars*. This net is shown in the sketch overleaf and as I describe it I shall refer to the letters in that illustration.

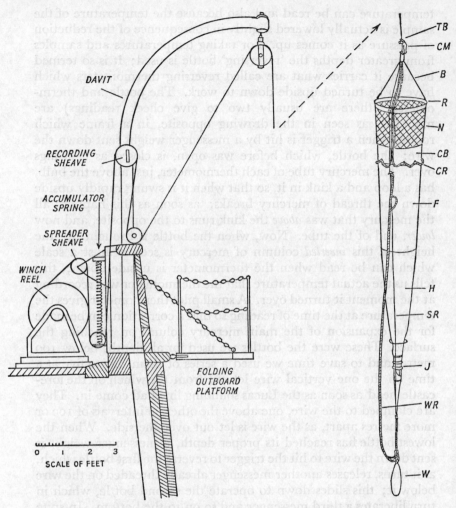

DAVIT

RECORDING
SHEAVE

ACCUMULATOR
SPRING

SPREADER
SHEAVE

WINCH
REEL

FOLDING
OUTBOARD
PLATFORM

0   1   2   3
SCALE OF FEET

TB
CM
B
R
N
CB
CR
F
H
SR
J
WR
W

t, a section through the rail of R.R.S. *Discovery* showing the light deck winch, davit outboard platform, etc., for hydrological and vertical plankton-net sampling. *Right* the 70 cm. diameter net rigged for vertical sampling; the reference letters refer to the description of the net in the text. (See also Plate 25, p. 304).

The main catching part of the net is a conical bag made of the silk gauze used by millers for sieving flour and known as bolting cloth; it is made in two parts, the front section (F) being of coarser mesh, 40 threads to the inch, than the hind section (H) which has 74 threads to the inch. This design ensures a good range of size in the animals caught: the wider mesh gives good filtration to secure the larger less abundant forms and the finer mesh sieves out a good sample of the smaller life. The front section (F) is sewn to a canvas band (CB) which is separated from the galvanised ring (R) by a cylinder of quite wide mesh netting (N). The ring is suspended from the closing mechanism (CM) by the three bridles (B). The hind end of the net (H) tapers to a canvas band which fits over and is clamped to the bronze collecting jar (J). Three stay ropes (SR) of phosphor-bronze run down from the ring (R) to take the weight of the jar off the gauze net and pass on to support the lead weight (W) below. There are a number of brass rings sewn to the canvas band (CB) and through these is loosely threaded the closing rope (CR) whose two ends pass up to be shackled to the closing mechanism (CM). The net is lowered open to the depth from which the vertical haul will start; and the weight below takes it down tail first so that it cannot catch any plankton on the way. When it is hauled up the canvas band spreads out and the net is full open for fishing.

The net may now be closed at any required depth by sending a messenger weight down the wire to hit the trigger bolt (TB) on the closing mechanism; this at once releases the ring holding the bridles so that the net falls and is caught by the closing rope (CR) which throttles the mouth of the net, at the canvas band, just like the string closing a sponge bag. The closed net is now hauled up hanging on this rope and we know that all the plankton in it came from the range of depth over which it fished without any additions from the water layers above as it came up.

The arrangement of the winch, the outboard platform, the davit and the recording sheave is shown in the same diagram; it is similar to that for the water-bottles farther for'ard. It is seen that the wire on leaving the winch drum makes a number of turns: it goes over the spreader sheave, down and round a pulley which is riding up and down in a frame against a strong spring accumulator and then up over the recording sheave before going out to the davit block from which the net is lowered. The function of the spring accumulator is to counteract to some extent the effect of the rolling of the ship; without it the net would be jerked up and down as it was being hauled up, and in excessive rolling might lose some of its catch if at odd moments it actually went down more than it came up.

Let me now quote from an account of the working of this gear which I wrote for the section on equipment and methods for vol. 1 of the *Discovery Reports* (Kemp and Hardy, 1929); it will give some idea of the attention that was required to prevent mishap.

'Three persons are required to work the plankton unit efficiently: two scientific officers and a deck-hand. Of the two officers one is on the outboard platform to adjust the closing mechanism and net before descent, to despatch messengers and to wash down and take the sample at the end of the haul; the other, who is in charge of operations, is inboard to control the engine, the depth reached and speed of winding, and to time the despatch of the messenger. . . . The deck-hand guides the wire on the drum, pulls up the weight and holds the net for washing down.

'After an examination, when the closing rope is seen to be open to the full extent, the net is lowered to the surface and the hands on the dials of the recording sheave adjusted to zero. This being done, the net is lowered to the depth from which the haul is to be taken. When the ship is rolling heavily—a not infrequent occurrence in the vicinity of South Georgia—the wire must be let out with great care. As the ship rolls to starboard, that is, away from the side of operation, the wire must be allowed to run out easily; as it rolls to port the drum must be checked by the brake or the wire may become slack, over-ride a sheave and possibly kink. The danger of this happening becomes less the farther the net goes out, because the strain on the wire is increasing with its own increasing weight; in hauling in the strain completely removes the danger. . . .

'As soon as the net reaches the required depth, the drum is stopped and put into gear, and the messenger, unless a haul to the surface is being made, is attached to the wire and held by a piece of line until the moment for despatch. The net is wound up at the speed of 1 metre per second. An even and exact rate of winding may be maintained, after a very little practice, by regulating the steam valve whilst watching the metre-recording sheave in conjunction with a stop-watch. The times that the particular messenger in use takes to fall to the different depths required have been calculated from previous trials. Thus when the haul is (say) from 750 to 500 metres, the messenger, which is known to fall 500 metres in 160 secs, is released from the surface when the metre wheel records that the net, in its upward passage, has reached 660 metres depth. The upward haul is continued without a break, so that the net meets the messenger at 500 metres and is closed. After this the net, no longer fishing and offering less resistance, may be hauled more quickly, but never more than 4 or 5 metres per second if damage to the net is to be avoided. In the haul from 1,000 to 750 metres the messenger, which takes 240 secs. to fall 750 metres, must be released when the dial reads 990: i.e., 10 secs. after the haul is started. At greater depths it may be necessary to release the messenger and wait before starting the haul: thus from 3,000 to 2,500 metres one must wait 5 minutes. A table of dial readings and times is easily drawn up for any particular type of messenger. Careful winding should ensure accuracy of release to within 1 or 2 metres in the shallower hauls and not more than 10 metres in the 1,000-750 metres haul. When the ship is drifting before a wind so that the wire is off the vertical a slightly longer time must be allowed for the falling of the messenger. . . . The spring accumulators afford a means of checking the accuracy of the haul, for they indicate by their sudden extension the exact moment when the closure of the net is effected.

'On reaching the surface the weight is pulled up by its special rope (WR in diagram) and the net washed down on each side with water from a bucket. The brass net bucket is now detached, replaced by another, the net fully opened and the mechanism reset for the next descent.'

It was with the plankton work that I was principally concerned and throughout most of the voyage Rolfe Gunther worked with me: he on the outboard platform and myself in control of the engine and depth timing. It was often far from comfortable working on the platform outside the rail, especially in these early days when the old ship rolled so abominably before we had the extra sister keels fitted; I shall have more to say on this presently. Rolfe was magnificent to work with, as was 'Jimmy' Fraser[1] who worked with me during a later part of the voyage when Rolfe was away on the *Scoresby*; and as a deck-hand we usually had either Will Wadden or Alf Briggs, both excellent men for the job.

I have now I think given some idea of the routine followed at a standard vertical station and of the difficulty of working if the wind was getting, as so often, towards gale force. Now let me return to my journal.]

Thursday, 16th February. I was called just before 6 o'clock this morning to be told by William the cadet that there was a fine iceberg ahead of us. It was our first iceberg. Throwing on a heavy coat I was soon on deck; and there it was, still many miles ahead, the rising sun reflecting off its glistening sides and peaks with a brilliant yellow light. It slowly changed shape as we approached and appeared to be swinging round. It was not until 9 o'clock that we were close to it. It

[1] Now Dr. F. C. Fraser, C.B.E., F.R.S., late Keeper of Zoology, British Museum (Nat. Hist.).

was truly a very large one; on being measured it was just over 300 feet in height. I made the water-colour sketch reproduced on Plate 9. It was a typical barrier iceberg, we were told by the captain who has had much experience of Antarctic ice. The barrier is the edge of that great sheet of ice that covers the Antarctic continent as an ice cap many hundreds of feet thick; it has been accumulating by the fall of snow over long periods of time and then, as its weight increases, it slowly slides off the sloping surface of the land like a vast glacier. As it reaches the sea it floats and pushes farther and farther out from the land as the barrier; it then breaks up into separate pieces of all sizes to give the characteristic flat-topped tabular icebergs, some of which are huge ice islands rather than just icebergs.

The iceberg before us had this typical flat top which was now somewhat inclined, no doubt due to irregular melting; and its edges were broken into peaks and turrets reminding one of some old Norman fortress. Since ice floats with nearly eight times as much of its mass below water as above it, we can imagine how great was the thickness of the barrier that gave it birth. Its sides were beautifully sculptured and there were deep caverns and clefts in them; in these was seen that most remarkable, almost luminous, ice-blue; so different from the blue of the sea or the sky. For a mile or more around it the water was dotted with little fragments of ice which had broken from its sides; they are known as 'bergy bits,' an expression of the old whalers. We steamed so close that at one time it was impossible to get the whole iceberg into my camera's field of view. The captain steered the ship among the bergy bits to give us for the first time the sound of broken ice upon her bows and sides: a musical scrunching sound, a little like the shovelling of broken glass.

Just as we were directly opposite the iceberg, there came a roar like thunder. For a moment we expected to see the whole castle crack from top to bottom or heel over; but no, this seemingly portentous sound was just some minor cracking on another side. Such icebergs break up by flat pieces carving from their sides to form the dangerous submerged icebergs called 'growlers.'

We were to have had a station at 8.30 but put it off till a few miles past the berg on account of the abnormal local conditions, the colder and less saline surface layer, due to the melting ice. We are now coming over still deeper water, our sounding giving 5,000 metres. Once again we brought up Radiolarian ooze; our position this time (at Station 11) being 50° 26' 00" S, 30° 27' 00" W. We were able to sample the water down to a depth of 4,500 metres and again we worked the closing vertical nets down to 500 metres. A very rich haul of copepods was taken in the upper plankton net and we have seen them gradually increasing in numbers on the rolls of the continuous plankton recorder which we have been using for some time. The surface temperature at this station had dropped another two degrees, being 5·36°c, and we noted for the first time a remarkable cold layer at a depth of 100 to 200 metres sandwiched between two warmer layers. Why did this cold water not sink below the warmer water under it? It was exciting that our samplings were so soon giving us challenging results. [It was present at the next station too, only more so. The varying temperatures at different levels from the surface down to a depth of 1,000 metres taken at the last four stations on this line are compared in the accompanying table. We had made an important discovery and revealed a unique character of the hydrology of the Antarctic seas, one which we will meet with again and again; only later did its true significance become apparent (pp. 317-320).]

TABLE OF SEA TEMPERATURES (IN °C) approaching S. Georgia
The unexpected cold layer found at Stations 11 and 12 is shown in heavy type.

Position	Station 9 46° 11' 30" S 22° 27' 30" W	Station 10 46° 35' 00" S 24° 15' 30" W	Station 11 50° 26' 00" S 30° 27' 00" W	Station 12 51° 55' 00" S 32° 27' 30" W
Depth in metres				
0	7·23	7·43	5·36	3·82
10	7·23	7·46	5·36	3·32
20	7·23	7·43	5·36	3·10
30	7·19	7·41	5·35	3·10
40	7·18	7·38	5·38	3·05
50	6·88	7·37	5·33	2·61
75	5·13	6·54	2·38	**0·51**
100	4·78	5·96	**0·89**	**0·25**
150	4·53	4·94	**0·36**	**0·02**
200	3·80	4·38	1·08	**0·39**
300	3·29	3·49	1·60	1·64
400	2·93	2·81	1·94	1·82
500	2·74	2·64	2·02	1·85
1000	2·58	2·54	1·95	1·58

Wednesday, 17th February. One thing which has surprised me very much, and indeed the captain has commented upon it, is the way in which the wind and the sea have recently risen and fallen in what seems an extraordinary short space of time. In the morning it may be calm with not a breath of wind; by the evening it may be blowing a gale with high steep seas; and by the following evening it may be calm again or perhaps there may be a wind in quite the opposite direction.

By the time yesterday's station was completed a light breeze had sprung up; it quickly increased, as did the height of the waves, so that we spent a most uncomfortable night. Few slept, I think, for it was difficult to keep in one's bunk, the ship rolled so heavily. This morning the gale was at its height and the effect magnificent as the sun shone brilliantly on a blue sea lashed into white foam and breaking waves; I tried to take photographs, but with the ship tumbling this way and that it was difficult. Just at the moment for the best picture, when the vessel is heeling at its biggest angle and a wave breaking over its side, then one must hang on for dear life or be shot across the deck with the violent lurch of the ship. By midday the wind was dying and by this evening only the big swell remains and that is calming down rapidly.

Friday, 19th February. Two more large icebergs were seen yesterday and this evening at 7 o'clock we saw a curious effect. On the horizon, standing out against a grey overcast sky, was a perfectly rounded iceberg of purest white; it was like a white setting sun, as if all the colour had gone out of some diseased world. . . . I was writing this in the deck laboratory just on midnight when a voice for'ard calls out 'Iceberg on the starboard bow!' It is a dark night and difficult to see; we pass a large iceberg barely fifty yards away. A little earlier we had passed another large one to port, the captain said. We are now going very slowly and there is much phosphorescence in the water. Many whales have been seen yesterday and to-day, both blue and fin whales, but we were never near enough to mark them.

We made another biological and hydrographical station yesterday (Station 12), and the temperature of the surface water had dropped again, to 3·82°c. There was a marked change in the plankton sample given by the uppermost net; instead of the profusion of copepods, there were now only a few and their place was taken by a rich growth of diatoms (particularly *Rhizosolenia* and a naviculid). This change is interesting; we are now entering the regions of rich phytoplankton characteristic of the polar seas. It is a change reflected in the deposits on the ocean floor. At this station our sounding lead brought back, from a depth of 2,744 metres, our first sample of diatom ooze. Our position here was 51° 55′ 00″ S, 32° 27′ 00″ W. It was an excellent sample made up of countless siliceous shells of diatoms, almost all of them recognisable species, together with some of the typical little skeletons of what are called silico-flagellates (p. 327). Here we could see brought up from the bed of the ocean, from thousands of feet below us, the dead skeletons of the same kinds of diatoms and flagellates as we are catching in our surface tow-nets. From the vast number in the deposit we gain some idea of the continuous rain of dead and dying

A piebald berg, black with volcanic ash, probably from a glacier of one of the South Sandwich Islands, drawn from a photograph.

material which must be sinking from the upper sunlit layers to support both the plankton animals in the dark depths on the way down, as well as the creatures living on the sea-bed.

To-morrow we should sight South Georgia. We have made a remarkably good passage from the Cape across what is normally a very difficult piece of ocean; we might well have had strong westerly winds against us most of the way. We are in better time to do some work in the present whaling season than we had dared to hope earlier in the voyage.

Saturday, 20th February. I was called at 4 o'clock this morning to see an enormous iceberg of *black* ice. I had told all the officers when on watch to have me called at any time if any unusual sight was to be seen. It was not yet light: the whole scene was dark, cold and grey. The iceberg might almost have been land. A line of ice, like a coast, stretched away on either side of a great raised portion which presented a black front to us for all the world like a massive face of rock. [Such icebergs, which may be most dangerous because almost invisible if met at night, have usually come from the glaciers of the active volcanic islands in the South Sandwich group; here black ash continually falls on the ice and becomes embedded in it. These may well have given some of the early navigators the impression of land and so account for some of the islands on old charts which have subsequently been shown to be false. We shall later see curious piebald icebergs, blotched black and white, which are formed in this way and in the distance may look like huge cows resting on the horizon.] As it became clearer we could see some magnificent formations of ice; behind some low-lying floes two sharply pinnacled icebergs appeared in the uncertain light of dawn to have a greatly exaggerated height.

By breakfast time South Georgia was in sight. Going on deck we saw an immense panorama of jagged snow-covered peaks stretching along the horizon. 'It might be the Himalayas seen from Simla,' said Dr. Kemp, 'if only one substituted cloud for the sea.' All morning they became more and more distinct; we could now see the glaciers and moraines winding down the valleys and then the lower-lying foothills of the coastline came over the horizon.

Approaching South Georgia from the north-east.

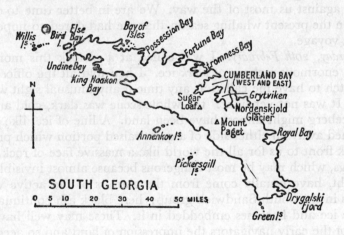

CHAPTER 7

SOUTH GEORGIA—FIRST ENCOUNTER

20th February (*continued*). South Georgia is a narrow island, about 100 miles long by some 20 miles across, formed by a range of mountains like the Alps rising steeply from the sea. It runs roughly in a north-westerly-south-easterly direction and lies between 54° and 55° south, almost at the same latitude as Cape Horn, which is just over 960 miles to the west of it. Its long north-east coast which we are approaching has many fjord-like bays running deeply into it. These provide sheltered access to the whaling stations placed at their head and a good anchorage for the factory ships; they must be quite reminiscent of home for the whalers who are nearly all Norwegians.

As we neared the land we saw our first penguins. Several schools of them passed the ship swimming under water and continually breaking surface for all the world like small porpoises. They appeared to be gentoo penguins which are said to be very common at South Georgia. They swim as if they were 'flying' under water; their flipper-like wings go through the movements of a wing in flight, but more slowly on account of the much greater resistance offered by water than by air. While they look like birds flying as seen in a slow-motion film, they nevertheless swim fast, for the wing strokes give a great thrust in the water.

By the early afternoon we were steaming into Cumberland Bay. It is the largest indentation of the coast with a mouth some five miles across, and it soon divides into two separate fjords, East and West Bays, which diverge almost at right angles from one another. We swing round to port into the East Bay and there, at the head of its larger branch to the left, for it divides again, is the vast Nordenskjold Glacier descending in a broad sweep from the snowfields of the Allardyce Range to break off in the sea as a brilliant blue wall of ice some two miles wide. Here is scenery which, on a crystal clear day like to-day, must hold its own with any in the world. We gaze and drink it in; there is a hush as we who have not seen it before stand in a group and watch it unfold. A photograph is on Plate 8 (p. 121).

159

Mount Paget, 9,550 feet[1], is the highest point of the range but there are many other peaks; the more spiky Sugar Loaf to the right, because it is more slender and a little nearer, appears just as high, but is actually only 7,823 feet[1]. The other branch of East Bay, that to the right, is Moraine Fjord, with steeper sides, two smaller glaciers at its head, and an entrance guarded by a chain of rocks; still farther to the right of this is a small headland jutting out to hide the mouth of yet another, much smaller, bay, King Edward's Cove. We point our bows towards it for round here lies our shore station laboratory and the whaling station of Grytviken.

Except where there are precipitous sides of rock, or walls of glacier ice, the lower slopes round the shore are mostly green with mosses, tussock grass and burnet. Apart from the grasses there are very few flowering plants here, but the burnet (*Acaena ascendens*) grows profusely on the lower slopes.

As we near the little headland, the Marine Station motor-boat with the members of staff, N. A. Mackintosh, J. F. G. Wheeler, L. Harrison Matthews and A. J. Clowes, come out to wave a welcome to us. Finally we pass round this last bend and see a perfect little natural harbour. There, with its back against the mountain, is the whaling factory with its huge sheds, flensing platform and clouds of steam; and here, across the small bay, on the little promontory that forms its sheltering mouth, stands our laboratory and living quarters for the shore party, together with the house of the British Magistrate, the wireless station and the Argentine Meteorological Observatory. It is a compact little colony on a small spit of flat land jutting out below the sheer cliffs of the mountain side. So steeply does the land drop away into the water that we were able to drop anchor within some fifty yards of the station jetty; this we did about tea-time.

Now we had our great reunion with our friends who had been eagerly awaiting us for so long and whom we had not seen since the autumn of 1924 when they sailed south ahead of us; we had so many stories to exchange. Later some of us went over to see the Marine Station. It is beautifully fitted up. It was quite a strange experience to see for the first time 'in the flesh' the laboratory that one had oneself, nearly two years ago, helped to design on paper. (I have already related, on p. 49, how the planning of this building with Mr. Rose the architect was one of my first tasks when appointed.)

Sunday, 21st February. Early this morning, before I was awake, the ship moved over and made fast alongside the quay at the whaling station. Here, while we are getting a supply of fresh water and coal,

[1]Recently revised height estimates.

10. A busy day at the whaling station at Grytviken, South Georgia, sketched from the deck of the 'Discovery', anchored in diluted blood

we are right in the middle of the factory smell. And what an appalling stench it is. I can only describe it as being like a mixture of the smell of a tanning factory and that of a fish meal and manure works together with a sickly and almost overpowering odour of meat extract. We are told that we shall soon get used to it, but this seems hard to believe. [Actually that is indeed true, in a day or two we hardly noticed it; yet, as we came to say, it was a smell you could almost see, for the meaty vapour before long gave our white paint a slightly brownish tinge.]

From our deck we look right over the factory. Before us is the flensing platform or 'plan': a scene of great activity for the fishing just now is exceptionally heavy. Floating in the water, belly upwards, are many fin and blue whales, blown up like balloons, waiting to be dealt with. They appear like this for two reasons; firstly, when killed, they have compressed air pumped into their body-cavities to make them float, but then if, as now, the fishing is heavy, there may be some delay before they can be dealt with, so that the gases of decomposition add to their internal pressure. It is a fantastic scene. The water in which the whales float, and on which we too are riding, is blood red. On the platform itself there are whales in all stages of dismemberment. Little figures, busy with long-handled knives like hockey sticks, look like flies as they work upon the huge carcasses; and from time to time these massive remains are pulled about the platform by steel cables or chains working round bollards from steam winches in the background. Then there are the factory buildings themselves, ejecting clouds of steam, and, sheer above it all, is a mountain peak of dark rock splashed with brilliant sunlit snow towering against a clear blue sky. This blue of the sky reflects on the blood-red water below us to give a curious lilac tint; on the quay-side to the right are the rows and rows of oil drums awaiting shipment: the produce of the factory. I shall later [in the next chapter] say more about the process when I am dealing with the industry; here I am giving just the first impressions. I made a sketch of the scene, shown here in Plate 10.

All around the fjord rise the mountains, giving, on calm days such as this, superb reflections in the water. And the water itself is remarkable for its range of colour: far out towards the entrance, where small icebergs float, it is a pure blue; it then becomes a vivid turquoise and passes into green. [This latter effect is due to the combination of two elements: firstly the water has become somewhat opaque and milky owing to a fine oily emulsion from the factory and then it is turned green by a rich growth of tiny microscopic plants.] Finally the green passes through brown to a rich red near the flensing platform where it receives the crimson streams from this gargantuan butchery.

F

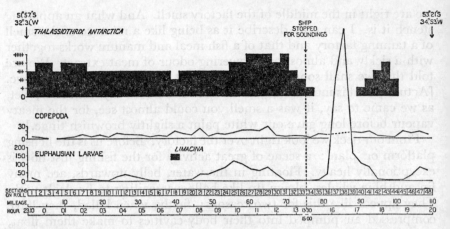

Graphical representation of a record obtained with the Continuous Plankton
Recorder on approaching South Georgia from the north-east in February 1926.
From *D.R.*[1], vol XI.

We must now add to the scene the sight and clamour of at least ten
thousand birds. Near the factory the water is alive with Cape pigeons
screaming and fighting over scraps of floating offal, and there are some
giant petrels too, a little farther out. In contrast to these scavengers of
somewhat revolting habits, are many delicate little black and white
birds, Wilson's petrels, which flutter over its surface like butterflies
with just their toes touching the water; they snap up morsels from the
surface as they hover and only settle farther out in the cleaner water.
These are well shown in Plate 16 (p. 200).

I spent this morning finishing off an analysis of two records taken
with my plankton recorder on approaching the island; they showed an
interesting zone, over seventy miles in extent, of rich phytoplankton,
mainly the diatom *Thalassiothrix*, followed by patches of young krill
as we got nearer the whaling grounds. I reproduce the record above.

After lunch Rolfe Gunther and I were taken by Wheeler and Clowes
to see the view from the top of the peak of the small mountain, Mount
Duse, 1,800 feet, immediately above their shore station. It is a steep
pull up over the craggy rocks which are much broken by the frost and
you have to use great caution to be sure that the piece of cliff you are
hanging on to will not come away in your hand. There are little gullies
full of broken bits of rock which begin to slip and form streams of stone
as you try to ascend them. The view from the top is truly rewarding:
how tiny the whaling station looks below us. Across the fjord, and part

[1]In this and later captions *D.R.* stands for *Discovery Reports*

of the way up on the other side, we look down upon a very green lake; above it and beyond rise the mountains of the Allardyce range, the backbone of the island, with Mount Paget and the Sugar Loaf. As we approached the top of our little peak we saw our first example of 'red snow,' a well-known mountain phenomenon; the snow, in patches, was generally more pink than red, but here and there it was quite a deep rose colour. The effect is produced by vast numbers of tiny single-celled plants, *Haematococcus*, which are distributed by the wind and multiply on the surface of snow; instead of having the green colouring of chlorophyl they have a bright red pigment haematochrome. We brought back a sample to look at under the microscope, and a fine sight it made: thousands of little fiery red cells glowing brilliantly in the bright transmitted light.

I have not yet commented on the name of the whaling station. Grytviken means in Norwegian *great pot* and it was given to the site because the whalers on their arrival found the large cast-iron pots which had been used long ago by the early American sealers for boiling out oil from the elephant-seal blubber.

Thursday, 25th February. Stormy weather has kept us within the fjord so that we have not yet been able to work on the whaling grounds outside. Yesterday morning we spent dredging in Cumberland Bay from the station motor-boat and obtained a good collection of

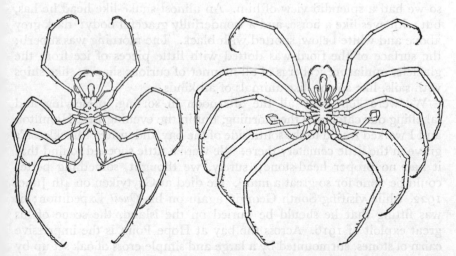

Antarctic pycnogons or 'sea-spiders' drawn from specimens taken at South Georgia, each a little less than half size. The rare ten-legged *Decalopoda antarctica* on the right is compared with a typical eight-legged species *Nymphon charcoti* on the left.

invertebrate animals of many different kinds: shrimps, prawns, polychaete worms, molluscs (including an octopus), sea urchins, starfish, etc. Of special interest to zoologists was one of the rarest of the sea-spiders or pycnogons, *Decalopoda*, of which only two or three specimens are known, all from the Antarctic. Like land spiders, typical pycnogons normally have *eight* legs, but our prize specimen had *ten*; hence its name. The surface waters were crowded with beautiful comb-jellies (*Ctenophora*) of which there were at least three different species, some reaching five inches in length.

I should here say that presently we found the pycnogons or sea-spiders to be very numerous both at South Georgia and further south. They are remarkable in being nearly all limbs and 'next to no body' as shown in my foregoing sketches of *Nymphon* and *Decalopoda*. These long-legged kinds walk delicately over soft muddy bottoms, shorter-legged forms are common on more rocky terrains. We were lucky later to find six specimens of *Decalopoda antartica* and eleven of *Decalopoda australis*, the only two species known of these ten-legged forms: more than any other expedition has found; we also brought back members of eleven entirely new species of the more normal eight-legged forms as reported by Dr. Isabella Gordon who worked out our collections (*Discovery Reports* Vol. vi, pp. 1-138.)

Whilst we dredged a sea leopard kept popping his head up out of the water to look at us; he came quite close, to within four or five feet, so we had a splendid view of him. An almost snake-like head he has, but with eyes like a horse, and a wonderfully graceful body: dark grey above and white below, spotted with black. The morning was superb; the surface of the fjord was dotted with little pieces of ice from the glaciers, miniature icebergs of all manner of curious shapes: like ships with sails, like swans, like animals of all kinds.

We were kept busy all the afternoon in sorting, preserving and labelling our catches of the morning, but in the evening Erik Hamilton and I walked round to the south side of the bay and visited Shackleton's grave in the little cemetery there. We were a little shocked to find that it had no proper head-stone; surely, we thought, something better could be done for so great a man[1]. He died at Grytviken on 4th June, 1922, while visiting South Georgia again on his *Quest* Expedition; it was fitting that he should be buried on the island, the scene of his great exploit of 1916. Across the bay at Hope Point is the impressive cairn of stones, surmounted by a large and simple cross of oak set up by his comrades before the *Quest* sailed on to complete the voyage he had planned.

[1] A granite headstone was sent out in 1927.

Saturday, 13th March. It is more than a fortnight since my last entry and in this time we have only had two days, the 3rd and 4th, when a drop in the wind has allowed us to venture out to work on the whaling grounds; clearly the region round the island has more disturbed weather than the open ocean we have crossed. Before getting out we made several more dredging excursions in the fjord bringing up again a great wealth of material including a number of large ascidians (i.e. 'sea-squirts,' see p. 76) and sponges; one of the latter had the form of a very large vase, over four feet in height and more than two in diameter, with holes (oscula) and pointed projections about its sides. Amphipods are also a feature of the grounds in both quantity and quality, including some remarkable spiny ones. The zoological highlight of these hauls was the finding of one of the remarkable walking medusae, a little jellyfish, which, instead of floating and swimming in the plankton as one would expect, has taken to walking over the surfaces of rocks and seaweeds by using its tentacles as *legs* and browsing as it goes upon the small life it finds there.

At last, early in the morning of the 3rd, we began the real work we had come to do: a study of the plankton of the whaling grounds and the conditions which favour its development. We want to know just why the whales come in such large numbers to South Georgia. We are principally concerned with the krill, the shrimp-like *Euphausia superba*, which our party at the shore laboratory have found in such quantities in the whale stomachs they have examined at the whaling station. Mackintosh and Wheeler examined the stomachs of 519 blue and fin whales and found all but 68 to contain food and usually in large quantities. [They write in *Discovery Reports*, vol. 1, as follows:

The whales caught at South Georgia (excluding the sperm whale) feed exclusively on *Euphausia superba* and have no other food whatever in their stomachs apart from a few specimens of the Amphipod *Euthemisto*, which is so abundant in the plankton round South Georgia that the whales can hardly help swallowing a certain quantity ... The enormous abundance of the krill round South Georgia is revealed by an examination of the stomach contents of the whales caught there. Normally the stomach was found to be well filled with comparatively fresh Euphausiids and an empty stomach was at most times an uncommon occurrence.]

It is an impressive sight to see a whale stomach cut open (Plate 14, p. 177). One is amazed that these whales with their great baleen filter mechanisms—like gigantic tow-nets—can be apparently such 'selective' feeders; the krill must be on the grounds in enormous quantities at the present time, for just now their stomachs are particularly full.

[Rolfe Gunther and I, in our joint *Discovery Report* (vol. XI) on the plankton of these whaling grounds, discuss the place of the krill in the Antarctic fauna as a whole, quoting a number of other naturalists. I give the following abridged version:

One is tempted to believe that ecologically it is the most important zooplankton organism of the Antarctic. . . . Hansen (1908) writes that '*E. superba* seems to live everywhere in the Antarctic Ocean as it has been taken by every expedition touching or exploring any part of those seas,' and Tattersall (1913) that 'it is the Euphausian "par excellence" of the Antarctic Ocean. It is circumpolar in distribution. . . . It forms the major part of the food of the crab-eating seal and of certain of the penguins.' The Australian Antarctic Expedition found it in the stomachs of the Weddell seal and Emperor penguin; and Clark (1919), in describing the biological observations of the *Endurance* Expedition, writes that '. . . during the winter spent at Elephant Island, our total catch of gentoo penguins amounted to 1436. . . . All these birds were cut up . . . for food and fuel. At the same time the stomachs were invariably examined, and . . . the largest proportion of these contained the small crustacean *Euphausia*, and this generally to the exclusion of other forms. . . . The quantity in most of the stomachs was enormous for the size of the birds. . . . Euphausiae, then, seem to be present in sufficient quantity in certain, if not in all, sub-Antarctic waters during the southern winter. . . .'

Different expeditions have found it in a number of bird stomachs, and the South Georgian whalers are familiar with the congregations of Nototheniid fish which collect to feed upon the swarms of this Euphausian on the whaling grounds. . . . (We go on to quote the findings of Mackintosh and Wheeler regarding the krill as the food of the blue and fin whales and then to recall that Racovitza (1903) had already drawn attention to its importance as the food of the humpback whale).

We want, of course, to study not only the distribution of the krill itself, but that of all the other important plankton elements which will help us to understand the whole pelagic community of which it forms a part; and in addition we must have the accompanying physical and chemical data to give us the basic background to it all. We began by making a line of five stations, the first 5 miles from the land, and then at 10 mile intervals, out north-east from Larsen Point which marks the northern side of Cumberland Bay. At each we took a complete set of physical observations and vertical hauls with the

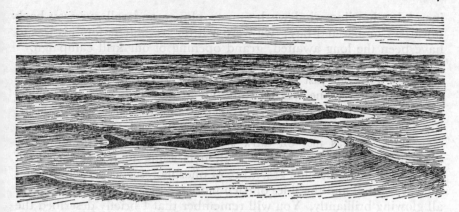

Two fin whales come to the surface close alongside us.

70-cm. diameter plankton nets (as outlined on pp. 146 to 153) as deep as the sounding would allow; these nets, while giving us the distribution of the smaller plankton forms, would hardly sample the krill efficiently; so that we followed the smaller nets at each station with similar vertical hauls using our large 2-metre diameter nets. We reached our first position at 9 o'clock in the morning and finished the fifth station just after 1 o'clock next morning; in this time we took 65 water samples and 31 plankton net hauls.

We had crossed the whaling grounds, right through the area of most intensive hunting at the present time, and seen many whales; yet we had caught hardly any krill at all! Perhaps they were very patchy in their distribution, so that we were missing the main concentrations by sampling at positions 10 miles apart? We steamed back to the coast and began another set of stations this time only 5 miles apart, on a line parallel to the last and 5 miles from it, running out north-east from Cape Saunders. It was 11 o'clock before we got to the position of the first station and we finished the fourth one on the line by 7 o'clock in the evening. How baffling, still no krill! And the sea and wind were now rising rapidly.

We knew the krill must be on the grounds in enormous numbers, yet we were failing to capture them in nets of the right mesh and with a mouth opening twice that of those usually employed for the collection of animals of similar size. They must either be even more patchy than we imagined so that all our vertical hauls came up between their shoals, or, if they were fairly well spread in the water, then the vibrating cable, above the mouth of the net as it came up, must have scared them out of the way of the net before it reached them. Against an

increasing howling wind we began to plunge and roll our way back
towards Cumberland Bay; we were a little crestfallen, for this was to
have been the long awaited, grand opening of our krill campaign.

As we staggered on we now towed behind us two of the 2-metre
diameter nets, one just below the surface and one at some 60 metres
depth; the lower one was let fully out at 8.20 p.m. and the surface
one put out ten minutes later. We kept them down for over an hour,
the surface one being taken in at 9.40 p.m. and the lower one at
9.50 p.m. It was just on dark when they came in. Imagine our
excitement and joy as we saw both nets rising to the surface as if
aglow with fire—the blue green fire of phosphorescence; each tow-net
bucket was full and the sides of each net were plastered thick with krill
all glowing brilliantly. You will remember that I briefly described the
luminous organs of a typical euphausiacean (p. 72) as little bull's-eye
lanterns; they stud the lower side, two pairs of them under the main
body and a line of four down the mid-line of the tail and, in addition,
there is one of a somewhat different kind on the underside of each of
the two stalks that bear the large compound eyes. In Plate 20 (p. 224)
is reproduced a coloured drawing I made of *Euphausia superba*, the
krill, and in the sketch below I give an impression of two of them
flashing in the dark. We tipped them out into a great bath on deck,
which we had to rock to keep the water in it as the ship rolled, and
saw them all swimming round, thousands of them, each like a little
ship with rows of portholes lit up. How well named they are: *superba*!
An hour earlier we had scarcely imagined we were going to celebrate

A drawing of two specimens of the krill, *Euphausia superba*, natural size, seen at night
with their luminous organs lit up; one seen from the side and the other with its
underside turned towards us. A coloured drawing is shown in Plate 20.

our opening season with such a grand firework display! We live and learn; we now know how to catch our krill.

That was just over a week ago. We have all been impatient to get out again for a second crack at the whaling grounds, but we have been held up once more, first by wind, then by thick fog. When we arrived there was no snow upon the lower slopes but recently we have experienced several quite heavy falls making the whole landscape white and very beautiful with delicate grades of blue shading.

On Tuesday when the ship was coaling Dr. Kemp, Rolfe Gunther and I walked over the pass in the deep snow to Maiviken on the West Bay to see the sea elephants[1] (or elephant seals, if you prefer it) on the beach there. On the way down we passed three lakes at different levels and a beautiful waterfall. In the lowest lake were two species of fresh-water copepod and some water beetles and their larvae. The burnet flowers push their heads up through the snow presenting a curious appearance: hundreds of little dark red balls on slender stems with no leaves showing.

Once down on the coast we found a series of small bays separated from one another by little rocky headlands and there were many low rocks sticking out of the sand in the bays themselves; behind them rose dunes and slopes of thick tussock grass. It was on the beach and in the grass that the elephants are lying. We came across a great many; most of them were young ones only five or six feet long, but there were several full-grown females and one large bull at least fifteen feet in length. The breeding season was now long past, the pups being born in September when the cows 'haul out' of the water after their sojourn in the sea during the winter; the bulls come out a little later, collect their harems together and pair with the cows about a month after they have given birth. It is at this time that the males fight savagely with their rivals for the possession of as large a harem and territory of beach as they can command. They remain on land, fasting, for about two months and go to sea to feed in December. In February and March they come ashore again for a period whilst they moult, and it was in this condition that we now found them. Harrison Matthews while at the shore station made a careful study of these seals which is published in volume 1 of the *Discovery Reports* pp. 233-56; I am indebted to his account for much of my information. The hair comes off curiously in patches 'being held together by a layer of the epidermis which is shed, taking the hair with it'; in this condition they present a somewhat unkempt appearance.

They are so fat that they can only move very slowly and, if you do

[1] *Mirounca leonina*, Linn.

not molest them, they will not attempt to get away, but may rear up, open wide their mouths and utter a horrible roar. It is advisable not to have your face too close to them when they do this, for their breath is distinctly unpleasant. They cannot be described as handsome. On the land they must be among the few of nature's creatures which may be called ugly; in the sea, however, they are swift, agile and full of grace. The females and young have short stub noses, but the grown bulls have a very long snout which they can inflate to look almost trunk-like, hence the name of sea elephant. Their eyes are large, like big calves' eyes and are always wet with tears which trickle down their faces. They present a picture of injured innocence. What a pity Landseer never painted them.

If provoked too much, they will make off towards the sea with much effort, heaving their heavy bodies along with their flippers. Normally they move very slowly and make tracks in the snow like those of a tank; there is the wide groove made by their bulky bellies and on either side, at very short intervals, are the impressions of their flippers, which remind one of a tank's caterpillar tracks. Whilst the females just move off with roars of angry protest, the bull shows a certain amount of fight. We came across a large bull lying in the tussock grass. He looked at first like a benevolent old lady; I think if you look at Plate 18 you will see what I mean. On approach, however, he did not remain placid for long. He reared up, stretched out his great bull-like neck, arched up his long snout and emitted a most terrifying blast of sound. As he got more angry, he reared up not only his fore body but his hind quarters as well, so that his whole body was curved like a 'U.' Then he advanced towards us in a great fury, but only got a short way; we just stepped smartly aside and after several attempts at attack he realised it was impossible to reach us and so turned aside and made for the sea. As he went down the beach he turned every few yards, rearing himself up and trumpetting as if making a fresh attempt at attack, but each time he thought better of it and proceeded seawards.

Saturday, 20th March. The weather conditions at South Georgia certainly make work at sea difficult in a ship like the *Discovery* which rolls upon the slightest provocation. As we noted on approaching the island from Tristan, storms in these regions arise and disappear with startling rapidity and recur all too frequently. This last week it has been a matter of snatching what opportunities we could. We sailed last Sunday, made a vertical station five miles off Merton Rocks at the south end of Cumberland Bay; this was followed by horizontally-towed 1-metre diameter nets just below the surface and at 60 metres depth. We now began a line of stations running north-east at which we again towed these two 1-metre nets; we put them out at points 10 miles, 18 miles and 26 miles from the coast and aimed at towing each set for an hour at 2 knots. We were getting good catches of krill but at the third set in the series the rising wind and sea forced us to haul them up after only 35 minutes and make for shelter in West Cumberland Bay. Here next morning we made some hauls with both the rectangular and the conical dredges; the former takes samples more from the surface of the bottom but the latter digs deeply into it, in this case thick mud, bringing up a sample with all its burrowing animals complete. There were great quantities of tube-forming worms and a mud-living sea anemone not unlike our English *Halcampa*. Into this West Bay descend a number of magnificent glaciers. In the afternoon we approached close to the foot of one of these where there is a deep-blue cliff of jagged ice jutting out into the turquoise green waters of the fjord. It was a brilliantly sunny day but the mountains were partially hidden by clouds and showers of snow or sleet; they kept appearing and disappearing between the squalls. For a little time rainbows hung above the glaciers as the sun caught the sleet; I rapidly made a sketch (Plate 9, p. 129).

After a night and morning in Grytviken fjord we started off next afternoon and made another two days' survey working a line from the coast to some sixty miles out and back taking stations every ten miles; we worked continuously through the two nights, but were then again forced to break off and return by heavy weather. At each station we towed the 1-metre nets for 3 miles at three levels at the same time: near the surface, and at depths of about 50 and 90 metres. At some of the night stations it was distinctly difficult to keep our feet or avoid spilling the plankton samples obtained in the tow-net buckets; the rolling was very heavy and squalls of sleet and snow produced a deposit of ice upon the deck. However there were no casualties to personnel or specimens. We are now getting splendid samples and collecting a great deal of valuable information on the distribution of the principal forms of plankton especially the species of *Euphausia*; in addition to *E. superba*, which is the true krill or whale food, we have also obtained many specimens of the related species *E. tricantha* and *E. frigida*. In the present season the krill is occurring in a definite thick zone some twenty miles from the coast; we have obtained many thousand in even one haul with the 1-metre diameter net. It is just in this region that the bulk of the whales are being taken. [All the positions, in latitude and longitude, at which the whales were shot by the catchers were provided for us by the different whaling companies so that we could

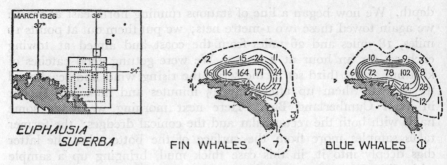

Euphausia superba and whale distribution in March, 1926. From *D.R.*, vol. XI.

plot them and thus contour their distribution month by month. The concentration of both fin and blue whales and that of the krill as found by our survey (shown by the relative sizes of the squares), are given in the charts above where we see how close is the correlation. The relationship is fully confirmed in the next season.] Almost as numerous as the krill are vast quantities of a planktonic amphipod, *Parathemisto gaudichandii.* (one of the Hyperiidae closely related to the *Themisto* that we met in our home waters soon after leaving Falmouth, as illustrated on p. 71); it occurs in the greatest numbers in a belt a little farther out than the krill. [Subsequent surveys appear to show that this amphipod was exceptionally abundant this season.] We also took a great many young euphausians of several different species. Scattered through this great bulk of material we find the rarer forms: pteropods, arrow-worms, tomopterids[1] (a particularly large species), young fish, etc. There is a striking paucity of diatom life in these coastal waters compared with its abundance farther out as was shown on the plankton recorder as we approached the island (p. 162).

Tuesday, 30th March. The weather continues to be stormy; it is not really cold but there are strong winds and snow squalls . . . On Sunday after three more days of violent weather we put out to make a 24-hour station in the middle of the region of the krill in order to study the changes in the vertical distribution of the plankton throughout the day and night. We attempted to repeat a series of vertical closing nets covering all the different ranges of depth from the bottom to the surface every two hours. We anchored in 265 metres of water, using the wire from the main winch, and began our first set of observations at 1 p.m. and made others at 3, 5, 7 and 9 p.m. By the evening, however, the wind had freshened again to such an extent that work became exceedingly difficult and after 9 o'clock we were

[1] *Tomopteris* is the beautifully transparent worm included in the picture on p. 43

dragging our anchor and being so buffeted by the waves that we were forced to give up. We lay to for the night and by the morning it was only with the greatest difficulty that we were keeping our position. It became very thick and it was not until late afternoon that we could see the tops of the mountains above a belt of fog and so find our position and make our way in.

[It was now a time of some frustration and disappointment; there was so much we wanted to do, but we now realised to the full the limitations of our old ship. She was no doubt an excellent vessel for work in the ice, but she had only auxiliary power. She was extremely heavily rigged to withstand the storms she might have to face, but all this stout tackle offered great resistance to the wind. And, being so underpowered, we were frequently blown far off course; or we had the greatest difficulty in making headway against the howling north-westerly gales which frequently swept the area and produced such mountainous seas. Somewhat like Nansen's *Fram*, the *Discovery* was built with a rounded bottom so that if she were caught in heavy ice pressure she would tend to rise out of it instead of being crushed; this was an admirable quality for ice navigation but it made her roll heavily in only a moderate sea. In typical South Georgia weather this truly terrible rolling nearly always made the working of nets and water-bottles difficult and it often made it impossible; it also severely handicapped us in our attempts to examine our plankton samples at sea as we went along. Harrison Matthews, of the shore party, who came out with us on several of these survey attempts, measured and timed our rolling. Referring to the *Discovery* in his book *South Georgia* (1931) he says, 'the writer has timed her rolling 35° to 40° each way nineteen times per minute, and sometimes she reached 45°.' He is of course measuring the angle of roll *from the vertical* i.e., the angle the mast goes through on either side. Let me now give a brief extract from Dr. Kemp's 4th Scientific Progress Report to the *Discovery* Committee dealing with this period:

About midday on March 17th we ran out for another attempt to take a line of stations off Merton Rock. The first station (St. 31) again proved that vertical observations were impossible: Mr. Herdman and Mr. Gunther were both immersed to the waist when working water-bottles and nets from the outboard platforms. We continued the line with a series of 1 m. horizontal nets, towed for three miles in every 10, with wind freshening from the SW., and the ship rolling violently in a heavy westerly swell. Captain Stenhouse found it necessary to heave to for the night and we continued the line in a moderate gale on the 18th . . .

An unusual cloud effect over South Georgia due to a sudden strong wind. Redrawn from a watercolour sketch made at the time.

The Committee which planned our venture had not perhaps really foreseen the type of work we should mainly have to do: the making of extensive surveys over the wide stretches of the whaling grounds and adjacent waters *as quickly as possible* to give us a picture of the conditions as a whole at one particular time. Only by doing this expeditiously could we hope to make a reasonable correlation between the plankton distribution and the hydrological conditions on the one hand, and the whale distribution on the other. We were trying to link the movements of the whales with the seasonal and other changes in their environment. With a very under-powered ship we could only make such a survey in bits and pieces. However, in spite of all these difficulties, by seizing every opportunity when the weather allowed we did manage to lay very valuable foundations for comparison with our later much more comprehensive surveys and I, for one, still loved the old *Discovery*. What she lacked in efficiency, she gained in charm and in the splendid zoological opportunities she gave us when beset.

This short first season's experience also made it clear that it was essential that we should have additional 'sister keels' added to our hull to reduce rolling. This the Committee at home, on getting our report, readily agreed to; so it was arranged that, after our visit to the Falkland Islands, we should return to South Africa to have them fitted in dry dock at the Naval Dockyard at Simonstown, to be ready for the next season south. And a really wonderful difference they made, as we shall see.

Since all our findings in this preliminary study of the whaling grounds only have significance when considered in the light of our later work, I propose to leave an account and discussion of them until they can be treated together in chapters 13 and 14. I will give only one more entry for this period and then go on in the next chapter to describe the actual whaling and the research accomplished on the whales themselves by our shore party who were now in their second season south.]

Wednesday, 7th April. Whilst kept in the shelter of the fjords by bad weather we have made a number of dredge and trawl hauls giving rich collections of the invertebrate fauna and the fish. Fish of the familiar groups, well known in the North, such as members of the cod family, or gurnards or flat fish are quite unknown here. Nearly all the fish of the Antarctic regions belong to a special group, the division Nototheniiformes, found nowhere else in the world, except for a few stragglers in places like Patagonia and New Zealand. The trawl-hauls we have just been making gave us a great variety of these fish including some notable rarities. [Actually when the collection came to be studied by Dr. J. R. Norman of the British Museum (Natural History) he showed in his account, *Discovery Reports*, vol. XVIII, that the three trawl-hauls made this week in Cumberland Bay (Stations 39, 42 and 45) yielded fifteen different species[1] of which two were quite new to science. The new fish are *Psilodraco breviceps* and *Pseudochaenichthysis georgianus*, discovered on account of the gales outside; it's an ill wind that blows . . . ! Most of the fish belonged to the genus *Notot9henia* which are quite good eating. There is one, *N. rossii*, which occurs in large numbers outside, where it collects to feed on the patches of krill and is fished for by the Norwegians who call it 'Torsk' because it reminds them of that fish at home. Harrison Matthews in his book *South Georgia* to which I have already referred, says concerning this fish: 'Curiously enough

[1]For those zoologists who may be interested I give the names of these fish as follows:
Nototheniidae: *Notot9henia larseni*, Lönnberg; *N. gibberifrons* Lönnberg; *N. nudifrons* Lönnberg; *N. augustifrons*, Fischer; *N. corriceps*, Richardson, and *N. rossii*, Richardson. *Trematomus vicarius*, Lönnberg and T. Hansoni, Boulenger.
Harpagiferidae: *Harpagifer b spinis*, (Schneider); and *Artedidraco mirus*, Lönnberg.
Bathydraconidae: *Psilodraco breviceps*, Norman and *Parachaenichthys georgianus* (Fischer).
Chaenichthyidae: *Chaenocephalus aceratus* (Lönnberg); *Pseudochaenichthysis georgianus*, Norman; and *Champsocephalus gunnari*, Lönnberg.

it was found, when the *Discovery* Expedition collected specimens, that in spite of the abundance of this fish only one dried specimen in the British Museum was hitherto known to science.' Another common fish, not so good to eat, is the so-called crocodile fish, *Chaenocephalus aceratus*, with a rather long pointed snout.]

Among the invertebrates large brittle stars with coiling tentacle-like arms were conspicuous, as were 'sea-lilies' (Crinoids) and quantities of beautiful gorgonians; around the branches of the latter were entwined some of those most primitive worm-like molluscs—of great interest to zoologists—members of the Neomeniidae, which I had never seen alive before. [I have already mentioned (p. 165) that the amphipods, the small shrimp-like crustaceans, were notable in both quantity and variety in so many of our dredge hauls; our efforts at South Georgia alone produced no fewer than twenty-seven new species, described by Dr. K. H. Barnard in his report on the Amphipoda in *Discovery Reports*, vol. v.]

I cannot resist recording that as the trawl was emptied on to the deck last Thursday morning with a big catch of fish, I introduced, unobserved, a life-size papier mâché model of a flat-fish—a dab—most realistically coloured. It had been given me, full of chocolates, before I left and I had kept it for just such an occasion. From its top side it looked perfect. I slipped it underneath a pile of fish and waited whilst my colleagues began to sort out the catch. Such a flat-fish from the Antarctic would indeed be a remarkable discovery. Yes—sure enough, the excitement was intense when it was seen—it even for the moment deceived our Director who cried 'Bless my Sam' as he pounced upon it! On turning it over the truth was seen; I had inscribed its white underside with the date: April the 1st! I had been on tenterhooks all morning for fear the trawl would not come in before 12 o'clock.

On Saturday afternoon we made another attempt at a line of stations outside but were again forced to give up in the evening after only completing two of them. By morning it was blowing a gale from the WNW. and we were being blown off to leeward. We were only thirty miles from land, yet steaming hard all day we only came up to the coast at night. It was too thick to make our way in the dark so we lay to outside and got in next morning. The wind increased and by the afternoon it was blowing in gusts of hurricane force, sweeping down from the mountains and carrying up clouds of spray from our little cove. I have never seen anything like it. A little way up the mountain we could see the water of a lake being blown out of it over its edge. We now started to drag our anchors; we had two of them out on sixty fathoms of chain. We kept steaming into the wind, but in spite of our

11. *Above*, the Grytviken whaling station, in King Edward's Cove at the end of East Cumberland Bay (see also Plate 10). *Below*, looking across the cove from near the whaling station towards the shore laboratory and the wireless station: in the foreground the piles of old bones, whale vertebrae and ribs, are a relic of the bad old days when only the blubber was used

12. *Above*, there she blows! A large blue whale. The gunner is ready to fire, but (*below left*) waits to get closer. *Right*, Bang! The whale has come up just below the bow and the ship jerks with the recoil of the gun; hence the photo (taken from the rigging) is a little blurred, but, at $\frac{1}{1000}$ sec. exposure, it catches the dark harpoon head just about to hit the whale

13. *Above*, harpooned, the large blue whale is making off full of fight and will be 'played' on the cable until it is exhausted and wound in for the second shot. *Below*, the final death flurry of a fin whale; it lashes the sea with its flippers, and the water is crimson with blood

14. *Above*, a blue whale on the flensing plan at the Grytviken whaling station.
Below, a fin whale stomach cut open to show its meal of krill which is gushing out;
only a part of the stomach is visible

High wind at Grytviken, South Georgia, raising flying sheets of spray from the water and blowing the *Discovery* ashore in spite of heavy ground-tackle. Drawn from a photograph by Dr. L. Harrison Matthews in his book *South Georgia*.

engines going full ahead we were being steadily blown to leeward. It was with great difficulty that we escaped being driven on to a rocky shore. For close on an hour we fought the hurricane, pulling round the yards to offer less resistance, trying this and that, but in the end we were beaten; although it seemed impossible, the wind increased yet in violence and we were driven back and back still pulling our anchors, still using every bit of power available. We were driven on to the new wooden pier, not yet completed, being built out from the little promontory on which our shore station stood. It was fortunate the pier was there; it broke the violence with which we should otherwise have been blown on to the shore. I'm afraid we altered its shape a little. There followed moments of great excitement as we leapt ashore and tried to fix anchors in the ground to hold the ship's bows; pulling the cables in the hurricane, through driving spray and sleet, was quite an effort, and all of no avail. The ship was pivoting on the pier corner as the anchors just pulled through the sodden earth; she swung round and grounded on the beach beside the pier.

How lucky it was that the beach here was steep and soft; it might so easily have been a reef of rock, and we should have been finished in that storm. After being pressed against the mud all night, we slipped off easily next morning without damage when the wind had dropped. [Harrison Matthews in his book *South Georgia* to which I have already referred, has a photograph of the *Discovery* being driven ashore; my sketch overleaf is based on this photograph. He spent two years on the island and writes, 'The characteristic feature of the climate of South Georgia is the wind: constant gales succeed each other in quick succession, and extremely fierce gusts blow down the valleys from the mountains without warning, raising clouds of spray like thick mist from the water in the bays. However, in the winter there is a greater proportion of fine weather than in the summer. Between the blizzards occur spells of a week or more of calm sunny weather and it is then that the scenery of South Georgia is at its best, sparkling with brilliance in the keen clear air.']

Our first round in the battle with the elements was over; we had very nearly been knocked out. I pointed out at the beginning of the chapter that this rocky and mountainous island is in just the same latitude as Cape Horn; it is exposed to just the same wild weather and gigantic seas. Plankton collecting and hydrological sampling around the Horn, even in the most powerful of ships, would be no picnic; in a wooden windjammer, with only low power auxiliary steam it would certainly be a gamble, and so, indeed, we found it was at South Georgia. If we were disappointed at not making greater progress, we were not too discouraged; we had learnt much from our experience which would stand us in good stead when we entered the ring for round two in the next season.

CHAPTER 8

WHALING AND WHALE RESEARCH

Thursday, 15th April, 1926. While the *Discovery* has been taking on coal for our voyage to the Falklands, I have been out on a whale-catcher to see how the hunting is done. The little ship is as powerful as a trawler but shorter, so that she can turn at full speed in a surprisingly small space; this by the way can be quite frightening at first, for she heels over at an appalling angle with the gunwale awash. She has only one mast, the foremast, which has the lookout barrel at its head; and her bows are built up to form the platform for the harpoon gun. Three or four such catchers will serve a single factory. I was lucky to get on the *Tiburon*, the latest and crack boat of the station. Calling round on Monday evening, just as she had come in, I found the skipper, Captain Hansen, at his supper and he gave me a hearty welcome; as there was no spare bunk available, he most kindly invited me to share his cabin and sleep on his long comfortable settee. Being due to sail at 5.30 in the morning I decided to go aboard that night.

In the modern catcher the captain has a commodious cabin. Here it was above the galley and messroom and below the bridge proper; the three levels forming a tall structure with a lower bridge running round the outside of his cabin like a balcony. He said he would most likely be late and asked me to turn in when I liked; this I did and awoke next morning as the engine-room telegraph rang and a gentle motion told me we were under way. By the time I was up we were at the mouth of the fjord nosing our way into a stiff breeze and a big swell with the sun just rising into a cloudless sky. During the last week whale had been very plentiful in the early morning close into the coast; this morning, however, there were none to be seen, so we headed straight out to sea.

At a quarter to eight we had breakfast, and were ready for it. A steaming dish of pork and beans was followed by cold sausage made of a mixture of whale and pork which unexpectedly proved to be a delicious concoction; and there was brown bread, butter and marmalade, and excellent coffee. The little mess next the galley under the bridge just comfortably seats four: the captain, who here is also the gunner (although this is not always so in other ships), the mate or second gunner, the chief engineer and myself. The captain speaks English almost perfectly and the others, while less accomplished, insist on doing so for my benefit. What a fine people the Norwegians are; they combine the strength and determination of the explorer—the old viking spirit—with a genuine kindness and good nature. I have never met one whom I did not like; perhaps it is that I have mainly come across the sea-faring folk, as I have met them here or in the fishing ports of Norway and in Iceland. I remember some years ago being much struck by this spirit of good-naturedness which formed a dominant note in J. J. Bell's delightful studies of Norwegian whalers in Iceland, in his book *The Whalers*. But here is a frightening paradox: no human activity could be more cruel than theirs.

Breakfast is over and we are heading into a big swell, throwing up sheets of spray. There comes a call from the barrel. The only similarity between our little ship and the old-time whaler is this barrel to accommodate the look-out man at the mast head. 'Hval! Hval!' he cries and points to starboard. But it is unnecessary, the captain has already seen the little 'puff of steam'—the 'blow' of the whale— far over on the starboard bow and without comment is swinging the nose of the ship in its direction. It is almost uncanny the way these fellows spot a 'blow.' They stand on the bridge looking over the sea. A 'blow' may appear far over to port or starboard and you feel sure they haven't seen it, because they don't appear to be looking in that direction; then just as you are going to call their attention to it, they automatically swing the bows round—that is if they are not already on the track of another. They must be continually sweeping the horizon with their eyes.

Those who have not seen a whale blowing are apt to think of the fountains of water so often shown in the old pictures as rising from the head of the whale; usually, however, only a little water is shot out of the blow hole, just as they surface, that which has filled the nasal passages. What is really seen is the breath of the whale condensing in the cold atmosphere as a cloud of vapour, just as does our breath in winter; indeed in the cold Antarctic it is almost like the puff of steam from a locomotive. The blow hole, of course, represents the whale's nostrils which in the course of evolution have moved up on to the very top of the head to act like the snorkel on the conning-tower of a sub- marine. In many whales the two nasal passages run together to open by a single aperture. [Actually what I wrote here years ago may not be the whole truth; it now seems likely that there may be an oily emulsion[1] discharged with the breath which may help to make it visible, especially in the tropics where the 'blow' can also be seen. That the breath of the whale should be so clearly visible in such a warm atmosphere had puzzled many people (myself included), but, as Professor Slijper points out in his recent book[2], this is not really difficult to understand; the breath, being exhaled at high pressure as it is forced out through the very narrow blow-hole, immediately undergoes great expansion outside and so at once becomes cooled as does any expanding gas by the simple laws of physics.]

Ah! There it blows again, much closer. It is a big blue whale. The captain hurries to the forward platform and we slacken speed. The gun, already loaded, is a stout cannon, well balanced and mounted so that it can swivel this way or that (as in sketch on p. 33). The steel shaft of the harpoon fits the barrel and out in front projects its head. It has a pointed shell-like nose containing the explosive charge and behind this are four large steel arms folded backwards; these are hinged barbs which, when a pull comes on the cable, will open out under the blubber and hold it fast in the whale's body. Linked to the shaft, by a ring sliding in a slot, is the thick yet flexible rope—it is a massive hemp cable—which lies coiled below the gun platform and then leads aft to the winch system. But now, suddenly and unexpectedly, before the captain has actually reached the gun, the monster breaks surface right alongside under the port bow. The captain jumps to the gun, but the whale is too close and actually astern of the gun. He cannot get a shot: a most unusual situation. The whale blows and sounds at once. We have scared it and it does not blow again for a long time and then far over to port. We are off after it, but it turns this way and that, only blowing at long intervals. It is no use chasing a scared whale, the captain says, and we give up.

We now come upon two fin whales, but they too are very shy and travelling fast. It is exciting gradually getting up to them and expecting every moment to be near enough to fire, but we are never quite in range and the captain waits. We chase all morning but again have to give up; we cannot catch up with them. Dinner time comes: another excellent meal of meat rissoles, gravy and potatoes followed by a boiled pudding with fruit syrup.

In the afternoon we resume the chase, hot on the trail of another big finner. From the bridge it is impossible to get really good photographs on account of all the rigging of the foremast between you and the gun platform. I therefore decide to climb half-way up the rigging on the

---

[1]This is further discussed on p. 459.
[2]*Whales*. London, 1962. (Translated from the Dutch *Walvissen* of 1958.)

port side and perch myself with my legs sticking through the ratlins; and from this splendid view point I overlook the gun platform and the water immediately in front. Whilst a wonderful position, it is not altogether comfortable for the ship is pitching and rolling heavily which makes hanging on, and at the same time holding your camera, somewhat precarious; and every now and again you are caught in a sheet of spray.

The whale rises repeatedly in front of us, throwing up his puffs of steam. We are gradually catching up. Each time you feel sure the captain will strike; but no, he withholds his fire. He's not satisfied—

The harpoon strikes—a whale-catcher off South Georgia.

he will get still closer. The gunners never fire at a range of more than fifty yards and usually much less. The whale, although large, only exposes a small part of himself above the water at once. He rises arching his body over in a curve; first the snout and blow hole show, and then dip forward as the back comes up to be again followed by the dorsal fin. His action has been aptly likened to a great wheel turning with only a small fraction of the rim showing above the surface. He presents a small target for a gun which is continually jumping this way and that as the ship pitches and rolls. The gunner—our captain— is on his toes, his knees are bent and he looks like a boxer sparring as he rises and falls with the ship, swinging the gun barrel to keep it facing into the water just ahead of us.

From my vantage point I can now see the great beast rising through the clear water just ahead of us. He breaks surface. I can look into his blow holes. I can smell his breath. Now comes his back, and just as his dorsal fin begins to show—Crash! All is smoke. The ship jerks with the recoil. The blocks scream as the cable goes tearing out. Then as the smoke blows away you see the whale disappearing below the surface with the long thick cable flying after him. The captain is shaking his head. 'A bad shot,' he says. It was apparently too long a range and the harpoon struck too far aft; it glanced off the backbone to one side and the explosion has blown the harpoon partly out again. 'I think we shall lose him,' he says.

The coil of rope below the gun platform is rushing out. The other end of this, as I have said, passes aft, but it does not go direct to the steam winch; it first goes up to the mast-head, round a block and down again. At the winch it makes four turns round two drums and passes to the hold below where more of it is ready coiled. This device of passing the rope up the mast is one to overcome shock; the block at the top is attached to a steel cable which passes over another pulley above it and goes down to connect with a most powerful spring in the body of the ship. It thus gives the system the flexibility of a giant fishing rod. We are now about to 'play' the whale on its line as we might play a salmon; we are playing a 'fish' almost as long as the ship. Our line consists of four lengths of 120 fathoms each fastened end to end. The cable we are now using is on the starboard side of the ship; the whole system is duplicated on the port side with a cable ready for a second shot if the first harpoon fails to kill.

Away runs the whale. The blocks roar and rattle. He strikes the surface again, blows once or twice and then down. On he careers, sounding and rising; the block at the mast-head saws up and down. He is pulling away for all he is worth, but he must be badly wounded, poor beast. Each time he comes up you can see a great crimson patch on his back, and as we pass each point where he has broken surface we see a blood-red patch in the water. Then down he goes deep. He has now run out three lengths of cable, i.e., 360 fathoms. Down, down he dives, until, judging by the angle that the cable makes, he must be at least a hundred fathoms down. Now the angle of the rope is lessening; he is rising. There he blows ahead of us, with streams of blood coming from him. It is indeed like playing a fish. We wind in a little cable and then let more out. Then when we think he is sufficiently weakened we gradually wind in more and more. We wind him in, getting closer and closer.

All this time the second gunner and one of the crew have been busy preparing the gun for the second shot: cleaning it out, ramming in masses of wadding, fitting the second harpoon on to the other cable, pushing it home into the barrel and screwing on the explosive head. All is now ready for his final despatch. In creeps the rope bit by bit. The whale lashes about in the bloody water and then sounds again. It is amazing how he can fight so long and lose so much blood. He is making a last desperate effort to get free. Down he goes; and down goes the cable abruptly. The captain signals to let the line run out, but it is too late. There is a sudden jerk on the cable and it becomes slack. He is away. The harpoon has pulled out and we have lost our whale. The captain waves his arms in a despairing gesture and comes aft shaking his head.

'Coffee time,' he says philosophically, and we retire to the little messroom for the Norwegian equivalent of 'afternoon tea,' at about 3.30 p.m.; there is coffee with bread and butter and marmalade, and cold whale sausage for those who want it.

After this we hunt the seas until dark, but whales are scarce; although we see an occasional 'blow' in the distance we do not get close enough. The wind has been increasing all day and now there is quite a big sea which, when we run against it, sends great sheets of spray right over the top of the bridge. As the light fails we run in towards the coast; it is too rough and the night too long to allow us to remain out drifting as we would have done had it been summer. In the darkness we creep in and anchor behind the jagged 'Wake-up' Rocks off St. George's Bay. We smoke and talk of whaling and the habits of whales till supper, another good meal, at 7.30; a bottle of whisky I have brought is much appreciated. After more talk it is early to bed at 9 o'clock.

At 5.30 next morning we are off once more, with the wind dropped, a calmer sea and the sun rising once again in a cloudless sky. We make farther south this time but do not meet with any whales before breakfast. This morning the meal is of fried fish 'balls,' but not what *we* would call fish balls; they are the shape and size of eggs, made of ground up dried fish, and peculiar to Norway, I believe, being made at Stavanger—not really very palatable I thought. After breakfast I again take up my place in the rigging as we sight several little white puffs in the distance. We are off at full speed towards them. A number of most strikingly patterned dolphins now appear. They are sharply marked in jet black and purest white: white below with a prominent white tongue marking running up diagonally on each side into the black of the back. They are all round the ship; there must be forty or fifty of them and they keep crossing and recrossing in front of the bows in groups of five or six. We are now drawing closer to the whales. There are many, for their 'puffs of steam' appear in all directions, but two

together are right ahead of us. We get closer and closer. Then up
they come right below the bows; I can see them as clearly as before
coming up through the water, but this time so close that they seem
almost to graze our stem. They are two large blue whales. Bang!
Clinging to the rigging with my legs I take a photograph at a thousandth
of a second and by remarkable luck catch the harpoon head just about
to penetrate the whale before it is blotted out by smoke. The picture
(Plate 12) is a little blurred, however, and no wonder, for at that
precise moment the rigging jumped at the shock of the recoil. Away
goes the line. It seemed a good shot, but he is far from being dead
and is pulling away in front. He blows every now and again and is
bleeding hard. His companion or mate does not fly off like a scared
whale, but swims bravely and pathetically beside him, as if offering
sympathy and encouragement. [This is probably not such sentimental
nonsense as many may suppose; observations on the behaviour of
dolphins in the oceanaria of America would seem to show the distress
of comrades who have been separated and their obvious pleasure and
recognition when reunited.] Clouds of Cape pigeons circle round and
keep settling and rising again over the bloody water.

The gun is quickly got ready again and after playing him for about
a quarter of an hour—winding him in and letting him out again—we
tire him out. He does not go far below the surface and gradually we
wind him slowly in—or wind ourselves up to him, which is it? He is
a huge whale, he appears almost as big as our ship. Panting, tugging,
blowing, there he goes just ahead with the harpoon in his side clearly
visible. We are gaining on him a few feet at a time. Next time he
comes up we shall get him; the line is almost in. The captain is ready;
his one hand is on the trigger and the other signals to the helmsman who
turns the bows a little this way or a little that as required. Up the
monster comes again. Bang! Over he turns, his ribbed belly gleaming
in the sun. His flipper gives one last flap in the air and he spouts a jet
of deep crimson. His huge mouth opens and closes, and he is dead.
The ship has stopped and he lies across the bows. His companion is
now nowhere to be seen. The cable is wound in to keep him at the
surface. At once all is activity; every man quickly but without flurry
does his job. To a long pole is fixed a hollow lance which is connected
to a rubber hose-pipe coming from an air compressor in the engine-
room; the lance is now driven deep into his body cavity and he is
inflated to make him float. Whilst this is being done a chain is passed
round his tail flukes and he is securely fastened to the ship. As soon as
the lance is withdrawn, one of the hands standing on the carcass plugs
the hole with a wad of tow. The harpoon lines are cut and the gun is

being reloaded. The whale is now brought along and secured to one side of the vessel, the starboard side on this occasion, for towing with the tail pointing forwards. In another few minutes the tail flukes are cut away with a flensing knife for they have little oil value and not only impede the ship by their extra water resistance but tend to make steering difficult.

We are off again. Whales are everywhere. In a moment a tall staff, with the flag of the company flying from it, is driven into our dead whale, and it is cast adrift. Already we are getting close to our next whale. He rises and blows but is still too far ahead for a shot. He is near enough, however, for me from my vantage point to see a remarkable effect; as he blows in the strong sunlight his jet of steam is like a rainbow—just as if he was blowing out puffs of coloured smoke. He has now gone down again. We steam on, but presently the captain signals slow ahead and we go gently forward waiting. It is remarkable how these gunners seem to know exactly where the whales will rise; with a little movement of his hand he signals to the man at the wheel, first a little to starboard, then a little to port. We wait; it seems an age.

At last, again just below the bows, the great beast rises. He might be a submarine co-operating with our ship; he comes up perfectly in line and straight ahead. He comes just to the surface; whether he sees us or not we cannot tell, but he hardly breaks the water at all and doesn't blow. Bang! Off he goes. Away screams the cable again. He appears at the surface once or twice, but seems very weak. Then he sounds. He goes right down to the bottom for the line is pulled vertically down for over a hundred fathoms. We are stopped and waiting, and then bit by bit we begin to heave slowly in. 'He is dead,' the captain says. There is no tugging at the rope, it comes straight up; it is like the cable of a crane lifting a heavy weight.

It is a relief that there is not this ghastly playing on the line; for one can only look on it with horror. It is a barbarous business. These creatures are mammals like ourselves, and I have no doubt that they feel pain. It is amazing that they can put up such a long fight as they sometimes do, after an explosion has occurred in their insides and when every effort they make to get away must increase the agony of the cable pulling in the wound. Perhaps as often as not the whale is killed almost at once, as it should be if the explosive shell reaches the proper target: the main thoracic cavity; but as we have seen it may not. It would never be allowed if it took place on land. Think what an outcry there would be if we hunted elephants with explosive harpoons fired from the cannon of a tank and then played the wounded beasts upon a line! Each time you eat margarine, or wash with soap for that matter, you are quite likely to be using the products of this chase. Of course the whales are huge and the harpoon is relatively small compared to their bulk; it has been pointed out that the size of the explosive head in relation to the size of the large whale is no more, or even less, than that of the service bullet in relation to the body of a man. But, of course, a steel bullet is different; the idea of shooting human enemies with explosive, barbed bullets on lines does not bear thinking of. It is indeed a paradox: I have already emphasised the kind-heartedness of the whaling folk to their fellows. It is amazing how blind and unfeeling man, the carnivorous hunter, can be.

I am reminded of a vivid passage in William Scoresby's *An Account of the Arctic Regions* (1820) which was written only a few years before he became a Christian minister (see p. 31):

The maternal affection of the whale . . . is striking and interesting. The cub, being insensible to danger, is easily harpooned; when the tender attachment of the mother is so manifested as not infrequently to bring it within the reach of the whalers. Hence, though a cub is of little value, seldom producing above a ton of oil, and often less, yet it is sometimes struck as a snare for its mother. In this case she joins it at the surface of the water, whenever it has occasion to rise for respiration; encourages it to swim off; assists its flight by taking it under her fin; and seldom deserts it while life remains. She is then dangerous to approach; but affords frequent opportunities for attack. She loses all regard for her own safety, in anxiety for the preservation of her young;—dashes through the midst of her enemies;—despises the danger that threatens her;—and even voluntarily remains with her offspring, after various attacks on herself from the harpoons of the fishers. In June 1811, one of my harpooners struck a sucker, with the hope of its leading to the capture of its mother. Presently she arose close by the 'fast-boat'; and seizing the young one, dragged about a hundred fathoms of line out of the boat with remarkable force and velocity. Again she arose to the surface; darted furiously to and fro; frequently stopped short, or suddenly changed her direction, and gave every possible intimation of extreme agony. For a length of time, she continued thus to act, though closely pursued by the boats; and, inspired by courage and resolution by the concern of her offspring, seemed regardless of the danger which surrounded her. At length, one of the boats approached as near, that a harpoon was hove at her. It hit, but did not attach, itself. A second harpoon was struck; this also failed to penetrate; but a third was more effectual, and held. Still she did not attempt to escape; but allowed other boats to approach; so that, in a few minutes, three more harpoons were fastened; and, in the course of an hour afterwards, she was killed.

There is something extremely painful in the destruction of a whale, when thus evincing a degree of affectionate regard for its offspring, that would do honour to the superior intelligence of human beings; yet the object of the adventure, the value of the prize, the joy of capture, cannot be sacrified to feelings of compassion.

But we must return to our own hunt, and be thankful that there is now a regulation which prohibits the harpooning of mothers accom-

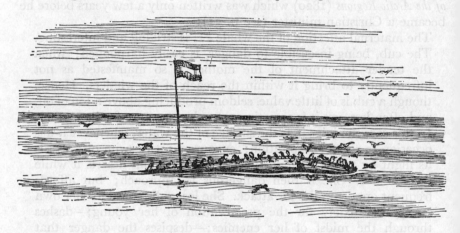

A dead whale marked by a flag whilst another is being pursued: a great attraction for petrels and gulls that come to feed on the blubber.

panied by their calves; it is, however, I am afraid, a law made for economic reasons and not those of compassion. I shall refer to more humane methods of hunting in chapter 20 (p. 463)

Slowly, slowly, our second whale is being pulled up. He is brought nearly to the surface when a very unusual accident occurs. There is a sharp crack, almost like a rifle shot. The large block over which the cable passes at the mast-head comes crashing to the deck, narrowly missing one of the crew. Under the heavy strain the steel cable which supported the block and passed to the spring accumulator below, has broken. This means delay; the rope holding our whale has to be changed over to the other side. At last this is done and the great body of our prize is pulled up into view; it is quite dead and is dealt with exactly as we saw before. We now steam back to pick up our first whale. Its carcass, as we approach, with its orange and red flag fluttering in the breeze, almost reminds one of a holiday pleasure steamer with a crowded deck, but its passengers are birds; they are mostly Cape pigeons pecking away at the blubber like mad, but here and there among them are a few 'stinkers' as the whale-men call the giant petrels. When the whalers first took to casting a dead whale adrift, they sometimes returned only to find no trace of it; or occasionally they came just in time to see it disappearing below the surface with a hissing sound of escaping air. In pecking at the blubber the birds sometimes pulled out the plug from the lance hole and so scuttled their meal; to prevent this the wad of tow is now soaked in kerosene to make it unpalatable. As we approach the birds fly off screaming angry protests at us. We pick up the whale and then to dinner.

The breakage of the tackle is a great disappointment to the captain, for the whales are very plentiful just now; but he dare not risk working with only one available line and must return to port to get the system repaired for to-morrow. He says we should have got at least two if not three more whales to-day if he had not had this rare accident. There was never any mention of my being a Jonah; but I wondered what they thought! It was 3 o'clock before we had dinner, and, as we were a long way south, it took us till nearly 7 o'clock before we reached home. We passed many beflagged whales waiting to be picked up by other boats; the catchers from some five other stations were at work. After the captain had had a nap we whiled away the afternoon with coffee and talk. Most Norwegian whalers are making money as fast as they can in order to get enough to start a farm and then to leave the sea for the land as they get older. It is of farms that they so frequently talk. The captain now talks of the one he has actually started and how his wife and nephew are running it for him whilst he is away; he talks of the cows and horses he has almost with affection, and of the peace of the woodlands that surround his land.

It is a wonderfully clear evening as we steam in to the coast. Every mountain of South Georgia is standing out sharply against the sky; as the sun gets lower and lower and finally sinks, the lights on the snow pass through shades of primrose to brilliant gold, rose and crimson, whilst the shadows change from pale sky blue to the deepest purple.

It may be of interest at this point to recall the remarkable prophecy of Dr. George Forster, who accompanied Captain Cook on his voyage in the *Resolution* when he discovered and laid claim to South Georgia in 1775. He wrote in his account of the voyage as follows:

If the northern ocean should ever be cleared of whales by our annual fisheries, we might then visit the other hemisphere where

Flensing a large blue whale at the Grytviken whaling station, South Georgia; the flensers begin by making long cuts in the blubber from head to tail. Sketched from a photograph.

these animals are known to be numerous. However, there seems to be little necessity to advance so far as New Georgia in quest of them, since the Portuguese and North Americans have of late years killed numbers of them on the coast of America, going no farther than the Falkland Islands. It should therefore seem probable, that though Southern Georgia may hereafter become important to mankind, that period is at present so far remote and perhaps will not happen, till Patagonia and Tierra del Fuego are inhabited and civilised like Scotland and Sweden.

Friday, 16th April. I have not yet described the whaling station in any detail. I briefly sketched its first sight appearance in the last chapter, but I must now explain its working. The whole factory is grouped around the central flensing plane or platform; this is an area of wooden planking some 50 yards square sloping gently to the water. The whales brought in by the catchers are tied up to buoys just in front of this and there they float, belly upwards, until they can be dealt with. From time to time a man in a boat comes off from the platform pulling a long steel cable with a great grapnel at its end, which he clamps to the whale's tail; he now unties the whale from the buoy, signals to a man driving a steam winch at the back of the platform, and slowly the huge carcass is drawn up on to the wooden staging. It has hardly come to rest before the flensers with their big curved knives, mounted on long wooden handles, climb upon it and begin to make long continuous cuts through the blubber from head to tail.

The blubber completely covers the body of the whale with a thick layer (except on the flippers and tail flukes) below quite a thin skin; its thickness varies from say 4 inches in a small fin whale to as much as 11 inches to a foot in a big blue whale. It serves a dual purpose in the whale's economy. For one thing it acts as an overcoat, an insulating layer, preventing loss of body heat in the cold polar seas. [The fact that the blubber must be reduced to a very thin layer on the flippers and tail flukes (also on the dorsal fin) to give good swimming qualities presents a problem concerning heat loss which evolution has solved for the whale, speaking metaphorically, in a most ingenious way. P. F. Scholander and W. E. Schevill (in the *Journal of Applied Physiology*, vol. 8, p. 279, 1955) have shown that the arteries carrying the warm blood to the fins and flukes are closely surrounded by the veins bringing the blood back, so that an exchange of heat takes place: the blood leaving the main body warms up that returning to it from its chilly extremities.] The other function of the blubber is to form a great reserve of food on which the whale can draw when he leaves the rich feeding grounds of the far south in the winter to migrate into warmer waters where the plankton is not so abundant. Like the hump of the camel, it is gradually reduced in a period of food shortage. It is unlike any other fat that I have ever seen; the only substance with which I can compare it is freshly cut pineapple. It is juicy and fibrous.

[In chapter 2 I described how, when preparing for our expedition, I went for a cruise with Professor Johan Hjort on the *Michael Sars*. I had an experience then which gave me an insight into the nature of blubber as nothing else could. I will quote from the obituary notice of Hjort which I wrote for the Royal Society[1].

I joined him in Oslo and we travelled together to Trondhjem where the *Michael Sars* was preparing for the voyage. There was some delay in the delivery of some new apparatus and we spent a week waiting to sail. Here I saw something of Hjort that I have

[1] *Obituary Notices of Fellows of the Royal Society*, vol. 7, 1950.

never seen recorded elsewhere—I saw Hjort the inventor of industrial machinery. At Trondhjem he had set up a small experimental factory to deal with the extraction of oil from blubber on quite novel lines using machines of his own design. In the usual boiling process of extracting the oil a good deal of the oil is lost in forming an emulsion with the water and is difficult to recover. Hjort had made a histological examination of blubber and from the results of this he had devised a mechanical means of extraction. He saw how the large drops of oil were held in the adipose cells of the tissue; he found that by hitting the blubber by quick sharp strokes in rapid succession—not too strong, not too weak—he could cause the cells to break down and then the oil could be squeezed out from the mass of connective tissue fibres running through the blubber just as if one was squeezing out water from a floor cloth. I went with Hjort on his first visit to see in operation the machinery he had designed; he was then fifty-five but he might have been a schoolboy in his excitement and enthusiasm. Strips of blubber had been brought from a nearby whaling station. We saw the long strips, rigid with the consistency of pineapple, fed in between two rapidly rotating rollers which had projecting ridges on them like the teeth of a cog wheel but extending along their whole length; we saw them emerge on to a moving banding like long strips of soft sponge. Any oil that escaped was caught in troughs below. The spongy strips now passed on into a helical press from one side of which the oil gushed in a steady stream while from the other side there emerged a continuous mass of white material—like cotton waste— the connective tissue fibres squeezed practically dry of oil. I witnessed with the inventor the birth of a new process. I forget the actual figures, but I remember Hjort a day or two later, when a proper analysis had been made, telling me with glee that he had succeeded in extracting something like 95 per cent of the oil, as against a much lower percentage by the boiling process.

After this digression let me return to the men who have just made the long cuts in the blubber from the whale's head to its tail.]

The blubber is still attached to the body in long strips. Next, the steel cable from the winch is again brought forward, this time with a hook at its end like a large meat hook, which is now stuck into one of the strips of blubber at its head-end. The strip is loosened with a knife and then—full steam on the winch! It is torn off backwards, pulled from the body with a terrific rending sound which I can only

15. *Above*, in the Roaring Forties. *Below*, typical Southern Ocean scene, sketched near South Georgia

liken to that of tearing calico but magnified many, many times. Strip after strip is torn off. A huge 90 foot blue whale may be bereft of its blubber in a matter of some twenty minutes. It is just like peeling a gigantic banana. As they proceed the whale's body is rolled over by other hooks on chains working round bollards from the side, again pulled from the steam winches in the background. By the same means the carcase, as soon as it is fully stripped, is dragged over to the other side of the platform to make room for the next whale and to have its flesh cut off. Meanwhile the blubber strips are cut up into suitable blocks to be sent up in hoists up the front of the boiler building on the

Flensing a humpback whale, lying on its back, at the Grytviken station. The undersides of the tail flukes and the flippers are white. Drawn from a photograph taken by Dr. L. Harrison Matthews.

right of the platform (looking from the sea) and so dropped into oil boilers from the top. My watercolour in Plate 10 (p. 160) shows the general arrangement.

The flesh, which is next cut off, goes up similar hoists into the flesh factory to the left where a certain amount of oil is extracted before it is made into cattlemeal or fertiliser; actually some of the flesh, if the whale is fresh, is kept for food for the whaling colony and very good meat it is too as I have already indicated. The remaining skeleton is drawn up a steep incline to a platform on the top of the bone boilers; here the vertebrae of the backbone are separated with axe-like choppers and the skull is cut in pieces with cross-cut saws to be dropped through openings into the cauldrons below. It is surprising how much oil can be got from the bones.

G

Nothing is wasted. What remains of the flesh and bone after the oil has been extracted is taken by trolley to the drying kilns. Each of these is a very long cylinder in an almost but not quite horizontal position and so arranged that it can be made to rotate about its axis; there is a furnace at the lower end and a chimney at the other. Inside the cylinder is a rail coiled in a spiral and fastened to its inner surface. The meat and bone remains are fed into the kiln at the furnace end and as it slowly rotates the spiral rail gradually guides the contents along towards the chimney end; in the process they are roasted and dried by the hot gases traversing the length of the cylinder from the furnace. Loops of chain hanging inside the kiln help to break up the remains into small pieces which, when fully dried, fall out through a slot at the chimney end. The products are now ground to powder in a mill. If only fresh meat has been used it forms a feeding meal for cattle; if the meat is less fresh it is mixed with the bone to form a manure which is usually sold as 'guano' I believe; and bone by itself yields bone meal. [I was writing of a typical shore station as I saw it in 1926; on the great factory ships of to-day the equipment is more modern.]

The sight of such a whaling station working at full pressure is one not easily forgotten. It is butchery on a fantastic scale, and the butchers, almost an army of them, are dwarfed by the huge blocks of flesh. It is difficult to connect the stripped and bloody carcasses on the platform, or indeed even the whole floating inflated bodies waiting to be flensed, with the graceful active creature we have seen blowing and diving at the surface of the sea. The smell I have already described. Walking on the platform requires some care if you are not to slip; it has a surface of blood and slimy intestinal contents. Here as at most stations a stream from the mountains has been diverted so that it can be directed over different parts of the platform to help wash the refuse away, but on a busy day it makes little impression till the work is over.

In the last chapter I mentioned the large number of birds that congregate to fight over the scraps of offal washed down from the plane. There are always several thousand to be seen, but last week, with fog and stormy weather outside, they have been driven in in millions. This is no exaggeration. It must be seen to be believed. The water is covered and the air is thick with them. I have photographs taken at this period in which there are the dark streaks across the water in the distance looking as if they were shadows but are actually masses of birds: Cape pigeons for the most part. In addition to the Wilson's and the giant petrels mentioned previously, a number of large Dominican gulls came in too.

To complete the account of the Grytviken whaling station I should not forget the settlement of wooden houses, like a Norwegian village, with its little wooden church, which lies behind and to one side of the station. Some two hundred people are employed in the factory. All the skilled work is done by Norwegians, but a lot of the rougher work is done by a strange mixture of nationalities recruited for the season from the cities of the Argentine.

Sunday, 11th April. [I have transposed this entry by a few days because it includes a visit to a floating factory which will be better understood after the description of the shore installation which I have just given.] To-day Mr. Esbensen, the manager of the Grytviken whaling station very kindly put at our disposal the small sealing ship S.S. *Karl* (always known as the *Little Karl*) to make a visit to the penguin rookeries at St. Andrews Bay some three hours' steaming to the south; here there are King penguins as well as ringed and gentoos. We made up a party: Dr. Kemp, Captain Stenhouse, Rolfe Gunther, Cadet Francis Pease and myself. The *Little Karl* is actually a very old whale-catcher originally used in the north and from her, years ago, the Kaiser, as a young man, shot a whale; she is only about 75 feet in length.

It was a gloriously sunny day, but the high winds of yesterday had left a heavy swell and it was a great disappointment to find on arriving at our destination that it was too rough to attempt a landing. It is so difficult to forecast, from the shelter of Grytviken, what it will be like on a more exposed part of the coast. However, we came close in and got good views of King penguins on the beach, but the rookeries were farther in among the tussock.

We put back to New Fortune Bay to visit the site of an abandoned whaling station; at the end of this sheltered arm of the sea we were able to run alongside the old neglected jetty and land. The mountains, deeply covered in snow, for we have had heavy falls in the last few days, come precipitously down on one side of the fjord and less steeply on the other. Opposite the jetty is the hulk of a wrecked three-masted sailing ship. By her build, and the port-holes along her side, the captain says she is an old coolie transport ship used for taking native labour from India and Africa to the West Indies; she has finished her last days in the whaling service of the south. We see threads from many different parts of the world drawn together and ended in this barren spot; in the little cemetery behind the derelict station we find, among the graves of the Norwegians, two much older ones of American sealers who died here in the 1870's.

The old station itself is certainly a remarkable sight. Thousands and thousands of pounds must have been sunk here—and no doubt redeemed in the quick profits of this southern Klondike; yet what an appalling waste it all seems.[1] Apart from the jetty and the long stone sea wall which must have taken much labour to build, there remain old houses, tramway lines, boilers, winches, quantities of harpoons and other gear; and, what seems almost pathetic, overturned in the snow, like a child's toy, lies a disused locomotive. The broken remains of great cog-wheels stick up through the snow and all around the fjord, in a broad band, are piled the bones of whales, as indeed there are along stretches of Cumberland Bay; thousands of whales must have gone to make this vast array: a reminder of the days before the Government forced them to use the flesh and bones as well as the blubber. Up on a wide ridge above the station we could see some rein-deer, descendants of those introduced from Norway some years ago and said to be doing very well; they provide some sport for the whaling managers and give them a welcome addition to their larders as a change from whale, or the mutton sent from the Falklands.

On the way back to Grytviken we called on the manager of the floating factory *Thor*, which is anchored in Godthul harbour. This is a very big ship converted to carry all the equipment of a shore station with the exception of the flensing platform. The whales are flensed in the water alongside by men working from a large punt-like pontoon, the strips of blubber being torn off and hoisted aboard by hooks and cables from the ship's derricks; on the deck above the blubber is cut up and passed to the boilers below. The meat from the carcass is then cut up into convenient 'joints' and similarly passed up to the ship. What a sight it is to see the men on the deck cutting at great hunks of flesh bigger than themselves and dragging the pieces on hooks to the circular openings that lead down to the boilers. The surface is slimy with grease and blood; it is a wonder that they do not slip and get carried with their sliding burdens into the awful cauldrons below and so become converted into meal. I believe it has happened. To say that the ship had all the equipment of the shore station is not quite true, for it had not the complete 'guano' plant to use the entrails; intestines and other in'ards floated away covered with fighting and screaming birds: Cape pigeons and giant petrels.

The factory ship stores its own whale oil and at the end of the season carries it all back under its own power. It also has the advantage that

[1]The Compania Argentina de Pesca, which founded the Grytviken station, the first at South Georgia, is recorded by L. Harrison Matthews in his *South Georgia*, 1931, as having paid a 70% dividend in its first year.

it can change its location from year to year if necessity should so demand. It should not be confused with the new pelagic whaling vessels which are now being experimented with and of which the S.S. *Lancing* is the first. This is a large floating factory which has a steep incline up which the whales are drawn by cables to be flensed on deck. Such a ship is independent of sheltered water and can work in mid-ocean, cruising about the seas following the concentrations of whales. Working outside the 3-mile limit, it can evade all taxes, licences, and regulations. It may well be feared that, if this experiment should be a success and international control cannot be brought to bear, the end of whaling through overfishing may be in sight.

[This was written nearly forty years ago. The pelagic factory ships have, of course, been a tremendous success, as we shall see later on, and nearly all the shore stations and the old type floating factories have gone. In spite of the work of the International Whaling Convention the great southern fishery has now been brought to the verge of collapse. Can it be saved? We shall return to this question when in chapter 19 we have reviewed the more recent research that has been done since our expedition and seen how we can now estimate the actual size of the stocks of the different species of whales. Here we must look at the beginnings of all this work.

I have stressed that in addition to our studies in the ocean of the factors which may govern the whales' distribution there are the equally important researches on the whales themselves, on their anatomy, growth and reproduction, which must be carried out where they are caught. Here will be a good place to consider the work done at our special Marine Laboratory at Grytviken or at other whaling stations.

Although much has been done since, the solid foundations of all that has followed were laid by the tireless efforts of Drs. N. A. Mackintosh and J. F. G. Wheeler, members of our shore party, during the first two years of the commission, 1925-7. Their massive report on the blue and fin whales, upon which I base this brief account, was published two years later[1]. When the South Georgia factory ceased work for the winter they transferred their activities to one at Saldanha Bay, South Africa, to study the stocks there; this gave a most valuable comparison. I have given a glimpse of conditions on the flensing platform—blood, guts, slime and stench; these formed the background of their everyday work. They were dwarfed by their enormous specimens upon which they had to climb or into which they had to cut

[1]'Southern Blue and Fin Whales,' *Discovery Reports*, vol. I, pp. 257-540.

or dig; their tasks of dissection and measurement were indeed Herculean. During the first two years' period they examined, measured and reported upon no fewer than 1,683 whales.

As they say in their monograph, their work was 'guided by three main objects', and these may be summarised as follows:

1. The determination of the characters of southern blue and fin whales in order to find out if there were any racial differences between these stocks and those of other areas such as might be brought about by their separation or different migrations.

2. An investigation of the reproductive processes, breeding habits and growth.

3. The examination of the interrelations of breeding, nourishment, distribution and local fluctuations of the whales.

In fulfilling the first object they collected a vast array of data on the sizes and bodily proportions of the blue and fin whales at South Georgia and South Africa which showed that, for both species, no distinction could be demonstrated between the stocks fished in the two localities. They have built up a body of knowledge, continually added to by later *Discovery* work, which will be invaluable for reference in relation to all future statistics collected in other parts of the world. We now know very much more about these whales in the southern hemisphere than we do of those in the north; as far as the poorer information regarding the latter will allow a comparison, there do not appear to be any structural differences between the members of either species in the two hemispheres such as would suggest the existence of distinct geographical races except perhaps a slight difference in size[1]; nevertheless, as we shall see in a moment, it appears most unlikely that there can be any interchange of stocks across the equator.

It was in respect to their second object, the investigation of breeding and growth, that Mackintosh and Wheeler, by their dissections and almost endless daily measurements, revealed one of the most surprising of all biological facts: the extraordinary rate of growth of these huge animals, both before and after birth. Pregnant females were, of course, continually being brought to the flensing platform. When the fœtuses were large there was no difficulty in finding and measuring them, but in the early stages of pregnancy the embryos are naturally minute, only a few millimetres in length, and thus exceedingly difficult to locate. Before the *Discovery* Investigations it was generally, but only vaguely, inferred that these blue and fin whales must, after spending

---

[1]It appears that the southern members of the species are a little larger at sexual maturity, but this may just be due to richer feeding in the south.

the summer months feeding on the rich polar plankton, migrate to warmer latitudes for breeding in the winter. No one had ever found their true breeding grounds, and this is still true to-day; thanks, however, to Mackintosh and Wheeler taking observations at South Africa as well as at South Georgia, and then combining their findings from both localities, they have fitted two large pieces of the puzzle together to give us a very remarkable picture of the main events in the breeding cycles of these two species. These conclusions, which I shall only be able to sketch in the broadest outline, were achieved in the

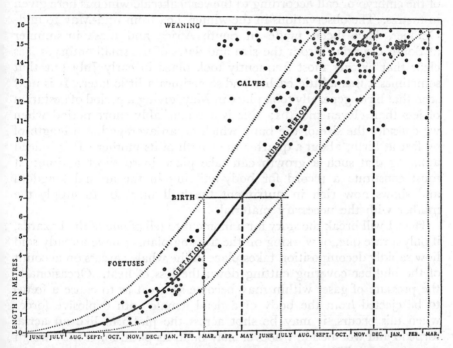

The mean curve of growth for the young blue whale during gestation and nursing, obtained by Drs. N. A Mackintosh and J. F. G Wheeler from their research at South Georgia and South Africa. From *D.R.*, vol. 1.

strenuous early years of the investigations and have only required minor alterations with the collection of much additional data in later years.

The story they have to tell is best conveyed in two diagrams, in graphs in fact. The first, that above, shows the lengths of all the blue whale embryos (fœtuses) and calves they measured and the second, while including the curve from the first graph on a smaller scale, continues with the sizes of the young whales between weaning and maturity. Similar graphs, except for slight time differences, could be shown for the fin whales, but to avoid repetition I shall confine the account to the blue whale. In passing I should mention that both species normally have only one calf at a time, although twins have occasionally been recorded. In the first graph we see along the base line a scale of months from June in one year, through the whole of the next year, to March in the year following, and against the date of each observation we have a dot in a position representing the length of the embryo or calf according to the vertical scale which is here given in metres. The observations in the winter, i.e., from mid-May to mid-October, have been made in South Africa and those in summer at South Georgia. From the size and dates of the small embryos it is clear that pairing most frequently took place in early July but that sometimes it was a little earlier and sometimes a little later. It is next seen that birth generally took place in May, giving a period of gestation of less than eleven months; this is a remarkably short period when we consider the size of the baby which on an average has a length of 23 feet at birth, about a quarter the length of its mother. It is indeed amazing that such a growth can take place in so short a time; it must constitute a record for body-building in the animal kingdom and shows how rich in nutriment the krill must be to supply the mother with the necessary material.

Here I will break the story for a moment to tell of one of the hazards, if only a rare one, of working on the flensing plan. I have already said how rapidly decomposition takes place in the whale carcass on account of the blubber covering cutting down the loss of heat. Occasionally the pressure of gases within may become so great as to cause a fœtus to be ejected from the body of a dead female with explosive force; when this occurs, it may be shot across the platform like an aerial torpedo and woe betide whoever may be in its path, for it may weigh a ton or two! The photograph on Plate 17 shows such a fœtus on the flensing platform at Grytviken.

Returning to the life history we see the calves accompanying their mothers until they are weaned some six months after birth by which time they have travelled to the rich krill feeding grounds of the south and their baleen plates have grown large enough to form effective collectors. The teats of the mother, when not in use, lie hidden in grooves on either side of the reproductive aperture, but in suckling they are protruded to be taken by the calf. At weaning the blue whale calf has reached a length of some fifty-two feet—as big as an adult humpback or a sei whale; how rich must be the mother's milk, and

16. Flocks of petrels feeding on the refuse coming from the Grytviken whaling station. The so-called cape pigeons (*Daption capensis*) are swimming in the filthy blood-stained water, but the more delicate Wilson's petrels (*Oceanites oceanicus*) dance gracefully like butterflies over the surface with only their toes touching it, for they will only settle in clean water

17. *Above*, Dr. Wheeler and Mr. Saunders examining and making notes of a foetal fin whale cut from a dead pregnant female. *Below*, a small embryo, seen through and in the middle of its foetal membranes, taken from a fin whale at the Saldanha Bay whaling station, South Africa. It is reproduced at about $\frac{3}{4}$ natural size

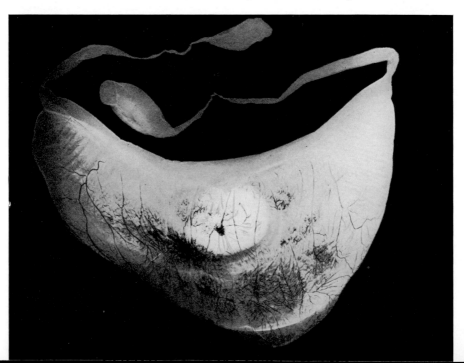

again how rich the mother's food—the krill. Then by the time the calf reaches its first birthday it will have added ten more feet to its length. We should now transfer our attention to the second graph where we see the growth of the young whale continuing. This, like the first, is based on observations made at both South Georgia and South Africa, i.e., summer and winter, and we see how perfectly the measurements made in the two areas fit together to produce one continuous curve;

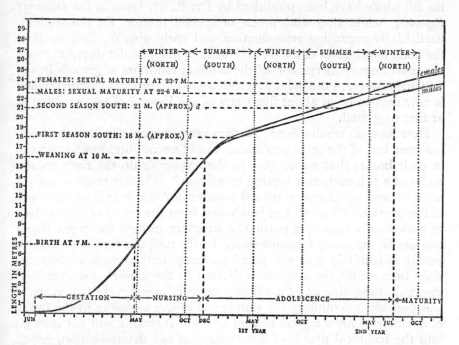

The estimated curve of growth for blue whales from conception to sexual maturity, also from the research of Drs. Mackintosh and Wheeler. From *D.R.*, vol. I.

in the south there were gaps in the records of measurement between about 61 and 66 feet and again between about 73 and 79 feet, and these gaps were exactly filled by measurements made in Africa. This gave valuable circumstantial evidence of migration for they must surely belong to the same stock; the direct proof in the case of fin whales from the evidence of marks, fired in one region and returned from whales killed in the other, only came much later and will be discussed in chapter 20 (p. 450). At two years old we see the young blue whale reaching a length of some 72 feet; a little later, at three or four years old, it becomes sexually mature but goes on growing until what is

G2

called physical maturity[1] is reached at between 90 and 100 feet. Again, is not this and the short time taken to reach a breeding age just as remarkable as the pre-natal growth?

I have already said that the authors give similar figures for the fin whale which is a little smaller; it is just over 21 feet at birth and reaches at physical maturity a maximum of about 80 feet. More recently two more detailed studies of the growth and reproduction of the fin whale have been published by Dr. R. M. Laws in the *Discovery Reports*[2]; while they add much of special interest for the student, particularly regarding reproduction and early growth, they confirm the main conclusions of the pioneer work of those earlier days. Perhaps the most important revision of the original estimates of growth in the fin whale concerns the point at which sexual maturity is reached which is now seen to be at about five years of age instead of two or three as at first suggested.

How long do whales live? To discover a means of telling their age has been one of the great problems. Could we not find some structure in their bodies that would give us the answer as do the rings on the scales of a fish such as a herring or salmon? Wheeler made a valiant attempt and developed a partial solution for the female in his study of the ovaries. When an egg is released from the ovary of a mammal, as periodically occurs, a particular structure termed the *corpus luteum* remains in the ovary for some time. In the rorquals similar structures persist indefinitely and are more correctly termed *corpora albicantia*. Now because all the evidence collected in the studies just described shows that the blue and fin whales normally breed every two years, it was possible by counting the number of *corpora albicantia* in the ovary of a female to have a good idea of how old it was. I will not here go into the technical details of this method of age determination, which are more complex than I have suggested, because a new method, indeed analagous with the rings on the scale of a fish, has at last been discovered; this will be discussed in chapter 20 (p. 461). The student of the subject however should consult Wheeler's pioneer paper in the *Discovery Reports* (vol. II, pp. 403-34) where he concluded that few whales at South Georgia were over 20 years old.

The bulk of the female whales, I have just said, breed every two years; they give birth to their young nearly a year after pairing, then

[1]Physical maturity, when growth stops, technically comes about when all the epiphyses of the backbone become firmly fused with the centra of their vertebrae; this process starts at each end of the column and proceeds till complete fusion takes place at a point nearer the head than the middle.

[2]1959: vol. XXIX, pp. 281-308 and in 1961 vol. XXXI, pp. 377-468.

suckle their calves for about half the next year and pair again when they go north at the end of that season. While this is certainly the general rule later information provided by Dr. Mackintosh shows that occasionally a whale will become pregnant while it is suckling a calf, and also that a few may remain in the south during the winter and so miss a breeding season.[1] Although we know so much less about the blue and fin whales of the northern hemisphere it would appear that they follow the same cycle but, on account of the reversed seasons, differing in phase by a six months' interval. For this reason, if for no other, it appears unlikely that there is any interchange of stock between the two hemispheres; again, it could be argued, had there been any interpolar migration we might have expected the populations of the north to have been to some extent made up from the south as they became depleted in the early days of the century, and there was no evidence of this.

Regarding their third object we have already seen in the last chapter how they have shown that these species in the south feed exclusively upon one particular kind of krill, the *Euphausia superba*; they have also shown that they take very little food in the winter when they are north. There can be no doubt that the movement south is a feeding migration and that the blubber, in addition to serving as an insulating layer, is the great food reserve which the whales have built up to last them over the winter in the warmer latitudes where, contrary to popular belief, the plankton is nothing like so rich as in the polar seas. Mackintosh and Wheeler in their studies show the blubber increasing in thickness as the summer season advances and then its great reduction in the whales coming south again after wintering in the north. They show much else of interest to the student, but I can only touch on two more points.

The blue whale used to be known to the old whalers by the name of sulphur-bottom whale because in the polar seas it often has a distinct yellow colour on its underside; but so also may the fin whale. This condition was first shown by Major Barret-Hamilton in 1913 to be 'a yellow slime, apparently due to algae.' In 1920 Mr. A. G. Bennett, when visiting the whaling station and the factory ships at Deception Island in the South Shetlands in the service of the Falkland Island Government, showed that it was caused by a coating of diatoms similar to the yellow bands often seen on ice-floes. He observed that the most heavily infected whales were those with a thick layer of blubber, indicating that they had been some time in the Antarctic, whereas the lean

[1] Indeed in the old days a little hunting was continued round South Georgia through the winter.

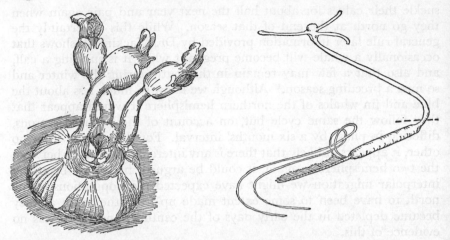

Left, three specimens of the 'eared' barnacle *Conchoderma auritum* attached to the whale barnacle *Coronula reginae,* from near the tail of a fin whale.

Right, the remakable copepod whale parasite *Pennella* firmly anchored with barbs inside the blubber with its body and its long egg sacs exposed to the outside. The broken line marks the outer skin of the whale.

individuals, recent arrivals from warmer waters, were usually free from diatoms. Mackintosh and Wheeler, who describe the external parasites of whales, notably the barnacles *Corunula* and *Conchoderma,* and the copepod *Pennella* (shown in sketch), and the amphipods *Cyamus* (p. 108), also studied this diatom film. They made interesting observations on both kinds of infection:

> It appears that whales become infected with these external parasites during their stay in the warmer waters, but lose them on migrating to the colder waters of the south. The film of diatoms is the only exception to this, for it is undoubtedly contracted in the summer in the Antarctic or sub-Antarctic waters. Early in the season it may be seen in its initial stages in the form of little round green patches on the skin, an inch or so in diameter. These patches appear to be growing colonies, which gradually expand from numerous centres and eventually cover perhaps the whole body within a few months.

Records and scrapings of the diatom film continued to be made at South Georgia. Dr. T. J. Hart, who joined the *Discovery* Investigations in 1929 and has made such important surveys of the phytoplankton right round the pole (pp. 484-490), published a *Discovery Report* (vol. x, pp. 247-82, 1935) on these records and a number of scrapings he had himself taken from whales at the South Georgia Station in the 1930-1 season. He fully confirmed the correlation between blubber thickness and diatom infection, worked out the communities of diatom species to be found in this unusual position and described a new species[1]. Space will only permit me to give two quotations. The first concerns a statement made by Mackintosh and Wheeler that, while all the mature whales were free of diatoms during the winter months at Saldanha Bay in South Africa, small spots of diatoms occurred on a few immature whales there in August and September; about this Hart says:

This is in good agreement with Bennett's conclusion that the skin film is acquired in Antarctic waters. It may now be considered as well established that a majority of the immature whales lag behind the larger mature whales on their southward migration (Harmer, 1931, pp. 107, 108), and it is therefore almost certain that their return to warmer waters is similarly belated.

He also describes the formation of reproductive spores in the commonest species of skin diatom (*Cocconeis ceticola*)[2].

Dr. Harrison Matthews, who at the shore station produced his *Reports* on the birds and the elephant seal of South Georgia (to be referred to on pp. 273 and 311) also did work here and at other whaling stations which he published some ten years later in four *Discovery Reports* dealing respectively with the humpback, the sperm, the southern right and the sei whales[3]; while based upon much less material than was available for the blue and fin whales, he produced, as far as possible, comparable data. These again are a mine of information for the student. The late Dr. Archie Clowes, our other scientist

---

[1]This he named after Dr. Wheeler: *Cocconeis wheeleri*. The commonest diatom to be found on the skin is the closely related species *C. ceticola*, but others including *Navicula* and *Lycmophora lyngbyei* may be present.

[2]. . . spore formation is commonest at the beginning and end of the season. As it seems certain that diatom film is only formed upon whales in Antarctic waters, it is thought that these spores furnish the chief means of dispersal of the species. The small nucleus of whales known to remain in the far south during the winter would serve to maintain survival, and the shedding of vast quantities of microspores into the sea in the following spring, when the schools congregate on the feeding grounds, apparently leads to rapid reinfection of the new arrivals. Spore formation was at a minimum in January, but showed a great increase in February and March. Examination of sei whales, which only come south late in summer, suggests that a period of about one month elapses between the arrival of whales within the Antarctic Zone and the formation of visible diatom film upon them. The great increase in spore formation at the end of the season will obviously tend to ensure that a majority of the whales that remain south through the winter become infected.

[3]All in vol. XVII, following one another, pp. 7-290.

at the shore station, was a chemist busily engaged in the analysis of the sea-water samples sent in from our surveys; some of the results of his work we shall see in chapter 14, and he worked on the composition of the whales' rich milk[1]. He also wrote the important *Report* on the phosphate and silicate in the Southern Ocean referred to in chapter 21 (p. 488).

The study of the migrations of whales by firing numbered darts into them will be described in chapter 20 together with the results of other more recent whale research. We must now get back to the voyage.]

---

[1]See an Appendix by him to Mackintosh and Wheeler's Report, *Discovery Reports*, vol. 1 pp. 472)

CHAPTER 9

DIPPING INTO THE DEPTHS

Monday, 26th April. We sailed into Stanley Harbour in great style on Saturday. It was just a week since we had left Grytviken expecting that the passage to the Falklands would be difficult; strong westerly winds are usually blowing and, if this had been so, we might well have taken three weeks or more. We were agreeable surprised to sail in a south-east wind; and except for Wednesday, it has remained in the east all the week, so that, with all sails set and the engine doing 70 revs., we have been flying along at 6½ to 7 knots—a splendid speed for the *Discovery*!

It has been an uneventful voyage. On Sunday when still within sight of South Georgia we passed three old whale carcasses floating and accompanied by a large number of Cape pigeons and giant petrels. Because these whales usually sink when dead, I think they must have been harpooned, inflated and cast adrift, and then lost through heavy gales preventing them being picked up before they had drifted too far to be found. But why no company's flags? Perhaps they lost them by being rolled over and over in the high seas.

Our first views of the Falkland Islands, seen under grey clouds and through frequent squalls of rain, were not inviting. The country looks somewhat monotonous with its low-lying hills, ridges of rock and stretches of rather yellow grassland unrelieved by trees. It was very much what one expected from the accounts of Darwin, Moseley and others. Stanley itself is a straggling town stretching along one side of the harbour. Shackleton once bitterly described it as a street about a mile and a half long with a graveyard at one end and a slaughter-house at the other. We shall see, however; first impressions are often false. Shackleton was naturally prejudiced as he was desperately trying to get a ship to rescue his expedition party, marooned on Elephant Island, before the ice closed in, and he had been told it might be several weeks before one could be sent.

Some of us have just returned from tea with hospitable Sir John and Lady Middleton at Government House, where we had an unexpected

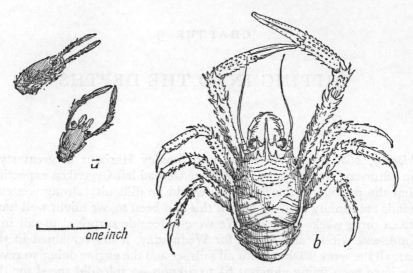

Left, the 'lobster krill', planktonic larval stages of the bottom living squat lobster *Munida gregaria* shown on the right.

and nostalgic glimpse of home. In contrast to the bleak climate their beautiful drawing-room led out into a conservatory which they have planted as an English garden; here roses and larkspurs were in flower, with a line of tall sweet peas and a fragrant mass of lavender. It was indeed a pleasant afternoon, with Sir John so interested in all the work of our expedition.

As with our Cape Town stay, I shall not take up much space with descriptions of the Falklands; such can be found in other books[1].

We spent some days trawling and dredging to the north of the islands obtaining good collections of invertebrates, but not many fish. We also surveyed the plankton to see what whale food there might be and came across large quantities of the so-called 'lobster-krill' which at times swarms in the surface waters so as to colour the sea bright red over large areas. This remarkable animal, up to about an inch in length, is indeed well named, for it has two long claws and is, in life, as red as a cooked lobster. It was originally thought to be an entirely pelagic species and was named *Grimothea*, but later it was shown to be the young stage of a rock lobster *Munida*. Our trawl hauls here have cleared up a little zoological problem; and one of whaling

[1] V. F. Boyson's *The Falkland Islands*, 1924, and Forrest McWhan's *The Falkland Islands Today*, 1952.

interest too. Let me quote Dr. Kemp's report to the committee at home on the scientific work of this period:

The identification of this form, which appears to be circumpolar in its distribution, has been the subject of much controversy, some authorities maintaining that *Munida gregaria* is not to be distinguished from *Munida subrugosa*. The question was, however, very fully discussed by Lagerberg in the results of the Swedish South Polar Expedition and the material we have obtained fully supports his conclusions. In our trawls and horizontal nets we obtained quantities of these two species of *Munida*, both in the post-larval and adult stages and were able to determine, without any doubt whatever, that '*Grimothea*' is the post-larval form of *Munida gregaria* and that this species is quite distinct from *Munida subrugosa*. In the latter species the post-larval form lives on the bottom, *Munida gregaria* being the only member of the genus in which this remarkable pelagic stage is known to occur.

These facts, apart from their scientific interest, are of some practical importance, for '*Grimothea*' is undoubtedly the 'krill' of the Falkland Islands. Sir Sidney Harmer informs me that he has recently learnt that it forms the food of the hump-back (whale) in New Zealand waters; Mr. J. E. Hamilton tells me that he has found it on various occasions at the Falkland Islands in the stomachs of shags and fur-seals and he also thinks that it is eaten by penguins. There is every reason to believe that it forms the principal food of the whales which frequent the locality, but unfortunately no record appears to exist of the stomach-contents of the whales formerly taken at the station on New Island.

L. Harrison Matthews, who was with us on this part of the voyage, has made a detailed comparison of the two species of *Munida* and reviewed the records of their circum-polar distribution[1]. We took large numbers of the adults of both *M. gregaria* and *M. subrugosa* in trawl hauls off the East Falkland Islands and after preserving many specimens the remainder were much appreciated in the ward-room and on the mess-deck. I give sketches of the adult and young opposite.

To give a slight impression of the country I will briefly quote from my journal, of 11th May, describing a week-end which Captain Stenhouse, Rolfe Gunther, Cadet Francis Pease and I spent riding over to stay with Mr. and Mrs. Langdon at their large sheep farm at Fitzroy, some 29 miles from Stanley.] . . . Winter weather had set in and, there having been a good deal of rain, the country was in a bad state for riding. All the year round there are numerous bogs which

[1] L. Harrison Matthews, Lobster-Krill, *Discovery Reports*, vol. v, pp. 467-84, 1932.

are dangerous to horses, but in addition to these much of the ground which would be dry in summer was in a soft marshy state. However, considering the conditions, we covered the distance quite well: 29 miles in 5 hours. The country we traversed may be regarded as typical of the islands, consisting of ranges of low hills lined along their tops with rough crags. The slopes are grass and heath, strewn with boulders and cut through here and there by sharp rock. Above any farm or settlement you see long trenches dug and peat stacked up ready for use; and Stanley has that pleasant smell of burning peat, reminiscent of West Highland villages.

After rising on to the high ground we crossed a ridge and down to a long arm of the sea which we skirted until we reached a point where we could ford it; and on the way we passed many sheep and two shepherds' cottages. Above the ridge three turkey buzzards were soaring; at times they came so low that we could clearly see the raw turkey-like head and neck which give them their name. They circle round and round, rising with steady outstretched wings on the up-currents formed as the wind strikes the slopes; or they may remain poised motionless upon the wind and then suddenly swoop down to within a few feet of the ground like a hawk.

We saw many of the so-called 'stone rivers' or 'stone runs'; one particularly large one is at the head of the bay about a mile and a half from Stanley. These broad bands of stones, lying just on the surface of the ground, as if scattered thickly from some giant cart, are caused by a movement—a slow flowing—of the peat. There was a time, it is said, when the Falklands were even wetter than they are to-day and when the sodden peaty soil was continually sliding down towards the sea and so exposing the rocks which line the hill tops. To-day the soil tends to flow only where little streams percolate through it; and here the fragments of rock which are continually broken off by frost from the crags above get carried down as a 'stone river.' They only move very slowly, like a glacier or even slower.

At Fitzroy, Mr. and Mrs. Langdon and their daughter entertained us; the kindest of people, they made us really at home. It was a delightful contrast to life on board a small ship: hot baths when we wanted them, big easy chairs with books and magazines in front of a glowing peat fire. The return was not so pleasant; snow made bogs difficult to avoid, we rode into a strong wind with frequent bursts of hail or sleet, and my horse took to shying at black rocks which stuck out of the snow like crouching beasts. Except for Icelandic ponies I had never been on a horse before, and I came off this one several times.

Thursday, 20th May. The fauna of Stanley harbour is very rich, as we saw from several expeditions we made with a motor-boat using a small 8 ft. beam-trawl and tow-netting at the same time. The water was full of the little jellyfish-like stages of hydroids in great variety; one kind in particular, probably a species of *Sarsia*, was worthy of note on account of its colouring: its manubrium—'the handle of the umbrella'—was a pure cobalt blue, and its radial canals and four long tentacles were a delicate lavender shade.

Anchored in the harbour are several old hulks whose sides, covered thickly in mussels, yield a wonderful variety of animals: sponges and hydroids of many different kinds, ascidians (sea-squirts), bright apricot-coloured holothurians (sea-cucumbers), polychaete worms, small crabs and pycnogons (sea-spiders). Armed with a long mussel rake we made a rich harvest, both for the laboratory and the table; the *moules marinières* and the mussel soup were excellent. The two larger hulks, old sailing ships, were the *Great Britain* and the *Queen Elizabeth*. The former had been famous in her day as a first-class sailing liner; one of the largest sailing ships, she was the first vessel in the world to be fitted with a screw propeller when she ended her days for a short time as an auxiliary steam craft. She is now used largely as a wool store. Her once luxurious state cabins on the upper deck were now used as temporary sheep pens for imported stock and the big panelled saloon below was piled high with bales of wool for export.

We sailed to-day and are now off once more across the wide South Atlantic, going back to the Cape to have our sister keels fitted. These will cut down the heavy rolling which has so much reduced our efficiency. First of all we are heading in a north-easterly direction to take soundings and examine a position at which the S.S. *Subra* in 1908 recorded breaking water and a sounding of only 8 fathoms; a similar report of breaking water was more recently made by Mr. Conor O'Brien (on his round-the-world solo voyage) at a position a little to the north-east. They have been called the Subra and O'Brien shoals; as no other soundings have previously been taken in this area, it is important for us either to confirm or confute their existence.

Sunday, 27th May. We are making satisfactory progress towards the Subra shoal and our nets have been yielding very good catches of plankton. Euphausians of several species continue to be a feature of the hauls and the lobster-krill is still with us but in smaller quantities. Salps, of four different kinds, have greatly increased in numbers and sometimes have filled the nets with their jelly-like bodies, making a true assessment of the other kinds of plankton difficult to achieve.

Last evening we caught an exquisite siphonophore, *Physophora*, another example of those remarkable composite animals which we saw

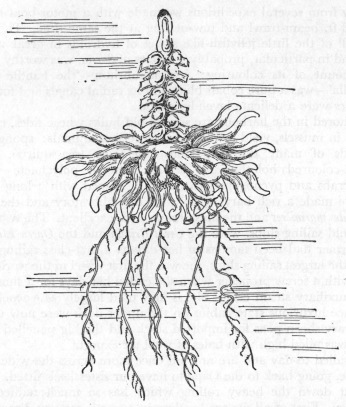

The siphonophore *Physophora hydrostatica* drawn natural size
from a watercolour painting of the living specimen.

and discussed in chapters 3 and 4, when we puzzled over the problem
of their individuality. Although not uncommon in the North Atlantic,
this is the first of this kind we have met with; it can either drift
passively or swim quite actively. It has a float at the very top, glistening
like an air bubble, and below it, on opposite sides of the stem, are two
series of five swimming bells of glass-like transparency; below these
again are two circles of so-called 'palpons,' rose-coloured and tipped
with orange, like the petals of some dahlia, but apparently serving
the purpose of protective bracts. From its centre hang some half-dozen
polyps trailing long tentacles with little branches bearing batteries of
stinging cells for the capture of their prey; and between these polyps
and the 'petals' are clusters of gonophores[1] bearing the sexual cells.

[1]A gonophore is a sack-like body producing the eggs or sperm; it is actually a modified
medusa which is never set free (cf. p. 74).

Why the highly-coloured 'petals'? Does it, like some gaudy blossom, attract planktonic 'bees' (perhaps amphipods) to carry out some 'pollinating' rites? Hardly. Yet bright colours in nature are almost always associated with advertisement. The colours of flowers are, of course, 'inn signs' inviting insects to sample the nectar, and those of fruits are similarly attracting birds to the feast: each with an ulterior motive—pollination in the former and seed dispersal in the latter. Few can doubt that the glowing hues of *Physophora* have a function. The highly-coloured sea-anemones are heavily charged with stinging cells, as are the 'petals' of our *Physophora*. It seems most likely that these flowers of the sea are not advertising to attract customers, but on the contrary are crying out 'Danger—keep away'; they provide most probably another example of the warning colours referred to on p. 142 and in its footnote.

Our *Physophora* does not always hang motionless, as I have portrayed it in my sketch, at times it will turn on its side and swim quite actively; then the swimming bells (modified into almost bellows-like structures) squirt out streams of water and so give jet propulsion. [This active swimming is well described and illustrated by A. K. Totton in his splendid 'Siphonophora of the Indian Ocean,' *Discovery Reports* vol. XXVII, 1934.] I should mention how very fragile these beautiful creatures are; nearly all the swimming bells had broken off and were found lying at the bottom of the tow-net bucket. In my drawing I have replaced them.

Friday, 28th May. Since Monday, that is for five days, we have encountered heavy weather: high seas and strong north-easterly winds. We are in the 'roaring forties,' but they are roaring in the wrong direction! This is most unusual.

We have been creeping slowly towards the position of the Subra shoal and to-day we passed close to it. In the high seas we were unable to make a proper sounding with the Lucas machine or use the outboard detonator for the echo apparatus; we did however manage to use the Kelvin sounding machine without getting bottom and this disposed of the alleged 8 fathoms sounding.

Both on Wednesday and to-day we have been visited by large schools of 'blackfish' *Globicephalus*; they differed from the common species by having a peculiar light-coloured lozenge-shaped patch slanting backwards on the side of the head in front of the eye. On each occasion their visits to the ship were very short and they never quite came within range of our harpoon gun; to-day we did have a shot at one but the harpoon fell short.

Sunday, 30th May. The gale continued into yesterday and while it

Southern pilot whales or 'blackfish' sketched from a photograph taken by Mr. A. Saunders on the *Discovery* and now on display in the whale gallery of the British Museum (Natural History). They are distinguished from the northern form of the species by the oblique white streaks on the side of the head.

was impossible to sound on the Subra position, to-day we have come back to that of the O'Brien shoal (43°, 20′ S., 46°, 02′ W.) and made a complete vertical station after finding bottom at a depth of 5,460 metres; this is the deepest sounding we have yet made, yielding a deposit of red clay with fragments of diatoms. So much for the supposed shoals! Some people, on seeing one of the large patches of floating kelp that one occasionally encounters drifting in mid ocean, are apt to imagine that it is anchored and must mean a shoal.

I have just mentioned making a vertical station; we are now about to take a series of such observations right across the ocean to South Africa. Each station where we stop the ship, will be like that described in chapter 6 (p. 146) where we take sea temperatures and water samples at different levels from the surface down to near the ocean floor, and at the same time make vertical hauls with the 70 cm. diameter plankton nets in a range of six depth stages from 1,000 metres to the surface. From this line of stations we shall, when we have worked out the results, be able to construct a chart showing a section of the ocean with all the contours of differing temperatures, saltness, oxygen content, alkalinity, etc., filled in and other such charts for the varying quantities of plankton of different kinds at different depths. We actually began our survey of the South Atlantic with the vertical stations between Tristan da Cunha and South Georgia where I described the procedure in detail. When we have made many more such observations we shall be in a position to discuss the general vertical distribution of the various water masses—those derived from the north and those derived from the south and the way they flow over or under one another— with their relative wealth of planktonic life. You may remember how we found that striking cold layer, between depths of 100 and 200 metres, as we approached South Georgia (p. 155). We are attempting to build up a picture of this vast hidden world by systematically fishing for the information we require by lines let down from the surface. At the end of such a vertical station, or between two of them, we shall tow much larger nets horizontally for two or three miles at different levels to show us something of the larger and rarer animals of this dark abysmal world. This is to be the special work of our present passage.

The station to-day yielded a number of interesting specimens. The 70 cm. net hauled vertically from a depth of 1,000 to 750 metres brought up a remarkable almost spherical medusa, with a small 'hollowed out' sub-umbrella cavity and short tentacles, radial canals and masses of eggs all of a bright brick-red colour. In the same haul was a large pelagic nemertine worm of the wide flattened type, *Pelagonemertes rollestoni*, with the ramifying branches of the gut of a chocolate brown. From time to time it would throw out a long white proboscis several times the length of its body and roll it in again— outside in; this organ, which is thought to serve for the capture of prey, is normally kept contracted in a sheath within its body. I show a sketch of it on p. 217.

Following the vertical work with the nets and water-bottles, we lowered away, for the first time on the voyage, the Petterssen young-fish trawl to a depth of 2,000 metres. This, in its original form, as used here, has a rectangular mouth, 6 ft. by 4 ft., which is kept open by otter boards (like a normal otter trawl) but is used as a mid-water pelagic trawl[1]; the net itself is made of stramin, a coarse open-mesh sacking-like material, and tapers to an end which is clamped to a metal bucket like a very large tow-net jar. It is a net which has been used most successfully in recent years in the North Sea for the capture of

[1]Later in the cruise, in fact after July 1926, the boards were discarded and the net, mounted on a 200 cm. diameter ring frame, used as an ordinary tow-net as had been done by Dr. (now Sir Frederick) Russell of Plymouth; in this form it is almost equally efficient and easier to handle.

young fish and some of the larger plankton animals. After towing for an hour it brought up a very large catch of deep-water animals. There were the typical bright red shrimps, prawns and mysids, but with them some greater rarities: large black and red amphipods; there were also, of course, hosts of smaller crustacea, especially scarlet copepods. There were orange-coloured arrow-worms and beautiful deep red and plum-coloured jelly-fish: *Atolla* and *Periphylla*. One of its most interesting captures, at any rate for the zoologist, was a remarkable ctenophore (a comb-jelly) whose comb-like plates not only did not beat in rhythm, one after the other, as they usually do, in such creatures, but did not beat as a *whole comb* at all; each comb allowed their long cilia to beat quite independently of one another. Why does the zoologist find this so exciting? It is just because it is so curious to find an animal having gone through the evolution of combining its once separate cilia into comb-like plates so that they *will* act together, now discarding this method of paddling locomotion for something much more like its primeval original design. There were, as well, of course, many deep-water fish.

Friday, 4th June. We made further vertical stations on Tuesday and yesterday, followed on Tuesday by a deep (2,000 metres) haul with the 4½-metre diameter net and yesterday by 1-metre diameter nets at the surface, 50 metres and 100 metres depth.

The 4½-metre net gave us another good catch of deep-water animals but it came up badly torn so we must have lost many specimens. Was the catch so big that its weight proved too great a strain, or did we catch, as we had supposed once before, some large and very powerful creature, perhaps a large squid, which tore its way out? A tantalising question to which we shall never know the answer. In the catch there were several fine pteropods[1] some of which we had not seen before; there was one curious globular and semi-transparent form *Thliptodon* and a number of the remarkable *Cymbulia* with wide wings like butter-flies, but also transparent, and each riding in what might be a glass slipper (as shown in my sketch). *Cymbulia* secretes this protective gelatin-ous 'shell'; it has the same consistency as the transparent swimming bells of many siphonophores or the bodies of salps.

We are again beginning to feel the shortage of our coal capacity and so using sail as much as possible and running on only one boiler; for this reason too we have had to abandon some of our proposed horizontal hauls between the main stations, except surface hauls when the speed is not too great, as we cannot continually be taking in sail. The contrary winds all last week upset our estimates considerably;

[1] A general note on the nature of pteropods was given on p. 77.

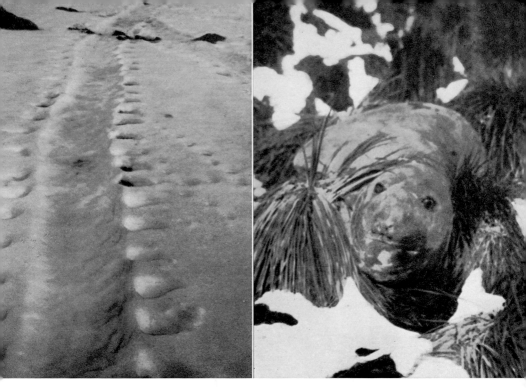

18. Elephant seals at South Georgia. *Above left*, the track of a large bull. *Right*, an old bull in the tussock grass. *Below*, harem of females at Undine Bay with the *William Scoresby* in the background

19. Rival bull elephant seals fighting for the possession of the beach and its harem, South Georgia; a remarkable photograph taken by Mr. A. Saunders

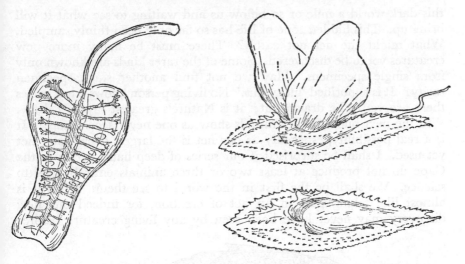

Left, the deep-water nemertine *Pelagonemertes rollestoni* and *right,* the pteropod *Cymbulia* and its glass-like 'slipper' (pseudoconch) drawn natural size.

they were quite unexpected in these latitudes. While we had a good following breeze at the beginning of the week, it has now dropped and we are making very slow progress.

We are being followed all the time by numbers of birds: great wandering albatrosses, sooty albatrosses, mollymauks (or mollyhawks as the sailors always call them) and Cape pigeons. These last are always fighting over the little scraps that fall from the ship. To-day, as we went very slowly along under sail alone, at barely 2 knots, we hung over a piece of salt pork on a line so that the Cape pigeons paddled at the side of us fighting over it. So intent were they at pecking at the bait that we were able to catch them easily in the hand-net; they soon got out of the net, however, and flying away were back at the pork in a moment or two, not in the least put off.

We lowered a 70 cm. net this afternoon and as we drew it in it was followed closely by a pilot fish (*Naucrates,* p. 81). We kept the net close under the stern for some time endeavouring to catch the fish with a hand-net; it swam close against the net, first at one side and then the other, or underneath it, but was finally scared away. It must have thought the net some very unusual fish!

Saturday, 5th June. We made another deep-water haul to-day with the 4½-metre net going to 1,500 metres, getting a very good catch. There is something very exciting about sending a large net down into

this dark world a mile or so below us and waiting to see what it will
bring up. This hidden zone of life has so far only been thinly sampled.
What might the net not catch? There must be many more new
creatures yet to be discovered. Some of the rarer kinds are known only
from single specimens. May we not find another single-specimen
rarity? It is a glorified 'lucky dip.' No living person knows what prizes
there are yet to be drawn out; it is Nature's greatest mystery draw.
Will the next bucketful of animals show us one never seen before? It
is a real possibility, especially as our net is the largest deep-water net
yet used. I shall be surprised if our series of deep hauls across to the
Cape do not produce at least two or three animals entirely new to
science. We shall be the first in the world to see them. I feel it is
almost like taking part in an act of creation, for indeed our new
discovery may never have been seen by any living creature before;

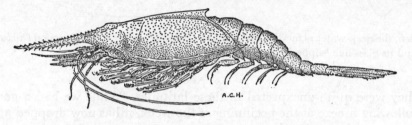

The deep-water scarlet mysid, *Gnathophausia gigas*, natural size.

we may be drawing it up from a pitch black world in which its very
shape and colour have never before made any impression upon a
living sensory system.

> *Full many a gem of purest ray serene*
> *The dark unfathom'd caves of ocean bear:*

It is indeed an exciting moment when the great net comes in view
as the last few fathoms of cable are wound in. With what eagerness
we await the untying of the bucket from its end and watch the contents
being gently decanted into an awaiting bath on deck. It is predomin-
antly a catch of red, orange and black. In to-day's haul there were,
as well as many of the dark red jelly-fish *Atolla* and *Periphylla*, some
beautiful golden-brown bell-like medusae (*Crossota brunnea*). There
was a magnificent flat nemertine (*Pelagonemertes*) with a brilliant orange
branching gut. Among the deep-water fish (many black stomiatids
and myctophids) was a fine specimen of the extraordinary eel-like
Nemichthys (p. 228) with its pointed curving jaws which make one
wonder how it uses them. Among the more usual concord of scarlet
crustacea was a very fine specimen of that big red mysid *Gnathophausia*

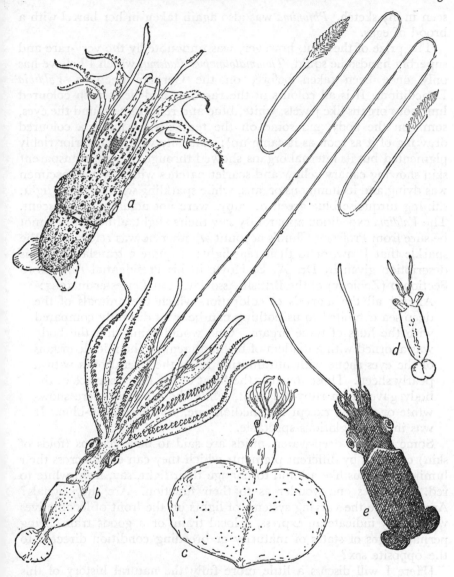

Some deep-water squids. *a. Histioteuthis bonelliana* ($\times \frac{1}{2}$); *b, Chiroteuthis veranyi* ($\times \frac{1}{3}$); *c, Octopodoteuthis sicula* ($\times \frac{1}{2}$); *d, Taonidium* sp. ($\times \frac{1}{2}$); *e, Benthoteuthis megalops* ($\times \frac{1}{2}$). From the author's *The Open Sea*, Part I. Note the large number of luminous organs on the underside of *Histioteuthis*.

seen in my sketch. *Phronima* was also again taken in her barrel with a brood of eggs.

The prize of the haul, however, was undoubtedly the very rare and superbly handsome squid, *Thaumatolampus diadema*, which I believe has only once been taken before, on the German deep-sea *Valdivia* Expedition. It is all colours of the rainbow and beset with coloured luminous organs like jewels, white, blue and red: some round the eyes, some on the body and some on the tentacles. I made a coloured drawing of it as soon as it came up[1]; not only was the exterior richly pigmented but its internal organs showed through its semi-transparent skin showing canary yellow and scarlet patches within. Our specimen was dying and its luminous organs, while sparkling with reflected light, shining turquoise blue green or ruby, were not actually luminescent. The *Valdivia* expedition apparently saw theirs alight, although I cannot be sure from Professor Chun's account whether he was referring to the sparkle that I saw, or to their real light; I quote a translation of his description given by Dr. W. E. Hoyle in his Presidential Address to Section D (Zoology) of the British Association at Leicester in 1907:

Among all the marvels of coloration which the animals of the deep sea exhibited to us nothing can be even distantly compared with the hues of these organs. One would think that the body was adorned with a diadem of brilliant gems. The middle organs of the eyes shone with ultramarine blue, the lateral ones with a pearly sheen. Those towards the front of the lower surface of the body gave out a ruby-red light, while those behind were snow-white or pearly, except the median one, which was sky-blue. It was indeed a glorious spectacle.

Some of these deep-water squids are said to have screens (folds of skin) coloured by different pigments which they can draw across their luminous organs like a blind to change their light, say, from white to red. It makes one wonder as to their function. Are they signals? Are they like the varying systems of lights on the front of locomotives which may indicate an express, a local train, or a goods train, being perhaps signs of states of maturity or breeding condition directed to the opposite sex?

[Here I will discuss a little more fully the natural history of this hidden realm into which we are dipping with our nets. The animals we are drawing up are examples of what is technically known as the bathypelagic life; by this is meant the deep-water life which is not actually on the ocean bed but living freely in that great zone above. It is a region inhabited mainly by creatures which never touch the

[1]Shown in Plate 21 of my book *The Open Sea*, Part I.

bottom (except as sunken corpses) or never reach the surface; they are living in a vast aquatic continuum, swimming to right or left, up or down, but never moving out of their dark and endless fluid world.

We are apt to think of these animals—some with gigantic mouths, or of grotesque body shape, or perhaps studded with luminous organs— as most unusual creatures. To our eyes they do indeed appear extraordinary; yet, if we consider the matter for a moment, we shall realise—as I have stressed elsewhere (in my book *The Open Sea*)— that they are actually some of the most characteristic kinds of life to be found upon our planet. 70·8 per cent of the world's surface is sea; and as much as 86 per cent of this extends for more than a mile below the surface and 50 per cent of it is over $2\frac{1}{2}$ miles deep. In other words more than half (60·8 per cent) of the whole surface of the globe is water over a mile in depth. Considering its vertical range, this habitat is undoubtedly the world's greatest zone of life and, except for the little deep pocket of the Arctic Ocean, it is continuous round the globe; the deep waters of the Atlantic, Pacific and Indian Oceans connect with one another round the southern extremities of the great continents.

Just as the *Challenger* Expedition gave us our knowledge of the life of the ocean floor by using the dredge, so the German *Valdivia* revealed the wealth and variety of the life of this bathypelagic zone with large mid-water nets; and a little later Johannes Schmidt on his Danish *Dana* Expeditions added much to these findings. For the most part these investigators did not attempt to close the mouths of their nets before hauling them to the surface; while they towed the nets at a particular depth for much longer than the time taken in hauling them up, there can be little doubt that some of their captures must have come from levels higher up than that of the main haul. It was Sir John Murray and Professor Johan Hjort, on their Atlantic cruise on the *Michael Sars* in 1910, who made the advance of closing their large nets before hauling them up and so ensuring that they knew the depth from which their various specimens came; on the way down the nets catch little because they are run out at about the same speed as that of the ship and sink without fishing. It was Hjort in that great book *The Depths of the Ocean* (by Murray and Hjort, 1912) who so ably discussed the leading characteristics and adaptations of these bathypelagic animals. We, on our voyage, by using large closing nets were attempting to provide corresponding information regarding this deepwater life of the southern Atlantic Ocean to compare with the results of the *Michael Sars* expedition in the northern half. I have already described how I went to study Hjort's methods before we set out.

Undoubtedly the most striking feature of these hauls, as just mentioned, is the great preponderance of black or red animals. In the course of the voyage I have from time to time mentioned the black fish, scarlet prawns or purple-red jelly-fish that we have drawn up from the depths; but I have not, I think, given a true idea of their numbers. One bucket may contain some fifty fish and several hundred crustaceans. Nearly all the fish, of many different families, are jet black; and the few exceptions are a very dark brown. Among the crustacea there may be a few black isopods, but the great majority are a vivid scarlet. There are many different kinds of scarlet prawns, belonging to two distinct groups (the Penaeidea and the Caridea), there are equally red mysids (the so-called opossum shrimps) and amphipods, ostracods (curious little crustacea with bivalve 'shells') and copepods of the same hue. The arrow-worms (Chaetognatha), which have species as transparent as glass in the surface waters, are represented in the deeper layers by others which are orange or red; and the same is true for the planktonic bristle-worms of the genus *Tomopteris* which have a handsome crimson relation living in the depths. In addition to the plum-coloured jelly-fish I have already mentioned (*Atolla* and *Periphylla*) there are others of a rich madder-colour (*Nausithoe*), or scarlet (*Aglisera*, *Halicreas* and others). My painting in Plate 20 (p. 224) gives a general impression of a typical deep-water haul.

Now let us compare such a collection of animals with a group of those typical of the surface layers, such as is shown on Plate 1; the contrast is indeed striking. At the surface most of the plankton animals are perfectly transparent so that we may have a glass vessel full of sea-water containing many different kinds of animal, yet see hardly any sign of them. Others like the siphonophores *Velella* or *Porpita*, the pelagic snails *Ianthira*, and many fish may be a beautiful blue. By being transparent or coloured blue to match their background of oceanic water they are camouflaged against the attacks of predators. This seems natural enough; but why black and bright red in the depths?

The light entering the sea is of course composed of the whole spectrum of colours but the rays towards the red and orange end are absorbed by the water much more quickly than those at the blue and violet end. In the graph shown opposite we see the results obtained by the American scientists Drs. Ostler and Clarke in the Sargasso Sea; they demonstrate very clearly the difference in the degrees of penetration of the rays of different colours. Faint blue light penetrates down to some 1,200 metres depth, but all the red and orange light is cut off at only about some 100 metres down. Below this 100 metre level any red animal will appear just black, and only blue or violet

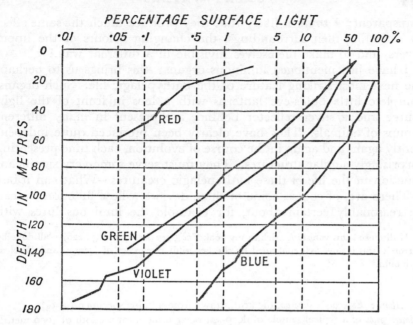

Curves showing the percentage penetration of the colour components of daylight at different depths in the Sargasso Sea. Redrawn from Oster and Clarke.

objects could show up by reflecting back the blue and violet rays; hence we see that black and red are the pigments selected at these depths to render their possessors as inconspicuous as possible. It seems that it is in the nature of fish to produce black pigment (melanin) more easily than red, whereas the crustacea more readily form the red (carotenoid) pigments; but in the depths they both look the same.

The existence of fish with silvery sides in the upper layers is interesting. They extend down to depths of some 500 metres but are usually those which may make extensive migrations up towards the surface. Notable examples are those unusually flat hatchet-fish (*Argyropelecus*, see p. 239) with their eyes pointing upwards and groups of luminous organs on their underside pointing downwards, or the lantern fish (*Myctophidae*) which, as their name suggests, are also provided with light organs and may sometimes come right to the surface at night. Silvery flanks and bellies are also characteristic of the surface-living fish of the seas, as for example members of the herring, mackerel and flying fish families. All of these have blue or blue-green backs which clearly match their background when looked at from above, but why should they have sides of silver? Such fish are, of course, too big to be transparent; I think it likely that they produce much the same effect by reflecting their surroundings, the changing colours of the upper layers, and so make themselves invisible in a different way.[1]

I have just mentioned luminous organs; this brings us to perhaps the next most striking feature of the bathypelagic life. Such organs, complete little bull's-eye lanterns with a lens in front of the light source and a silver reflector behind, are present in many different groups of animals. They have clearly been produced quite independently again and again in the course of evolution, each time presenting surprisingly similar structures. They must serve some very significant function in the life of these bathypelagic creatures—What can it be?

There are, of course, some of these devices, whose function we can be reasonably certain about, for example the luminous lures with

[1] I discussed this vanishing trick in my book *The Open Sea*, Part I (p. 226)—'all done by mirrors'; this is now well confirmed by the beautiful researches of Denton and Nicol at Plymouth.

20. *Above: Euphausia superba*, the krill, drawn from a living specimen ($\times 1\frac{2}{3}$).
Below: part of a typical sample of deep-sea pelagic life from a depth of 1000 metres after it has been emptied from the tow-net bucket into a white enamelled dish: the black fish, scarlet crustaceans and dark purple jelly-fish predominate, but there are other red or orange invertebrates as well. A key to the various animals is given below.

Jelly-fish 1. *Atolla bairdii*. 2. *A. vanhöffeni*. 3. *Nausithoe rubra*. 4. *Periphylla hyacinthina*.

Worm-like animals
    5. The nemertine *Pelagonemertes*.
    6. *Sagitta macrocephala*.
    7. A deep-water *Tomopteris*.

Crustaceans
    8. The ostracod *Gigantocypris*.
    9. Copepods of several kinds.
    10. The mysid *Gnathophausia*.
    11. Amphipods, *Lanceola*, etc.
    12. Penaeid prawn *Sergestes robustus*.
    13. Carid prawns *Acanthephyra*, etc.

Fish
    14 and 15. Myctophid and gonostomid fish respectively.

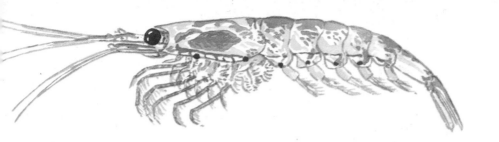

which some of the deep-water angler fish angle for their prey or the similar lures which some of the Stomiatid fish trail along on their long barbels for the same purpose. Some are perhaps making recognition patterns distinguishing one species from another in the dark or providing signals of sexual maturity as suggested above in the case of the squids which are said to be able to change the colour of their light from white to red. But why, in so many animals, do they shine *downwards*? That is the puzzle.

Such downwardly pointing light-organs occur in many species belonging to three quite distinct groups of crustaceans: the Euphausiacea (including the krill as we have already noted), the Penaeidea and the Caridea; members of the last two groups may have their photophores (as such organs are called) arranged in a very similar fashion, yet have been produced in the course of evolution quite differently, as so beautifully shown by Professor R. Dennell from the specimens collected by our expedition (*Discovery Reports*, vol. xx, pp. 307-82, 1940). Then many of the deep-water squids have their photophores on their undersides. Again among the fish no less than eight distinct families have such organs, all, or nearly all, pointing downwards. Dr. N. B. Marshall writes in his *Aspects of Deep Sea Biology*: 'When a long series of mid-water nets are towed at many levels in deep oceanic waters the probability is that four-fifths or more of the fishes taken will bear light organs.' Recent results obtained with photo-electric recording apparatus lowered into the depths reveal a much greater degree of illumination than had ever been suspected.

In some books of popular natural history it is assumed that the deeper one goes into the depths the greater will be the development of luminous organs: no doubt on the principle of the darker the scene the more light required. This was the old view which was disproved by the *Valdivia* and *Michael Sars* expeditions; luminous organs are most highly developed in the species in the upper 500 metres, are smaller in those down to some 1,200 metres and at greater depths are usually absent. Hjort also pointed out (*The Depths of the Ocean*, p. 702) how 'It was also very interesting to note the remarkable coincidence between the vertical migrations of the fishes and the development of their light organs.' After giving examples, he goes on 'A perfect analogy is found in the decapod crustacea. The deepest living species have no light organs and make no vertical migrations.'

I will now quote again from Dr. Marshall's *Aspects of Deep Sea Biology*: We have said that the main light batteries shine obliquely outward and downward, and this is true of the larger luminescent crustaceans and the squids. In the course of evolution, has there

H

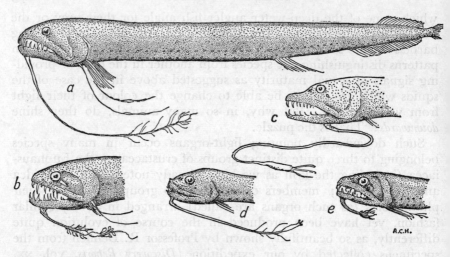

Barbels of various stomiatid fish, all natural size: *a*, *Flagellostomias bourenei*; *b*, *Echiostoma tanneri*; *c*, *Eustomias obscurus*; *d*, *Leptostomias ramosus*; *e*, *Chirostomias pliopterus*. From the author's *The Open Sea*, Part 1.

been a tendency for the light organs to be placed ventrally so as to endow the animal with greater chances of survival? Now in fishes it is the larger organs which contain a silvery reflector and it is these which are ventral in position. When an animal displays its lights there is a possibility that the photophores of a non-lighted neighbouring animal might show up as cats' eyes on the road show up in the lights of a car. If the more powerful photophores face downward the chances of their showing up by reflection will be reduced. . . .

Perhaps it is significant that both sunlight and living light stream downwards. If the lights from a fish or a squid or a crustacean were shot upwards, they might well obscure the animal's upper visual field, a field in which prey and enemies will be silhouetted against the down-going blue rays of the sun.

I devoted some space in my book *The Open Sea* to discussing some of the ideas that had occurred to me but wrote: 'The solution to a problem is so often only just round the corner, and when found, looks so very different from what we imagined it would be.' Since then Dr. James Fraser in his excellent book *Nature Adrift* (1962) and Dr. William D. Clarke in an article in *Nature*[1] (1963) have both, quite independently, provide what I believe must be the answer.

This is their idea. In these very dimly lit regions the various fish

[1]*Nature*, Vol. 198, pp. 1244-7

and other animals will hunt by looking upwards to see their prey silhouetted darkly against the blue background of light coming from above. We do in fact see so many of the eyes of deep-sea fish pointing upwards. Now the luminous organs are remarkably evenly spread over the underside of nearly all the animals that have them pointing downwards; they suggest that the lights tend to destroy the dark silhouette appearance and so make their possessors invisible when viewed from below. It might be thought at first that these discrete spots of light would make them more conspicuous; Dr. Clarke points out,

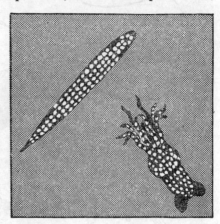

Sketches to illustrate Fraser and Clarke's explanation of the function of the luminous organs on the undersides of so many deepwater fish, squid and crustacea. *Left*, a fish and a squid without such organs silhouetted against the faint blue light coming from above when seen from below; *right*, the same but with a typical arrangement of light organs. Seen at a distance, and *out of focus*, the latter are much less conspicuous than those without lights.

however, that at a distance from the predator's eye they are most likely out of focus so that their appearance will be a blurred one giving just the right effect. I show a diagrammatic sketch of such a fish and squid with and without their photophores alight; if you now look at the drawing with a lens out of focus you will see that the ones with their lights on do indeed disappear whereas those which are not shining stand out in sharp contrast to the background. It is a beautifully simple explanation; indeed one which was just round the corner. How foolish one feels not to have looked in the right direction!

Whilst I believe that his hypothesis correctly explains the widespread occurrence of these downwardly pointing photophores I think in some species they almost certainly must be used for other purposes

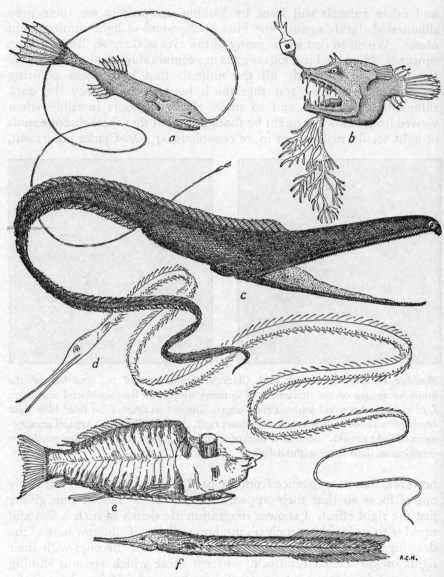

A selection of deep-water fish: *a* and *b*, two remarkable angler fish *Gigantactis macro-nema* and *Linophryne arborifer* ($\times \frac{1}{2}$); *c*, *Eurypharynx pelicanoides* ($\times 1\frac{1}{2}$); *d*, *Nemichthys scolapecus* (nat. size); *e*, *Opisthoproetus graimaldii* ($\times \frac{1}{2}$); *f*, *Cyema atrum* ($\times \frac{2}{3}$). From *The Open Sea*, Part I.

as well. Dr. R. H. Kay and I have found that the euphausiacean *Meganyctiphanes norvegica* will at times spontaneously give off bright flashes from its photophores when kept for many hours in darkness[1].

Another striking feature of the bathypelagic fish is the gigantic size of mouth which one sees developed. The gape is enormous; it enables them to take relatively very large prey. A meal may be most infrequent so it should be as large as possible. There is a nice gradation in the average size of animals as we pass from the surface to the depths. It is only in the sunlit zones of the upper layers that the plant members of the plankton (phytoplankton) can flourish and multiply, and we have seen that individually they are exceedingly small (p. 41). It follows then that all the life of the depths must depend upon these plants near the surface: they are their ultimate source of food. The herbivorous plankton animals tend on the whole to be small and these form the prey for other plankton animals which will be a little larger and these again form another link in a food chain to still larger animals. There will be a continual rain of dead and dying material from the phytoplankton above which will help to nourish animals on the way down; and some of this manna from heaven will fall all the way to provide nourishment on the ocean bed. As it falls, however, it is being used up so that beyond a certain depth there is not enough to support a large number of small creatures feeding directly upon it. At this point we get the chain of animals feeding one upon another. As we go down they will become a little larger and also fewer. Hence the need for the large mouths just mentioned: to take the large but very occasional meal. It is in this region that we get some of the curious angler fish and the gulpers such as *Eurypharynx* shown opposite. By having enormously expanding jaws and elastic stomach and body walls some of the angler fish can swallow other fish larger than themselves and a striking demonstration of this is seen in the sketch overleaf made from specimens in the British Museum.

The difficulty of one fish coming upon another in this dark abysmal world has not only given the angler fish a large mouth; it has had a most curious effect on the sex-life of many of the species. The younger stages of any animal will certainly be more numerous than the older ones, because their numbers are diminished as many of them become the prey of other animals; this being so some of the more numerous young males will have a better chance of finding partners than the older ones. The more precocious the sense of attachment the more likely it is to succeed. Attachment is the right word. Natural selection has favoured the early meeting of the sexes and the linking of the male

[1] *Journal of the Marine Biological Association*, Vol. 44, pp. 435-484, 1964.

to the female in preparation for the later act of reproduction. The young male becomes attached to the female, physically, for life; as a tiny fry he grips her with his jaws and then gradually becomes transformed into a small parasitic organism sharing the female's food supply by his body—and blood system—becoming continuous with hers. The tiny male, which may be fused on to his spouse in all sorts of positions—on to her face, or her flanks or her belly, will (no doubt stimulated by a hormone she will produce) supply the sperm to fertilise her eggs at just the right moment. The bathypelagic world is certainly a strange one.]

Sunday, 13th June. We have had a week of very rough weather so that since a station we made last Sunday, when conditions were far from good, until yesterday, when we took another full station followed by a Petterssen young-fish trawl, we have not been able to do any fishing with nets. For most of the time it was blowing a really hard gale so that it was a matter of preventing oneself from being thrown from one side of the cabin or laboratory to the other; under these conditions work becomes very trying. The effect, however, of the wind blowing the tops off the waves is a fine sight. I managed to wedge myself into a fixed position on the poop, hang a jar of water round my neck, and make some water-colour impressions of the great waves as souvenirs of the roaring forties; one is reproduced in Plate 15, and another on p. 255.

Yesterday's young-fish trawl brought up another excellent catch of deep-water forms including, in addition to the typical scarlet crustacea and dark red jelly-fish, some red and orange nemertines (*Pelagonemertes*) and bright red polychaete worms. Among the fish was another long eel-like fish but of a kind we have not had before: *Serrivomer beanii.* Among the crustacea we caught a magnificent prawn of the genus *Hoplophorus*; it has a remarkable series of luminous organs having bright blue lenses and red pigment spots, separated from the blue by a white crystalline layer, so making each look like a little red, white and blue rosette!

After the young-fish trawl O'Connor, the chief officer, showed us an old sailor's trick for catching an albatross. He made a simple device of four strips of metal drilled with holes and hinged to one another to form a diamond shape; a line is fastened to one corner by a ring and the opposite corner has a piece of fat tied to it as a bait; and then a piece of cork is fastened to the line just in front of it to make it float as it is thrown over the stern to be towed along the surface. Presently down comes a great wandering albatross to snap up the fat. As soon as it had picked up the bait O'Connor pulled on the line so

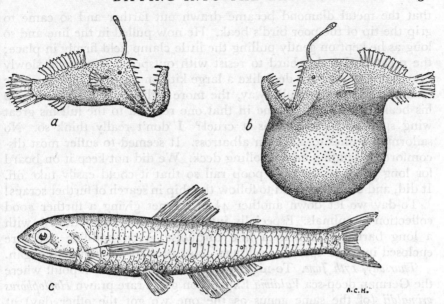

a and *b*, the deep-water angler fish *Melanocoetus johnsoni* before and after swallowing *c*, a myctophid fish *Lampanyctus crocodilus* nearly three times its own length. Drawn from scale models in the fish gallery of the British Museum (Natural History) ($\times \frac{1}{2}$).

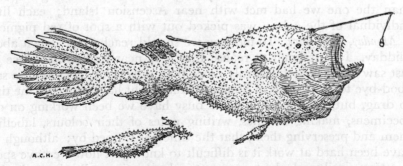

The female angler fish *Ceratias holbolli* with a small 'parasitic' male attached to it, and an enlarged view of the male. Drawn from specimens in the British Museum (Natural History).

that the metal diamond became drawn out farther and so came to grip the tip of the poor bird's beak. He now pulled in the line and so long as he kept on gently pulling the little clamp held firmly in place; the great bird trying hard to resist with outspread wings was slowly drawn down on to the deck like a large kite on a string. The more he resisted and tried to pull away, the more tightly did the clamp grip his beak. It was as he came in that one realised to the full his great wing span of 10 feet. Was it cruel? I don't really think so. No sailorman wishes to harm an albatross. It seemed to suffer most discomfort at standing on the rolling deck. We did not keep it on board for long but put it on the poop rail so that it could easily take off. It did, and then continued to follow the ship in search of further scraps!

To-day we let down another 4½-metre net giving a further good collection of animals. Especially interesting was a stomiatid fish with a long barbel ending in a fine turquoise green ball-like structure enclosed in a transparent swelling: most probably a luminous organ.

Thursday, 17th June. To-night we passed very close to a point where the German deep-sea *Valdivia* Expedition got a rare prawn *Hoplophorus grimaldii* (of the same genus as the one we got the other day) at 10 metres below the surface in 1899. Dr. Kemp was particularly anxious to obtain one so at 11 o'clock we lowered away a 2-metre diameter net in the hopes of catching some; and remarkable to relate, and much to Kemp's glee, we were duly rewarded by obtaining a single specimen. Either we were very lucky or, as I suspect, the species is more plentiful than was supposed; but it was curious to get it in just the same spot in the wide Southern Ocean.

There were some fine *Pyrosoma* to be seen in the wake of the ship and our net came up with many fragments of a much larger species than the one we had met with near Ascension Island; each little individual of the colony was picked out with a spot of red pigment.

Monday, 28th June. To-morrow we should reach Cape Town about midday. It is difficult to realise that it is nearly six weeks since we last saw land; it seems hardly more than a week or two since we said good-bye to our friends in Stanley. One might have expected the time to drag, but, on the contrary, so busy have we been working on our specimens, making sketches, writing notes of their colours, labelling them and preserving them, that the time has slipped by; although we have been hard at work it is difficult to know just how we have spent our time until we look at our constantly growing collection: the jars and jars of specimens, at intervals going down into the hold and their places taken by empty ones ready for the next hauls.

All the more interesting animals from each of the deep-water nets are picked out, preserved, labelled and put into separate specimen tubes so that on reaching home they may readily be sorted out and passed to the different specialists dealing with the various animal groups. Some are preserved in spirit, some in formalin, and a few in some special fixative desired by one or another particular worker. (As an example of the latter I may mention some of the smaller crustacea which the late Professor H. Graham Cannon wished to have preserved in Dubosq solution; for these we had a special jar, which I labelled 'Cannon Fodder'.) Flat-bottomed tubes were always used ranging in size from $1 \times \frac{1}{4}$ in. to $6\frac{1}{2} \times 1\frac{1}{2}$ in. and these, when filled, were plugged with a ball of cotton-wool wrapped up in tissue paper (to prevent wool entangling delicate specimens) and stored in large wide-mouthed jars. Each jar was lined at the bottom with a thick layer of cotton-wool and would hold from a dozen to a score of tubes; when full it would be filled up with the same preservative as in the tubes and another thick layer of cotton-wool added, to prevent the tubes from moving, before sealing up the lid. Stored in this way the danger of breakage is very slight and the method is greatly to be preferred to using corked tubes in boxes; corks often cause discoloration to the specimens and are liable to shrink and allow the contents to dry up. It was the careful preserving and labelling which took up so much of our time.

[To give an idea of the different kinds of life in these deep-water hauls and the amount of preserving and tubing we did on each occasion, I reproduce overleaf the lists from the *Discovery* Biological Log Book of the animals separately preserved after two of the deep-water nets had come in. The names will mean little to the average general reader who can just glance at the lists to get an impression of variety; the zoologists may find them more interesting. Both nets were of $4\frac{1}{2}$-metre diameter, the first at Station 81 from a depth of 650 metres towed for 2-3 miles and the second at Station 86 from 1,000 metres, towed for 3 miles.

Here the reader may like to know a little more about the laboratory in which so much of our time was spent. On page 236 I show a sketch which I made about this time; I drew it with the perspective slightly distorted to give a 'wide-angle' view so as to include as much of the laboratory as possible. This device makes it look wider than it really is; to get a correct idea of its size you should bend the page into a semicircle and look *into* it. For those who would like more of the details I will quote what I wrote in vol. 1 of the *Discovery Reports* (p. 169):

The Biological Laboratory, as already mentioned, is placed on the

STATION 81, JUNE 18, 1926, 32° 45′ S; 8° 47′ W

Colonial Radiolaria: few
Coelenterates:
 Medusae, several species, moderate
 Diphyids. several species, v. many
 Nectophores of large Siphonophore
  species
Crustacea:
 Copepods: *c.* 19 species, moderate
 Nebaliacea: Nebaliopsis 1
 Ostracods: 2 species several
 Mysids: Gnathophausia 1 small
  Spiny Mysids 2
  others, v. few
 Amphipods: Cystisoma 1
  Lanceolids few
  Phronima 4
  others, several
 Euphausians: Bentheuphausia? 1
  Thysanopoda 3 v. large
  Nematoscelis moderate
  others many, 1 carrying eggs
 Decapods: Sergestes, 2 large, many
  others
  Gennadas, many
  Acanthephyra purpurea 1 large, sev. juv.
  Acanthephyra sp.? 1 small
  Hoplophorus grimaldii few
  Hoplophorus sp. n.? several
  Stylopandalus richardi? 6
  Systellaspis 1
  Phyllosoma 2

Pteropods:
 Cymbulia 3
 Clio *c.* 24
 Limacina 1
 Spongiobranchaea? 1
Cephalopoda:
 4 species several
Tunicata:
 Pyrosoma, fragments
 Salps, large and small, moderate
Fish:
 Cyclothone many
 Gonostoma 2
 Photichthys 3
 Argyropelacus affinis 1
 A. hemigymmus 7
 Sternoptyx diaphana 12
 Astronesthes 1
 Chauliodus 6 (2 large)
 Idiacanthus 1
 Dactylostomias 2
 Echiostoma? 1
 Stylophthalmus paradoxus 1
 Diretmus argenteus 1
 Melamphaes 1
 Serrivomer 1 large 5 small
 Myctophum, few spp. several
 others few
Residue preserved

upper deck, at the after end of a deck-house which also contains the chart-room, a spare cabin and the wireless operator's room. It has a door on either side to the deck, and one leading into a vestibule at the head of the companion to the ward-room. The general arrangements are sufficiently well shown in the sketch, but one or two points perhaps deserve special mention.

The port-holes are 14 in. in diameter and are placed much lower than usual, $3\frac{1}{2}$ in. above bench level, in order to give the best possible light for microscopic work; and, in view of the large amount of bench space that would have been taken up by their dead lights and screw clamps, those on the after bulkhead are reversed and are opened and closed from the outside. The benches give seating accommodation for four and are so placed that those using the centre table face thwartships, a position which

STATION 86, JUNE 24, 1926, 33° 25′ 6° 31′E

Coelenterates:
 Atolla 7
 other Medusae moderate
 Diphyids v. many
Nematodes:
 found free, ?parasitic, v. few
Nemertines:
 very large red species 1
 others, 2 spp., 2
Chactognatha; many
Polychaeta:
 Tomopteris 2
Crustacea:
 Copepods. v. few
 Ostracods: Gigantocypris 4
  others, few.
Mysids:
 Gnathophausia ingens 1
 Gnathophausia sp. 5 (3 juv)
 Eucopia unquiculeta? 2
 others, few.
Amphipods: Phronima 1
 Cyphocaris 2
 Rhabdosoma 1
 Lanceolids few
 Dark brown Hyperiid 1
 others few
Euphausians: Thysanopoda 1 large
 Bentheuphausia? 4
 others, sev. spp. v. many
Decapods: Petelidium many
 Sergestes; red spp. 3
 Other Sergestes sev.
 Gennadas many
 Benthesicymus? 1 large

Decapods (Contd.)
 Acanthephyra purpurea
  16 medium & large, few juv.
 Acanthephyra sp. 1 small
 Systellaspis 4
 Notostomus 1 large
 Hoplophorus sp. 4 juv.
 Eryomicus 2
 Phyllosoma 1
Pteropods:
 Cavolinia 12
 Clio mod.
 Cymbulia 3
 other Gymmosomes 3
Cephalopods:
 several spp. 5
Tunicates:
 Pyrosoma, large, several; small 1
 Salps, few
Fish:
 Cyclothone species, v. many
 Gonostoma 3
 Vinciqu rria?
 Photichthys 1
 Malacostens 1
 Arqyropelecus hemigymnus 4
 Sternoptyx diaphana 4
 Chauliodus sloanei? 5 (1 juv.)
 Nemiclithyid 1
 Melamphaes spp. 5
 Scopelids, various, many
 Chiasmodon sp. 1
 Melanonus 5
 other fish many

is preferable for work in a rolling vessel. The chairs of the two side benches have folding backs; they run on brass rails flush with the deck and can be pushed under the bench when not in use. All microscope stands are drilled and can be bolted to a brass plate countersunk in the bench surface.

The swing table, 20 in. by 33 in., is built of teak, with iron stays carrying a tray below the table and a lead weight of 56 lb. This was a very essential part of the equipment: except in the calmest weather it was in constant use. It would have been improved with more space round it. Two small swing tables,

The main biological laboratory of the R.R.S. *Discovery* looking to starboard, and drawn as a *wide-angle* view to show as much as possible; to obtain the correct idea of its size bend the page in a semi-circular fashion and look into it. Note the large swing table, half out of the picture on the left, the long rack beyond the sink to hold the different sizes of specimen jars, and the whale-marking guns on the far wall, always ready for action.

bracketed to the after bulkhead between port-holes, were useful for small dishes of specimens.

The sink is supplied with fresh and salt water from two small tanks placed on the bridge, and above it, in an alcove built out over the companion, are three 20-litre glass jars containing 75 per cent spirit, 10 per cent formalin and formalin of full strength. The supplies from these jars are led by rubber pipes to glass taps, mounted close together on a wooden base. The jars are refilled by means of a small Merryweather hand pump, provided with rubber intake and outlet pipes. In practice this arrangement proved very convenient, but much labour would have been saved if it had been possible to accommodate larger jars. Successful hauls yielded vast quantities of material, and even when all the larger animals had been separately accommodated in tanks or stoneware jars, 20 litres of spirit frequently proved insufficient. The dilute formalin jar also had to be refilled continually during plankton investigations.

The rack for bottles added greatly to the efficiency of work in confined quarters. It is built over a set of baize-lined drawers in which tubes were stored, and holds, in felt-lined pigeon-holes inclined at an angle of 20° from the horizontal, all the types of bottle used for the preservation of specimens. The main supply of bottles was kept in one of the holds, packed in felt-lined boxes and in the rack there is room for more than a boxful of each size. When it was found that only a few empties of a particular size remained in the rack, a fresh box was brought up from the hold and empty and full bottles interchanged. Large specimen tubes, 12 to 24 in. in length, were stowed in a special rack built behind two of the book-shelves on the after bulkhead, the tubes, when wanted, being withdrawn from below. A row of lockers above the bottle rack was useful for miscellaneous articles.

The numerous other fittings used need not be mentioned in detail. Bars were required to keep books on their shelves and to prevent thwartships drawers from opening, while special chocks, brackets and racks were necessary for glass bowls, dishes and tubes, measuring cylinders, reagent bottles, trays, Kelvin tubes and other apparatus. At first it seemed that to accommodate all necessary gear would be impossible, but eventually a place was found for everything. Tidiness in such cramped surroundings was essential and breakages were inconsiderable, even in the worst weather.

On the main deck below was a smaller chemical laboratory which also served as a workshop and contained a large plate-glass chart table lit from below for the tracing of our survey positions from the Admiralty charts. Leading off from this was a photographic dark-room as shown in the drawing overleaf. Now let us return to the journal.]

So engrossed have we been in dealing with all the material from our nets during the last ten days that I have quite neglected my diary. We have made an excellent series of eight more deep-water hauls and worked a further four complete vertical stations. I will only mention the remarkable *Pyrosoma* colony which we took in the very last net of our series: the 2-metre diameter net which had been down to only 180 metres. We had been getting fragments of large colonies of a red *Pyrosoma* in our nets on several occasions since I mentioned them in my last entry on the 17th (p. 232). As the 2-metre net came up to the surface—it was 3.30 in the afternoon—we saw clearly through the water this huge *Pyrosoma*, at least 8 feet, if not 10 feet, in length caught about its middle by the frame of the net. Unfortunately, as it broke

The smaller hydrological laboratory of the R.R.S. *Discovery* with the photographic dark-room leading off it.

surface, the half on the outside of the frame was torn away and lost; the other half, although much broken by being carried down the net in the rush of water, could be pieced together. You will remember, from the description of the smaller kind given on p. 111, that *Pyrosoma* has the form of a long cylinder closed at one end like a thimble. The diameter of this large specimen at the point of fracture was about 10 inches; the part of the cylinder we had caught in the net was close on 5 feet in length and we judged, from the brief view we had of the whole, that that was just about half of it. There must have been close on a million individuals in the whole colony, for each individual was but a tenth of an inch in length; as each had a bright red pigment spot they gave the whole colony a rich pink appearance. The *Challenger* caught a similar giant *Pyrosoma* in a deep-sea trawl and Moseley in his *Notes by a Naturalist* writes of it as follows: 'It was like a great sac, with walls of jelly about an inch in thickness. It was four feet in length and ten inches in diameter. . . . I wrote my name with my finger on the surface of the giant *Pyrosoma*, as it lay on deck in a tub at night, and the name came out in a few seconds in letters of fire.'

[I had said a little earlier in my journal (p. 218) that I should not be surprised if we got two or three species new to science; actually, apart from the prawn *Hoplophorus*, mentioned on p. 230, which was independently discovered by another expedition about the same time, we brought to light—and in this case how appropriate is that phrase—ten new species on this single crossing of the Atlantic. It is impossible, in most cases, to be certain at once that our finds are really new; we

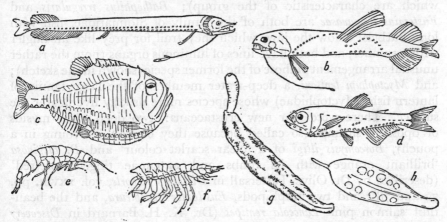

Eight of the ten new species we fished from the depths of the southern Atlantic Ocean on our voyage from the Falkland Islands to Cape Town: *a, Eustomias trewarasae; b, Bathophiles irregularis; c, Argyropelecus gigas; d, Myctophum tenisoni; e* and *f,* the amphipods *Eusiroides stenopleura* and *Lanceola remipes; g* and *h,* the nemertine worms *Bathynemertes hardyi* and *Probalaenanemertes irenae.*

pick out several in a haul, that appear to us to be unusual, for closer examination and then consult the large monograph reports of former expeditions. Luckily we carried on the ship a splendid library of the complete sets of volumes of results of all the earlier deep-sea expeditions. Eagerly we scan their pages and plates, and our prize group of candidates for novelty dwindles. One has been taken twice by the *Valdivia* expedition and once by the *Sipoga*, another was found by the *Challenger* and so on, but, how exciting, there remains one from the haul that does not appear ever to have been caught before. We cannot be absolutely certain that it is new until it has been examined by the leading specialist in the group at home. We make careful notes on colour, or perhaps colour-drawings and take measurements before such rarities are preserved; usually the colours so quickly fade and the specimen may shrink in the preservative.

I give a brief note of the new species we obtained in this one crossing of the ocean with a reference to the *Reports* in which they are described and named; and overleaf I give little sketches of eight of them. There were four new deep-water fish (described by J. R. Norman in *Discovery Reports*, vol. II, pp. 302, 311, 313 and 321 respectively): *Argyropelecus gigas* is a beautiful silver hatchet-fish which, while only 3½ inches in length, is the largest species of this family yet discovered (note in the sketch the prominent luminous organs on its underside which are characteristic of the group); *Bathophilus irregularis* and *Eustomias trewavasae* are both of the family of Stomiatidae, fish with long barbels[1] below the jaw, which they trail for prey like an angler with a spinner, and both have lines of luminous organs (note the rather unusual arrangement of those of the former species shown in the sketch); and *Myctophum tenisoni*, a deep-water member of the large family of lantern fish (Myctophidae) whose species more usually live nearer the surface. There were four new crustaceans: two deep-water mysids or opossum shrimps (so called because they carry their young in a pouch), *Boreomysis illigi* of a 'clear scarlet colour' and *B. bispinosa* 'brilliant orange with its limbs and antennae tinged rose-red' (described by Dr. Olive Tattersall in *Discovery Reports*, vol. XXVIII. pp. 72 and 78); and two amphipods, *Eusiloides stenopleura*, and the beautiful salmon pink *Lanceola remipes* (Dr. K. H. Barnard in *Discovery Reports*, vol. V, pp. 192 and 255). Then there were two new bathypelagic nemertines, those curious worms with a large proboscis which can be shot out of a hidden sheath for the capture of prey, *Bathynemertes hardyi* and *Probalaenanemertes irenae* (described by Dr. J. F. G. Wheeler, *Discovery Reports*, vol. IX, pp. 280 and 287). Wheeler kindly named the former species after me because I, realising it was almost certainly new, made a detailed coloured drawing of it; it was a vivid scarlet flecked with black and unusually large and massive for a pelagic animal[2]. The second species was a much more delicate organism; we obtained two specimens, one noted as being 'scarlet with orange spots down its sides' and the other 'pale orange with deep rose pink

---

[1]Rolfe Gunther made a colour sketch of the barbel of *E. trewavasae*; the large bulb in the terminal portion was an exquisite turquoise blue.

[2]I could hardly believe it was a truly pelagic species and began to think that the net must have been fishing near the bottom; actually, however, the net fished no deeper than 1,000 metres in a region of the ocean some 5,000 metres deep. The coloured drawing I made is reproduced in Plate XVI of *Discovery Reports*, vol. IX and also in Plate 10 of my *The Open Sea*, Part I.

spots down sides.' In addition to these ten new species was a new sub-species *purpurea* of the pelagic octopus *Elledonella massayie* (described by G. C. Robson in *Discovery Reports*, vol. II, p. 379).

The real value of our deep-water results is not, however, to be measured in terms of these new animals; it lies rather in the very large collections of other specimens, in so many different zoological groups, which, being described and discussed by various specialists in the *Discovery Reports*, such as those just referred to, add so much to our knowledge of the bathypelagic community of the South Atlantic as a whole for comparison with that of the northern hemisphere and those of other oceans.

Or again our spoils have provided the material for a number of outstanding zoological researches on the anatomy of these little-known animals, such as those of Professor Dennell on the luminous organs of the prawns already referred to; particularly would I draw students' attention to the superb studies by the late Professor Graham Cannon on the deep-sea ostracods[1] and on that remarkable and most primitive crustacean *Nebaliopsis*[2], or again those of Dr. Norman Marshall on the swim bladders of the bathypelagic fish[3].

We made many other deep-water hauls during other passages, but I shall only rarely refer to them, except perhaps just to say that they were taken; I must not overdo the study of the depths in this general account of our voyage.]

Tuesday, 29th June. This afternoon, in perfect weather, we sailed into Table Bay on much the same course as that we had taken in December; the full expanse of the Table remained hidden until the last, when it suddenly opened out as we rounded the Lion. Friends from our former visit came out in a motor-boat to greet us and came on board. It is pleasant to be back in the welcoming old city.

[1] *Discovery Reports* vol. II, pp. 435-83 and vol. XIX, pp. 185-244.
[2] *ibid.*, vol. III, pp. 199-222.
[3] *ibid.*, vol. XXXI, pp. 1-22.

CHAPTER 10

BACK AT THE CAPE—THE SHIP
IMPROVED

[It was not until 27th October that we sailed south again; for the greater part of our stay at the Cape the ship was in the Royal Naval Dockyard at Simonstown having her new sister keels fitted. I shall only give a few extracts from my journal to give continuity to the story and I shall omit dates except for the last.]

After our arrival we remained at Cape Town for a little over a week and then made our way to Simonstown under difficulties. An epidemic of influenza broke out in the ship and more than half of the ship's company, including three of the four stokers, were confined to their bunks with high temperatures. I luckily escaped and was able to do a watch in the stokehold, for I had now become fairly proficient with the shovel. It is difficult to get sufficient exercise on a ship like the *Discovery* with so little deck space; during the last passage, when not working a station, I went down to the stokehold every evening to stoke and trim coal in the bunkers for an hour, and by so doing won a rare commodity: a bucket of boiling fresh water for a bath in the engine-room before dinner. Having been well instructed in the art of stoking and raking the fires by my friend Bill Alsford, I was able to take his place in the passage round from Cape Town.

Simonstown is situated on the shores of that wide and beautiful False Bay which is immediately to the east of the Cape of Good Hope; it lies at the foot of the mountains running south from the Table and looks across to the range of the Hottentots which run out to end in Cape Hanglip at the opposite side of the Bay. This distant view, especially in the evening, reminded me of the Sorrento peninsula seen across the Gulf of Naples, and the little town itself seemed Mediterranean with its balconies jutting out over the pavement, its tall aloes by the water's edge and mimosa-like trees in full bloom. The whole of the Cape region is richly planted with many varieties of these mimosa-like trees, all, I believe, of Australian origin; the commonest is the Australian wattle, sometimes called the Port Jackson willow. Some of the houses are draped with bougainvillæa and the Admiral's residence has a particularly handsome deep brown-purple variety contrasting with the more usual magenta shade. The street life too is full of colour: on the pavements the British blue-jackets contrast with the many-hued clothing of the Kaffirs, and the red fezes of the Moslems of Malay origin, while in the roadway are wagons drawn by large teams of donkeys or oxen [It was 1926, remember].

For a few days we lay in the main basin and it was quite a surprise on looking over the rail to find that the harbour walls, up to the water-line, had the appearance of a tropical reef; they were richly encrusted with soft corals (gorgonians) of bright red and orange and a great variety of sea-anemones of many different hues. We made a good collection of specimens including some fine sea-slugs (of the Dorid family) and in the full sunlight, swimming at the very surface of the water, we found many large flat-worms (Polyclad turbellarians) of the genus *Thysanozoon*. These last are grand relations of the more humble little flat-worms found crawling over surfaces in our ponds and ditches at home. Over two inches in length, of a rich pinky-purple colour, and with long fleshy papillae on their backs, they swam with graceful undulating movements like ribbons waving in the water.

As soon as the ship went into dry dock we moved into the British Hotel with magnificent views across the Bay, and found the space of even quite modest rooms a welcome change from the confines of our cabins. A mountain, or Red Hill, as it is called by the Navy, rises abruptly behind us; in fact the town actually hangs upon its slopes. After making the steep climb to the top—or, if less energetic, being swung up on the aerial ropeway to the Naval Sanatorium—you come upon a wide plateau covered with rocky ridges and with still higher crags to the east. It is like a gigantic rock garden planted with an almost infinite variety of xerophytes and heaths; I could not have believed that so many different kinds of heath could be found living together. Here and there, in more sheltered places, huge Proteas bloomed. There are troops of baboons in these mountains but they are so wary that it is difficult to catch sight of them; occasionally, however, you will see their sentinels on the skyline, and once we saw a party of half a dozen chasing an unfortunate brother out of the troop, tearing after him across the rocky mountain slope.

From the topmost rocky ridge you can see the sun setting over the Atlantic behind. On one memorable evening we saw the sun, a fiery ball, hanging over the sea, whilst opposite, over the rose-flushed Hottentots, soared the full moon, appearing enormous and brilliantly silver. As we faced the moon, long purple shadows stretched out like fingers over the plateau from the hummocky ridge on which we stood, and then, sweeping upwards, cut off the flush of light on the crags to the east.

Farther along the lower slopes of the mountain side, about a mile from the town in the direction of Muizenberg is a Kaffir settlement, consisting of little ramshackle shanties of wood and rusty iron (flattened out biscuit tins) clustering one above the other. In daylight the squalor is pathetic; in the evening, however, when approaching darkness hides the detail, it presents a not unpleasing picture of little fires flickering red and sending to heaven tall columns of blue smoke, while groups of figures in the foreground, some with coloured blankets or shawls, make their way homeward after the day's work.

[These entries may perhaps suggest one long holiday, but that was far from the case; they are included to give an idea of the colourful background to our work. It was a period of intensive re-organisation and planning for the next season.]

All our gear, our nets, instruments, wires, etc., had to be carefully gone over and repaired where necessary. Our first survey at South Georgia, although much curtailed by bad weather, had given us a good knowledge of the type of plankton we were dealing with; we now knew something of its distribution in depth during different times in the twenty-four hours, finding that more animals than not made migrations upwards at night and that some tended to be massed together in strong concentrations rather than more evenly spread. I spent much time in going through this material and in the light of the picture gained Kemp and I replanned our coming campaign. We realised that to get adequate samples of the krill, which was shown to be very patchy in its distribution, we should have to make much more use of long horizontal tows with nets at several depths in addition to our vertical hauls. Our devices for closing horizontal nets, after they had been towed at some particular depth, to ensure that they would not catch animals from other levels on the way up, had been designed for the larger 2-metre and 4½-metre diameter nets. We must have smaller, simpler devices to enable us to use two or three 1-metre diameter nets at different levels on the one towing rope and similarly to use 70 cm. diameter nets of finer mesh for the capture of the young stages of the krill. It was my task to redesign this equipment and to get the mechanisms made by an engineering firm in Cape Town.

It was important that we should cover as wide an area of the whaling grounds as possible in a relatively short time so that we could get a true picture of the plankton distribution in relation both to the physical conditions and to the whale concentrations before they changed. The new little full-powered ship, the R.S.S. *William Scoresby*, was now on her way out to join us; she was specially provided to undertake whale marking for tracing their migrations and to make a trawling survey of the Falkland Islands banks to explore the possibility of developing a fishery there. Because the old *Discovery* was so slow, Dr. Kemp, in his report on our first season's work, had recommended to the Committee that the *William Scoresby* might work with the *Discovery* on a great combined survey of the South Georgia whaling grounds next season. Kemp had just received the sanction for this and so we now planned accordingly. In the operations Kemp and I would work together each on our own ship: he on the *Discovery* and I on the *Scoresby*. Plankton was my special subject and he generously gave me a very free hand in the design of the survey. It was going to be an exciting attempt to make a really complete study of the relation of the plankton to the movement of the whales in perhaps the roughest seas of the world: the two ships working together in constant touch by wireless. It was a challenge to modern oceanographical methods. It meant increased numbers of tow-net rings, buckets, bridles, closing mechanisms, etc., to give us plenty of spares; for we must expect to lose some in our fight with the elements. All these had to be made and additional nets as well. The period of the ship's refitting was certainly not an idle time, but an intensive recasting of our plans and equipment in the light of last season's work.

The R.S.S. *William Scoresby* under the command of Lt.-Commander G. M. Mercer, D.S.C., R.N.R., duly arrived at Simonstown on 1st August. It was a great moment when we welcomed her in. You can imagine with what excitement I viewed her; the little ship which should be mine in the boisterous campaign to come. It was a happy reunion too with David Dilwyn John and Francis Fraser, our two new zoologists who had been with us for a short time at Dartmouth before we sailed, but who then remained to complete the scientific equipment of the new ship. The *Scoresby* is a vessel of the modern whale-catcher type, built by Messrs. Cook, Welton and Gemmell, Ltd., of Beverley, Yorks, a firm famous for the building of trawlers; she has a displacement of approximately 370 tons but is only 125 feet long at the water-line. She is actually a compromise to satisfy three distinct purposes: whale-hunter, trawler and research ship. She has the whaler's look-out barrel at the mast-head, her built-up bow (for firing marking darts instead of harpoons) and a good turn of speed (12 knots). On her port side she is a trawler with the typical steel gallows fore and aft for handling the otter boards of a full-sized commercial trawl; and she is equipped, of course, with the necessary powerful winch. On her starboard side she is the research ship with the small winches and davits similar to those on the *Discovery* for operating water sampling bottles and plankton nets, but without the outboard platforms which are not necessary. Although small, she is a strong and powerful vessel which promises well for the battles ahead, and I was well pleased with all I saw.

On the first Thursday of each month a tug leaves Cape Town to carry mails and stores to the lighthouse on Dassen Island which lies off the west coast some 35 miles to the north. It is famous for its enormous colony of black-footed or jackass penguins (*Spheniscus demersus*). It is said to be one of the largest penguin colonies in the world; there must certainly be over a million[1] birds concentrated on this small island which is about two miles in length and varying from a half to a mile in breadth. During the last few years a large trade in penguin eggs has been developed and annually during a period of five months some 500,000 eggs are gathered; a periodic collection of guano is also made. The eggs are sold at many shops in the Cape Peninsula and when properly cooked—they take some twenty minutes' boiling—they are (in my view) very good eating. Some find their yolk too rich and others are put off by the transparent and gelatinous 'white' which never becomes the firm white of a hen's egg; however, once the latter prejudice is overcome the eggs may be greatly enjoyed. I got permission from the lighthouse authorities for three of us, Dr. Marshall, Dilwyn John and myself, to pay a visit.

The island is low and sandy and strewn with boulders, with here and there rocky ridges; part of it is covered with low vegetation, mainly a plant in size and appearance somewhat like the English ragwort. Big Atlantic rollers break upon its shores and only in one sheltered bay may a safe landing be made. It is 'governed' by a Portuguese, a cheery fellow with a wonderful flow of language, who came to greet us; on the beach as well, also it seemed welcoming us, were two large groups of penguins. Except for the somewhat aberrant race of small penguins on the Galapagos Islands, the jackass (with its close relatives in South America and the Falkland Islands[2]) is the most northerly of the tribe. It is a striking, if somewhat comically marked bird, with a black beak and cheeks surrounded by a prominent white band which curves up on either side and arches over the eyes

[1]Cherry Kearton who subsequently spent some months on the island estimates their number at five million (*The Island of Penguins*, 1932).

[2]The Humboldt penguin (*S. humboldti*) in South America and the Magellan penguin (*S. magellanicus*) in the Falkland Islands and Tierra del Fuego.

like broad exaggerated eye-brows; and the white below the face is separated from that of the breast by a thin black band which at a distance might well be mistaken for a black bow-tie.

Having about five hours on the island we were able to cover all its ground. The egg-collecting season was just over and the birds were now left in peace to rear their young. The birds lay two or occasionally three eggs and only one is supposed to be taken; it is said that if this is done, they will lay another one to replace it. We soon saw that the whole island is covered in nesting birds; some were spread throughout the region of low vegetation, but the great majority were crowded together in vast colonies on the exposed sandy patches. Typically their nests take the form of a burrow in the shape of a letter L so that the sitting bird is hidden except for its head; but in the more sandy parts, where the walls of a burrow will fall in, they make nests which are mere shallow depressions in the ground. Where good burrowing is possible the ground is so honeycombed with holes that you have to walk with extreme caution to avoid putting your foot through the roof of a nest and on to an unfortunate sitting bird. Many take advantage of the shelter afforded by the boulders scattered over the island's surface and, burrowing in underneath, have a massive stone roof for protection; others may merely nest in a gap between two rocks, apparently finding sufficient shelter from the walls of stone on either side.

The sitting birds could not be frightened from their holes, but stretched out their necks in defiance, uttering harsh guttural cries or opening their mouths ready to snap at the intruder. Their beaks are very sharp and powerful and it is said that if one is imprudent one may easily lose a finger. The noise of the colony is tremendous. You very soon learn why they are called jackass penguins, for, in addition to the short sharp cries which they frequently utter, they will at times make a noise just like a braying donkey; and with so many birds there are many braying at the same time. Here and there you will see a bird carrying in its beak a bunch of foliage to his mate on the nest. Often he may be followed by several others trying to wrest it from him, but I never saw one succeed; he would hurry all the more, trying to run and then sometimes falling down, but at last proudly handing to his beloved spouse his contribution to the home. The nests are lined with a rough litter of such dried sprigs and leaves. There is a continual coming and going; husband and wife each take a turn at incubating the eggs; whilst one is sitting on the nest the other is away fishing for food. [Their main food is small fish rather than krill-like crustacea; there are vast shoals of sprats on this coast.]

I have said that after the collection of eggs for the market the birds are left in peace, but I am afraid this is hardly true; man, unfortunately, is not the only one who levies a toll upon them. Continually circling over the colony were a number of large and beautiful Dominican gulls, white with black-tipped wings, reminding one, at first sight, of gannets at home. We had not been watching very long before we saw one swoop down into the colony and rise again almost at once with an egg—and they are large eggs—held in its extremely wide open beak. He circled round once or twice followed by many of his screaming companions; doubling this way and that he managed to get clear of them and, when over a flat stretch of rock, dropped the egg from a height of about 40 feet and in a flash, before the others could get there, he dived down to polish off the omelet. It must have been a young bird well advanced for we hurried to the spot and found that he had left no trace save the bits of clean white shell. We now watched and reckoned that, from the large colony we were observing, an egg was taken by the gulls on an average about once every two minutes. It was not always a case of a gull swooping down to carry off some egg left uncovered for a moment; we saw prolonged manœuvres taking place. One sitting penguin, which we watched, not only refused to uncover her egg while a gull either jumped about in front of her, flapping its wings and screaming, or jumped from one side over her back to the other, but she made every attempt to peck it. The marauder was apparently trying to make the brave mother dizzy, but after a long struggle he had to give up the attempt. With another bird, however, we saw the gull succeed; the unfortunate mother was so harassed that in the end she was driven off her nest and saw her egg at once carried up into the blue; and, if her eyesight had been good enough, she would have seen it dropped and its contents gobbled up. We came upon a large expanse of rock which was covered with broken egg shells; it reminded me of the 'anvil' stones at home on which thrushes break their snail shells, but this was shell breaking on a grand scale.

Along the edge of the shore we found penguins who had one or sometimes two fluffy youngsters with them; they had evidently left the colony and sought the shelter of the rocks coming nearer to the food supply. We then saw a number of shags and some fine ibis with their long curved black beaks. Apart from insects, mostly flies, the only other living things we saw were tortoises of which there were a great many living under the foliage or basking in the sun; it was a strange community in which penguins and tortoises were the principal members.

Some 25 miles north of Dassen Island is Saldanha Bay where Messrs.

Irvin and Johnson[1], the big South African fishing company, have a whaling factory. This station on the west of South Africa and the one at Durban on the east coast attack the whales as they migrate from the south up into the warmer waters to breed in the southern winter and again on their return journey south in the spring. At Saldanha Bay Mackintosh and Wheeler have been continuing their studies on the anatomy and reproduction of whales ever since they arrived from South Georgia at the end of May. [I have already referred (p. 201) to the valuable work they have done here in showing that their series of measurements of both blue and fin whales in African waters exactly fill gaps in their ranges of measurements made at South Georgia; this gave strong circumstantial evidence in favour of the supposed whale migrations between the waters of the south and those off the coasts of Africa. This inference is now indeed proved correct by whales in one region being found to carry marks fired into them in the other regions as we shall presently see (p. 450).]

Later in August Kemp and I paid a visit to the whaling station, spending a week-end there. Mr. Gurdon, the manager for Irvin and Johnson's, very kindly put his car at our disposal. The road took us via Malmesbury through agricultural land and then across the veldt which was beginning to be gay with flowers; in places it was brilliant with carpets of vivid orange, white and crimson mesembryanthemums. We came eventually to Langebaan, a small and now almost deserted seaside summer resort, and completed the journey to the whaling station by boat across a wide and shallow lagoon. The station was arranged on the same general lines as the one we were familiar with at South Georgia and seemed most efficiently run; it was quite a contrast to the south to see black labour employed on the flensing platform. At the time of our visit they were catching many rather small fin whales and a few sei whales[2]. In addition to their work on measurements, Mackintosh and Wheeler were studying the rate of embryonic development in whales and had found in both blue and fin females during July and August some of the smallest fœtuses yet obtained measuring no more than between 20 and 30 mm. It was difficult to say exactly how old they were, but it seemed probable that conception had taken place not less than several weeks earlier. We saw one of these tiny embryos, a blue whale barely an inch in length. It seemed scarcely possible that so small a creature should grow to a length of nearly 23 feet by the time it was born only sone ten months hence; yet this astonishing rate of growth is firmly established. When we visited the

[1] Now operated by the Saldanha Whaling Co.
[2] See p. 32.

station the *William Scoresby* had just arrived on the whaling grounds and news came of the first two whales she had successfully marked.

Simonstown, Tuesday, 26th October. To-morrow we shall be sailing south again for our second season's work. Since my last entry we have made two short cruises: one of about a fortnight over the whaling grounds off Saldanha Bay and the other for only five days to take a series of hauls with the large 4½-metre diameter nets at different depths. Both were most successful. The special sister keels, which we have just had fitted, have made a great improvement in the behaviour of the ship; they run on either side of the central keel and have been attached in short lengths by bolts which will draw under exceptional strain so that they will break off if the ship is caught in ice pressure and allow her, with her rounded hull, to rise up instead of being crushed. The difference they have made is almost miraculous; not only is the extent of the rolling greatly reduced, but its period is longer and the jerk or lurch at the end of the roll, which was such an aggravating feature before, has been completely eliminated. We can now continue to work in quite rough weather.

In the first cruise we made a series of five full stations with vertical plankton nets and physical observations every ten miles on a line at right angles to the coast and a sixth station fifty miles farther out in deep water. Each was followed by horizontal hauls with the 1-metre diameter nets towed simultaneously at the surface and at depths of about 70 and 140 metres and a similar series of 70 cm. diameter nets of finer mesh; before being hauled up, the two deeper nets in each series were closed by the new, lighter and simpler, closing mechanisms which I had designed and had made in Cape Town. I was much relieved to find they worked perfectly. It was very satisfying because this cruise, in addition to giving us valuable information on the plankton off the African coast, was, of course, something in the way of a dress rehearsal for our coming new attack on the whaling grounds of South Georgia.

The surface waters were teeming with a very beautiful small blue salp accompanied by large numbers of the brilliantly iridescent *Sapphirina* which we have previously noted having such an association (p. 132). They shone more often blue and green than red and gold, whereas those we saw here last December flashed with all colours almost equally; they may belong to a different species. They presented a notable spectacle, spangling the deep blue waters with flashing points of sapphire. The salps themselves occurred in such numbers in the surface nets as to be a real nuisance in obscuring the occurrence of other plankton animals; they literally came up in bathfuls.

Among the more interesting captures in these hauls were a number of those curious pelagic molluscs classed as heteropods. Some measured as much as six inches in length and they belonged to two genera *Carinaria* and *Pterotrachea*; both almost entirely transparent. The former has a small shell like a cap of liberty and floats upside down (compared with a snail) with the shell hanging underneath as a keel; the latter lacks a shell altogether and has its head drawn out into a long trunk-like process. The two forms are shown in my sketch below. At first sight you would hardly suspect that *Pterotrachea* was a gastropod mollusc related to a snail, yet among the heteropods we can see all stages in the modification of the body to this floating life by the gradual

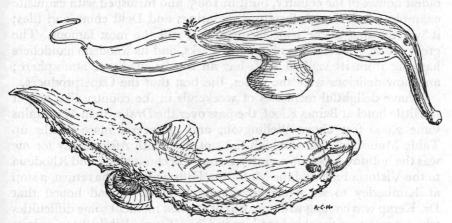

The heteropods (pelagic molluscs) *Carinaria* and *Pterotrachea* (upper drawing), × 1½.

reduction of the shell and the expansion of the so-called foot. We can pass from forms like *Oxygyrus* and *Atlanta* which are distinctly snail-like (see the sketch on p. 91) to our *Carinaria* where the shell is greatly reduced and so to *Pterotrachea*; I am not, of course, suggesting that this is the real path taken by evolution, that *Pterotrachea* is actually descended from *Carinaria*, or *Carinaria* from *Atlanta*, but the existence of this series shows how the general course of modification can have proceeded. We have now seen that four quite separate groups of the gastropod (snail-like) molluscs have taken to a planktonic life: these heteropods, then the shelled and the shell-less pteropods which were evolved on quite independent lines, and the sea-slug *Glaucus* which we saw sprawling on the very surface in the tropics.

After working several series of deep-water nets we arrived back in

Simonstown on the 18th and have had a busy week making final preparations for our coming second voyage to the south. On Thursday the 21st the *William Scoresby*, which had returned on Tuesday from Saldanha Bay, set out direct for South Georgia ahead of us; Hamilton went in charge of her with Mackintosh, Harrison Matthews, Clowes and Fraser. To-morrow we ourselves will be taking a different course.

[There are many more entries in my journal for this period of South African interlude, but they are not directly connected with the voyage. I will skim over just a few of them to give a little more background to the picture. There was the memorable afternoon and evening when some of us, with Kemp and Stenhouse, were guests of the De Villiers at their beautiful and historic home of Klien Constantia, one of the oldest houses in the country, built in 1685, and furnished with exquisite examples of old Dutch furniture, paintings and Delft china and tiles; it was the first of the wine farms and is still the most famous. The great cellar, with its rows of gigantic casks, and its wooden chandeliers hanging from its vaulted roof, has an almost medieval atmosphere; and how delicious were the wines, the best that the Cape produces.

I have delightful memories of weekends in the country like one at the little hotel at Baines Kloof, the pass over the Drakenstein Mountains some 2,000 feet above Wellington, and of several more climbs up Table Mountain. But the high-light of the South African stay for me was the holiday I took up country through Bechuanaland and Rhodesia to the Victoria Falls and the Matoppos Hills, with, on the return, a stop at Kimberley to see over the diamond mines. I had hoped that Dr. Kemp was coming with me, but at the last moment some difficulties which arose over the ship kept him in Cape Town. Whilst I went alone I was never lonely for I met so many interesting people on the long train journey. To describe this tour—four nights in the train—passing over the Karroo, up the side of the Kalahari Desert and on through the Rhodesian forests to the Falls would take a chapter in itself; so would the joys of the days by the great Zambesi and at the Falls, but they do not relate to the main theme of the book and are no doubt similar to the impressions gathered and recorded by very many travellers. For a time I thought I might have dragged in the wonders of the Falls under my title of *Great Waters*; but no, I must resist the temptation, they do not really belong.]

CHAPTER II

SOUTH AGAIN—TO BOUVET ISLAND
AND THE PACK ICE

Wednesday, 27th October, 1926. We sailed from Simonstown with a good send off from the Navy at 3 o'clock this afternoon. We start upon the second half of our voyage—by far the more important part. The first year was bound to be to some extent preliminary: exploring the ground and the best means of attack. Not only this, with our delayed start last season, we arrived late on the whaling grounds; this year, whilst not having days to spare, we have more time. And there are other factors to improve the picture. The *Discovery* is now quite ladylike in comparison with her former behaviour. Our remodelled equipment and method of working nets promise well, and whilst we cannot make the old ship, with only auxiliary steam, less a plaything of the storms, we are now joined by the full-powered *William Scoresby* to help us through. We therefore set out full of optimism.

Our immediate plan, subject always to alterations, is as follows. Instead of going to South Georgia via the northern route as we did before, plugging against the westerlies most of the way, we shall go due south to the pack ice cutting across the latitude of the 'roaring forties' as quickly as possible. As spring advances there is, peculiar to this region, a belt of pack ice coming up from the Weddell Drift with a zone of clear water to the south of it; and here, to the south of the westerly winds, it is often fairly calm and there may sometimes even be winds blowing from the east. We hope to push through the pack to this quieter region, proceed westward and come up to South Georgia from the south, if possible via the South Sandwich Islands. For part of our voyage we shall be traversing what we believe to be virgin water, never before crossed by man. It is always tempting to dream of the possibility of discovering new islands: islands perhaps, through volcanic action, providing a warm 'oasis' in the chill surroundings and so inhabited by a strange fauna of their own—perhaps relics from a bygone prehistoric age, visions of Conan Doyle's *Lost World.* . . .

It is a vain dream, of course, but harmless and pleasant to contemplate. We have the tracks plotted of all known former expeditions in the area: there certainly are spaces not yet covered. We hope to visit Bouvet Island, the position of which was such a mystery for so long.

All along our route, every other day, we shall attempt to take tow-nettings at the surface and at 50 and 100 metres depths with the 1 metre and 70 cm. diameter tow-nets at both 9'clock in the morning and in the evening; at every 200 miles we shall attempt to take a full vertical station of physical and plankton observations. We know, of course, that with storms and contrary winds we shall often not be able to maintain the programme, but it is there to work to as closely as possible. The *William Scoresby* is taking a similar series of hauls on her more direct course; we shall thus have two sets of observations across the Southern Ocean on different lines at the same time which should give us a very valuable picture of the plankton distribution in this part of the southern hemisphere.

At South Georgia, as explained, we shall work on the whaling grounds with the *William Scoresby* during December and January and then we, on the *Discovery*, will go south to the South Orkneys and South Shetlands and work along the west coast of Graham Land (part of the Antarctic continent itself) as far as time and ice will permit. This South Shetlands region, shown in the map on p. 376, was at the time of our expedition the next most important whaling area to that at South Georgia and had its fleet of 'floating factory' ships concentrated at Deception Island. A line of observations will then be attempted from the Antarctic, across Drake Strait, to Cape Horn: a notoriously difficult piece of water to investigate, but oceanographically so important as the link between thePacific and Atlantic Oceans. The campaign certainly promises well.

Tuesday, 2nd November. For the third time we are crossing the 'roaring forties'—and they are roaring with a vengeance. It has been blowing a strong gale since Saturday and to-day we are very uncomfortable. We are rolling a good deal—35° from the vertical—but nothing to what we should be doing if we had not had the keels fitted. For two days we have been battened down, with huge seas sweeping over the decks and the atmosphere below is appalling. You can only read or write by firmly wedging yourself off in a corner of your cabin, and mine is leaking in two places: from a ventilator fitting over the settee and from a beam above my writing-table. With the constant drip, drip, dripping, I might almost be living in a grotto! But these are only very minor hardships. Nevertheless I have actually felt more

Rough weather in the 'roaring forties', redrawn from a watercolour sketch.

uncomfortable these last two days, I think, than at any former time on the voyage; this, however, is mainly due to the very rapid drop in temperature. Everything is damp, and it is bitterly cold.

On Thursday, the day after leaving Cape Town, when we took a full vertical station the surface temperature of the sea was 15·5°C and then on the following day it rose to nearly 20°, and on Saturday at another full station it was still 18·9°C and the warm water extended down to 200 metres depth, which gave 16·69°. On Sunday it fell to 12° at the surface and yesterday it fell again rapidly to 6°. The wind too is bitterly cold and it is now blowing at gale force with squalls of snow and sleet. Only a few days ago we were enjoying strawberries and cream in a sweltering hot spell at Cape Town; no wonder we feel rather miserable!

The zone of warm water which we crossed after leaving the Cape is of considerable interest, for it cannot have come from the westward. It is in fact warm Indian Ocean water, as deep as the Gulf Stream, and is a continuation of the Agulhas Current which flows down the east of Africa, rounds the Cape and is then bent back on itself to the eastward again as it meets the great West Wind Drift. As we dealt with the tow-net samples on Saturday we felt we were washing our hands in warm water, so great was the difference between the temperature of the water and air. The plankton of these samples was characterised by the very large numbers of the amphipod *Phronima* in their transparent barrels fashioned from the tests of salps or *Pyrosoma* colonies; most of the barrels carried clusters of developing young on their insides.

We had a swallow on board on Friday and Saturday, migrating perhaps from England, swept off its course and carried past its goal to perish in the waste of the South. We were unable to catch it and it disappeared.

Thursday, 4th November. Yesterday the weather moderated sufficiently for two sets of hauls with the 1 metre and 70 cm. diameter nets in the morning and evening. *Pyrosoma* and *Phyronima* have disappeared and the amphipod *Parathemisto* is now increasing in each sample. In the evening nets the large Antarctic pteropod *Spongiobranchea australis* appeared in large numbers; we had taken a few of it before around South Georgia last season. To-day has been comparatively calm and we are now used to the cold and do not feel it so much. After a full vertical station we towed a large 4½-metre diameter net for two hours at a depth of some 900 metres. With a wealth of deep-water fish and crustacea we obtained some twenty or more fine specimens of the large orange ostracod *Gigantocypris*; I had never seen so many before and they were fairly lively waltzing round and round the dish paddling themselves with their feathery oar-like antennae. Their large eye reflectors gleamed like jewels and through their semi-transparent shells one could see the remarkable 'fifth leg'—a long flexible appendage bearing bristles like a bottle-brush—continually at work cleaning the inside of the shell. A *Gigantocypris* is seen in the deep-water sample painted on Plate 20, p. 224.

Since last Sunday, when the temperature dropped, small ice petrels or 'whale birds' have been with us; and to-day while on station a penguin popped up to have a look at us. We are nearly a thousand miles from the nearest land; it gives one some idea of the great distances these birds can swim. Cape pigeons and albatrosses have been with us all the way.

Tuesday, 9th November. We are once again beginning to experience some anxiety concerning our coal supply; not that we are actually short of it yet, but the quality of the South African coal is so bad we are getting very little power from it. Since Thursday winds have been unfavourable so that our daily run has averaged only 60 miles.

While it has not been calm enough to work vertical stations, our

21. Jackass penguins (*Spheniscus demersus*) on Dassen Island, South Africa. *Above*, off for a swim. *Below*, part of the main colony. The males in the foreground are carrying material to their spouses for lining their nests in hollows in the ground

22. *Above*, southward bound through the "roaring forties". *Below*, the *Discovery* entering loose pack-ice south-east of Bouvet Island

towed nets have given us a wonderful selection of pteropods: quite a feast of sea-butterflies. The 1-metre diameter nets near the surface have given us shelled forms not unsimilar to our *Clio* and *Limacina* of home waters, a beautiful deep pink *Clione* with wide semi-transparent 'wings,' a large chocolate brown *Spongiobrachaea* and a remarkable form of great rarity, *Procymbulia*, of which only one specimen has ever been caught before. It has been supposed that the last named, like its relative *Cymbulia* (p. 217), must have a pseudoconch (that curious slipper-like shell), but this is not known for certain and we found no trace of such in our sample. It is a handsome creature, with a stout mousy grey body and broad widely expanded 'wings,' reminding one of a bumble-bee or some large bombyx moth. Then to add to our satisfaction a deep-water haul with the 4½-metre diameter net on Thursday provided us with another example of the equally rare pteropod *Schizobrachium* which, until we obtained a specimen between the Falkland Islands and the Cape, had only been known as a single specimen taken by the German *Valdivia* Expedition in the Pacific. We called it 'Henry of Navarre' on account of the wonderful white plume which it carried on its head: actually covered with numerous small suckers. To-day four more penguins were seen, swimming round a patch of floating kelp; like the one we saw a few days ago they were 'Antarctic' or ringed penguins.

Thursday, 11th November. To-day with a short blast on the whistle and the stoppage of the engine, we marked the two minutes' silence at 1 o'clock, corresponding to 11 o'clock English time.

On Tuesday evening we sighted our first iceberg of the season and passed close by it soon after 8 o'clock. It was about a hundred feet in height and a little more than a hundred yards in length. It was an old iceberg, much weathered, and had obviously capsized for we could see an earlier water-line making an angle of about 45° with the present one; above this sloping line the surface was much weathered like a rough crag, while below it was perfectly smooth like glass that has been long in the sea. There was a good swell running and big waves were breaking upon it and sending broad tongues of very blue water up its pure white surface. Later that night a strong gale sprang up which lasted all day yesterday and has only moderated to some extent to-day. The waves were enormous, with great angry tops curling over and breaking in line after line of tumbling white foam: quite some of the biggest I have seen. The decks, of course, were awash all day and my cabin has again been leaking abominably. I have now rigged up a system of 'gutters' slung with string under the beams, a crazy device made from old biscuit-tin lids which calls forth derisive comment from my friends; it is effective, however, and carries most of the water into my basin.

This evening we have passed three more icebergs. One at 6 o'clock was a large one and quite close to us; it was of blue barrier ice, with a depth of colour in the fissures in its sides reminding one of that luminous blue seen in the grotto at Capri as the sunlight filters up into the cave from below the surface of the sea. From some of its projecting edges hung lines of long icicles reaching down to meet the foam of the waves which from time to time leapt up its broken face. I came up from my hour in the stokehold to have a look at it; the change from the heat of the furnace to the chill of the icy air was great and I did not expose myself (in thin vest and shorts) for long— I looked, admired and hurried back to the fires below.

The temperature of the sea surface yesterday and to-day has been *minus* 0·5°c.

Saturday, 13th November. Yesterday we passed several small icebergs and to-day there are gigantic ones, as well as 'growlers'—the smaller fragments broken off the larger ones. The surface water temperature has dropped still further to minus 0·85°c and to-day there has been fog giving a trying time for the officer of the watch. This morning a magnificent barrier iceberg loomed out of the mist on our port beam; it had the typical flat top but very irregular sides standing some 200 feet above the water. And this evening we passed on our starboard side a still larger piece of the barrier—quite an ice island over two miles in length with white cliffs like a coast of marble. Here and there were dark caverns and at one or two points there were hollow 'chimneys' up which the waves dashed to produce great fountains of spray. The many little pieces of ice, miniature icebergs, like swans on the surface of the sea, which we had been passing earlier in the day, may have broken off from this great mother iceberg; they reminded me of those which often covered the surface of Grytviken fjord at South Georgia—broken from the Nordenskjold glacier.

Yesterday our tow-nets, both morning and evening, gave us very thick samples of plant-plankton in the surface layers; like green-pea soup, this is the real polar phyto-plankton we have read so much about. Here it is made up chiefly of a *Phaeocystis*-like form (vast colonies of small green flagellates in jelly globules, very similar to the *Phaeocystis* common in the North Sea in spring) and long slender diatoms of the genus *Rhizosolenia* and the pill-box-like kinds of *Coscinodiscus*.

If the fog lifts and fair weather continues we may sight Thompson's Rocks to-morrow and Bouvet Island the following day; but the position, or even the existence, of the former, is doubtful.

Sunday, 14th November. To-day we have made our first acquaintance with the pack ice. And as for icebergs—has ever a man seen more in one day than we have?

As we came on deck this morning we found it covered with fragments of ice which had fallen from the rigging and every few moments pieces, sometimes small but sometimes almost dangerously large, came hurtling down. Icicles hung from stays, yards and ropes. The falling of ice continued throughout the day and you had to be quite wary as you walked. The fog thickened and thinned at intervals, but lasted till evening; sometimes it melted away to give a visibility of two miles or so, at others closing closely round us. Between daylight and noon we passed over forty large icebergs, many of them over 200 feet high. Our officers have had an exceedingly anxious time, particularly at night; we would steer out of the way of one, only to find a moment later another, still larger, looming up ahead of us. It was fascinating to see these floating 'cliffs' of ice take shape through the mist, sweep past and then melt phantom-like into the white wall behind. What a still more wonderful sight it would have been if it had been clear with the sun shining on their glistening flanks: fleets of them to the horizon on either side. Upon several of the icebergs were groups of penguins. Upon one they all seemed to be struggling up a steep slope of snow as if to reach the top to get a better view of us! We must indeed have seemed to them a strange object emerging from the mist. In between the icebergs the surface was again covered with innumerable small fragments of ice of all sorts of grotesque shapes.

We were called from lunch to see the first real pack ice. The fog had cleared to some extent and about two miles away on the port beam was a long white line. The sea, as we advanced, became covered more thickly with small fragments of ice and then sheets of broken pack appeared ahead and on the starboard bow. At first these floes were just two or three hundred yards across with a mile or so of clear water in between. Then they became larger and larger till we were pushing our way through belts of broken pack over a mile wide and stretching to right and left as far as we could see. Each mass of ice is made up of closely packed pieces. It is a strange sight: the dull grey sky above, the almost black water, and the dazzling white ice rising and falling on the gentle swell. The water appears like ink because it receives so little of the light which is nearly all reflected off the ice; it has the darkness of a cave. The whole scene is one of reversed values. The ice floes, which take the place of land, are as brilliantly light as the sky should be whereas the sky itself is grey and dark in comparison and the water darker still. You at first get a curious feeling as if you

A penguin colony on an iceberg drifting north, redrawn from a watercolour.

were living in a photographic negative. Yet there is colour within the ice. Every little crack and hollow appears as if lit by blue light: not a sky blue, an ice blue—the colour is quite distinctive. There is no blue in the sea or sky for it to be reflecting; it is the real blue of transparent ice. Some of the blocks are discoloured green-brown at the water-line by deposits of diatoms. That 'photographic negative' feeling may perhaps be indicated in my sketch on p. 264.

The sound of the ship's bows striking the ice and of ice bumping along its side is a peculiar and exciting one, a scrunching sound, with something of the tinkle of breaking glass. Sailors are busy aft with long poles pushing away the larger pieces from the propeller, which from time to time has to be stopped when we are passing very heavy floes. For all the rest of the day we have been pushing through such large pieces of pack, with here and there an iceberg. To-night the pack is stretching all around us and just before it got dark we saw 'ice blink' for the first time: a band of white light in the sky—a reflection on the cloud above of the white ice below. The wind has been increasing all afternoon so that now it is blowing almost a gale, but, sheltered by the ice, we are as steady almost as if we were in dock.

For two days we have been unable to take sights so that we are navigating on dead reckoning; it has been much too thick to get any view of Thompson's Rocks which we are thought to have passed about 3 o'clock this afternoon. This evening there was an opening in the pack just sufficient to allow a 70 cm. diameter net to be towed. Never before have I seen such a thick sample of diatoms; it filled a 5 lb. jar with a green concentration of minute plants. A drop of this under the microscope revealed close on a score of different species and of all manner of beautiful shapes[1].

Monday, 15th November. Before turning in last night I spent some time on deck between 12 and 1 o'clock when we were pushing through some

An iceberg in a big swell producing a 'fountain' through a crevasse as each wave passes; redrawn from a watercolour sketch.

really dense pack. Some of it was quite hummocky as it is called when blocks of ice become piled one on top of the other through pressure. It was splendid to feel the ship smashing her way through these heaving masses, cracking huge blocks, rearing them up and pushing them aside. The old *Discovery* with her greatly strengthened bow, and with its cutting edge, certainly has fine qualities in the ice. In among cracks in the ice were some large brilliantly phosphorescent organisms. For several nights previously we have passed some fairly large creatures giving out a bright green light; judging by their apparent circular shape we considered they were probably luminous jelly-fish.

All to-day we have been passing through broad bands of more broken pack. The fog lasted until nearly midday but then lifted to give us a glimpse of the sun. Sights were at once taken and it was

[1]There were the long delicate hair-like species of *Rhizosolenia* and *Thalassiothrix longissima*, chains of *Chaetoceros* cells with their long spines spreading sideways, pill-box-like cells of *Coscinodiscus*, boat-shaped *Navicula* and long chains of *Fragilaria*, to say nothing of masses of *Phæocystis*.

found that with the recent north-westerly gale we had been driven some
90 miles to the south and east of Bouvet Island. The wind having
dropped we are now making our way towards it. There have been
just as many icebergs to-day as yesterday; at one time there were
fourteen large ones in sight together, and some were as fantastically
peaked as those seen in the old prints of Arctic whaling days, almost
too good to be true. Many have ringed penguins on them and on some
of the floes were crab-eater seals and young sea leopards. The 'crab-
eater' does not actually eat crabs as was originally thought from the
crustacean remains found in its gut, but feeds principally on euphausian
shrimps—mainly krill. Their teeth are most remarkable in that they
are deeply serrated so that when they come together they can strain
the shrimps from the water which is passed out through their teeth much
as the water is passed out through the baleen plates in the mouth of a
whale.

There are other petrels with us now besides the Cape pigeons and
'whalebirds': Antarctic petrels with brown and white wings and
snowy petrels of the purest white which seem to disappear as they flash
over the bright floes.

We are all busy at various tasks: and how different they are. At
one moment Dr. Kemp is examining the Euphausiacean crustaceans
we have caught; Wheeler is trying to get specimens of birds; Gunther
is making estimates of the contents of the 1-metre diameter net samples;
Dilwyn John is up on the forecastle hoping to shoot a mark into one
of the whales which come up to blow from time to time in the lanes of
water between the ice; whilst I, with the high power of the microscope, am exploring the world of tiny planktonic plants. We are
investigating the life of the area from the largest to its very smallest
components. Kemp, by the way, is showing us very interesting changes
in the distribution of the species of *Euphausia* as we have passed south
from Cape Town, through the sub-tropical to the sub-Antarctic
waters of the West Wind Drift, back to the sub-tropical as we sampled
the tongue of the Agulhas Current for a short time, into the West Wind
Drift again and finally across the Convergence into the true Antarctic
water. The following were the principal species encountered:
Euphausia recurva, E. similis and *E. spinifera* characteristic of the sub-
tropical waters; *E. luceus, E. longirostris* and *E. vallentini* of the West
Wind Drift; and *E. tricantha, E. frigida* and *E. superba* of the Antarctic
water.

Particularly fine was the pack in the late afternoon. At times the
ice was quite heavy; the ship would rise up on to a great block of it,
fall back, then rise again, and then finally cut its way through. From

Evening in the pack, near Bouvet Island, redrawn from a watercolour.

the top-mast we obtained some striking photographs of the track of the ship stretching away through the ice behind us. Later there was an unusual sunset effect. A band of brilliant gold lined the horizon beneath a very dark grey sky; the water in narrow lanes between the white floes showed up as black as jet and on the horizon, cutting into the streak of gold was a many-pinnacled cathedral iceberg with deep-blue shadows on it. In the foreground alongside the ship a group of ringed penguins flapped their wings and excitedly called out to us 'Quark, quark'. My drawing of this scene is above.

To-night, after writing the above, I have just been on deck about midnight; the sky has cleared and there is a brilliant, nearly full, moon shining down on this gleaming white world. It is indeed cold, but indescribably beautiful. I remember that barely two months ago I was on the banks of the Zambezi revelling in the glories of the tropical forest. I say to myself what I have said again and again: fancy being paid for this!

[We now found that the pack was becoming much thicker than we had expected it to be at this time; it had been piled up into hummocks by the high winds. We were making little progress and using up our coal supplies in trying to force our way through. There was clearly a risk that we might get stuck in the ice for a long period; there would be no danger to life for we had a two years' supply of food on board, but it would have been disastrous for our work. It was decided to abandon our attempt to get through and to retreat north-westward and make our way to South Georgia north of the pack after all.

I will quote a short statement on the position from Kemp's official report to the Committee at home:

At first the pack was loose with wide leads of open water, but as it went on it became much closer; it was clear that if we were ever to make our passage to South Georgia we should have to abandon the route we had planned. We were then to the east and south of Bouvet I. and we turned north-west laying a course for the island.

On 16th November it blew strongly from the WSW., driving the pack ice close and making it very difficult to penetrate. Everywhere icebergs were hemmed in by the pack and they, in the high wind that then prevailed, gave cause to some anxiety. The pack drifts fast before the wind, while the bergs with their greater hold on the water move so slowly that they might almost be islands. In the comparatively heavy ice in which we found ourselves we could make scarcely any progress on our course but drifted rapidly to leeward.]

Wednesday, 17th November. All yesterday morning we were pushing

A scene in the pack-ice on an overcast day, with a grey sky and very black water between the floes. Two Weddell seals are on the ice.

very slowly through thick pack, with very few and short stretches of water in between. Icebergs were as numerous as before. Some of them were discoloured a deep brown along their ledges and in hollows indicating that penguins had made a habit of collecting there; and some of them still carried numbers of them in such positions[1]. When we got sights, as the sun came out for a brief spell, we found we were still some 50 miles south of Bouvet. There were many seals on the ice, mostly crab-eaters and sea leopards. Some would appear blasé and hardly take any notice or just roll half over for a glance at us; others, rearing themselves up at both ends in a most comical manner, would display considerable anger as the ship jostled the ice on which they lay.

The wind was now driving the pack before it along the surface of the sea, and us with it. The great icebergs, although almost stationary because so much of their bulk was below the surface in the deeper layers, appeared in relation to us and the moving ice to be like great battleships cutting their way through the pack. Icebergs that at first appeared far away on the horizon gradually advanced upon us; they fortunately passed to port or starboard, throwing up the great blocks of ice before them as a plough turns the earth. If we had actually found ourselves, fixed in the pack, in the path of one of these, what chance would we have of survival? It was not a pleasant thought. As the icebergs kept on passing us we began to realise that if these conditions prevailed much longer we must surely, by normal probability, expect to find ourselves in just such a position. And sure enough in the afternoon we did indeed begin to be in this predicament.

The strong wind from the SW. had increased in force and was producing a marked swell in the pack; the massive floes undulated and crashed against one another. A barrier iceberg of medium size, a little distance from us, was rocking to and fro, and, as we watched, it suddenly turned over through 90° and presented quite a different outline. Just before this we had been moving rather more freely, pushing the ice aside but now as we were getting horribly near this rolling iceberg we encountered an exceptionally heavy piece of ice. We crashed at it, but made no impression. We now realised that we were certainly being carried to the iceberg—indeed it appeared as if we were stationary and it was bearing down upon us intent on our destruction. In spite of the roaring wind the captain ordered more sail—and, of course, all power from the engines possible. Nearer and nearer we came to the cliff of ice and saw the floes being piled up against it and tossed aside. It was undoubtedly unpleasant. Then

[1]The sketch on p. 260 was drawn from a watercolour I made of one of these bergs.

crack—rearing up, we smashed down on the floe in front of us; it split in two. The *Discovery* proved herself mistress of the ice. We escaped literally by yards. The photograph on Plate 24 shows our track through the ice just after we had got clear of it. To the left of the iceberg is what looks like a shadow; this is a patch of clear water behind the iceberg as the pack is being swept past it on either side. See how the level of the pack is higher on the other side, as it is being pushed up against the ice cliff. It was in that position that we were ourselves a few minutes before I took the picture.

[In case my account may be thought to over-dramatise the event let me quote again from Dr. Kemp's restrained official report in which he makes brief reference to it:

One berg we escaped by little more than ten yards and since a considerable swell was breaking on it a collision might have resulted in serious damage. The berg, moreover, was not one with which we desired near acquaintance; it was evidently in unstable equilibrium and, while we were within a short distance, rolled over through an angle of 90°. By crowding on more sail than he normally would have done Captain Stenhouse succeeded in clearing this berg and after some hours, under both steam and sail, we succeeded in breaking our way out of the pack.]

The pack, having increased so much in thickness, ended abruptly and we came out into open sea. There was a big swell and the many small fragments of ice, rising and falling on the long sweeping waves, produced a quite remarkable effect. Very soon we were out of sight of the pack, in a rough sea and in almost a gale. Save for a few large icebergs here and there in the distance the world of ice was gone.

Very soon big seas were sweeping over the rolling deck which later became covered with ice making progress about the ship somewhat difficult. Later in the evening the wind, shifting to the north, became a head wind and reduced our speed considerably so that we did not sight Bouvet until this morning. It was first seen through squalls of snow, at about 6 o'clock, but as the snow became heavier it did not become visible again until nearly ten and then only for a very short time. From this aspect, from the south-east, it appeared almost completely covered in snow. The land rose by a gentle slope from the south to a high ridge which dropped away steeply to the sea on the northward side. I show a sketch of this view opposite. On the leeward side of the island, and away to the south as far as one could see, there was thick pack ice, in places very hummocky.

Thus we were prevented from getting as close to the island as we had wished; coming, however, as near as the pack would allow, about 4 miles off, we took a vertical station getting a sounding of 1,700 metres. We had hoped to dredge here, but could not get into the shallower water which was a disappointment. As it was we had to cut the station short on account of the pack working its way up towards us; we sampled as far down to 750 metres with the vertical nets. As we moved off from the position we towed the usual series of 1 metre and 70 cm. nets—now in a hard snow storm. It was bitterly cold. The decks were covered with ice and the sea water on the nets froze very soon after they came up. The snow falling on the surface of the sea did not melt, but gathered together in drifts, forming irregular white patches all

Bouvet Island from the south-east with an expanse of pack ice along the horizon behind it, redrawn from a watercolour.

over its surface—a most curious effect. It was Bruce of the Scotia Expedition who, I think, remarked that plankton work in the Antarctic is not child's play; he was right. The handling and washing out of the nets in a temperature much below freezing, and in a blinding snow storm, is not an ideal form of amusement; we were glad when it was over and could carry our spoils into the warm laboratory.

Diatoms were abundant but the samples were not so rich as those of the previous station; they consisted of a high percentage of *Thalassiosira*. We were surprised to find no krill in the samples in spite of the fact that there were many whales about. Eight whales, mostly blue whales, were seen yesterday, although for a great deal of the time we were in thick pack ice; and to-day when our visibility has been much reduced by snow squalls, we saw nine. They seemed to be as numerous here as at South Georgia, but they never came quite within range of our marking guns.

Our way to the south being blocked by heavy ice, we passed round to the north of Bouvet and between 6 and 7 o'clock in the evening, it became much clearer so that we could make sketches and take photographs. From this aspect, Cape Circumcision, the northerly point, was very prominent. It was so named by Bouvet after the holy day on which he discovered it—New Year's Day 1739; seeing it veiled in fog, he thought he had found the great southern continent which some of the early navigators believed to exist. We also saw Cape Valdivia, named, of course, after the German expedition ship, which was the last vessel to visit the island before us—in 1898. Patches of rock and cliff showed through the snow and we obtained a good view of the highest point, covered by an ice cap, and named Kaiser Wilhelm Peak by the Germans.

Later there was a magnificent sunset with Bouvet standing out very clearly on the horizon; ahead of us some fine icebergs were silhouetted against the flaming west, whilst others behind us brilliantly reflected all the rose and golden glory of the sky. We passed close by a large barrier iceberg, over half a mile in length; it had a perfectly flat top from which the wind was blowing sheets of snow far out beyond its precipitous deep blue 'cliffs.' Then after the sun had set we saw a most curious effect. There were a number of long low clouds separated from one another to form parallel lines across the sky; these being no longer lit by the sun, appeared a cold grey against a rich crimson background—the afterglow in the sky behind them, as the sun still illuminated a band of haze at a higher level. On the horizon a large iceberg gleamed white, and above the band of crimson was the blue sky of evening in which swam a gibbous moon— white and luminous— perhaps to some extent lighting and making colder still the grey clouds below. Never before have I seen such a contrasting mixture of cold and warmer light.

Sunday, 28th November. Since my last entry there has been little to record save growing anxiety over contrary winds and shortage of coal. Even now, within 700 miles of South Georgia, we are not sure whether we shall make it. It is now evident that it is impossible with the old ship to attempt long passages and to work stations at the same time; we have had to cut our work to the minimum, using only towed nets.

[Let me once again call upon Kemp's official report to describe the situation:

As we went further our anxieties greatly increased and eventually weof und that even if the comparatively good weather that had prevailed were to continue—light to moderate headwinds, a smooth sea and moderate swell—we had not sufficient coal to carry

us through. Captain Stenhouse and I frequently discussed the
probable necessity of turning back to Cape Town, though we
realised how serious this would have been and that it would have
wrecked the whole season's programme. Actually we were within
an ace of returning and, if at this time we had had a westerly gale
lasting two days, this course would have been forced upon us.]

Since leaving Bouvet we have gone somewhat to the north and
passed out of the region of thick diatoms. Copepods and young
euphausians now make up the bulk of our plankton samples. Last night
with the continuous plankton recorder I obtained some specimens of
the true krill *Euphausia superba*. This is important for we were beginning
to consider, from our own and previous observations, that it was
confined to relatively shallow water; here, however, we are in the
middle of a vast stretch of deep ocean, so clearly we were wrong.

We continue to pass large barrier icebergs and the other evening
came across one which was particularly noteworthy; its whole mass,
except for some grotesquely-shaped white pieces at its foot, was of the
deepest cerulean blue. The sun was not shining and it was approaching
dusk, yet its great bulk, with two peaks, was like some enormous
irregular crystal—a mountain of copper sulphate—floating upon a
grey sea beneath a leaden sky.

[Here is another short extract from Kemp's report:
Owing perhaps to the position of the wircless station at Grytviken
we were unable for a long time to get into touch. We succeeded
when 800 miles away and instructed the *William Scoresby* to fill her
bunkers and hold herself in readiness to meet us. Fortunately for
our pride we managed without having to be towed. For the last
four days we had strong favourable winds and when finally we
reached harbour we had enough coal in hand for rather more than
two days' steaming.]

Saturday, 4th December. On most days of this week we have been
hemmed in by fog making it a very anxious time for our navigating
officers with so much ice about. Thursday and yesterday it was like
sailing up a great avenue of icebergs, for they appeared to form a
line on either side of us. This may perhaps have been an actuality
rather than the mere effect of not being able to see those farther over
to the right or left. It is just possible that the icebergs, carried in the
West Wind Drift, are for a time held up behind South Georgia and
then, being carried round each end of the island, may form two long
streams which will gradually tend to come together at the other side;
if this was so, then we, sailing west and aiming at the middle of the
island, might well be travelling between the two converging lines.

['The year is without doubt an abnormal one,' writes Kemp again in his report when discussing the ice conditions and he continued, 'I learn that floating factories have been unable to reach Deception I. and have been working off the edge of the ice in the neighbourhood of the South Orkneys. According to Mr. Hansen, Manager at Leith (South Georgia), the season is more severe than any since 1916'.]

CHAPTER 12

SOUTH GEORGIA: SECOND ROUND

Wednesday, 15th December. As we steamed in towards the coast of South Georgia on Sunday, the 5th, there was fog outside and only here and there could we get glimpses of the lower headlands; the mountains were entirely hidden. Soon we sighted our little companion ship, the *William Scoresby*, coming out to meet us; after a happy exchange of greetings she set off for a day's whale marking whilst we turned into the familiar entrance of Cumberland Bay.

The fog had now risen to become cloud at about two hundred feet so that all the edges of the fjord and bases of the mountains were clearly seen but cut off sharply by a dense white ceiling—a not uncommon effect here. Very soon we were tied up at the buoy in Grytviken harbour just as if we had come back from only a day or two's cruise. We learn that this year's whaling is exceptionally good, there being many large blue whales in excellent condition, yielding an average of 110 barrels of oil instead of the more usual 75.

For the next few days, while the ship was coaling, we were busy with the plankton collections made on the way over. I have been specially interested in those taken by the *Scoresby* so as to compare them with ours from the more southerly route. Whilst exact analyses will follow later, I have taken volumetric measurements and made rough percentage estimates of the more important constituents to give us a good general idea of the plankton of the Southern Ocean. The map we have made shows (overleaf) the limits of the great phytoplankton zones which lie to the south, the populations of copepods in the different regions, and the distribution, from the larger nets, of the euphausiaceans, the pteropods, amphipods, etc.

Yesterday we walked over the Maiviken pass to the West Bay to do some shore collecting and try some tow-netting in the lakes on the way. Last year in March we found a great many of two species of freshwater copepod in the lowest lake. Launched on a large block of ice, I punted myself well out into the middle and was then pulled back by a rope as I towed the plankton net. We drew a blank, however, as

271

regards copepods; it was evidently too early in the season for them, but we got a number of small water-beetles. We collected mites, spiders, beetles and earth-worms under stones. The snow was quite deep in the little shaded valley running down from the lakes, and the stream, much swollen by the thaw, dived in and out of tunnels through the drifts, turning this way and that, sparkling and gurgling as it went.

Along the Maiviken beach and in the tussocks behind there were very many more elephant seals than last year: hundreds of them lying

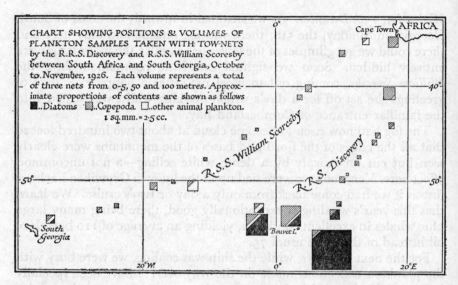

CHART SHOWING POSITIONS & VOLUMES OF PLANKTON SAMPLES TAKEN WITH TOW-NETS by the R.R.S. Discovery and R.S.S. William Scoresby between South Africa and South Georgia, October to November, 1926. Each volume represents a total of three nets from 0-5, 50 and 100 metres. Approximate proportions of contents are shown as follows ■..Diatoms ▨..Copepoda □..other animal plankton. 1 sq. mm. = 2·5 cc.

A chart of the relative plankton quantities taken by the *Discovery* and the *William Scoresby* on their respective cruises between the Cape and South Georgia, from the author's account in *The Geographical Journal,* vol xxii, 1928.

together in groups of a dozen or more, and a few others floundering about in the water. These groups are evidently the remains of the several harems for the breeding is now over and at this time they are almost ready to go back into the water before coming out for the second time to moult (as when we saw them last year). The full-grown bulls are no longer savagely guarding their harems from the younger bachelor bulls which a little earlier would hang round outside trying every now and again to get a cow or two for themselves or even challenging the overlords to a fight for the whole harem. These seals carry a thick layer of blubber which yields sufficient oil to make their exploitation well worth while. In the old sailing-ship days the sealers visiting South Georgia and other islands to the south combined the hunting of the fur seal for their skins and the sea elephants for their oil. They exterminated the fur seal in many places and reduced the elephants to very small numbers. To-day at South Georgia the fur seals as in other Dependencies of the Falkland Islands, are protected and the elephant seal hunting is now carefully controlled so that they have increased greatly in numbers. Harrison Matthews gives a very good account of this modern sealing in his 'Natural History of the Elephant Seal' in *Discovery Reports*, vol. 1. With his kind permission I quote from him as follows:

At the present day the hunting is carried on by one of the whaling companies, under a licence issued by the Government of the Falkland Islands. The first licence for taking seals was issued in 1910 and the same company has continued hunting until the present time. The coast of South Georgia is divided into four roughly equal divisions, of which only three are worked each year, the fourth forming an unmolested reserve. The licence allows the taking of adult bull seal only and stipulates that 10 per cent of the bulls shall be left on each beach. As the elephant seal is polygamous there are always many bachelor bulls on the beaches; further, it may be assumed that the proportions of the sexes born annually are about equal, so that the excess of bulls may well be exploited commercially without diminishing the numbers of the species; in fact the numbers may be increasing in spite of the hunting. The taking of seals is prohibited during the close season between November 1 and March 1. During the winter, from the beginning of May until the end of August, sealing is impracticable owing to the absence of the seal, bad weather and the closing of the whaling station. Consequently the actual period during which the seal are taken is limited to the four months September and October, March and April. . . .

For hunting an old whale-catcher is used, the crew being Norwegian and Russian. She visits the various beaches and anchors off them as near the shore as possible, and sends ashore a 'pram' with the hunters. The selected seal are driven down to the water's edge and there shot by rifle. The killing shots are the back of the head, or, if the seal stops to roar, as he frequently does, up through the palate into the brain while the mouth is open. When the seal is killed the iris of the eye relaxes so that the retina throws a green reflection. This fact was noted by Pernety in 1764, who says: 'I remarked that when they were expiring their eyes changed colour, and their crystalline lens became of an admirable green'. As the elephant seal, like all seals, is very tenacious of life, the sealers sever the carotids by gashing the side of the neck after the seal have been knocked down by the rifle shot. The quantity of blood that runs from a large elephant seal is very great, a fact which much impressed the early voyager. The blubber is flensed off with the hide by cutting through it along each side just above the ground as the seal lies on his belly. . . .

The elephant seal are of extremely low intelligence, as the survivors take no notice at all of the slaughter of their companions. A slight disturbance is caused in the rookeries in driving the bulls out of the harems, which they are loth to leave, and down to the water; but as soon as the hunters have passed through the rookeries the seal all settle down again, and the spare bulls proceed to annex the harems and fight amongst themselves for them. The blood and carcasses, and the presence of the sealers cause no disturbance, nor does the sound of rifle fire, as it is possible to shoot many in succession right alongside each other. Sometimes the spare bulls get sufficiently scared to enter the water, but they do not go away and soon haul out again. The cows and pups take no notice whatever of the killing.

When we had left the shore we looked down from the cliffs a little farther along and saw two young bull elephants fighting in the water. It was evidently just a practice sparring bout in preparation for the more serious fights to come next season when, as adult bulls, they would fight for the possession of a harem and the nuptial rights over part of the beach. The two were in the shallow water and time after time reared themselves up against each other, breast to breast, uttering the most horrible cries. They would then strike at each other's chests with heads and flippers and fall back after a short spar to prepare for the next round. It seemed only play, not the fight that one has heard described when they gash each other's breasts with their sharp canine tusks. They were no doubt just young 'lads' growing into manhood. A splendid photograph by Mr. A. Saunders of two bull elephant seals fighting in earnest is shown on Plate 19, p. 217.

Having come from Grytviken by the usual track to the right of the lakes, we decided to return by the other side of the valley, keeping as high up as possible. The lower mountain sides form screes of broken fragments of rock which are mostly flat; at times you may lose your foothold and go shooting down amid a clatter of rattling 'tiles'. These flat pieces, flaked off from different bits of the mountain by frost, have a wide range of colour and often, when lying on an even surface, give the appearance of a crazy pavement.

Before climbing up the mountain side we passed through a small colony of wreathed terns (*Sterna vittala georgiae*, Reichenof) with beautiful roseate legs and bills. They were much agitated at our approach and flew over us uttering shrill cries and every now and again swooping down to attack us. Dr. Marshall who visited a larger colony in Moraine Fjord, and shot a specimen for the scientific collection, was repeatedly pecked on the head; although he was wearing a cap they pecked him so severely that they drew blood in two places—heroic little birds!

One of the most interesting sights of the last few days has been the swarming of the krill, or whale food, within the fjord. One day last week, for a whole day there was a dense aggregation, like a red cloud, of closely-packed euphausians (*E. superba*) against the jetty at our shore station. There must have been thousands and thousands in a close swarm some four feet across. They were all swimming hard and going round and round, sometimes in a circular course, sometimes in a figure of 8, but never breaking away from the one mass. The cloud would thus change shape and elongate this way or that. (There appeared to be some guiding principle—almost as if there was some leader in command of the whole!) At times they would form into two such moving parties and one would tend to separate from the other, so that the swarm became dumb-bell shaped; but as soon as the connecting link became of a certain thinness the one part would turn back and flow into the other to form one big mass again. It was drawn into the whole like the pseudopodium[1] of an amoeba; indeed the whole swarm appeared to behave as one large organism. It was for the most part at the surface, but at times it would sink down almost out of sight to rise again. This would happen apparently spontaneously, or again happen if some sudden disturbance occurred, the approach of a boat for instance. They were so close to the pier, at times even below it, that one could look straight down on to them and observe them with ease. I put in my walking-stick and stirred the whole swarm up quickly so as to scatter them in all directions; but within half a minute they were all back again in their old formation.

Other swarms were recorded by fishing parties out by the kelp at the entrance of the harbour and on another day we had a similar display close to the ship in mid-harbour, just a few hundred yards from the whaling station itself. They were half-grown specimens just developing their reproductive organs. It was interesting finding them right inside like this; last March we had caught much younger stages 20 or 30 miles

---

[1]The semi-fluid limb-like process thrust out and re-absorbed in the primitive animal *Amoeba proteus*.

off the coast. Do they always occur, even when adult, in such swarms? I have seen dense patches of the northern krill, *Meganyctiphanes norvegica* off Iceland when on the *Michael Sars* with Hjort—and from the very heavy catches we made with our nets last season it looks as if they must. If so, it is not difficult to realise how these huge whales find sufficient nourishment; two or three mouthfuls of such concentrations must fill their huge stomachs to repletion. It is to be hoped that during the coming months we may be able to throw more light upon this question.

Sunday, 26th December. Just over a week ago we began the great survey of the plankton and water conditions of the whaling grounds: the second round, with the two ships working together, which we have long been preparing for. For the time being I have transferred to the *William Scoresby* to be in charge of one half of the work in co-operation with Dr. Kemp in the *Discovery*.

I joined the *Scoresby* on Thursday the 16th, but before we could start the survey we had first to pick up Commander Chaplin, Cadet O'Conor and Able Seaman Smith who for the past ten days had been engaged in quite another type of survey. The map of the island has been far from exact and as its proper charting—and that of other lands farther south—is of vital importance for the whaling vessels, Commander John Chaplin, R.N., of the Hydrographic Department of the Admiralty, was specially seconded to us to undertake this work. They have, just now, been determining—or fixing I think they say—the precise position of the extreme northern end of the island. Thither we set off on Friday with a Norwegian pilot, Captain Johannsen, to take us through the dangerously narrow passage between Bird Island and the mainland. The map on p. 158 may here be useful.

Travelling in the *Scoresby*, which can do over 10 knots, was a great change from the slow *Discovery*. We swept up the wild coast; glacier after glacier, rocky headland after headland, and island after island, came and went. Few landscapes can present a more spectacular array of fantastic pinnacles and peaks; and all along the way were stranded icebergs of every size, shape and shade of blue. Stromness, Fortuna Bay, Antarctic Bay and Possession Bay, passed swiftly by, each with its own grandeur. It was at the last named bay that Captain Cook, on January 14th, 1775, 'landed at three different places, displayed our colours, and took possession of the country in His Majesty's name, under a discharge of small arms'[1]. So it was that it became called Georgia.

[1] I quote from Cook's 'A Voyage Towards the South Pole and Round the World,' London, 1777.

After rounding the rugged headland of Cape Buller we passed close by the Welcome Isles which are covered with gentoo penguin (*Pygoscelis papua*, Forst.) rookeries and nesting Dominican gulls (*Larus dominicanus*, Licht.). By half past seven we were approaching the thrilling Bird Island passage, and this is no idle expression for our course lies between two submerged, invisible and jagged rocks which are so close together that the slightest mistake means disaster. No doubt in time they will be buoyed; for the present, the secret of their navigation is in the hands of just a few sealing captains. Bird Island lies at the extreme north of the main island. As we approached the passage we passed Else's Harbour, a little bay bitten into the coast so as almost to join with Undine Harbour on the other side. Here we gave a blast on our whistle to prepare Chaplin for our aproach. In a moment, still at full speed, we were sweeping through the passage. The little island is well named for it is covered with nesting birds: mollymauks[1], Dominican gulls and shags[2], with here and there crowded penguin rookeries. The air was full of protest as wheeling gulls screamed defiance at our approach. Johannsen, alert on the bridge, gives orders to the helmsman. Suddenly he points down to the water close at hand on the right and then runs to the other side and points down again equally closely to the ship; his face now breaks into a triumphant smile and he claps his hands. We are through 'the most dangerous channel in the world' he tells us—and I could well believe it. A moment later we are swinging round Cape Paradise between rocky islands into Undine Bay. We pass beside a large rookery of macaroni penguins (*Eudyptes chrysolophus*, Brandt.)—the first we had seen—built on the steep rocky banks of a stream; with our glasses we can see the little tufts of yellow plumage which decorate these quaint birds. 'Stuck a feather in his hat and called it Macaroni' says the old song.

We soon see the tents of the campers and have a boat away. All along the beach there are hundreds of sea elephants with some quite big bulls amongst them. Our party had to build a 'stockade' of sharp jagged stones around their camp, for at dawn on their first morning they found two of these monsters lying on their tent flaps, just beside them, with only the canvas in between. Unpleasant companions if they had rolled over! Quite the most striking feature of the scene is the number of wandering albatross (*Diomedea exulans*, Linn.) on their nests; specks of white, like sheep, they dot the hillsides all around. We could get right up to them without disturbing them from their tall nests built up in the tussock; some were fast asleep and did not

[1] or black-browed albatross (*Diomedea melanoparys*).
[2] *Phalacrocorax georgianus*, Lounberg.

wake up until we had been standing close beside them for some time, when they would suddenly arise with a most startled expression, stretch out their wings—a span of some ten feet—and strut off the nest. They had not begun to lay yet, and it was too late in the evening for us to see anything of their quaint courtship dance [which we shall see in the next chapter]. South Georgia and Kerguelen are among the very few places where these great birds breed; they must have these gentle slopes towards the sea to enable them to become airborne.

We also visited a gentoo penguin rookery after eggs, but here we were too late. I was glad, for the sight of the newly hatched and actually hatching chicks was worth many breakfast eggs, fond as I am of them. The chicks, little balls of fluff, stretched out their necks and uttered shrill cries like their parents who strutted round the nest shrieking at us. What a commotion there was as we approached: thousands and thousands of outraged birds giving cry at the same time; the hills echoed with the din. Many of the eggs were just cracking; there was a hole about half an inch square chipped in the shell through which we could see the beak of the little chick within pecking away at the shell and chirping all the while.

We were astonished to find on the edge of the colony a solitary King penguin: a magnificent bird, with brilliant orange neck, black and pink beak and a beautiful glossy back. He—or she, it is difficult to tell which—remained motionless as we approached. They make no nest, but we suspected that she was carrying the egg between her feet and we tried to push her to one side to see. I call the bird 'she,' but the male takes an equal share in incubating the egg. Would she move?—not a bit of it. She held her ground, striking out savagely with her sharp beak, dealing heavy blows with her powerful wings and from time to time uttering shrill cries of defiance. One of the party threw his muffler over her neck and pulled her suddenly over and for a moment we caught sight of the large white egg. She was up in an instant with the egg carefully concealed again. She then moved a pace or two away carrying the egg in the white down covered folds round her legs so that you would never guess that she carried so large an object. I would rather have left her with her precious possession, but —— would take it for the collection. No doubt he was right; she would probably lay another anyway, as most penguins do when robbed, but I could not bear the robbery. A savage battle ensued; never have I seen an animal put up a more heroic or energetic fight. Time after time she was pulled over with the muffler, but each time kept the egg hidden beneath her. At last, inevitably, came the

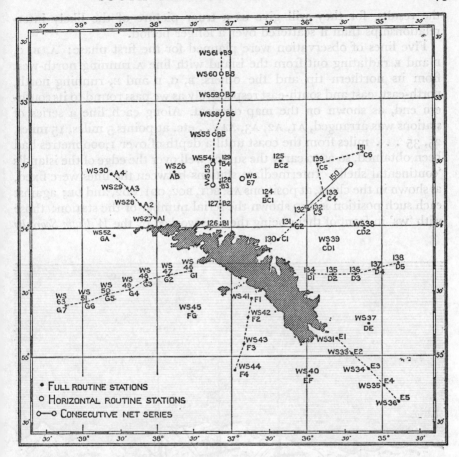

Chart showing the positions of the observation and sampling stations in the South Georgia plankton survey, December–January, 1926-7. From *D.R.*, vol. xi. For further explanation see text.

chance to snatch the prize. The combat was over. She walked away slowly, silently, a picture of injured dignity.

We returned to the beach as the last of Chaplin's equipment, theodolites, chronometers, etc., were being passed into the boat, and, steaming through the night, reached Grytviken early next morning. After landing the survey party on the *Discovery*, the two ships were now ready to start on their great joint enterprise.

Our object is to cover the whole area of the whaling grounds with a network of exactly similar observations in as short a time as possible; the nearer they are to one another in time the more valuable will be the results, for they will give us a truer picture of the likely inter-relationships than if scattered over a longer period.

Five lines of observation were planned for the first phase: A, B, C, D and E radiating out from the island with line A running north-west from its northern tip and the others, B, C, D and E, running north, north-east, east and south-east respectively as we pass round to its southern end, as shown on the map overleaf. Along each line a series of stations was arranged, A1, A2, A3, A4 . . . etc. at points 5 miles, 15 miles, 25, 35 . . . miles from the coast until a depth of over 1,000 metres had been obtained, so as to carry the survey well over the edge of the island's 'continental shelf'. Intermediate stations between the lines were fixed, as shown in the chart, at positions AB, BC1, BC2, CD1, CD2, and DE; against each such position is also shown the serial number of the station: those with 'ws' in front of them being the ones worked by the *William Scoresby*

The *Discovery* working a station on the survey of the South Georgia whaling grounds, drawn from a photograph taken from the *William Scoresby*. Mount Paget is behind the ship and the Sugar Loaf to the right.

in contrast to the others worked by the *Discovery*. At each station exactly the same routine was to be followed:

A sounding with a snapper lead (see p. 145).

Water-bottle samples for salinity, oxygen content, phosphate determinations, alkalinity measurements, etc., as well as temperature readings at the surface and at the following depths in metres: 10, 20, 30, 40, 50, 60, 80, 100, 125, 150, 200, 300, 400, 500, 750, 1000 and 1500, as far as soundings would allow.

Vertical plankton hauls with the 70 cm. diameter net from 50 metres to the surface, from 100 to 50 metres, 250 to 100 m., 500 to 250 m., 750 to 500 m., and 1000 to 750 m., again as far as soundings would allow, for the collection of the smaller plankton animals and the study of their relative abundance at different levels. In addition a haul was made from 100 metres to the surface with the 50 cm. diameter net of the finest silk gauze (200 meshes to the linear inch) for the sampling of the tiny plants (the phytoplankton) which are confined to the upper sunlit layers.

Each such series of vertical observations is to be followed by horizontal hauls of 1 mile each at a speed of 2 knots of three of the 1 metre diameter nets towed at the same time at just below the surface, at 50 and at 100 metres depths for the capture of the larger plankton animals, particularly the krill. The two nets at the lower levels are to be closed by our new mechanisms at the end of each tow before being hauled to the surface so that they will not catch anything on the way up and so give us a true estimate of the life at the levels we are sampling[1]. As soon as the 1 metre nets come in, another similar series is taken, at the same depths, with three of the smaller and finer mesh 70 cm. nets (also arranged to be closed), but each towed for only a quarter of a mile, for the capture of the young stages of the krill.

I have already described the working of the vertical part of such a station (p. 146); the towing and closing of the horizontal nets we have already practised off the African coast and a drawing of the method is given on p. 50. After the completion of this first part of the survey other lines to the west will be taken.

I was indeed glad that Dr. Kemp had let Rolfe Gunther come with me on the *William Scoresby*, for we had always worked together at the plankton nets; for the hydrological work John Wheeler and Archie Clowes came from the shore station to help us.

[1] As already explained the nets catch little on the way down because they are veered away at almost the same speed as the ship goes forward.

[In the preface I have recorded how Rolfe Gunther was tragically killed, by an accident, when on active service in the early days of the War. As a tribute to him, let me quote from the obituary that I wrote in *Nature*[1]:

He was a man of sterling qualities. Working with him day and night, often under the difficult conditions presented by the Southern Ocean, one was continually impressed by his deep sense of duty, his devotion to his work, and his tireless energy. His enthusiasm was always combined with a scrupulous regard for accuracy: both in the field and the working-up of data. After working at the nets and water-bottles for thirty-six hours on end, except for odd moments snatched for hurried meals, it was only the fear of being inaccurate in the readings and recordings, not fatigue itself, which persuaded him to rest. He had a love of the sea and the open life; he was a real deep-water oceanographer, with the determination to bring back results.

We two worked together so much as a team. He also kept a journal of the voyage and when we returned a large part of it was published in *The Draconian*, the magazine of the Dragon School, Oxford, where Rolfe was a pupil before going on to Winchester; this was reprinted with many of his photographs and sketches in a privately published volume: *Notes and Sketches made during two years on the 'Discovery' Expedition 1925-1927*. It is a delightful volume prized by many of his friends, and in it he gives a vivid account of this plankton survey. With the kind permission of his widow, Dr. Mavis Gunther, I am quoting extracts from it for they will not only increase the interest, by giving an entirely independent version, but will add lively passages of beautiful descriptive writing. They show too how closely we worked together and here, I must admit, my vanity is no doubt also prompting me to include them for the kind allusions he makes to my part in the operations. It will be remembered that at stations Rolfe worked on the outboard platform whilst I controlled the steam winch, the timing of the hauls, etc., from inboard; and I have already, on p. 173, quoted Dr. Kemp's report to the Committee at home on the first season's work: '. . . Mr. Herdman and Mr. Gunther were both immersed to the waist when working water-bottles and nets from the outboard platforms.' I shall quote his journal at intervals as we go along with the account of the survey, but let me begin here by showing how he saw things from his position over the rail:

On a sunny day there are few pleasanter places than the outboard platform, as the ship rolls lazily and the grid-like stage is now

[1] *Nature*, vol. 146, p. 123, 1940.

near, now far from the heaving swell. When one can keep dry
shod there is a charm in gazing into glorious depths, to see the outrunning wire vanish into dimly-lit depths fathoms down; to see
the 'messenger' ride up and down the straying wire, its release-
string held like reins; then to release it, to watch its plunge into
the abyss, to watch the bubbles as they wriggle their way to the
surface and, bursting, sprinkle it with fairy fountains.

But when at midnight one has to turn out into a cold drizzle,
and work in inky blackness, a station has less charm. A dim cargo
'cluster' hangs above the winch, but does not light up much of the
outrunning wire or of the murky waves. It is then that all the
accidents happen, and one turns to Hardy for humour and support.
'Changing tyres' was a memorable comment as he handed a
new net to replace the one which in the darkness had 'gone
west.']

The two ships steamed out to start the survey on Saturday morning.
It was arranged that we on the *William Scoresby*, the faster ship, should
take the two outlying lines to the north and south, A and E, and the
intermediate stations AB, CD1, CD2, and DE, whilst the *Discovery* should
work the lines B, C and D with the intermediate stations BC1 and
BC2.

The *William Scoresby* was under the command of Lt.-Comdr. G. M.
Mercer, D.S.C., R.D., R.N.R., who came to us from being an officer on
the old four funnelled *Mauritania* of the Cunard fleet; he left that
greatest of liners for our tiny vessel for the prospect of more interesting
work in the south. I found him an excellent collaborator. It is sometimes difficult for a scientist in charge of a research cruise and the
captain to see eye to eye when difficult decisions have to be made;
the scientist desperately wants to complete his programme if he can,
but the decision to continue work must rest with the captain who has
the safety of the vessel in his hands. I have always found that if one
tries to understand the difficulties and responsibilities of the captain
and at the same time gives him a clear idea of what one is trying to
achieve, so as to excite his interest too, there is never any trouble.
Captain Mercer had a splendid set of officers and crew. The Chief
Officer, A. Irving, who had been a trawler skipper from Orkney, was
specially appointed for the fisheries survey the *Scoresby* would later be
doing on the banks between the Falkland Islands and South America.
The Second Officer was Lieut. M. C. Lester, R.N.R., who had already
seen Antarctic service in the Graham Land Expedition of 1923-4.
The Chief Engineer was J. W. Ridley, and the Second Engineer was
G. Brabender.

[There was a friendly rivalry between the two ships in this enterprise, happily noted by Gunther as he writes of it in his journal: 'The *Discovery* was slightly ahead of the *William Scoresby* in casting off her moorings, and as her work lay close to Cumberland Bay she had an unfair start. It made us keener to adjust things.']

To give a complete, detailed account of the intensive work of the next few days would make tiresome reading. It is a record of haul after haul, station after station, with the small ships' company working watch and watch through day and night—and the scientists snatching such sleep as could be got as the ships steamed from one line to another. We worked continuously for two periods of 24 hours each, with only a few hours' sleep in between. There might just be time between stations to snatch a hurried meal; as a rule, however, you were hard pressed to complete all the preserving, labelling and recording of samples, and writing up the log, before you heard the call from the bridge 'Prepare for station' and knew that in five minutes the ship would be slowing down for the next. Every man was working to his utmost, and the *Discovery* was going equally hard. The two ships were in wireless communication so Dr. Kemp and I could compare notes as we went along. When we had bad weather they were sometimes working in perfect conditions, and *vice versa*.

We finished station AB soon after midnight getting very heavy catches of krill at the surface: 42,500 in the 1-metre diameter net, and 59,500 in the 70 cm. net—according to rough sub-sampling estimates. We started the A line off Bird Island at 6 o'clock next morning and completed it at A4, with a sounding of 2,582 metres, in the very early hours of the following morning. (You will remember that each line was to be continued out from the coast till a station of over 1,000 metres depth was encountered.) After the vertical sampling at A1 the lowest of the three horizontally-towed 1-metre diameter nets accidentally touched the bottom, fortunately without damage, bringing up a perfect bouquet of invertebrates from the deep. There were sea-cucumbers (holothurians) of rose and salmon pink, starfish white and orange, large anemones like dahlias and lavender-tinted sea-urchins; most conspicuous of all, however, were the scarlet ascidians (sea-squirts), which contrasted with deep-magenta sponges.

[Now let me give another quotation from Rolfe Gunther's account:
A midday telegram informs Hardy that the *Discovery* is one station ahead of us. Unused to conditions obtaining on a new ship, last night we spent six hours on our first station.

Recovery is but a matter of time. To the message Hardy makes a happy retort, enquiring whether the *Discovery* is operating

Secchi Discs. This, a measurement of seawater transparency, we generally shirk.

Life is a giddy rush: three-quarters of an hour are all that we have between stations because of the greater speed of the steamer.... Every plankton sample, and there are twelve to a station, has to be concentrated, preserved, labelled and stowed; lumber accumulates. For the convenience of stewards meals are only snatched when they are laid out. Day runs into night. To the southward an orange sunset fades to yellow and grows fainter, but never becomes quite so sombre as the long low cloud flung across the heavens. At midnight, when we were towing our last horizontal nets, the daylight streak still lay upon the horizon, and by two o'clock when we turned in, the decks were illumined by the dawn.

The midnight station he is referring to is the A4 at the northern end of our first line. I describe the same sky in my journal and then go on as follows.] It was after completing these towed nets that we had a little adventure with my continuous plankton recorder which I was hoping to run from this point, the farthest north in the survey, to the most southern line which we were next to work. It was perhaps unwise to try to use it on a new ship with a new crew, at such an hour when we were all dead tired, but enthusiasm makes fools of us at times; in any case it was a somewhat tricky undertaking to get it neatly over the side, on account of various stanchions, guy ropes, etc. The main winch, whose cable we had to use, was not yet properly 'run in' and so somewhat fierce. We were all holding on to it, ready for launching from a davit, when I gave the order 'Raise gently, two feet.' Crack! Nearly three hundredweight (see Plate 38) leapt like a grasshopper. An officer and two of the hands were knocked flat on their backs. The winch, in one violent jerk, had wound in some two fathoms of cable instead of two feet. The machine which had sprung skywards, luckily stopped just short of the davit block and was wildly swinging about and knocking into stanchions. It was lucky that no one was seriously hurt and the machine, too, sustained no damage. I decided, however, to postpone further attempts until the eccentricities of the winch were fully understood—and we had had a little needed sleep.

We arrived at our 'E' line, off Cooper Island in the south, at 4 o'clock in the afternoon, after steaming down the east coast all day in brilliant sunshine. [But I will here let Gunther tell the story:

Line A finished, we make a dash for the southern end of the island. On passage we were not roused until eight o'clock breakfast, and were thankful for so much sleep. Woke to the sunniest calm day

with a cloudless azure sky. Against it towered the deeply cleft
white mountains of snow-laden South Georgia. Dark shore-line
rocks, the green tinge of glaciers and brilliant snowfields each were
reflected in the lively mirror; wavelets broke the reflections with
ripples of contrasting green. Merrily we sped, scattering sheets
of glistening spray as the ship's head plunged through the sunlit
waters. To port, deep in shadow against the noonday sun,
appeared the little *Discovery* with her cocky bowsprit pointing
towards South Georgia. She was dwarfed by huge icebergs, some
tabular, others canted by uneven melting but all the more
precipitous. A formal dipping of the flag was all that passed
between us.]

The entrance to Drygalski Fjord, South Georgia.

No sooner had we reached Cooper Island and our first E line
station, when a rapid change in the weather was noticed. The sky
clouded over and a strong breeze from the west set in. Station EI,
in shallow water, was carried through in less than two hours, yet by
the time we reached E2, ten miles farther out, the breeze had become
half a gale and the sea very steep. We were forced to heave to, hoping
it would moderate as quickly as it had arisen. Morning, however,
brought no change so we decided to seek shelter and, while waiting for
an improvement, to explore the large Drygalski Fjord which penetrates
some ten miles into the coast just inside Cooper Island. With the
smaller Larsen Harbour which opens out of it on the left as you enter,
it is recognised as the most beautiful fjord in all South Georgia. The
entrance is narrow and a very striking one; on either hand the
mountains descend sheer into deep water, and their crests are bristling

with pinnacles. At the head of the fjord two large glaciers come
together to form a long barrier of ice; smaller ones along the sides
make a steep descent, some reaching the water, others hanging above
precipitous cliffs.

[Here let me interject another little quotation from Gunther:
'Weather conditions still too heavy for station work. We run into
Drygalski Fjord. Wireless from the *Discovery*—"Transparency disc
not deemed expedient. Sorry to hear work impossible. D line proceeds

The R.R.S. *William Scoresby* in Larsen Harbour, Drygalski Fjord, South Georgia.

under ideal conditions." They were four stations ahead of us this time,
and the hint of sarcasm we sensed in their condolence determined us
to set the pace.']

The fjord did not give us the shelter we had expected; it formed a
funnel for the NW. wind which whistled down it with gale strength,
throwing up white clouds of spindrift. We turned into the narrow
side-branch of Larsen Harbour which is so serpentine as to be completely screened by its wall-like sides. The whole scene is compressed
laterally; from the narrow fjord of emerald green water everything

rushes upwards to the sky, and here the snow peaks merge into the clouds. . . . By early afternoon the weather appeared to be moderating so that we ventured out and managed to complete stations E2 and E3 under difficulties; by midnight it had much improved and by the time we reached E5, it was excellent. The soundings along the line were 77·5, 135, 121, 161, and then, suddenly over the shelf, 1,242 metres. We completed E5 at nine in the morning having worked all through the night. We reached DE at three in the afternoon and CD2 at half past nine. We now had to take soundings with the wire on the hydrographic reel because the bearings of the Lucas machine had cracked at E5; this caused a considerable delay as we went to 2,013 metres, 'no bottom,' with the full extent of the wire out, and CD2 was not completed till four in the morning. CD1, our last station, was reached at 6 o'clock and finished at 8.35. [Now let me give Gunther's version of this:

Not until half-past three were we working on the position evacuated yesterday (E1). Half-past three soon merged to half-past five, ten, midnight, and so midsummer night was passed—doing stations, bottling catches, pushing forward. At intervals we carried raids into the galley, where are cocoa, sandwiches and buttered toast. By the first watch we had completed the second line and so, with breakfast as our dinner, we turned in, not expecting to be on station again before tea-time. But no such luck; our relentless engine-room forged ahead and brought us out again at two in the afternoon, with puffy eyes and hands inflamed by bruises, cuts, salt and formalin, with skin engrained with dirt and cracked. We plunged into the fray again, having slept, in all, for scarcely five-and-twenty hours in the last six days. By 10.0 p.m. there remained but two stations, the first of which was deep and lengthened by an accident.

Thursday, December 23rd. One more station. We had heard nothing of the *Discovery*, we were racing against time. Then came a telegram—'*Discovery* hove to, waiting for abatement of gale before completing last station'—Ha-ha! In a few minutes our last was completed and over what seemed the most luscious of breakfasts Hardy was able to ruminate a reply which began: 'Sorry your conditions impossible . . .']

Actually the *Discovery* finished her part of the programme in the early hours of the same morning; it was as good as a dead heat. In five days the whole survey was completed (except the western side to be done later). This must be the first time that such an intensive plankton and hydrological programme, taking so many observations

23. The ship forced to a standstill in heavy pack-ice

24. Pack-ice being driven past an iceberg in a gale, and the path of the *Discovery* through the ice after narrowly missing ship-wreck on the berg

at each point from near the bottom to the surface and covering some 10,000 square miles of sea, has been completed in so short a time. In 5½ days 29 stations were worked yielding 370 water samples and 307 plankton net hauls. [Writing 35 years later I can say that I doubt very much if it has yet been equalled.] Every man on each ship did his utmost to make it a great success. On the *William Scoresby*, with so small a crew, we were very short-handed for such work, but all knew what we were trying to achieve—with the odds, the chances of frequent storms, heavily against us—and they entered into the spirit of the contest; without being asked, the stokers, whenever they could, turned out to help with the nets. As we steamed home I received a wireless message of congratulation on our performance from Dr. Kemp. I at once posted up the following message on the notice boards of the ward-room and the mess deck:

To the Captain, Officers and Ship's Company of the R.S.S. *William Scoresby*:

I have just received Dr. Kemp's congratulations on excellent piece of work. In passing this on to you I wish to take this opportunity to express my great appreciation of, and admiration for, the way in which every man on the ship has done his utmost to achieve this success. There is no doubt that the results will be of great value in the investigations we are engaged upon and we may have every hope that they will form a permanent contribution to oceanographical science. Thank you all very much.

A. C. HARDY

So, a happy ship, we steamed into Grytviken, and it was two days to Christmas.

All the expedition were together, the two ships and the shore party. On Christmas eve we met for a punch-bowl party at the Marine Station and a jovial evening we had with songs, games and high-jinks of one kind and another. It was a memorable occasion; after the hard work of the past week everyone was ready to enter into the carnival spirit. [I believe it was on this occasion that I first launched my parody of 'Yip-I-Addy-I-Ay' which I'm afraid then became a traditional act at all such future occasions; yes, it is even known from time to time to-day to echo from the past when old members may gather for a reunion somewhere in Soho. I cannot really sing a note in tune, yet one song from my school days I have always remembered: it was that ditty sung by George Grossmith in 'Our Miss Gibbs' in the heyday of Edwardian musical comedy. This is how my parody went:

K

Doctor Kemp our Director, world famed dissector,
    Collector of all forms of life,
Led a great expedition, to put down sedition
    'Mongst whales where 'twas said to be rife.
With high nets and low nets and all kinds of tow-nets
    He fished up the life of the sea,
But when someone below, sang this song that you know,
    He flung it all back in his glee!

                              (as if he would!)

Yip-i-addy-i-ay-i-ay, Yip-i-addy-i-ay!
    I don't care what becomes of me,
When you play me that sweet melody,
        Yip-i-addy-i-ay!
    My heart wants to shout out 'Hooray',
    Sing of joy, sing of bliss,
    Home was never like this,
                              Yip-i-addy-i-ay!

Now Stenhouse our skipper, a hard-case old ripper,
    Since he was a nipper of nine,
Took command of this barque, 'Cutty Sark' of an ark,
    And sailed her far over the brine.
He'd coal short and pack-ice, and fog that was not nice,
    Conditions most sure to annoy,
But when the Chief at the keys, played with such breezy ease,
    He set the wheel spinning with joy!

Yip-i-addy-i-ay-i-ay, Yip-i-addy-i-ay! etc.

Among my old *Discovery* papers I found a caricature of myself by
J. W. Ridley, the Chief Engineer on the *Scoresby*, which was drawn
after this occasion if I remember aright; I reproduce it opposite to
give the flavour of the festivities.]

On Christmas morning we had a simple service on the *Discovery* with
the old Christmas hymns—I think everyone enjoyed it—and at midday
our Christmas dinner. Dr. Marshall and I were looking after the
decorations and arrangements generally, so we had a busy time
beforehand fixing up paper festoons, lanterns, holly and mistletoe
(artificial) and crackers on the table. Mr. Binnie, the magistrate,
brought us a fine rose and some sweet-peas from his greenhouse for our
centrepiece; they were much appreciated. We were all rather like
children; we gave each other presents, things bought from the canteen,

Caricature of the author singing 'Yip-i-addy-i-ay'
drawn at South Georgia, Christmas, 1926, by J. W.
Ridley, Chief Engineer of the R.S.S. *William Scoresby;*
he is depicted with a tow-net in one hand and
waving his plankton recorder (in miniature) with the
other, with a cloud of krill above his head and one
of the small winches for working nets in the background.

often quite absurd things, wrapped up in absurd ways. Each man had some kind of present and they were drawn out of a bag by Father Christmas (the Doctor, of course, in fine cotton-wool beard). . . .

It was indeed a happy Christmas. The two ships working together had splendidly won round two in the battle for our knowledge of the whaling grounds; and we shall presently, in chapter 14, see just how much that was.

CHAPTER 13

ROUND THREE

Tuesday, 4th January, 1927. Whilst a thorough analysis of the plankton can only be made on our return home, we must have an idea of its general distribution before planning the rest of the survey; I have, therefore, been busy with the collections and will here sketch the main features.

To the eastward of the island, along its whole length, there is a zone against the coast occupied by small copepods and comparatively few diatoms[1]. Outside this, and at each end of the island, are rich patches of diatoms, composed largely of *Corethron valdiviae*, at times yielding a settled volume of over 60 c.c. per sample; it is one of the most characteristic species of the Antarctic. Farther out the diatoms are fewer, but of many more kinds. Over this groundwork are spread, in different patterns, the larger planktonic animals: the ctenophores (comb-jellies), the hyperiid amphipods (*Parathemisto*), the larger copepods, the euphausiaceans (particularly the krill) and the salps.

Euphausia superba, the krill or whale food, which is, of course, the focus of our attention, appears by inference to occur in numerous patches; at one time the smaller net (70 cm. diameter), towed for only a quarter of a mile, makes a very heavy catch whereas the larger net (1 metre diameter), towed for 1 mile immediately before it at the same depth, yields hardly any, or *vice versa*. Nevertheless, by consider-ing the total krill caught in all the towed nets at each station, we are able to arrive at a good general idea of their distribution. We find most to the north and north-east, with the heaviest catches at the end of the lines where the shelf drops away into deep water; there is little to the south-east. Conditions are thus very different from those at the end of last season when all the krill were so much nearer the coast.

To complete the survey three pieces of work seem necessary: (1) to

[1]This brief account of the plankton is based in part on my original journal and part on a rather fuller statement written at the same time as part of a scientific report ('Second Report on the Scientific Work of the *William Scoresby*') which I sent to the Committee at home.

293

run similar lines of stations on the other side of the island, to the west and south-west; (2) to continue the lines B and C, at the ends of which quantities of krill had been taken over deep water, to see how far they extend; and (3) to take one or more continuous series of towed nets to try to determine the frequency, size and density of the patches of krill[1]. The last seems most important in order to determine what reliance can be placed on observations from a single station and also to find out if such concentrations are typical; the reader will remember the swarms of immature krill that we saw in Grytviken harbour early in December (p. 275).

In addition it may be possible to take current measurements at each end of the island to determine the rate of the westerly drift. It seems likely that South Georgia, placed almost at right angles to the current from the south-west, may provide a set of conditions peculiarly favourable to the growth of plankton. Waters rich in phosphates and nitrates stirred up from deeper levels as the current strikes the continental shelf, may give rise to an exceptionally rich phytoplankton which, carried round the ends of the island, may be held for a time in an eddy on the eastern side; here, in the lee of the island, and fed by the fresh supplies of diatoms from either side, may well be an exceptional 'nursery' area for the krill, and so explain why South Georgia is so rich a whaling ground. Here at any rate was a hypothesis to test.

On Thursday the *Discovery* set out to do some trawling but no sooner had she got outside than the glass began to fall steeply and the north-west wind came shrieking down the valleys in savage gusts. In the afternoon we received a wireless saying she was in difficulties and so at once made ready to go to her assistance if it should be necessary, although it would take us the best part of an hour to get steam up. The wind was rising to hurricane force and the fjord was blotted out as clouds of spindrift, carried upwards in spiral columns from the water, were whirled across the scene. Then came the better news that the *Discovery* was slowly making her way back. She indeed made slow progress and at 10 o'clock was only just holding her own off Sappho Point at the entrance to East Bay. We reached her just as she went aground. To get shelter she had cut it rather too fine, and a strong gust from an unexpected quarter had struck her stern and swung her round. She was lucky again for it was only a bank of gravel. By the time we got up to her and had made fast with lines she had actually got off. Ending well, it was an exciting little incident while it lasted;

[1]The full grown krill are too large to be successfully sampled by my continuous plankton recorder; they generally fail to pass through the narrow slit by which the catching silk leaves the sampling tunnel on its way to the storage roll.

it was no easy matter, in the darkness, with sweeping sleet and spray, to manœuvre alongside without our rigging becoming entangled in her spars, sheets and shrouds, which loomed above us. We were soon in port again.

To-morrow the two ships should start on the third round of our survey: the *Discovery* to take a continuous series of nets to study the patchiness of the krill and to extend the lines of observation over deeper water, and we on the *Scoresby* to go to the west to complete the survey of conditions right round the island, and also to explore some of the little-known western coast.

To-day we witnessed a pathetic sight: the arrival of the three-masted sailing ship *Fortuna* from Norway; this is the end of her last voyage, for she has come here to die, to become a hulk for mere storage. Having no auxiliary power she was towed up the fjord by a whale-catcher and I was reminded of Turner's famous picture 'The Fighting Temeraire being towed to her last Berth'; here was the same sense of sadness.

Sunday, 16th January. We were delayed again by gales until the 6th. On our way round to the west, we landed Chaplin's party in Drygalski Fjord to 'fix' the position of the southern end of the island, and then set off at daybreak next morning. Exactly the same procedure was to be carried out at each station as before. We were to work two main lines of stations: F running s. 15° w. of Pickersgill Island with the first station FI between the island and the mainland, and G running w. by s. from Cape Nunes, each to be continued, as before, till we reached a depth of more than a 1,000 metres; then there were to be inter-mediate stations (EF, FG and GH) between the lines at the points shown in the map on p. 279.

The weather was remarkably fine so we kept going continuously, completing thirteen stations in just over three days. The ship's crew worked watch and watch, but we, the scientific staff, Wheeler, Gunther, Clowes and myself, having tried to do the same, working in pairs, found it impracticable and we all kept on. We started EF at 6.30 a.m. on the Friday morning, finished G6 at 5.56 p.m. on Sunday night and then did GA, off Willis Island, on Monday morning. In contrast to the F line, which gave a sounding at F4 of over 1,400 metres, the G line was exceptionally shallow; the shelf ran out far in this direction, so that the sounding at G6 was still only 210 metres.

Normally we should have gone at once to complete the G line till we were over deep water but I considered some rest was essential. Except for hurried meals, every moment of our time between stations was taken, as before, in labelling, concentrating and preserving our catches, and writing up the scientific logs; and at stations it was of course continuous action. Since the few hours' sleep we got when we tried to take watch and watch on Friday night, Gunther and Clowes had done 36 hours' continuous work and Wheeler and I had done 34; I decided we must take eight hours' sleep whilst we went to GA and then we could return to complete the G line refreshed. There comes a time when, while it is physically still possible to carry on, there is a danger of making mistakes in the reading of thermometers and metre wheels; then it is essential to rest, if the quality of the work is to be maintained.

We began station GA badly with an accident. No doubt due to being just roused from sleep when still overtired, we committed the awful and dangerous crime of catching our first vertical net in the propeller; in our eagerness, we lowered it too soon—before getting the signal from the bridge. The ship had stopped, but the captain had not quite finished manœuvring. It might indeed have been serious if we had been unable to get it clear, with its wires, hoop and heavy lead tightly jammed; we were off a rocky lee-shore with mist closing down and a wind freshening from the west. After turning the propeller slowly and pulling on the wire had failed, the captain and one of the hands made a splendid effort and freed it with boat-hooks from a dinghy. It was a dangerous operation, working under the counter, rising and falling in a fair swell and jabbing with the hook; now pulling on the wire, and now ordering a turn on the propeller, they finally succeeded. We were now getting short of water and so, after completing the station, we proceeded round the north of the island to Prince Olaf Harbour; with its present equipment the ship is not able to condense sufficient water for its needs when working close stations. As we went the mist became thick fog and at one time we found ourselves between three icebergs, narrowly escaping collision.

As we steamed to Prince Olaf we were able to make a rough examination of the plankton on the western side. Close against the coast, as on the other side, was a zone comparatively free of diatoms and occupied by small copepods, but here they were much more numerous. Outside this was a great belt of diatoms of a density even greater than that of the patches on the north-east side and not the same 'almost pure culture' of *Corethron*[1]. This richer diatom formation in a belt just inside the edge of the shelf and curving round the south side of the island, together with the fact that we got hardly any krill on this side of the

---

[1] With the *Corethron* and greatly predominating over it, was a very small species of *Chaetoceros* (*Ch. socialis*), with the addition at different stations of varying quantities of other diatoms (*Fragellaria, Rhizoselenia, Thalassiothrix* etc.)

island, seems to give good support to our idea that the whale food is concentrated in an eddy in the lee of the island fed by a rich phytoplankton generated by upwelling on the western side. We were duly elated. [Actually, although not a bad guess, later considerations call for a slight reinterpretation of this view, as we shall learn in the next chapter.] Whilst there were very few krill, there were many of the amphipod *Parathemisto* and over the wide continental shelf were large numbers of mysids (opossum shrimps) *Antarctomysis maxima* which we had not met with at all on the other side of the island. There were also a number of the large purple *Beröe* (Ctenophores or comb-jellies) which had been quite a feature of the plankton off Grytviken last season; one very large one which we caught at night was brilliantly luminous down its eight longitudinal bands of comb-plates.

On arrival at Prince Olaf Harbour we learnt that the *Discovery* had again been forced back to Grytviken by bad weather without extending the B line or doing a continuous net series. I therefore decided, after a night's rest, to leave next evening and run a series of continuous nets through the night to arrive at B4 in the early morning; there was an advantage in taking the series at night as we knew from our earlier experience that the krill would be right up against the surface in darkness, and so the experiment would be more easily done.

Before sailing we spent a very pleasant afternoon at the Bay of Isles to the north. In almost freak weather—warm like an English summer day—we looked out over this beautiful wide-sweeping bay studded with little rocky islands and with a high glacier at its head.

The continuous series of nets, which we ran through the night from 9.30 p.m. to 3.15 in the morning, when we arrived at B4, gave us a striking record of patchiness. We worked the line with two 1-metre diameter tow-nets which were exactly alike in every particular. They were towed alternately just below the surface, each for exactly a quarter of an hour at a constant speed of as nearly as possible 2 knots; as one net was hauled in over the starboard quarter the other was let out to port and *vice versa*. Thus a series of 23 consecutive samples was taken, each net traversing approximately half a mile of water.

[Our record of patchiness was exciting, but it was nothing to that which the *Discovery* got a few nights later when she made a splendid series of 49 hauls on the 'c' line. I will discuss the two sets of results together. The *Discovery* series gave very much higher catches of *Euphausia superba*, the krill, of the amphipod *Parathemisto gaudichaudi* and also the salp *Salpa fusiformis*[1]; it appeared that the area of the c line was much richer in zoöplankton generally than the B line, and the

[1]Now *S. thompsoni*, see p. 500.

degree of patchiness was greater than we could possibly have imagined. The results I believe make quite a new contribution to the natural history of the plankton. The area crossed by the *Discovery* series begins some 30 miles from land, and extends for another 30 miles; the patchiness cannot have been caused by the water being continually broken up by coastal disturbances. It has often been assumed that the plankton is more or less evenly distributed, at any rate over distances of a few miles together; actually it was my doubts about this that led me to invent my continuous plankton recorder, but here was a patchiness far exceeding what I had expected.

Instead of giving tables of numbers[1] I will reproduce opposite one of the histogram charts from our report in *Discovery Reports*, vol. xi, which shows the patchiness of the krill (*E. superba*). The *William Scoresby* results (Station w.s. 53), are inset in the larger graph of those of the *Discovery*. The consecutive nets in each series are labelled A.B.C.D. . . . etc. and against each is a scale of time and distance[2] (in miles); the *Discovery* series ran from daylight through darkness to daylight again, whereas the shorter *Scoresby* series was entirely at night, as indicated by the time-scale being blacked in between sunset and sunrise. The main concentrations of krill are lying in an area some 15 miles across. The catches between R and Y in the *Discovery* series alternate rather regularly between high and low values: 11,604—1,419—7,774—873—7,758—535—9,231—201 which might at first sight suggest that one net is fishing more efficiently than the other; if we look just before and after this part of the series, however, we see this is not the explanation, for they get 'out of step.' We see how exceedingly patchy the krill is; do these animals always remain in tight swarms such as those of the younger forms we saw at Grytviken? We will reconsider this (pp. 408 and 482) when further evidence has been gathered, but it is quite clear that they are most irregularly distributed into areas of higher and lower concentration. It helps us to understand how the huge whales are able to gather sufficient nourishment from mere planktonic shrimps; they are conveniently 'gathered together' in meals almost ready prepared. Indeed, if the whale krill of the northern hemisphere, the euphausiacean *Meganyctiphanes norvegica*, is shown to occur in similar dense swarms, as I believe to be so, then the evolution of the whalebone whales of this great size may well have depended upon the swarming habits of these small crustaceans.

[1] These can be found in tables iv and v of appendix ii to Hardy and Gunther's 'Plankton of the South Georgia Whaling Grounds . . .', *Discovery Reports*, vol. xi.

[2] The *Discovery* was unable to keep her speed to exactly 2 knots and was in fact a little faster, so that each of her hauls is a little less than half a mile in extent.

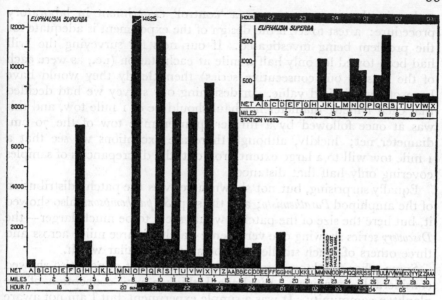

Histograms showing the variations in the numbers of *Euphausia superba* taken in forty-nine consecutive surface hauls with the 100 cm. tow-nets (A-AAA) at Station 150 and in another twenty-three similar hauls (A-X) at Station ws 53 (inset). From *D.R.*, vol. XI.

Mackintosh and Wheeler (in their big *Discovery Report* of 1929) make an interesting observation in commenting on the krill found in the stomachs during the 1926-7 season. They state that:

The krill differed from that of other seasons in the fact that there was in most cases a noticeable mixing of Euphausiids of different sizes. These were not always mixed indiscriminately in the stomach. Large or small individuals might be found together in different parts of the mass of stomach contents, or patches of large ones might occur in a mass of smaller forms, suggesting that the whale had been feeding on separate shoals which differed in respect of the sizes of the individuals . . .

Another object of these experiments, as we said at the beginning of the chapter, was to determine, in view of possible patchiness, 'what reliance can be placed on observations from a single station.' If, as in our survey, stations are ten miles apart, can each one be considered as reasonably representative of the area around it? In other words, if the plankton was so very patchy could the isolated hauls give us such representation? These consecutive hauls are to be looked upon rather in the same way as is a 'control' experiment in laboratory procedure: a test to see if the design of the experiment is adequate for the problem being investigated. If our nets for surveying the krill had been towed for only half a mile at each station (i.e., as were each of the nets in our consecutive series) then clearly they would have been of very limited value. In designing our survey we had decided that each 1-metre diameter net haul should be of 1 mile tow, and this was at once followed by a further quarter mile tow of the 70 cm. diameter net; luckily, although there are exceptions we see that a 1 mile tow will to a large extent 'iron out' the discrepancies of samples covering only half that distance.

Equally surprising, but not shown here, was the patchy distribution of the amphipod *Parathemisto*; and the salp, *Salpa thompsoni*, also showed it, but here the size of the patches would seem to be much larger—the *Discovery* series showing one very dense patch of three miles across and three others of much smaller numbers but of similar width.

Some other plankton animals from the same set of nets also showed considerable patchiness. We have I think a new conception of the plankton community. It was a simple experiment, but I am not aware of it having been made before. We took two more such series in the Brandsfield Straits much farther south when we surveyed that area; these gave equal evidence of uneven distribution (see chart, p. 409). Let us now, after this digression, return to where we have completed the *Scoresby*'s line of consecutive nets and arrived at the position of B4 where we repeated the station made there earlier by the *Discovery* as a prelude to extending the line much farther to the north.]

Daybreak was a wonderful one; the whole range of the South Georgian mountains was clear cut along the skyline to the south and flushed with the light of dawn, and nearer to us were icebergs of many shapes reflecting the same rosy glow. For some hours after sunrise the water was a flat calm like the sea in the doldrums and it seemed warm too; just as the previous afternoon at the Bay of Isles had been like an English summer, so also did this morning appear almost unreal for South Georgia. The water was very blue and clear and as we worked the station we saw many long chains of salps swimming near the surface, evidently part of the patch we had been recording in the last hauls of our series; and here and there we could even see individual specimens of full-grown krill and sometimes little companies of them, some thirty or forty, all swimming together in one direction. Actually we did not catch many krill in our horizontal nets at this station or at the next B5.

As we began to proceed towards B6 under conditions ideal for work came the frustrating report from the engine-room of a breakdown in

the water feed pump which necessitated an immediate return to
Grytviken; it was really maddening to have to abandon this line and
further postpone our return to the west. Science at sea is not only at
the mercy of the elements. After a day in port for repairs we went
straight to the south to pick up Chaplin's survey party from Larsen
Harbour, where we found them well and comfortable in their camp.
The elephant seals, however, had proved rather a nuisance in that they
evidently objected to the erection of the tide-recording pole in what
they must have regarded as their favourite shallow water wallowing
pond; night after night they pushed it down. From Larsen we came
yesterday to Leith Harbour to land Chaplin's party for further surveying at Cape Saunders. Leith Harbour is one of three inlets in large
Stromness Bay which lies immediately to the north of Cumberland
Bay; the other two inlets in the bay are Stromness and Husvik
harbours and all three are the sites of flourishing whaling stations
[now abandoned].

It was from the mountain above Leith that the great avalanche of
1913 crashed down and swept a large part of the whaling station into
the sea; it lifted, we were told, some of the huge oil boilers bodily
from their places and hurled them right over the bows of a ship at
anchor. It was a lucky chance that the blow struck just at the dinner
hour when nearly all the hands had left the flensing platform and
boiler houses for the canteen; otherwise there would have been a
heavy loss of life. The scene, however, is more memorable, for just
across from here, down to the next whaling station, Stromness, came
Shackleton, Worsley and Crean at the end of their wonderful crossing
of the mountains, following their equally amazing open boat journey
from Elephant Island to get help for their ship-wrecked comrades.
Here, if ever there was one, is a scene to be held sacred in commemora-
tion of the spirit of human endeavour. Their ship, crushed in the ice
of the Weddell Sea to the south, was named the *Endurance*; ice, storm
and adversity could not crush the endurance of her company. There
is a passage in Shackleton's *South*, his story of his expedition, which is a
vivid example of a certain extraordinary type of human experience;
a collection of such examples will, I believe, in time be made and may
well provide an important contribution to the natural history of man.
I quote the passage from p. 209 in the first edition of his book:

When I look back at those days I have no doubt that Providence
guided us, not only across those snowfields, but across the storm-
white sea that separated Elephant's Island from our landing place
on South Georgia. I know that during that long and racking
march of thirty-six hours over the unnamed mountains and

glaciers of South Georgia it seemed to me often that we were four, not three. I said nothing to my companions on the point, but afterwards Worsley said to me, 'Boss, I had a curious feeling on the march that there was another person with us.' Crean confessed to the same idea. One feels 'the dearth of human words, the roughness of mortal speech' in trying to describe things intangible, but a record of our journeys would be incomplete without a reference to a subject very near to our hearts.

Sunday, 23rd January. Leaving Leith Harbour early last Monday morning we set out once more to work the B line, due north of Prince Olaf, to see how far the krill extended. On the way to our first position we came across, in the middle of the morning, a dense patch of birds. There were thousands upon thousands of them: small whale birds (*Prion*), Cape pigeons, and Wilson's petrels, with a few albatross, all gathered in an area about half a mile across; most of them were asleep on the water, although quite a number of the whale birds were flying round like flocks of starlings. We had heard about these patches of birds from the whalers who thought they always denoted a thick patch of krill and said that they usually caught quantities of fish there. I put out a series of three 1-metre diameter nets (one at the surface, one at 50 metres depth and another at 100 metres), and towed them towards the area, but we caught relatively little krill (9 near the surface, 137 at 50 metres, and none at 100 metres); we did catch rather more of the amphipods *Parathemisto* (464 at the surface, but only 8 and 6 at the lower levels) and possibly these may have accounted for the assembly. For the birds, clearly the feast was over; most of them as I have said were asleep as if gorged with food. Perhaps earlier in the morning *all* the krill were against the very surface but at the time we used our nets they had sunk to a level, say, between the surface and 50 metres and so been missed by us. We shot one of the *Prion* to see what it was feeding on, but its stomach was empty. Being pressed for time we had to hurry on, leaving the cause of the concentration unexplained.

At B6 we got about 700 krill in the three 1-metre diameter nets, but the numbers fell off as we went on over the deep water to work B7, B8 and B9: showing us that we had passed the areas of great abundance; at the last station we also did a full set of vertical observations.

We had next intended taking current measurements off Willis Island on our way to complete the G line but as we got there the glass fell violently and our 'little summer' was over for a time. We therefore went into Wilson Harbour which was the first of several west coast harbours we had hoped to survey and report on in some detail. On the following day Mercer and Lester undertook a survey under difficult conditions of mist and rain, and Wheeler, in spite of the poor weather, took an excellent series of photographs of this and Undine Harbour with their entrances and other prominent land marks each with a bearing given by Mercer or Lester.

I will not dwell on the details of the landscape, they were submitted in a report sent to the Committee at home; here I wish to convey more the impressions of the scene. Jagged precipitous mountains, blotched with snow and ice, appear and disappear in the driving mist and rain. Lower down at sea level are stretches of soaking wet tussock grass in which, at every few paces, lie half a dozen to a score of fat—monstrously fat—sea elephants wallowing in pools of their own filth, or there are colonies of screaming gentoo penguins with their fluffy youngsters like great dolls beside them; and over the shingle of the river beds swoop the graceful white terns. The elephant seals, like those we saw last season, have hauled out to moult and are continually scratching themselves to free the layer of epidermis which comes away with the hair; they scratch with their finger-nails in a very human fashion. I was surprised to find how large the young gentoo penguins were, since it was only a month ago that we saw the chicks hatching at Undine Harbour a few miles to the north; these were now standing about three-quarters the height of their parents, dressed in a coat of white and chocolate down. By the edge of a stream we collected not only the two species of burnet (*Acoena ascendens* and *A. teuera*) but the beautiful little Antarctic buttercup *Ranunculus biternatus*; there was also a rush, *Juncus scheuchzeroides* . . .

Along the beach, upon which lay the dried skeletons and many rotting carcasses of flensed seals, were groups of Dominican gulls and skuas. Some of the skuas were very savage when we came near their nests high up on the ledges above the valley. Time after time an enraged bird would fly like a bullet straight at our faces and then, when just a yard or two off, would skim up over our heads. The little tern (wreathed terns) were braver still and I experienced a massed attack as I walked up the shingle moraine in the valley; there must have been hundreds of them. At first they merely circled and swooped above my head crying loudly, but when I actually came to the site of their nests—or rather eggs, for, like all terns, they make no proper nest, they attacked in grand style. One after another they swooped down and pecked my head through the thick tweed hat I was wearing; thump, thump, thump, I felt the repeated sharp blows; my hat was luckily thicker than the doctor's cap, for in his case, as I have already related, they drew blood. This was kept up so long as I remained among their eggs, which with their blotched colouring were exceedingly difficult to see. On the shingle too were several very young Dominican gulls, balls of speckled fluff which, similarly camouflaged, would lie absolutely motionless as one stood over them and then, as soon as one turned away, would be up and running swiftly on their big legs which appeared all out of proportion to their little bodies. The parent gulls, although screaming overhead, were not so brave as the little terns and made no attempt to attack.

About four hundred feet up the side of the valley Gunther found many nests of the diving petrel *Pelecanoides georgicus*, a pretty bird with a white breast and dark grey back, head and bill; they make burrows two or three feet in length and often with a bend in them. Along the edge of the beach we saw many of the lark-like Antarctic pipit *Anthus antarcticus* which is found nowhere else in the world and is, in fact, the most southerly of all passerine birds. We never saw them fly more than a few yards, but they were continually on the run, this way and that, and round and round the tufts of tussock; they feed on small insects among the grass, and molluscs and crustacea on the shore. As we lay at anchor their song, or rather a constant twittering, came to us pleasantly across the water, but interrupted at intervals by the deep growls of the elephants.

The weather having greatly improved we set off the next day to continue the G line out past the 1,000 metre line; you will remember that before at G6 we only got a depth of 210 metres, so now our first objective was, of course, G7 ten miles beyond. We must have passed over the edge very soon and abruptly for at this station we got a sounding of 1,752 metres and worked a full vertical station. It is quite surprising how steeply the continental shelf falls away around the island once one comes to its edge; we have now defined its limits in all directions. On p. 305 is a contour chart of the sea bed around South Georgia based upon the many soundings taken during our survey journeys, for we often took depth readings between stations; and below it is a cross section (with an exaggerated vertical scale) through the line AB shown on the chart. I have written already about the rapid erosion of the island by frost. Does the 'continental shelf' or plateau around it represent the original size of South Georgia? It almost certainly does, and what we now see is but the last and (geologically speaking) quickly vanishing remains of a great mountain range, like part of the Andes, which originally occupied the limits of the plateau as we now find it. Year by year, slice by slice, it is carved away by frost and carried to the sea by glaciers. There are some days when one sees only the highest peaks of South Georgia standing above a line of clouds looking like a chain of islands in the sky, the rest hidden

25. Working a vertical plankton net on the *Discovery*. F. C. Fraser is on the outboard platform adjusting the net before it goes down and the author is at the winch ready to let it out and to control its speed of hauling with stop watch and depth recording wheel (see diagram on p. 150)

26–27. The great wandering albatross (*Diomedea exulans*). *Above*, photographed from the *Discovery*. *Below*, breeding on the tussock grass slopes at the north end of South Georgia: a protest at being disturbed. *Opposite*, different phases in the albatross courtship dance: a serenade, a bow and a kiss

28. The *Discovery* in a gale on passage from South Georgia to the South Orkneys, showing the sails almost blowing out and the sailors furling them

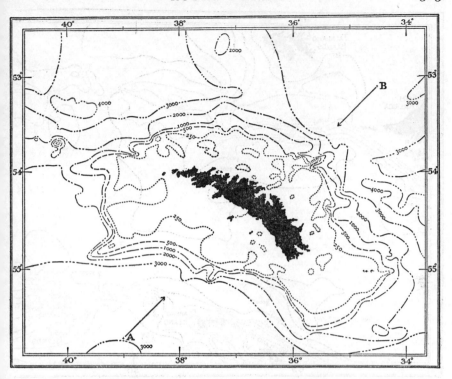

Contour chart of the the submarine plateau upon which South Georgia stands covering the main area of our plankton survey, with the depths shown in metres. AB indicates the line of the section shown in the figure below. From *D.R.*, vol. XI.

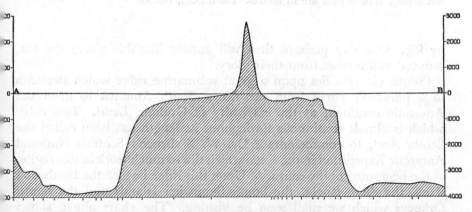

A section through South Georgia along the line AB in the chart above; with the vertical scale exaggerated. The heights and depths are expressed in metres; and the positions of the soundings are indicated along the base line. From *D.R.*, vol. XI.

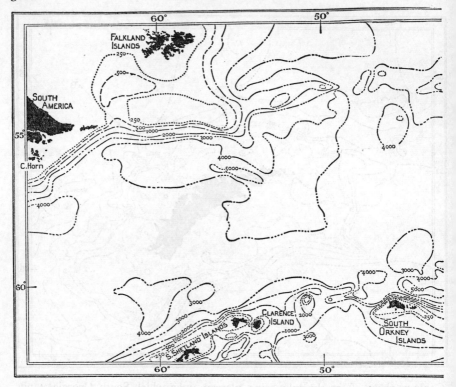

Contour chart of the ocean floor showing the position of South Georgia on the Scotia Arc, based largely upon soundings taken during the *Discovery* Investigations (after Herdman). The depths are in metres. From *D.R.*, vol. XI.

by fog. One day perhaps they will appear like this above the sea, reduced still further from their glory.

[South Georgia lies upon a great submarine ridge which stretches in a parabolic curve from the tip of South America to meet the Antarctic continent at the extremity of Graham Land. This ridge which is almost continuous throughout its length has been called the Scotia Arc[1], to commemorate Dr. W. S. Bruce's Scottish National Antarctic Expedition in the *Scotia* which did so much work in this region at the beginning of the century. Upon this ridge lie also the Burdwood Bank, the Shag Rocks, the South Sandwich Islands and the South Orkneys which we shall soon be visiting. The chart above shows the contours of the sea floor in this whole area. To the west the Arc

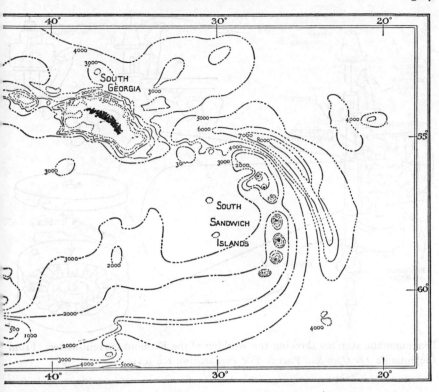

encloses a deep oceanic area, connected with the Pacific by the Drake Passage, and now known as the Scotia Sea. To the east stretches the great Southern Ocean, where, at a little distance beyond the ridge, depths of over 8,000 metres have been obtained by the *Meteor* and *Discovery II* expeditions. To the north of the Arc is the Atlantic Ocean and to the south lies the Weddell Sea. In the next chapter we shall see the influence of this configuration upon the flow of ocean currents which are so important to the understanding of the patterns of plankton distribution which our survey has just been revealing.]

Having completed our vertical station at G7 we ran a line of soundings to a position 10 miles NW. of those great mountainous rocks, Willis Islands, which lie just to the west of Bird Island and the northern extremities of the main island. They are as much covered with birds as Bird Island, or more so. Here we anchored in 137 metres and took current measurements with the Ekmann current-meter to find out how fast the plankton might be carried round the north end of the island by the general westerly drift.

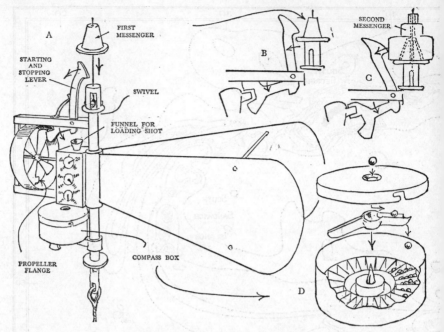

Diagrammatic sketches showing the working of the Ekmann current-meter. From the author's *The Open Sea,* Part I. For explanation see text.

Oceanographers will be familiar with the Ekmann machine, but it is such a beautiful and ingenious device that I think the general reader will appreciate a brief description of it. It is lowered into the water on a wire, and being provided, as shown in my sketch, with a vane like a weather-cock (actually a double one) it always points head on into the current. It has a little 'propeller' which will be turned by the water flowing past it; this, which is going to measure the flow, is held by a catch until the recording is about to begin. On the underside of the apparatus is a circular box, like a large and rather deep pill-box, whose lower half is divided into a number of compartments by partitions radiating from the centre like the spokes of a wheel; pivoted on a spike in the centre and swinging over the compartments is a stout compass needle having a slightly sloping groove on its upper surface running from its mid-point to the end pointing to the north. This, I think, will be clear from the sketch diagram. In addition this compass-box has a small hole in the centre of its lid and immediately above it is another little box containing a supply of bronze shot. To take measurements the ship must be anchored and the instrument lowered to the required depth, perhaps 10, 50 or 100 metres; then a small brass messenger weight, like the one we use to operate our water-bottles, is sent sliding down the wire to release a catch to set the propeller turning; after one, two, or more hours, as desired, a second, larger, messenger-weight stops the propeller and the machine is brought to the surface. The number of turns the propeller has made is recorded on a set of little dials from which the speed of the current can be calculated; in addition, after every so many revolutions the propeller shaft causes a little slot, at the bottom of the box containing the shot, to open and close and so at intervals to allow one shot at a time to drop into the box below and be guided by the grooved compass-needle into one or other of the little compartments. The compass box being fixed to the machine is always orientated to the direction of the current and the needle, swinging to the north, spreads the shot according to the variations in the current; thus by counting the shot found in each compartment at the end of a recording we know to what extent the current has varied in direction during the time of observation and also its average path of flow. The direction is given by the angle between the mid-line of the box (always pointing in the line of flow) and that of the compartment containing most shot which has, of course, most often been pointing to the north.

Our results showed a variation in residual currents from N.58 W. at 11.45 a.m. to S.20 W. at 3.35 p.m. (the flow expressed as coming *from* the directions named) and the speeds recorded varied from 3·6 cm. per second (·07 knots) or 1½ miles a day to 9·74 cm. per second (·19 knots) or 4½ miles a day; the variations in direction and speed are no doubt due to tidal action. Too much reliance cannot be placed on an isolated series of observations of this kind; they give, however, a provisional indication of what is happening. [We shall have more exact information, as to current directions and speeds, available to us in the next chapter.]

As we were finishing the current-meter station we saw more whales than we had ever seen together before; there must have been a school of fully a score or more large blue whales blowing about us, their white 'puffs of steam' showing up sharply in the cold sunlight. Perhaps they were a new school arriving at South Georgia from the west and had not yet found the rich krill to the north and east; for here we had found but little food for them. No sooner had we got the current-meter in, whilst we were still anchored, when a huge beast, seeming nearly as big as the ship, rose to blow almost under us, his head appearing just by our side. He must have grazed our hull; a lucky escape for our current-meter. So astonished were we that we had not time to snatch up the marking guns before he quickly sounded again, evidently quite as surprised as we were.

We had not yet used our big commercial-sized 90 foot otter-trawl with which the *Scoresby* would shortly be making a trawling survey off the Falklands; we wanted to sample the fish population on the west of the island to compare with the *Discovery*'s trawl catches to the east and this seemed a good time to try it out. We therefore went to the SW. of Willis Island to the middle of the wide shelf we had found which promised to be a favourable ground. The operation was under the charge of our first officer who had had special experience as a trawling skipper. The trawl went over the side perfectly, but alas, the *William Scoresby*, shorter and of a very different build to a typical trawler behaved in a manner quite unexpected by the old time trawler man; it swung in the wrong direction and in a flash one of the main warps was drawn into the propeller. With a frightful jerk the main engine stopped dead. How sorry I was for poor Irving.

The thick steel warp was tightly wound round the propeller shaft and matters were complicated by the presence of the great otter-board which hung down beside it. For two hours, turning the propeller slowly by hand gear and at the same time pulling on the warp, we tried to free it by every means we could think of. It was impossible. Darkness was falling and we were drifting out of control off a rocky lee shore acknowledged to be one of the most dangerous coasts in the world; we could anchor, of course, but exposed to the westerly gales which might come upon us with suddenness at any moment, it was not a desirable anchorage.

It was lucky that there were plenty of whales to the north of us so that there were several whale-catchers working not very far away; our wireless call for help brought a catcher to us very soon. She turned up with four whales in tow and without casting them off to be picked up later—it was now almost dark—she towed us quickly into North Undine Harbour where we could anchor safely in shelter.

The following day as we awaited the arrival of a whaler bringing a diver from Grytviken, we went ashore to have a look at the albatross. The low hills to the south of the bay are overgrown with tussock grass and studded with nesting birds; they do indeed look like sheep grazing on the hillside. These are the large wandering albatross which build up their nests on the top of tall grass tussocks; they are built up by pieces of peaty moss brought by the male and then put into position and stamped down by his mate. The sooty albatross, of which there were also a few here, nest in a hollow in the ground. When we were here before they had not yet begun to lay; now the eggs were well advanced and the birds were sitting closely. We could come right up to them now and usually they would show no alarm, unless we tried to push them off the nest to look at the egg, and then they resisted with all their might. In the morning, with few exceptions, there was just one bird at each nest, their mates being away after food; an occasional one or two circled overhead and sometimes when they swooped close over our heads we heard a noise, a rush of air, like an aeroplane gliding down to land with its engine shut off. In the afternoon I came across several pairs going through their delightful courtship and kissing act; a most remarkable display. Sometimes they would stand perfectly rigid with their necks and heads pointing straight up into the sky and then utter a guttural call; sometimes they would walk round with their necks stretched out as far as possible in front of them and their backs humped up in a curious way, making, at times, as they walked, a sort of low crooning sound. On approaching one another the male would stop, hold up his head and again stand rigid before his bride, spreading his wings out and high up so that their tips curved round pointing forwards towards her. Thus they would remain for half a minute or so—not a movement—as if carved from stone. Then they might start prowling round again with their necks out. Or they might come closer together and gravely bow their heads down and up, curving their necks so that their heads came close down in front of their breasts, an act which may be done once or several times; they would then stretch out their necks towards one another and bring their beaks together for an affectionate kiss. A very pretty sight it was, as may be seen in Plate 27 (p. 304).

[The foregoing account was written after only a little observation. Not being experienced in the study of bird behaviour I have no doubt that it is a far from accurate one and misses many of the subtleties which would be noted by the expert. For an excellent and more detailed account the reader should consult the paper on the birds of South Georgia by Harrison Matthews in vol. 1 of the *Discovery Reports*.]

The freeing of the propeller proved to be a longer task than we had anticipated. The diver did not arrive till evening and starting at 4 o'clock in the morning, and working in spells, it was noon before he got it entirely clear. The stern tube was found to be slightly damaged which will necessitate the ship going on the slip at an early date for repairs. Now on Sunday evening we are steaming back to Grytviken. This we must regard as the end of round three. Whilst we have been in the west the *Discovery* has been able to take more stations farther out on the c line. We have now covered the ground well, done all we set out to do, and must stay no longer. I shall rejoin the *Discovery* for her voyage to the south where we shall be doing a similar if less extensive survey of the whaling grounds in the Brandsfield Strait between the South Shetland Islands and the Graham Land coast of Antarctica.

[In the meantime, in the next two chapters, I shall deal more fully with the knowledge we have won on this South Georgian survey; if any reader should find them too technical he can skip to chapter 16 (p. 327) and join us as we go farther south.] Before I go on, however, I should record that while I was away on the *Scoresby*, Kemp on the *Discovery*, often prevented by bad weather from working outside, had done an immense amount of trawling and dredging in different parts of Cumberland Bay.

There can never have been a more enthusiastic collector than Kemp; he showed us how collecting should be done. After a trawl or dredge haul we first sorted out for separate preservation all the larger specimens, treating the various kinds in different ways to give the best result for later examination. Then we turned to deal with the contents of fine mesh nets which he had cunningly fixed to the back of the trawl to catch all the smaller creatures, largely crustaceans, which would otherwise have escaped through its mesees. Next we sieved the sand, gravel or mud for the tiny forms which might easily have been thrown away. Then had we finished?—dear me no! Kemp could extract much more from the haul and from his team working like slaves. He then showed us how by splitting open fragments of crumbling rock, kelp roots and bits of coral, what an assemblage af small burrowing forms of life were to be found in unexpected places. What a zoological education it was. I've said we worked like slaves—but we were not driven, we were compelled by his example and enthusiasm. If we stopped for a moment's relaxation, on he went, tireless, sometimes into the early hours of the morning. We compared ourselves— hauling on ropes, grovelling among the contents of the trawl, bespattered with mud and looking like a gang of pirates—with the naturalists of the *Challenger* Expedition. In the illustrations to their *Reports* they stand by, elegant, immaculately dressed, nonchalant, while the sailors soil their hands in picking out the contents of the dredge. Doubtless they were only the product of some Victorian artist's imagination, but there were times when we envied them.]

CHAPTER 14

THE KNOWLEDGE WON

For two chapters I am departing from my journal: in this to give
the results of our South Georgia survey—the facts—as they turned out
after all the material had been examined, and in the next to discuss
some theoretical considerations. I am giving only the main findings,
in as non-technical a fashion as I can; and space will not allow me to
give all the evidence so that the student should go to our full account
in the *Discovery Reports*[1].

Having seen our struggle with the elements, I think the reader will
like to know something of what we won. I hope, if he is not a zoologist,
he will not be put off by the scientific names of some of the animals,
for they are the only ones they have; he need not remember them and,
if he only regards them as counters in the game, he will see the pattern
of life revealed, which, for those who are not specialists, is all that
really matters. I hope, too, that he may also share in the pleasure of
seeing the picture of this hidden world gradually take shape as the
thousand and one pieces of the puzzle are fitted together. I am not
exaggerating here, for our findings are based upon 1,071 plankton
samples and a still higher number of physical and chemical observations: i.e., temperature, density, salinity, alkalinity (pH), phosphate
and oxygen values from many depths at each station. I use the term
'plankton sample' for a catch made by a standard net, and each of
these, of course, gave information as to many different species. Just
as there is excitement in snatching our samples between the storms, so
is there another fascination, quieter but no less real, of reconstructing
the course of nature from what at first appears to be a flood of data
almost equally opaque as the sea itself. The extent of the material
was certainly not a little daunting; one needed faith that something
worth while would emerge.

Plankton analysis is always a laborious process; there is no short

[1]Hardy and Gunther: 'The Plankton of the South Georgia Whaling Grounds and
Adjacent Waters 1926-27.' *Discovery Reports*, vol. XI, pp. 1-456, 1935.

cut if you want a knowledge of the whole community. I shall indent the description of the method so that it may more easily be skipped by those not specially interested.

First of all the volume of each sample was measured after it had been allowed to settle for 24 hours in a measuring jar; this, however, gave only a very rough indication of its bulk on account of the different settling properties of the organisms: spiny creatures, for example, do not pack so closely as do more rounded ones. Next the sample was spread out in a shallow dish and the larger animals, which could not be estimated fairly by our sub-sampling methods, were picked out and recorded; then the smaller, rarer ones were hunted with the microscope, for they too would not be properly sub-sampled on account of their scarcity. The final estimation of the main sample was now made by what is termed the 'stempel pipette' method invented by the German pioneer planktologist Victor Hensen.

This 'stempel' process requires a little description. The sample, made up by the addition of water to a particular volume, say 100 or 200 cc., is placed in a special spherical flask and the stempel pipette inserted. This device is a glass cylinder into which a metal piston with a groove round it can be drawn up by a rod with a handle, the groove being machined to have an exact volume of 1, 2 or 5 cc. according to the size used. The pipette is put into the plankton with its piston extruded; the flask is now shaken so as to thoroughly stir and spread all its contents as evenly as possible[1], and then the piston is pulled smartly up into the cylinder. The sub-sample so obtained is now spread on a glass slide engraved with fine lines into a grid of little squares each of a size that will just fill the field of view of the low power of a microscope. The slide is now moved backwards and forwards under the microscope on a mechanical stage until all the squares have been examined and the different species in them identified, counted and recorded.

From these counts we can easily calculate the total of each organism present: if our sample had been made up to 200 cc. and we had drawn out 2 cc., then all we had to do, of course, was to multiply the numbers of each animal counted by a hundred to give us our estimate. Various refinements were made for the different kinds of sample as explained in the full *Report*.

Counting, counting, counting—square after square, sample after

---

[1]Great care must be taken in this; if the sample is just swirled round, the heavier animals will be swung more to the outside and so not sampled properly.

sample—at times there seemed no end to it; but as the results began to show, one was buoyed up with the sense of achievement.

A number of people were concerned with the analyses. For the zoö-plankton Rolfe Gunther examined the samples from the vertical 70 cm. nets, Dr. Helene Bargmann undertook those from the horizontal 1 metre nets and the late Mr. Andrew Scott the horizontal 70 cm. nets; and I worked out the phytoplankton from the 50 cm. nets. Mr. Andrew Scott also examined the collection of copepods from all the nets; and in addition we received help in the identification of other specimens from many other people[1]. The hydrological analyses were made by Dr. A. J. Clowes at the Shore Station as the work progressed and all the physical and chemical data are recorded in vol 1 of the *Discovery Reports*.

Our aim was to bring together all the factors linking the great whales, through the plankton, to their physical and chemical background. The chain connecting them is fortunately short—quite remarkably so; it is indeed surprising that the largest animals in the world should be linked to a microscopic vegetation by only one intervening bond: the krill, which feeds directly on the tiny plants. Whilst this direct chain is short, there are, however, others linked to it; for example, those different little shrimps, the planktonic amphipods of the genus *Parathemisto*, feed extensively upon the young krill, so that if they are very abundant, as at times we have seen them to be, they may reduce next season's whale food in a particular body of water. The arrow-worms and comb-jellies too are voracious carnivores, and so on.

We are trying to give a picture of the whole community. A great deal of our work consisted in plotting the distribution of the different species around South Georgia and at different depths. It is true that the actual pattern of dispersion in itself, at this one time, will only be of limited value because a few weeks earlier, or later, it may have been very different according to the flow of currents and other changing conditions; nevertheless a study of the community at any *one* phase correlated with the physical and chemical factors *at that time*, may well reveal something of the general principles governing planktonic production. This is what we are really after. The various charts taken together present the 'anatomy' of the plankton community caught like a snapshot in one instant of time; a knowledge of the physics,

---

[1]   Dr. H. Bargmann—Chaetognatha   Dr. F. C. Fraser—Ostracoda
    Dr. H. K. Barnard—Amphipoda   Mr. E. Heron Allen—Foraminifera
    Mr. E. T. Browne—Medusae   Miss A. L. Massey—Pteropoda
    Mr. A. Earland—Foraminifera   Mr. C. C. A. Monro—Polychaeta
    Mr. G. P. Farran—Copepoda   Mr. A. K. Totton—Siphonophora

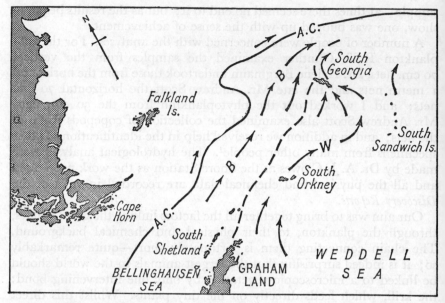

A chart showing the line of the Antarctic Convergence, A.C., which separates the
Sub-Antarctic water to the left (and north) from the Antarctic water to the right
(and south). The arrows show the main surface water movements, particularly the
two currents B and W, Bellingshausen Sea water and Weddell Sea water, which
influence South Georgia within the Antarctic Zone.

chemistry and motion of the water at that same moment helps towards
an understanding of its 'physiology': the vital interaction of the
community. It is as a living whole that I would try and present it.

Since I shall be using a good many charts and diagrams, it will
perhaps be more like an atlas with a running commentary, but in this
way I can cut down description. Let me begin with the physical background. Geographically speaking South Georgia is outside the
Antarctic Circle; but hydrologically it is some 250 miles within the
true Antarctic zone, so that our findings relate to the typical south
polar seas. The surface water is very cold, but less saline, and so lighter,
than that of the typical ocean because it receives icy *fresh* water from
the melting of the great barrier (and its broken-off icebergs); this ice,
as already explained, has been formed over thousands of years by the
accumulations of snow on the vast ice cap of the Antarctic continent
and slowly slid off like a gigantic glacier into the sea. This cold surface
water, which has a depth of some 200 metres, is being continually
added to by melting ice, and so moves northwards until it meets the

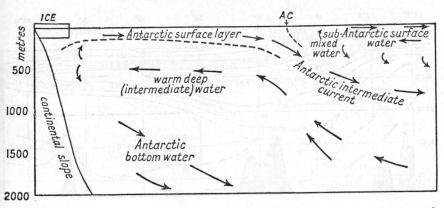

A vertical diagrammatic section of the Antarctic and Sub-Antarctic Zones, separated by the Antarctic Convergence, AC, to show the main water movements at different levels.

warmer surface water of the sub-Antarctic Zone; still going north, it sinks below this water which, although more saline, is actually lighter because it is warmer and so less dense. The front along which the Antarctic water dips below the surface forms the northern boundary of the Antarctic Zone and is called the Antarctic Convergence; it is shown in the map opposite. This northern flowing water is also deflected to the east by the westerly winds.

There is another stream of cold water but this is on the bottom, creeping northwards over the ocean floor; it has sunk because it is water which has been chilled, but not made lighter by the addition of fresh water. To take the place of these two northern-going streams, and indeed forming them, there is a warmer current flowing southward in between them; this becomes cooled against the ice and turned back: part of it, that diluted with fresh water, rises to the surface, and the rest sinks to the bottom. This is shown in the diagram above. Here we have a striking instance of waters at different levels travelling in different directions: the water going south flows in between the two layers going north[1]. We shall presently see some interesting consequences of this when we consider some plankton animals that make vertical migrations between two of the layers. This system is indeed important in relation to many of our problems. The likelihood of such a system was theoretically forecast as early as 1905 by Professor Otto Pettersson from his studies in the Arctic. Its existence in the south was revealed independently by two expeditions: the German *Meteor* and our own old *Discovery*. You will remember

[1]They are not strictly in *opposite directions* as each has a strong easterly component as well.

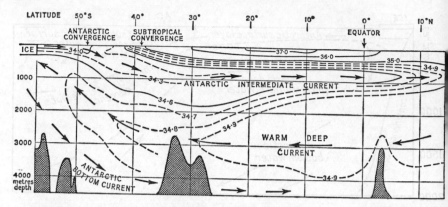

A section through the Atlantic Ocean, from latitude 55°S to 15°N along the meridian 30°W, showing the water of varying saltness (34.0 to 37.0 o/oo) and the direction of the main currents at different depths. It shows how the Antarctic icecap extends its influence into the northern hemisphere. Redrawn in diagrammatic form from Deacon.

how surprised we were when we first met signs of it on approaching South Georgia in 1926 (p. 155). It is discussed and described in detail in two *Discovery Reports*[1] by Dr. G. E. R. Deacon, now Director of the National Institute of Oceanography, who while taking part in the later voyages of the *Discovery II* has done so much to increase our knowledge of it.

This system influences the whole Atlantic Ocean. A more detailed chart of it above shows a vertical section through the Atlantic Ocean from latitude 55°S. to 15°N. along the meridian 30°W. with the varying saltness of the water as found by the *Discovery II* and the direction of the main water movements at different depths. We see that the Antarctic Intermediate Current (derived from the Antarctic surface water) flows well *north* of the equator; it can actually be traced as far north as 30°N. The Antarctic ice cap dominates the oceans of the world! In the north there is no corresponding polar continent with a great accumulation of ice[2].

Dr. Deacon has given us a remarkable time scale for reckoning the rate of flow of these vast water movements. As he went north on the *Discovery II*, up the meridian of 30°W. stopping at intervals to take water samples at different depths, he found, when he analysed them,

[1]Vol. VII, pp. 171-238, 1933, and vol. xv, pp. 1-124, 1937.
[2]There are only the glaciers from Greenland, Spitzbergen, etc., which are relatively very small; the ice of the North Polar basin, except for the odd bergs from these glaciers, is that of the pack—the frozen sea.

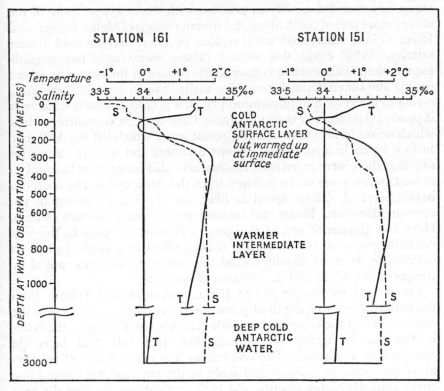

STATION 161   STATION 151

Temperature   -1°   0°   +1°   2°C   -1°   0°   +1°   +2°C

Salinity   33·5   34   35‰   33·5   34   35‰

COLD
ANTARCTIC
SURFACE LAYER
*but warmed up
at immediate
surface*

WARMER
INTERMEDIATE
LAYER

DEEP COLD
ANTARCTIC
WATER

Temperature and salinity-depth curves at two stations within the Antarctic Zone: 161 to the south-west and 151 to the north-east of South Georgia.

a very extraordinary thing. I should explain that the path and depth of this Antarctic Intermediate Current flowing north is determined by the points of lowest salinity in the vertical series of samples at each of the stations. As it goes along its salinity slowly increases as more salt diffuses into it from the surrounding water. It is also characterised by a high oxygen-content given to it by the great production of planktonic plants in the Antarctic; this also undergoes a change, being reduced as it goes north by that used in the respiration of the planktonic animals. Thus there is a progressive increase in salinity and decrease in oxygen, but not in the steady manner that one might have expected; on plotting a graph of them, from south to north, Dr. Deacon found that the curves gave a series of waves. In the graph of increasing salinity there were seven undulations, likewise in that of decreasing oxygen. Not only that, but the *crests* of the waves of one curve corresponded exactly in position with the *troughs* of those of the other; as we passed north along the stream regions of higher oxygen and lower salinity alternated with regions of lower oxygen and higher salinity. What could this mean? There seems only one possible explanation. This water was once at the surface in the Antarctic where during the summer much more ice melts than in winter; here also, owing to the growth of planktonic plants, a greater quantity of oxygen is produced in summer than in winter. Clearly these alternating values which we see in the curve must represent water which left the Antarctic surface layers in a succession of past summers and winters. Since we saw that there were seven such fluctuations, this water must have taken *at least*[1] seven years on its journey from the Antarctic to the northern hemisphere! A similar speed is likely for the water flowing in the opposite direction. Plants and melting ice give us a measure of time. Here is a glimpse of one of the great influences at work in the vast circulatory systems of the world; it is an effect in a vertical plane as opposed to the more usually considered surface movements caused by the prevailing winds and the rotation of the earth.

On p. 319 we see graphs of the temperature and salinity from the surface down to a depth of 3,000 metres at two stations, one to the south-west and the other to the north-east of South Georgia; the latter is the one at which we actually first met this cold layer on approaching the island. The continuous line curve is one of temperature according to a horizontal scale at the top and the broken line curve similarly shows salinity. At both stations we see how the cold Antarctic surface water, i.e., that above 100 metres, is warmed up by the summer atmosphere and sunshine so that as we go down we strike the colder layer below; the salinity on the other hand is reduced right against the surface due to the effect of melting ice and precipitation (both rain and snow). In our plankton survey the shallower regions over the continental shelf were flooded with the cold Antarctic surface layer similarly warmed up near the surface in contact with the atmosphere.

A little earlier, on p. 294, I suggested that South Georgia, being at right-angles to the West Wind Drift, might give rise to an upwelling of water rich in phosphates and nitrates, and so to an outburst of plant plankton, on its western side; and that this, flowing round each end of the island, might feed a nursery of krill on the sheltered leeward side.

[1] I have said *at least* here because Dr. Deacon tells me that he now fears there are not sufficient observations along the path of the current to make their number quite certain; but as this estimate agrees well with other estimates he feels it gives a fairly reliable time scale.

29. *Above*, icebergs to the north of the South Orkney Islands. *Below*, pack-ice coming out of the Weddell Sea, with a large tabular berg looming out of the mist in the background

30. Birds on Coronation Island (South Orkneys). *Above,* sheathbills (*Chionis alba*), pretty creatures but scavengers on the penguin rookeries. *Below left,* a giant petrel (*Macronectes giganteus*) with chick. *Right,* the chick taken just a second before it discharged the contents of its stomach all over the photographer (the author)!

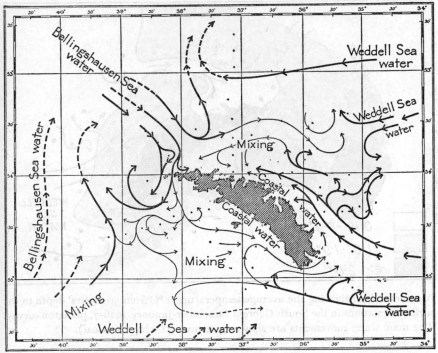

———←——— Path of Bellingshausen or Weddell Sea water according to label.
———←——— Probable mixture of the two, also with Coastal water.
‒ ‒ ‒ ‒ Probable path outside area investigated.

A chart of the surface-water movements round South Georgia in December-January, 1926-7, prepared by Dr. A. J. Clowes by means of dynamic calculations. From *D.R.*, vol. xi.

This idea, which I also put forward in my lecture to the Royal Geographical Society[1], now requires some modification. The late Dr. Clowes who worked up the hydrological data for this survey has shown that the water does not reach South Georgia in quite such a simple way as I had imagined. The island is at the meeting of two streams: one from the Bellingshausen Sea coming up through the Drake Passage from the coast of Graham Land to strike the north-west end of the island, and the other from the Weddell Sea, being influenced by the ridge of the Scotia Arc, curving round to meet its eastern side. Both streams are of Antarctic surface water. There is a considerable mixing of the two waters on either side of the island as is seen in the chart shown above specially prepared for our *Discovery Report* by Dr. Clowes.

[1]Published in their *Geographical Journal*, vol. LXXII, pp. 209-34, 1928.

L

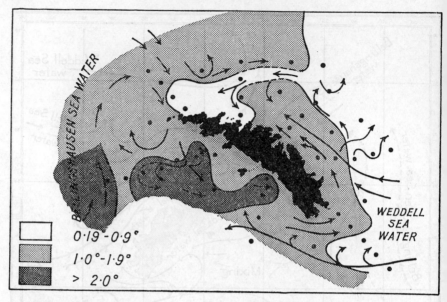

A contour chart showing the average temperature in°C from 50 metres' depth to the surface at stations in the South Georgia December-January 1926-7, plankton survey. The main water movements are shown by arrows (cf. chart overleaf).

The Weddell Sea water, being slightly colder than the Bellings-hausen Sea water, gives an interesting picture of its influence if we plot the averages of the temperature readings from 50 metres' depth to the surface at each station, as we have done in the chart above. This gives us the physical background.

Now let us look at the chemistry of the water; again our simple hypothesis must be revised. Although there is indeed likely to be upwelling due to both streams of water striking the shelf on which South Georgia stands, the surface waters of the Antarctic do not appear to require a replenishment of phosphates and nitrates as do our temperate upper layers; there is never a scarcity of these salts which might limit the growth of the plants as in our own seas. We must seek some other factor to account for their prolific growth in some parts round the island but not in others; let us look now at the regions of their main production.

When we set out, the more modern methods of comparing the quantities of phytoplankton had not yet been invented[1]. We could only either estimate the total number of plant cells in each standard

[1]To be mentioned on p. 485.

sample, expressing them, say, in millions, or we could use settled volumes. Neither method is entirely satisfactory, either because of the great range in the size of diatoms—or of their different settling properties—spiny ones taking more room than rounded ones; nevertheless the same main areas of production are clearly shown in charts using either method and the truth probably lies between them, as is represented by the one on p. 324 which is drawn as a compromise between the numerical and volumetric charts.

Now let us look again at the phosphate values which I have plotted on p. 325 where the average phosphate-content from 50 metres to the surface at each station is expressed as milligrams per cubic metre. These values, ranging from 78 to 111·5 mg. per cubic metre, are all very high compared with those of our own seas which average only some 15 or 20 mg. per cu.m. for the middle of the North Sea. They show, however, an interesting picture which I bring out by shading the areas in which the values exceed 90 mg. per cubic metre; the areas of lower values, left white, now correspond very closely with the regions of dense phytoplankton production and show how the plants have reduced the phosphate content of the water. The chart in fact beautifully confirms that of the phytoplankton abundance; it even shows the little patch off the north end of the island. We see indeed that the phosphate chart is its *negative* image. This is important in relation to a discussion we shall presently have on whale distribution. There are some differences in detail between the phosphate and phytoplankton charts, but they in themselves are instructive[1]. Such results give us confidence that we are indeed gleaning some truth from our sea of data.

It is also seen[2] that the two main areas of plant production are just at the *mixing* of the two kinds of water: the Bellingshausen and the Weddell Sea waters. This is not an infrequent phenomenon, often we find that where two current systems meet there is a rich growth of plankton along the line of junction. Why this should be, we are by no means certain but we can make a plausible suggestion. We are beginning to realise that in addition to the main nutritive salts, the phosphates and nitrates, there are other substances in the sea, such

[1]For example, the areas of reduced phosphates are nearer to the south-west coast of the island than are the areas of maximum phytoplankton production, but, if we look at the flow of water as indicated by the arrows on the phosphate chart, we see that the area near the coast is flooded with water which has just come *from* the regions of greatest production; again round the south-east corner the low phosphate area extends further up the east coast than the high plant production for just the same reason.

[2]Especially if we look back to the detailed chart of the water movements on p. 321.

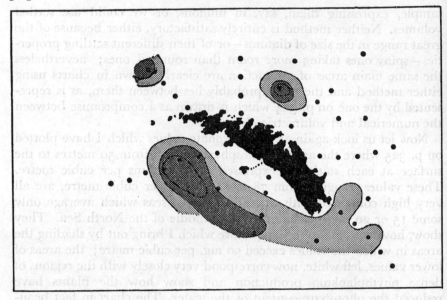

A contour chart showing the total quantity of phytoplankton in the South Georgia
December-January 1926-7, plankton survey collected in vertical net hauls from
100 metres' depth to the surface taken at each station whose positions are shown as
black dots. The darker the shading the greater the quantity of phytoplankton.

as vitamin-like substances, which must be present, although in minute
traces, to give healthy growth to the plankton. Vitamin B12
(Cobalamin) is found to be one of them, and there are probably more.
Let us suppose in our hypothesis that there are several such trace
substances, say A, B and C, vitally necessary for the growth of phytoplankton, and let us suppose that, in the course of time, one or other
of these substances may become used up in one particular body of
water so that the phytoplankton production is reduced; now if this
water meets and mixes with another body of water which may still
have a supply of the missing element then production may leap ahead.
Two different water masses such as the Bellingshausen and Weddell
Sea waters on meeting and mixing may fertilise one another with the
necessary vital ingredients for renewed productive vigour. It is, of
course, equally possible that upwelling may have a similar effect. The
waters down below the phytoplankton zone may still possess the
precious substances which have been used up near the surface so that
when they flow up against the shelf and mix with the surface layer the
deficiencies of the latter may be repaired; if this were so, then my ori-

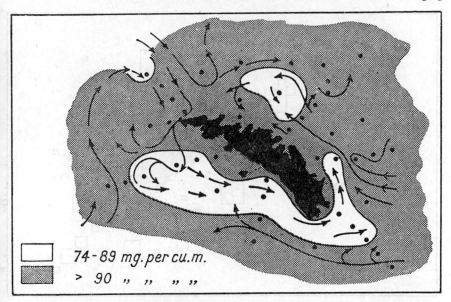

74 - 89 mg. per cu. m.
> 90 ,, ,, ,, ,,

A chart showing the distribution of phosphate values from 50 metres' depth to the surface at stations in the South Georgia December-January 1926-7, plankton survey. The lower values, 74-89 milligrams per cubic metre of water are in the areas left unshaded and the higher values, over 90 mg. per cu.m. are in the shaded areas. The main surface water movements are indicated by arrows.

ginal hypothesis (p. 294) would be correct if we substitute these 'other substances' for the phosphates and nitrates which I there postulated.

I should now say a little about the nature of the phytoplankton; in the last chapter, when considering the rough analysis made on the spot, I mentioned the importance of the very small diatom *Chaetoceros socialis*, which occurred in such enormous numbers on the western side of the island, and of the much larger diatom *Corethron valdiviae* which was particularly abundant on the eastern side. The diatoms, of which 71 different species were recorded, made up by far the most important part of the planktonic plant life; the dinoflagellates, forms such as *Peridinium* and *Ceratium* (p. 67) appear to play an insignificant role in the Antarctic compared with their importance in the north[1]. The little bright-green spherical alga *Halosphaera* was very abundant, but at only three stations, to the south-west of the island; and the

[1] Our results in this respect confirm the early findings of Professor Mangin who reported in 1915 on the phytoplankton collected by Charcot's expedition in the *Pourquoi-pas?*

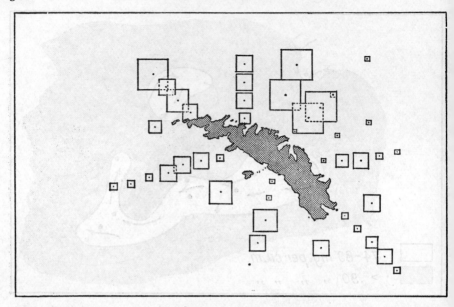

Distribution of the diatom *Corethron valdiviae* round South Georgia in the December-January 1926-7, survey; the squares indicate the relative quantities from less than 10,000 (smallest square) to over 1,000,000 (the largest square).

beautiful little silicoflagellate *Distephanus* was recorded at a number of points. The relative importance of these four main groups of planktonic plants in our survey may be indicated by the following total numbers, in round figures, as estimated in our standard samples.

Diatoms	1,846,000,000[1]
Protococcoids (*Halosphaera*)	84,000,000
Silicoflagellates (*Distephanus*)	420,000
Dincflagellates	283,000

[1]For those who may wish to know which were the more important diatoms, I list the first twenty species in order of abundance, the figures representing the total recorded in *millions*:

*Chaetoceros socialis**	1,493	*Chaetoceros dichaeta*	0.4
*Nitzschia seriata**	211	*Ch. schimperianus*	0.4
Corethron valdiviae	24	*Dactyliosolen laevis*	0.4
Fragilaria antarctica	10	*Biddulphia striata*	0.2
*Rhizosolenia styliformis**	9.8	*Ch. curvatus*	0.2
*Chaetoceros atlanticus**	6.4	*Thalassiosira antarctica*	0.2
Ch. criophilum	6.2	*Rhizosolenia obtusa**	0.2
Thalassiothrix antarctica	0.5	*Rh. curva*	0.2
Coscinodiscus oppositus (?)	0.5	*Pleurosigma directum*	0.2
Eucampia antarctica	0.4	*Coscinodiscus bouvet*	0.1

*Species which are also found in northern waters.

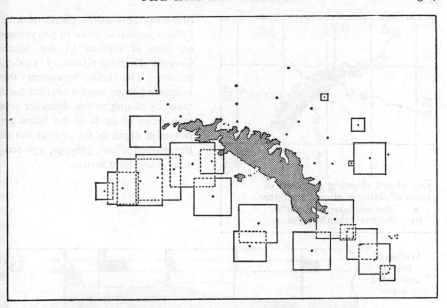

Distribution of the diatom *Chaetoceros socialis* round South Georgia in the December-January 1926-7, survey; the sizes of the squares indicate the relative quantities from less than 10,000 (smallest square) to over 100,000,000 (largest square). The dots without squares indicate none found at these positions.

The general appearance of these planktonic plants is very similar to that of related species in our home waters shown on p. 41. Here I give just two examples of the distribution charts of separate species: *Corethron valdiviae* and *Chaetoceros socialis*. Similar charts are given in the main *Report* for all important species and we can recognise groups of species which were characteristic of the different waters.

We must now leave the plants for the animals—the zoöplankton—of which 182 species were recorded. Among the Protozoa (single-celled animals) were Foraminifera (*Globigerina* and its allies) and Radiolaria. The coelenterates (the jellyfish-like animals) were represented by ten species of Siphonophora and eight other Hydromedusae; and the ctenophores (or comb-jellies) by *Beroë* and *Pleurobrachia*. There were four species of arrow-worm (*Chaetognatha*) and eleven pelagic bristle-worms (Polychaeta). The Crustacea, of course, made up the greater bulk as follows: ostracods (8 species), copepods (100 species), mysids (1), amphipods (8), isopods (2), euphausiaceans (8). There were five kinds of pteropod, and two of salps. Relatively few species, however,

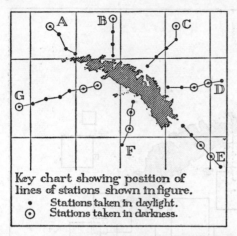

Key chart showing position of
lines of stations shown in figure.
•   Stations taken in daylight.
⊙   Stations taken in darkness.

Showing the vertical distribution of *Calanus propinquus* down to 500 metres on lines of stations in the South Georgia December-January 1926-7, survey. The scale represents the numbers per 50 metres vertical haul taken by closing 70 cm. diameter nets in a series of hauls of the following ranges of depth as far as contours of the sea-bed allow: 500-250, 250-100, 100-50 and 50-0 metres.

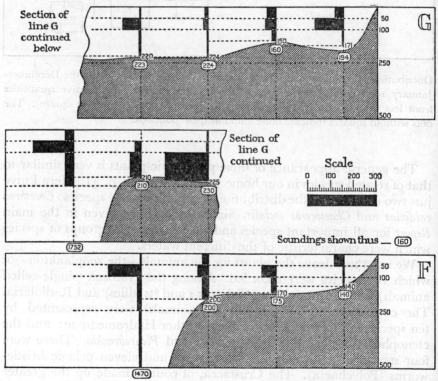

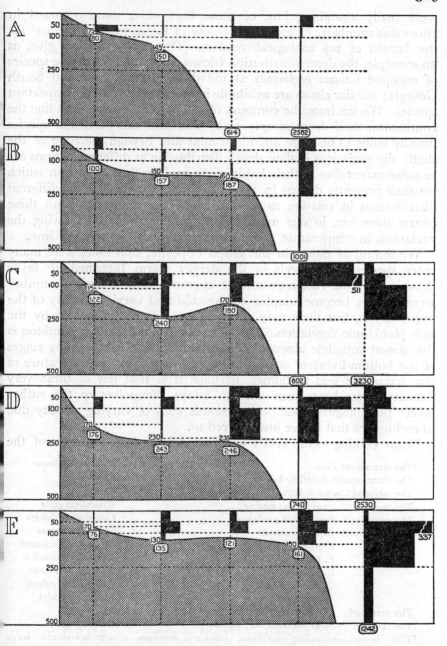

were really abundant, but, of those that were, some occurred in enormous numbers. I give a list below of the commoner species[1] for the benefit of my zoological readers. The charts overleaf give, as an example, the depth distribution (down to 500 metres) of one species of copepod *Calanus propinquus* at the different stations round South Georgia; similar charts are available in our *Report* for all the important species. We see from the contours of the bottom how on each line the continental shelf drops steeply away and how this particular species usually tends to be more abundant near and beyond the edge of the shelf; the variations in their depth distribution at different stations are to some extent due to their habit of diurnal vertical migration which we shall presently discuss (p.343). Different species show us different distributions in relation to the sea-bed. For comparison with these charts there are, in our main *Report*, similar ones but showing the variations in temperature and salinity with depth along each line.

We found, as shown in the graph opposite, that there were many more species of copepods in the deeper warm Intermediate layer than in the cold Antarctic surface current; only a limited number seem to have become adapted to the cold and varying salinity of the upper layers, but these may multiply exceedingly supported by the rich planktonic vegetation. A curious feature of the polar plankton is the almost complete absence[2] of the planktonic ciliated young stages of the bottom-living or coastal animals which form such a feature of our temperate seas at home; perhaps it is that few of these very delicate forms have been able to adapt themselves to the rather severe physiological conditions (osmosis etc.) of varying salinity due to melting ice that I have just referred to.

Before coming to the krill I will just include three examples of the

[1]The ctenophore *Beroë*.　　　　　　　　　The copepods: *Calanus simillimus*
　The Chaetognath *Eukrohnia hamata*　　　　　　　　　　*C. propinquus*
　The ostracod *Conchoecia hettacra*　　　　　　　　　　　*C. acutus*
　The mysid　　*Antarctomysis maxima*　　　　　　　　　*Rhincalanus gigas*
　The amphipod *Parathemisto gaudichandi*　　　　　　　*Clausocalanus laticeps*
　The euphausids *Euphausia superba*　　　　　　　　　　*Ctenocalanus vanus*
　　　　　　　　E. frigida　　　　　　　　　　　　　*Drepanopus spectinatus*
　　　　　　　　E. triacantha　　　　　　　　　　　　*Pareuchaeta antarctica*
　　　　　　　　E. vallentini　　　　　　　　　　　　*Scolecithricella minor*
　　　　　　　　Thysanoessa vicina　　　　　　　　　　*Pleuromamma robusta*
　　　　　　　　Th. macrura　　　　　　　　　　　　　*Metridia gerlachei*
　The pteropod　*Limacina balea*　　　　　　　　　　　*M. lucens*
　The tunicate　*Salpa fusiformis* var. *aspera*　　　　　　*Oithona frigida*

[2]There is one outstanding exception, *Auricularia antarctica*, a large holothurian larva (i.e., the young of a bottom-living animal related to a sea-urchin and often called a sea-cucumber).

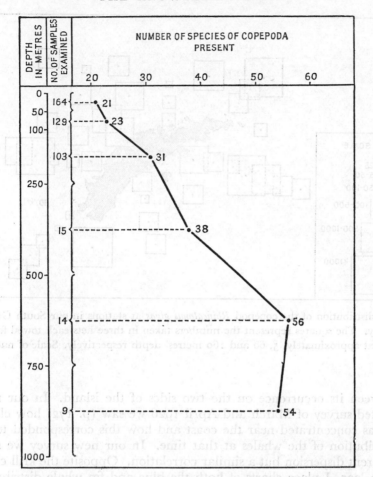

A graph showing the increasing number of species of copepods with increasing depth in the South Georgia region of the Antarctic Zone.

distribution charts of some of the other more important plankton animals on the next two pages: *Rhincalanus gigas* (copepod), *Parathemisto gaudichaudi* (amphipod) and *Antarctomysis maxima* (mysid) as shown by the 1-metre diameter towed nets.

Now for the krill, *Euphausia superba*. I have already described (p. 298) how we always found it in dense swarms and how essential this is for the feeding of the whales; a most important item in the knowledge we gained. In the chart on p. 334 we see what a contrast there is

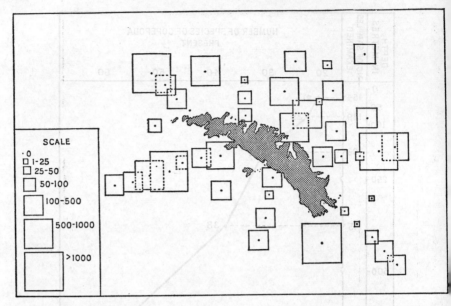

The distribution of the copepod *Rhincalanus gigas* at stations in our South Georgia
survey. The squares represent the numbers taken in three nets each towed for one
mile at approximately, 5, 60 and 160 metres' depth respectively. Scale of numbers
inset.

between its occurrence on the two sides of the island. In our more
limited survey of March and April 1926 we saw (p. 172) how closely
it was concentrated near the coast and how this corresponded to the
distribution of the whales at that time. In our new survey we see a
different dispersion but a similar correlation. Opposite the krill chart,
on p. 335, I place charts of both the blue and fin whale distribution
as reported in the same period by the whaling gunners; the reader will
remember that the position of every whale shot was given us by the
different companies so that we could make such monthly distribution
charts. It must be admitted that the correspondence is remarkable. It
is, of course, what we would expect; the whales during their summer
feeding season will naturally be concentrated in relation to their food.
It is good, however, to know that our methods show it. The next step
should be to explain the distribution of the krill.

In the curious way things happen, I had, by chance, before coming
out to the Antarctic, been specially interested in the distribution of the
herring in the North Sea in relation to dense patches of phytoplankton
which sometimes form there in the autumn in the neighbourhood of the

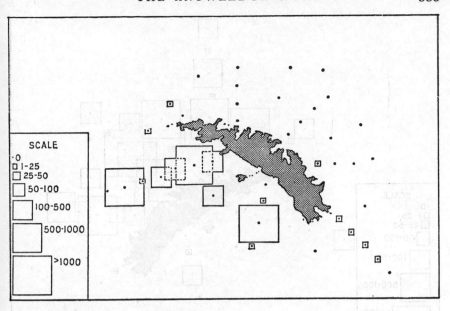

The distribution of the mysid *Antarctomysis maxima* in our South Georgia survey; arrangement as before.

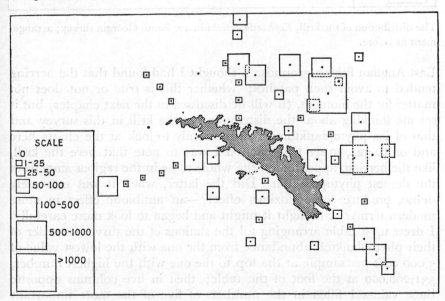

The distribution of the amphipod *Parathemisto gaudichaudi* in our South Georgia survey; arrangement as in the previous figure.

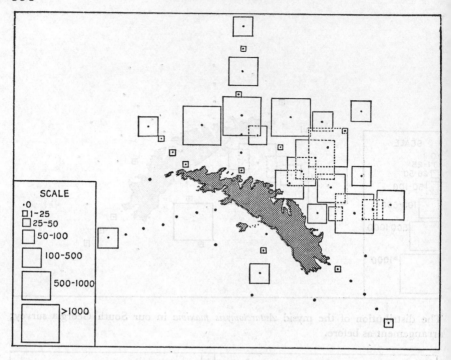

The distribution of the krill, *Euphausia superba* in our South Georgia survey; arrangement as before.

East Anglian fishing grounds. I thought I had found that the herring tended to avoid such patches; whether this is true or not does not matter for the moment, (it will be discussed in the next chapter) but it set me thinking about the distribution of the krill in this survey and that of the phytoplankton. You have only to look at the charts here and on p. 324, to see how excited I was to note that here the krill, like the herring, appeared on the whole to be in the regions *away* from the densest phytoplankton. Did the latter, when it was extremely dense, produce some noxious effect?—an antibiotic effect in more modern terms? I thought it might and began to look more carefully. I drew up a table arranging all the stations of the survey in order of their phytoplankton abundance from the one with the lowest value of 3,000 cells per sample at the top to the one with the highest number, 531,200,000 at the foot of the table; then in five columns opposite these values I filled in the numbers of five of the more important zoöplankton species which were taken at each of the stations. There are 43 such stations. I have here summarised the table by grouping the

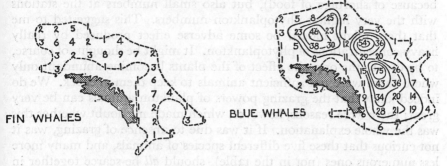

FIN WHALES   BLUE WHALES

The distribution of fin and blue whales in December, 1926, as revealed
by the records of the positions of the whales shot by the whalers hunted
around South Georgia. From *D.R.*, vol. XI.

stations into six groups, the first of which contains the eight stations
with the lowest phytoplankton values, and each of the other five
groups contain seven stations going up in order of phytoplankton
abundance. On the left of my summary table I give the *average*
phytoplankton values (in numbers of cells) for each of these six groups
of stations: ranging from an average of 57,500 for the eight stations in
the lowest value group to an average of 315,125,000 for the seven
stations in the highest group. Then opposite these values I give the
average number of each of the five zoöplankton species taken in the
corresponding groups of stations, and then I have indicated those
which are above *the average for the whole column* in **heavy type**.

Phytoplankton values averaged	Euphausia Superba	E. frigida	Thysan- oessa	Para- themisto	Salpa fusiformis
57,500	289	3	17	48	38
290,000	**1913**	**44**	57	**266**	**1781**
483,000	**951**	**47**	94	44	**1051**
2,064,000	**369**	**76**	**136**	**87**	**675**
50,936,500	31	15	**138**	53	246
315,125,000	41	2	69	45	49

It is now that one reaps the benefit of all that counting which at times
had seemed almost hopeless; the numbers begin to show us things
about the life of the whole community that we might not have suspected. We see that on the whole there tend to be smaller numbers
of animals at the stations with the sparsest phytoplankton (perhaps

because of shortage of food), but also small numbers at the stations with the very highest phytoplankton numbers. This suggested to me that there might indeed be some adverse effect produced by really heavy concentrations of phytoplankton. It might be thought, of course, to be due to the opposite effect of the plants becoming abundant only where there were not sufficient animals to keep them in check. We do indeed know that the grazing powers of plankton animals can be very great; there were reasons, however, which made me doubt whether this was the whole explanation. If it was due to absence of grazing, was it not curious that these five different species of animals, and many more less numerous ones (not in the table), should *all* be scarce together in the regions of dense phytoplankton? And why were there not more plants where the animals were scarce at the *top* of the table? Again the concentrations of plants seemed to be formed in relation to definite hydrographic conditions, areas of mixing or upwelling. This idea of the dense plant concentrations having an influence on the animals, one which I called the hypothesis of animal exclusion, will be discussed further in the next chapter. Whether it is true or not—and, as will be seen, I am still not sure of the answer—does not matter for the moment, here I am only discussing *the fact* that the krill (whatever the cause) were not in the regions of dense phytoplankton.

We have seen that the distribution of the whales, both blue and fin, during the feeding season was closely related to that of the krill; when the krill was against the coast as on our first visit so also were the whales, and when it was more widespread and away from the coast, as in this second season, so also were the whales. We have also seen that the krill occurs away from the dense phytoplankton, and that a chart of the phosphate values was the negative image of the phytoplankton distribution. If these relationships always held could we not deduce the areas of whale abundance direct from phosphate values, or at least say where we should *not* expect whales to be? It was now possible to make several tests of this.

In the years following our survey the new ship, the R.R.S. *Discovery II*, and sometimes the *William Scoresby*, made further surveys at South Georgia and the phosphate values they found were published in the station lists[1] and as before the whalers kept records of the positions of all the whales they took during these years[2]. There were three surveys at South Georgia when such a test could be made. The first was in December 1928 and for this the phosphate values are plotted on a

---

[1] *Discovery Reports* vol. III, pp. 1-134 (Station List 1927-9) and vol. IV, pp. 1-232 (Station List 1929-31).

[2] These were charted by Kemp and Bennett in *Discovery Reports*, vol. VI, pp. 165-80.

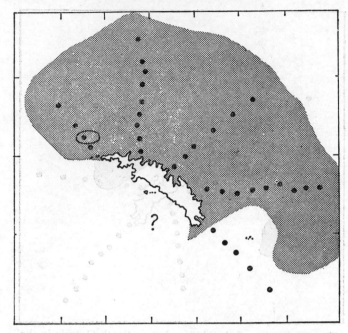

Distribution of phosphates values at South Georgia in
December-January 1928-9. At all the points in the shaded
area the values exceeded 100 milligrams per cubic metre of
water and in the unshaded area they were below it.

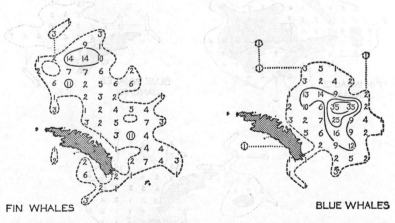

FIN WHALES   BLUE WHALES

The fin and blue whale distribution round South Georgia in December 1928.

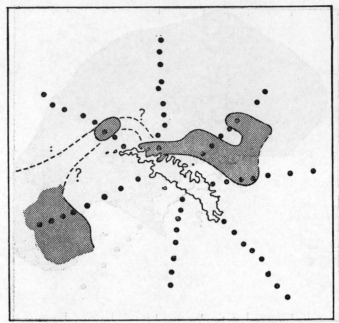

The distribution of phosphate values at South Georgia in the January-February 1930, survey; in the shaded areas they exceeded 90 milligrams per cubic metre of water and in the unshaded areas they were below this value.

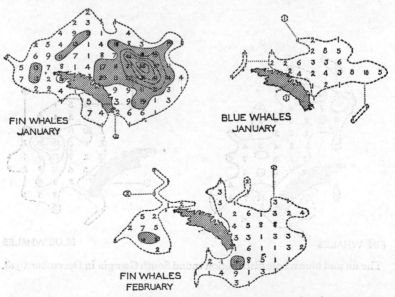

Whale distribution round South Georgia in January and February, 1930.

chart on p. 337; from this, if the relationship just suggested is correct, we should expect the whales to be widespread to the east of the island, but *not* to the south of it. When we look at the accompanying whale distribution we see that our deduction is correct. In the next survey, that of January—February 1930 we see, in the chart opposite, a widespread reduction of phosphates with smaller areas of higher figures which suggest, if our relationship stands, that the whales should be found concentrated in these places. We see the whale distribution in the next chart; in January there were very few blue whales but those there were, and the dense concentration of fin whales, were over the limited area of higher phosphate values to the east. In February there were no blue whales and the fin whales (as if they had exhausted the confined area of krill) were now scattered with some over to the west where there were also high phosphate values. In November 1930 the phosphate values and the whale distribution were as shown overleaf; the correspondence of higher whale numbers with areas of higher phosphate values is again apparent. In no case were there concentrations of whales where the phosphate values were low.

It was amusing to think that it seemed likely that by sitting in my study at Hull, for I was then professor there, and looking at the phosphate values sent to me, I could say where the whalers would *not* catch whales at the opposite end of the world and where they might expect to. While this could have no immediate practical value, it would, if true, give us a better understanding of how the whales' distribution was related to their planktonic background and this might well *eventually* be of economic importance. It would not be of direct practical benefit, of course, because you must have a ship to gather your phosphate measurements and from your ship you could see your whales blowing, if they were there, long before you could work out the phosphate values! Now these were deductions; I was not making real predictions because the whale distributions were actually worked out before I looked at the phosphate values. True prediction is the satisfying and exciting test of hypothesis. The chance for this now came.

Looking through the whale charts in Kemp and Bennett's *Report* I found that there was a striking occasion when the distribution of both blue and fin whales, that of February 1928 as shown on p. 341, was the exact opposite to that found in our survey. Now no phosphate measurements had been taken at this time but the *William Scoresby* had made a plankton survey at the end of February and the beginning of March; the samples, not yet analysed, were all with the *Discovery* collections at the British Museum (Natural History). I wrote to Dr. Kemp to ask if they could be examined and *predicted* that when they

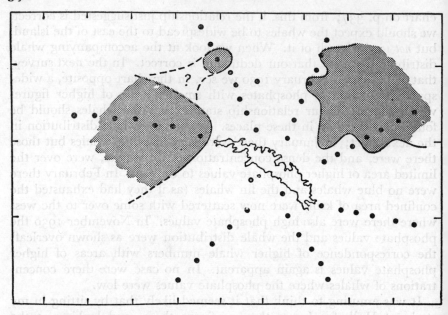

The distribution of phosphate values at South Georgia in November 1930; the areas
of higher values are shaded as before.

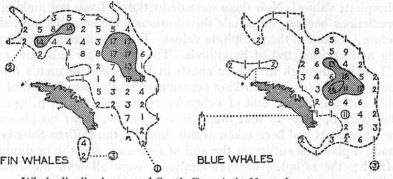

FIN WHALES   BLUE WHALES

Whale distribution round South Georgia in November 1930.

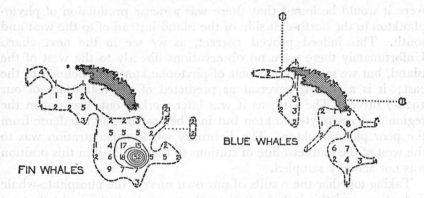

Whale distribution at South Georgia, February 1928.

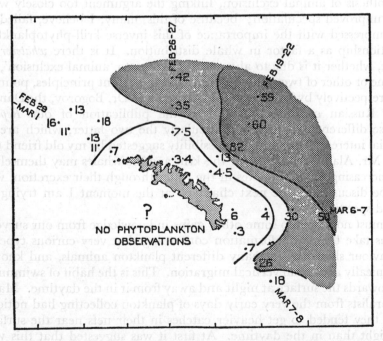

The distribution of the phytoplankton, measured by volume in cc. per sample, in the February-March 1928, survey at South Georgia.

were it would be found that there was a dense production of phytoplankton to the north-east side of the island instead of to the west and
south. This indeed proved correct, as we see in the next chart.
Unfortunately there were no observations directly to the west of the
island, but we see the great belt of phytoplankton well defined to the
east; it is a striking reversal as predicted of the conditions of our
1926-7 survey. The krill, as it was later worked out, was not in the
region of dense phytoplankton but in a belt separating the dense from
the poor phytoplankton. The February whale concentration was to
the west of the southern line of stations so that the krill in this position
was not actually sampled.

Taking together the results of our own survey, the phosphate-whale
deductions and this last prediction, there can be little doubt that we
have demonstrated an important factor governing the concentrations
of whales during their feeding season. Clearly they are linked with the
concentrations of krill and these in turn are *not* within the areas of dense
phytoplankton but may well be adjacent to them.

I realise now that in our former *Report* I emphasised too much the
hypothesis of animal exclusion, linking the argument too closely with
this unproved speculation; because of this, many, I believe, failed to
be impressed with the importance of this inverse krill-phytoplankton
relationship as a factor in whale distribution. It is there *whatever its
cause,* whether it is due to absence of grazing, to 'animal exclusion', or
to one or other of two quite different and important principles, pointed
out respectively by Dr. Steemann-Nielsen and Dr. Bogorov, the Danish
and Russian oceanographers, *after* the publication of our *Report.*
These different hypotheses, particularly the two latter, which are of
special interest for us, and the possibility suggested by my old friend the
late Mr. Alan Gardiner, that the krill and the whales may themselves
be increasing the phosphates in the water through their excretion, will
all be discussed in the next chapter; at the moment I am trying to
avoid speculation.

I must now turn to some other gains in knowledge from our survey;
let us take the new information concerning that very curious type of
behaviour shown by so many different plankton animals, and known
technically as diurnal vertical migration. This is the habit of swimming
up towards the surface at night and away from it in the daytime. Many
naturalists from the very early days of plankton collecting had noticed
that they tended to get heavier catches in their nets near the surface
at night than in the daytime. At first it was suggested that this was
due to the little animals seeing the net approaching in the daylight and
being able to dart out of the way of it, whereas at night it came upon

them unawares. It is likely, of course, that a proportion of the larger kinds and more powerful swimmers may well be able to escape the net in the daytime, and indeed we certainly know that this happens in the case of active young fish, but it does not explain the phenomenon in general. By taking hauls with tow-nets at different depths at the same time it is easy to demonstrate not only that there are *more* animals in the upper layers at night than in the daytime, but also that there are *fewer* in the lower depths, and vertical migration has also been demonstrated experimentally in the laboratory.

It is a most extraordinary thing that so many different plankton animals will expend so much energy in climbing up towards the surface at night only to sink or swim down again in the daytime. In the next chapter I shall discuss various ideas that have been put forward to explain this; here for the time being I want to stick to the facts— and they are remarkable enough.

There are various ways in which we can study this phenomenon. Dr. F. S. (now Sir Frederick) Russell, Director of the Plymouth Laboratory, for example, made a long series of investigations by taking series of horizontal tow-net hauls with a standard net at different depths at different times during the twenty-four hours in one place. Whilst we made some observations in a somewhat similar manner the greater part of our evidence was obtained differently. In carrying out our survey we used standard nets towed at three different depths at many different stations; we steamed from one station to another, day and night, and so obtained a large number of observations, taken at all hours of the day. By disregarding the fact that they were taken on different days, and in different positions (but all of them round South Georgia) we can arrange these observations in a sequence throughout the twenty-four hours. Let us take one species from our survey by way of example; it is the copepod *Clausocalanus laticeps*. On p. 344 we have prepared a chart of its occurrence as shown by the series of 70 cm. diameter nets towed horizontally at each station at three depths at the same time: i.e., at 5 metres and two lower depths which were usually about 60 and 120 metres, but varied considerably. We have seen that in heavy weather it was impossible to adjust the speed of the old *Discovery* with any precision, and changes in speed gave changes in depth of net; however, by placing Kelvin sounding tubes at the end of the line we could determine the depths the nets reached on each occasion. Along the top of the chart is a time scale in hours from noon to midnight and to noon again. Along this scale are marked off the positions of each station in the survey according to the time of day it was taken. That part of the chart lying between sunset and sunrise

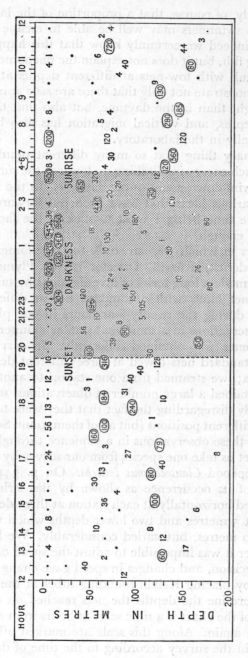

A chart showing the depth distribution of the copepod *Clausocalanus laticeps* at different times of the day and night as revealed by 70 cm. diameter nets towed at, usually, three depths at each station in the surveys round South Georgia. The results, according to the time of day of each station, are arranged in chronological order from noon to midnight and to noon again as shown on the scale along the top of the figure; more stations are taken in some hours than in others. The depth of each sample is shown by a dot or a number placed in relation to the depth scale on the left; the numbers represent the quantities of any *Clausocalanus* taken, while the dots mean that there was none. The shaded area of the figure indicates the stations taken during the hours of darkness, *i.e.*, between sunset and sunrise. Disregarding occurrences of less than 50 as being insignificant, a ring is placed round the highest number at *each* station; in general an upward movement of the majority towards the surface at night is clearly shown.

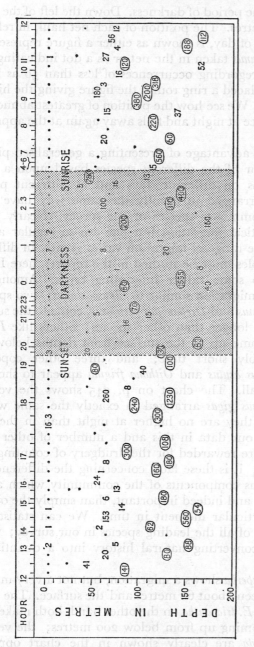

A chart showing the depth distribution of the copepod *Rhincalamus gigas* at different times of the day and night in the surveys round South Georgia. The arrangement is exactly the same as that described in the previous figure; here no vertical migration is seen at all.

is shaded to represent the period of darkness. Down the left of the chart is a scale of depth in metres. The position of each net haul, in relation both to depth and time of day, is shown as either a figure representing the number of *Clausocalanus* taken in the net or as a dot indicating that none was present. Disregarding occurrences of less than 50 as being insignificant, we have placed a ring round the figure giving the highest number at each station. We see how the position of greatest abundance tends to rise to the surface at night and falls away again at the approach of dawn.

This method has the advantage of presenting a generalised picture of the typical behaviour of the different species based upon a large number of observations on different days and at different places. Similar charts, each arranged in exactly the same way have been prepared for all the commoner species of our survey. Nearly all of them show such a vertical migration but few are so regular as the example shown, and the range of migration varies greatly in different species. Further examples must be studied in the report; here I shall just draw attention to some rather interesting types. Among the copepods some have a migration similar to *Clausocalanus*; two species, however, *Calanus simillimus* and *Drepanopus pectinalis*, come to the surface earlier and stay up for longer than other species; others like *Pleuromamma* and *Metridia* come up to the surface from depths below 200 metres in a remarkably short time; and three other copepods *Rhincalanus gigas*, *Calanus acutus* and *Oithona frigida* appear to show no vertical migration at all. The chart on p. 345 shows the vertical occurrence of *Rhincalanus gigas* arranged in exactly the same way as that for *Clausocalanus*; they are no higher at night than in the day. In being able to treat our data in this and a number of other ways we see again how we are rewarded for the drudgery of counting that alone made it possible; it is these facts concerning the differences in the habits of the various components of the community which are so much more interesting, and indeed important, than simply the overall distribution at one particular moment in time. We can statistically compare the behaviour of all the leading species in our survey; this is true ecology, we are converting natural history into a quantitative science.

The krill *Euphausia superba* shows a migration, but not a very marked one, going mostly between about 60 metres and the surface. The allied species of *E. frigida* and *E. triacantha* on the other hand, both make most extensive migrations coming up from below 200 metres; the vertical movements of *E. frigida* are clearly shown in the chart opposite, where we see with what speed they must rise from the depths at sunset

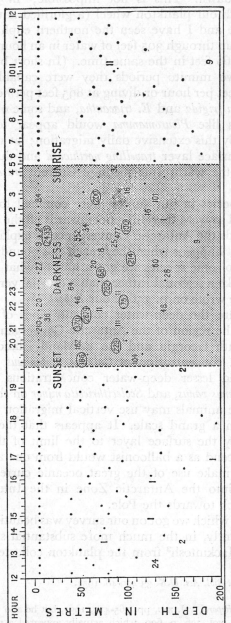

A chart showing the depth distribution of the euphausiacean *Euphausia frigida* at different times of the day and night round South Georgia as revealed by 100 cm. diameter tow-nets. These nets were used more frequently than the 70 cm. diameter nets; apart from the larger number of stations, the arrangement is the same as in the two previous figures. It shows how rapidly members of this species swim up towards the surface at dusk from levels below the sampling of our nets, and down again at dawn. From *D.R.* vol. XI.

and dive down again at dawn. This is not impossible; in later laboratory experiments[1] with our plankton wheel (a glorified aquatic 'squirrel's cage') Bainbridge and I have seen the northern euphausiacean *Meganyctiphanes* swim up through 305 feet of water in an hour and swim downwards through 566 feet in the same time. (In short bursts of speed measured over two minute periods they were capable of climbing at the rate of 570 feet per hour or diving at 895 feet per hour.) These two species, *Euphausia frigida* and *E. triacantha*, and some of the deeply migrating copepods like *Pleuromamma* would appear to be maintaining their latitude by this extensive daily migration; at night they are in the Antarctic surface layer *travelling northward* and during the day they are down in the warm Intermediate Current *travelling towards the south!*[2]

Most of the Antarctic species in our survey were confined to the upper 200 to 150 metres and so were travelling northwards all the time with this upper layer towards the Antarctic Convergence as explained earlier in the chapter. What happens when they reach this boundary? On our survey, in respect to some species we got a hint of what they may do; they appear to make a seasonal rather than a diurnal vertical migration. I quote what we wrote on p. 356 of our *Report*.

Particularly interesting are the deep-water concentrations of a number of Copepoda in the region of the Antarctic Convergence on the line between South Georgia and the Falkland Islands. There is a most marked concentration of *Calanus propinquus* at 750—1,000 m. . . . and lesser deep-water concentrations of *Calanus simillimus, Ctenocalanus vanus*, and *Scolecithricella minor* on this line, suggesting that these animals may use vertical migration as a form of 'navigation' on a grand scale. It appears that these animals, being carried by the surface layer to the limit of the Antarctic Zone, may descend as a balloonist would from one air current to another, and make use of the great oceanic current system to return again into the Antarctic Zone in the Intermediate layer flowing back towards the Pole.

The hint of this possibility which we got on our survey was beautifully confirmed, quite independently, in the much more substantial study later made by Dr. N. A. Mackintosh[3] from the plankton collected at

[1]Hardy and Bainbridge: *J. Mar. Biol. Ass. U.K.* 33 409-48, 1954.
[2]See footnote on p. 317.
[3]His full account is in *Discovery Reports*, vol. XVI, pp. 365-412, 1937, but he also had a preliminary note in *Nature* in 1935, vol. 136, p. 629, which actually appeared a month before our *Report* was published; when he wrote his *Nature* note he was unaware of our South Georgia findings.

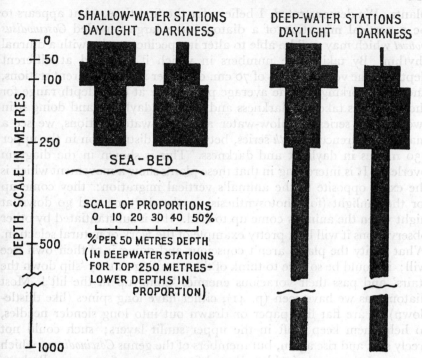

Histograms showing the average relative depth distribution of the diatom
Coscinodiscus bouvet during daylight and hours of darkness round South Georgia;
the results from the shallow-water stations, *i.e.*, those near the coast, and those
for the top 250 metres of the deep-water stations confirm one another and
strongly suggest a diurnal vertical movement which is the reverse of that
usually shown by the zooplankton.

different levels by the *Discovery II* on lines of stations running north
and south along the meridian of 80°W.; this will be referred to again
on p. 493 in chapter 20.

We have dealt with our findings in regard to patchiness in our last
chapter when we gave the results of our continuous net series. Among
other things we did, we correlated our results with the condition of the
sea, whether calm or rough, and also with phases of the moon; we
showed—a little surprisingly—that the state of the sea at any rate
up to force 7, had little bearing on the number of organisms in the
surface layers, and as to a lunar influence, possibly governing swarming, we found no evidence of it.

Before ending the chapter I will now return for a moment to the plants. We demonstrated, I believe for the first time, what appears to be a vertical migration of a diatom: the large rounded *Coscinodisus bouvet* which may well be able to alter its specific gravity with a diurnal rhythm. By taking the numbers in which it occurred at different depths in the vertical series of 70 cm. diameter nets at different stations, and then working out the average percentage at each depth range for those stations taken in darkness and those in daylight, and doing it in two distinct series—shallow-water and deep-water stations, we see a marked difference, in *both* series, between the distribution in the upper 250 metres in daylight and darkness. This is shown in the diagram overleaf. It is interesting in that these plants show a movement which is the exact opposite to the animal's vertical migration: they come up for the sunlight (for photosynthesis) in the daytime and go down at night when the animals come up to feed. If it is substantiated by other observations it will be a pretty example of the work of natural selection. What a pity the plants aren't conscious and doing it of their own free will; it would be so nice to think of them smiling as they 'slip down the stairs' and pass their voracious enemies 'going up in the lift'! Most diatoms, as we have seen (p. 41), either have long spines (like thistle-down) or are flat like paper or drawn out into long slender needles, to help them keep aloft in the upper sunlit layers; such could not freely sink and rise again, but members of the genus *Coscinodiscus*, which are rounded, are admirably adapted for such a performance. Perhaps in daylight they are buoyed up by bubbles of oxygen produced in photosynthesis and sink as the light fades and the oxygen is used up in respiration. It is instructive to see (in the diagram) the constant number at all depths below 250 metres, both day and night; this must be the perpetual rain of the dead and dying sinking to feed the populations on the ocean floor.

It is impossible in one chapter to deal with all the results of our survey when their description in vol. xi of the *Reports* fills 456 pages, but enough has been said, I think, to show that the old square-rigged *Discovery* and the little *William Scoresby* together got good value in their contest with the tempestuous South Georgian seas. And in thinking of these results we must not forget the work and devotion to the expedition's programme of all the members of the ship's company, both officers and ratings, which made the harvest possible.

IDEAS AND SPECULATIONS

I have separated the considerations which follow from the facts recorded in the last chapter so as to make it easier for the reader to distinguish what has actually been established; I think, however, he may be interested in some of the more theoretical ideas that have arisen from the South Georgia work. Some people abhor speculation. 'Let us stick to the facts,' they say, 'these are all that should concern us as scientists.' That I believe is a barren path to tread and a negation of the true spirit of science. Ideas, of course, are only worth while if they stimulate experiment or further observation; if they are proved right, it is an advance, and if wrong, we must think again. Hypothesis is the fuel of scientific progress.

I have discussed some of these ideas in two essays[1] published since the *Report*, but it is likely that they will have been seen only by professional zoologists.

At the end of the last chapter I described some of our observations on the curious habit of vertical migration possessed by many of the plankton animals; I will take up the thread from there and discuss the possible significance of this remarkable behaviour. By significance I don't just mean what is the immediate physiological process which sets the animals off in movement in relation to this or that external stimulus, although this is interesting enough and may be briefly mentioned first. There seems little doubt from the work of Sir Frederick Russell of Plymouth, Dr. George Clarke of Harvard in America, and others that the animals are reacting mainly to a changing light intensity. I will sketch the theory in its simplest possible form. The members of any given species appear, on an average[2], to 'prefer'

[1]'Change and Choice: a Study in Pelagic Ecology' in *Evolution: essays . . . presented to Professor Goodrich . . .* Edit. de Beer, Oxford 1938, and 'Some Problems of Pelagic Life' in *Essays in Marine Biology*, Oliver and Boyd London 1953.

[2]I have said on an average because all the individuals of the species will not be reacting to exactly the same light intensity, there will be a considerable range of variation as in most characters. We shall see presently too that individuals do not always behave in just the same way.

351

(i.e., to be adapted to) a particular rather dim light intensity which keeps them well below the surface when the sun is high. As the sun sinks at evening the zone of this special light intensity naturally moves upwards and so is followed by the animals which at darkness will come up near the surface; as the sun rises in the morning the light below the surface will gradually increase so that the zone of illumination to which our species is adapted will go deeper and deeper and the process be reversed. There is actually more to it than this; I am here over-simplifying it to show as briefly as possible the sort of physiological mechanism in operation. I am not, however, concerned with these reactions here. What interests me particularly is the significance of this behaviour in terms of advantage to the animal possessing it.

Why should evolution, natural selection, have brought about this particular reaction to light to produce this type of behaviour in so many different kinds of animals? It is a habit that has been evolved quite independently in almost every major group of animals in the plankton, some making shorter, others longer, migrations: protozoans, jelly-fish, comb-jellies, arrow-worms, polychaete worms like *Tomopteris*, the pteropods (planktonic snails), members of nearly all the many different groups of crustaceans, the salps and most young fish. Such a vertical climb every day must use up a great deal of energy, and the fact that the habit should be one so pronounced and possessed by so many different animals must mean that it is of profound importance in their lives. What can be the meaning of it?

We have seen that the ultimate source of food for all the plankton animals is in the upper layers where alone there is sufficient light to allow the little plants to grow and multiply. Can it be that the little animals are coming up to feed in this layer only at night when they may more readily escape from their enemies under the cover of dark-ness? Perhaps also the carnivorous animals are just following their herbivorous prey up to the surface, for both the predators and the grazing ones migrate up and down in much the same way. This may be so, yet it seems extraordinary that it should have become so universal a habit. If all the carnivores go up at night and down in the daylight, is it not surprising that at least for a few of the herbivores natural selection should not have evolved the opposite habit, or one of just remaining in the surface layers in the daytime and so saving themselves the arduous vertical climb? It is certainly a puzzle.

Is it possible that the plants in the upper layers are giving off some substances which are injurious to the animals—having some antibiotic effect as we should say to-day—and that consequently the animals can only come into these layers for a limited time each day? If so, then

31. Deception Island. *Top*, approaching Hell's Gates, as the entrance to the harbour is called. *Centre*, the fleet of whaling factory ships at anchor in the harbour. *Below*, the steaming water's edge within the harbour as the cold water laps against the hot volcanic beach

32. A stranded berg in Fournier Fjord, Anvers Island, in the Palmer Archipelago, off Graham Land

the animals might find it more advantageous to come up in darkness to escape from enemies as just suggested; or it might be that the antibiotic effect, perhaps some by-product of their light-stimulated growth process (photosynthesis) is stronger in the daytime than it is at night. At one time I thought this possible. The idea, indeed, receives some support from the fact that those animals which make little or no vertical migration, such as *Rhincalanus* as seen in the chart on p. 345, are characteristically found in the layers *below* the phytoplankton zone. There may possibly be something in this idea of a plant influence, and I shall return to it presently; it cannot, however, be the fundamental cause underlying vertical migration in general, for such behaviour is also characteristic of many planktonic animals which only inhabit the mid-water depths of the great oceans, far below the phytoplankton layers[1]. It seems clear that vertical migration must have some peculiar significance in the lives of nearly all planktonic animals, whether near the surface or not.

It might perhaps be, and this is my hypothesis, that vertical migration has been evolved because it gives the animal a continual change of environment which would otherwise be denied it. Planktonic animals, as we have seen, have been defined as those which are passively drifting in the moving waters; most of them have only very limited powers of locomotion which can only carry them a very little way in a day. If they had no vertical migration they would be at the mercy of their environment; if it should prove to be uncongenial they would have no means of escape.

We know now that the water masses are hardly ever moving at the same speed at different depths; the surface layers are nearly always travelling faster than the lower layers; this is partly because the wind drives the upper layers in different directions and partly because there are weaker forces, including the resistance of the sea-bed, acting lower down. While the forces that produce the deep and bottom circulation are not well understood, there are generally different water layers flowing in different directions; a good example was seen in the last chapter. An animal which can swim to right or left for only a few hundred feet may not get much change of environment for its effort; if, however, it sinks a hundred feet and climbs again next evening it may well find itself a mile or more from the point against the surface from which it dropped at dawn. There may well be a difference of a mile or two a day in the speed of the current at the surface and that at

[1]These interesting results are described by T. H. Waterman, R. F. Nunnemacher, F. A. Chance and G. L. Clarke in their paper 'Diurnal Vertical Migrations of Deep-Water Plankton' in *Biological Bulletins* vol. 76, pp. 256-79, 1939.

M

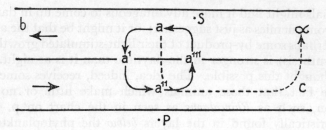

For explanation, see text.

only 30 metres depth. A drop in the morning and a climb of a hundred feet in the evening may give an animal a horizontal movement in relation to the surface layer of some ten thousand feet.

Some people appear to find these considerations of relative water movements difficult to grasp, but this is only because they think them more complex than they really are. Let us take, in the diagram above, the extreme instance of two water layers travelling in opposite directions at similar speeds; and from a position outside the system, say at P on the sea bed, let us observe the path of an animal as it migrates between the two layers, going up, say, at 6 o'clock in the evening and down at 6 o'clock in the morning. From a position a at midnight it will follow the path a^i, a^{ii}, a^{iii} and back to its starting point; this is its starting point in space in relation to the observer outside of the system at P, but it is *not* the same part of the surface water as it was in before. The water which surrounded it when it started at a has now moved on to b, and that which surrounded it at a^{ii} will have moved on to c by the time it is back again in this position in relation to P. Now if we could have watched the animal from a boat drifting in the surface layer, say at s, we should have seen the animal follow the path from a to $\propto$.

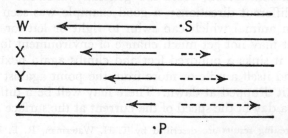

For explanation, see text.

More usually the layers of water may be travelling more or less in the same directions but at different speeds. If for example, as in the lower diagram opposite, the water layers w, x, y and z are moving to the left, as seen from the sea bed at P, with speeds corresponding to the lengths of the arrows, then if viewed from the surface layer at s, the lower layers will be moving to the right, relative to the observer, with velocities increasing with depth in proportion to the length of the broken-line arrows. Any animal going down from the surface into a lower layer will be carried to the right in relation to s.

Vertical migration, I believe, may be a means of providing a relatively weak and drifting animal with a powerful means of movement. It can make an 'inverted hop' from one part of its environment to another by sinking and rising again. Rather than speaking of movement, perhaps we should say that it is being left behind by the surface water out of which it drops for an interval each day; *relative* to the surface, however, it is moving along day after day.

Analogy can be dangerous, but it is often instructive if used with caution. Man is most like a plankton organism when he is up in an old-fashioned balloon drifting freely in whatever wind there is. Let us examine this parallel more closely. The aeronaut can control his movement to some extent; he can navigate within certain narrow limits. The wind is never at the same speed and rarely in exactly the same direction at different heights. The experienced balloonist in a competition, now, alas, almost an event of the past, goes up and down till he finds the wind that is likely to carry him either farthest from the starting-point or nearest to the particular goal he may be trying to reach according to the nature of the contest. He goes up by letting out his sand ballast; he comes down by valving out some gas from the balloon. Any independence he has over the environment is achieved entirely by *vertical migration*! I am not of course supposing for a moment that the plankton animals make any conscious navigation; even if they were conscious of their surroundings—or even indeed if they were intelligent beings—they could not judge how fast or in what direction the different water layers are moving any more than the balloonist can when he is travelling in the clouds cut off from the sight of land. I am suggesting that the development of a habit of regular vertical migration enables the animals continually to sample new environments—new feeding grounds—and so gives them a better chance of survival than if they always drifted in the same body of water.

We have as a matter of fact seen in the last chapter some remarkable examples of vertical migration serving as a means of unconscious 'navigation' enabling species like *Euphausia frigida* and *E. triacantha* to maintain their geographical position, or with a seasonal migration enabling, as Dr. Mackintosh has shown, many plankton animals to return southward during the winter after drifting northward during the summer.

It seems likely that vertical migration as a whole has been evolved as a means of giving planktonic organisms a greater degree of independence of their environment than could be achieved without it. If on coming up into a new environment they should find it not to their liking, then they can at once drop out of it again, stay down for a while and make another attempt later. I believe it to be a special adaptation to drifting life brought about by selection acting on variations in the innate behaviour patterns of the animals in relation to external stimuli such as changes in light intensity[1]. It is clear, I think, that any animal which might be inclined to make a vertical movement away from a patch of water which was uncongenial to it, would be more likely to survive and give more offspring to posterity than one doomed to remain drifting under adverse conditions. Such water might be uncongenial for a variety of reasons: shortage of the right food, too

[1]Recently my former pupil Mr. Peter David of the National Institute of Oceanography (in *Systematic Zoology*, vol. 10, pp. 10-16, 1961) has suggested a different evolutionary significance for vertical migration. Members of the same species, because they will not always behave in the same way, will continually be meeting with different members of their clan and so by breeding bringing about a continual interchange of new genetical material. It is in fact a mechanism which prevents the genetic isolation of members of the same species. This indeed must be true. On p. 306 of our original *Report* I wrote under the heading of 'Reassortment of the Plankton': 'The consideration of vertical migration leads one to recognise that there must be a continual reassortment of animals within the plankton community. If organisms A, B, C and D are together one night they may be considerable distances apart on the next night, if their vertical migration range is different and the speeds of the different water layers are not the same. Whilst the places of those passed on may be taken by others of the same species which have followed, often, owing to the patchiness of their distribution, the numbers of each different species brought together within a given body of water on consecutive nights must vary considerably.'

David is right to point out that it provides a mechanism for accelerating the interchange of genetic material, but I find it difficult to visualise how this potentially desirable quality could have led to its evolution by natural selection in the first place. Valuable as this aspect may be, I do not think it could have been the first selective cause of the habit, nor do I think it likely that it is its most important evolutionary factor. We must remember that it appears to have been evolved again and again independently in so many different groups; once the instinct is fixed by selection we see that it can have this important advantage of accelerating the interchange of genes in the population, but some quite different factor must have been the one upon which natural selection first acted in each case.

Professor V. C. Wynne-Edwards in his recent *Animal Dispersion in relation to Social Behaviour* (1962) gives yet another significance to vertical migration, but this again must be secondary to the original selective advantage.

high an alkalinity, the presence of some poisonous organism such as the notorious 'red-bloom' and so on. In this way hereditary variations which caused the animals to move vertically would tend to be selected; then eventually, by the further selection of other inherited changes in behaviour, the diurnal process, the rhythmic movement in relation to light which we know to-day, would gradually be perfected over the millions of generations of planktonic life. The animal comes to be presented with a continuous change of scene. This rhythmic movement in relation to the vertical changes in light intensity, as night alternates with day, is, however, not one that is rigidly fixed. In studying the results of our survey we do not see all the members of a species going up together; some seem to remain down on some nights, and on occasions others may be seen at the surface in bright sunlight. It is no doubt a pattern of behaviour that can be modified in relation to various circumstances: both differences in the nature of the environment and in the physiological state of the animal.

Once such a rhythmic vertical movement is established it must have a very profound bearing upon the patterns of distribution as seen in any survey. I have sometimes been a little surprised that more attention has not been paid to this aspect; the ideas I want now to present were all put forward in our *Discovery Report* based directly upon our South Georgia work. Here again I think perhaps unintentionally I obscured the issue by seeming to link my argument too closely with my speculations regarding the hypothesis of animal exclusion; actually the effects I want to describe are in principle entirely independent of that hypothesis. The idea I am about to describe is not actually a speculation at all; it is an account of what in fact must logically follow from the occurrence of the vertical migrational patterns observed in our survey and the movements of the water as independently established by our hydrologists. It is indeed as much fact as any of the items included in the last chapter.

In the shallower regions of the sea, over the continental shelf, where the bottom may be hollowed into troughs or raised up in banks, there may be a very different pattern of water movement near the bottom as compared with that at the surface; also where two currents meet, or where one stream is deflected by a mass of land, we may sometimes get a surface swirl produced: an upper layer of water rotating like a disc above another layer which is being guided along in some particular direction by the contours of the sea bed. Plankton animals migrating every day upwards and downwards between the upper and lower systems are going to be carried in all sorts of directions which we should never expect if we did not have an exact knowledge of the

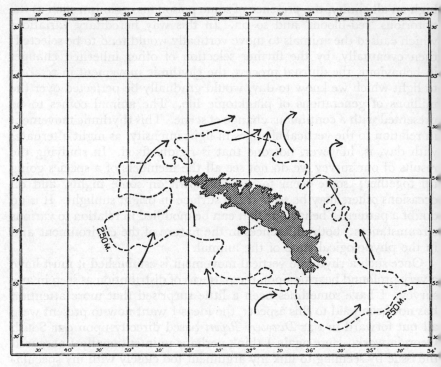

A chart showing the main water movements round South Georgia at a depth of 150 metres; this should be compared with the more detailed chart of the surface currents shown on p. 321. From *D.R.*, vol. XI.

relative movement of the two water layers. If we work out their paths in detail we see how in some regions they may be held up, almost marking time as it were, and in others hurried on apace.

In the last chapter, p. 321, I gave a chart of the *surface* water movements round South Georgia as prepared for us by the late Dr. A. J. Clowes by means of dynamic calculations; to compare with this I now reproduce above another chart from our *Report* specially prepared by Dr. G. E. R. Deacon to show, in less detail, the general movements at a depth of 150 metres. Neither hydrologist would regard these charts as exact, but they are as nearly correct as can be estimated from the data available. By considering both charts we can work out the approximate path that would be taken by animals migrating between 150 m. and the surface, assuming that the speed of the currents and the range of vertical migration remain more or less constant. The next chart shows an example. It represents in plan an area to the north-east of South Georgia bounded approximately by latitudes 53° 20′ and 54° 20′ and longitudes 34° and 38° W. In this diagram, and the four which follow, the fine continuous lines represent the direction of the surface currents and the fine broken lines that of the lower currents, in this case those at 150 m. The heavy black lines represent the paths of vertically migrating animals, the unbroken parts of the lines being their paths in the surface currents, and the broken parts their paths when below. If we start to observe an animal at

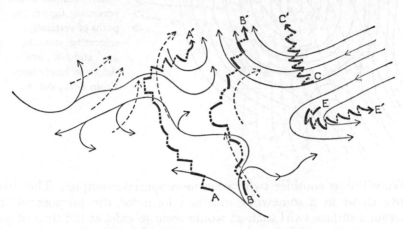

A plan of the water movements in an area to the north-east of South Georgia combining those at the surface, shown in fine continuous line, and those at 150 metres' depth, in fine broken line; in heavy line are shown the paths which would be taken by plankton animals A, B, C, and E if they spent the night near the surface and the day in the lower layers. From *D.R.*, vol. XI.

A it will follow more or less the path to A′ and one at B will go to B′. We see that at some points in their journey they may be carried farther apart than at others. The distance travelled in the surface current is shown as approximately equal to that travelled in the lower current. The surface current will likely be travelling faster than the lower one; but we have seen that the animals usually spend a shorter time in the surface layer and a longer time below. C will take the path to C′ and E to E′. So we could pick out numerous examples of the possible movements of migrating animals from different parts of the region; it must be remembered that these considerations are theoretical and based on the assumption that the range of migration remains more or less constant.

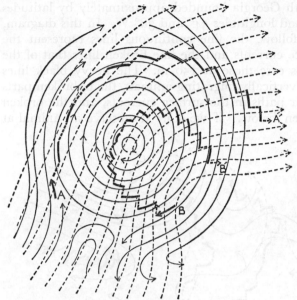

A plan of the water movements to the west of the north end of South Georgia where there is a swirl of water at the surface (fine continuous lines) but a regular flow of water below it (fine broken lines). Similar to the preceding figure, the paths of vertically migrating animals, A-A' and B-B', are shown in heavy line. From *D.R.*, vol. xi.

We will now consider two rather more special examples. The chart above shows in a somewhat idealised form for the purpose of the diagram a surface swirl such as would seem to exist at the time of our survey to the west of the northern end of our island. It is not necessarily a vortex descending in the centre, but perhaps rather a disc of surface water rotated by the moving water masses at its periphery. The fine broken lines show the likely movement at 150 m. Now our vertically migrating animals will follow paths from A to A' and from B to B'.

If a current in the southern hemisphere meets an obstruction it will tend to be curved round to the left; thus when two currents meet they may be deflected round in opposite directions. Now if the water of one current is perhaps warmer or less saline than the other, and so slightly less dense, it may, as it curves round, partly overflow the other, giving rise to a condition as shown in the next chart opposite. This diagram, for purpose of demonstration, is again ideal rather than usual; such a completely symmetrical system may indeed be rare, but not infrequently some may approach it in form. In this ideal diagram an animal starting at A would pass to A' and back to A again, and one at B to B' and back to B again. It will be noted that the animals are shown as travelling longer or shorter distances for each sojourn in the upper or lower layers as they pass out towards or inwards from the periphery of the curving current. In this manner an assembly of

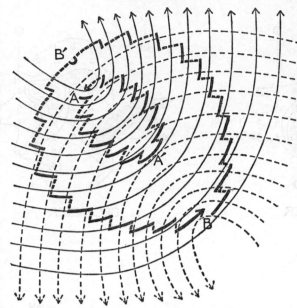

An extreme example of how animals migrating vertically day and night between the surface waters and a deeper layer might be held up in one locality if the water layers concerned were moving in opposite swirl directions as shown by the fine continuous and broken lines. The paths of two plankton animals at A and B are seen, in heavy line, to move to A′ and B′ and come back to their original positions again. From *D.R.*, vol. XI

animals might be kept circulating in one area whilst the water masses were continually passing on. In actual practice an animal would rarely be brought back to exactly the same place, but with swirling current systems as we see round South Georgia in the meeting and mixing of the two streams of Bellingshausen Sea and Weddell Sea origin, varying slightly in salinity and temperature, we may well get conditions which might tend to hold assemblies of animals for considerable periods in one neighbourhood.

This last proposition is of considerable interest in relation to whaling in regions like South Georgia or other areas where the meeting of currents may cause swirls. We have seen in the last chapter how closely the whales are associated with concentrations of krill. A study of the whale distributions, as plotted from the returns of the whalers by Kemp and Bennett[1], suggests that at times such concentrations of krill must be kept at one place for considerable periods of time; since we also know that round South Georgia the water is always likely to be on the move, it follows that some such swirl effects as those just outlined are most probably in operation. An example of such a maintained whale concentration is given in the charts overleaf.

My next step in what I have called the 'dynamics of plankton distribution' may be thought perhaps to be a little more speculative, yet

[1] *Discovery Reports*, vol. VI, pp. 165-90, 1932.

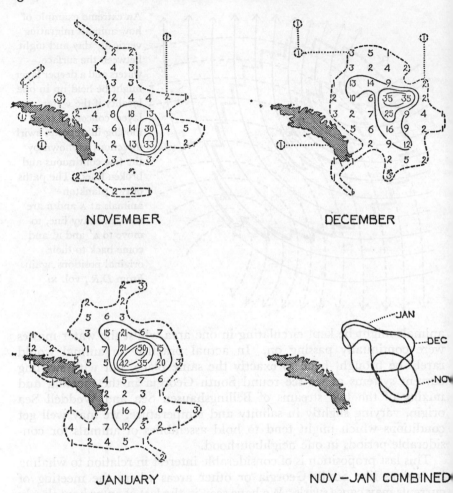

NOVEMBER

DECEMBER

JANUARY

NOV—JAN COMBINED

Concentrations of blue whales at South Georgia remaining in the same place from
November, through December, 1928, to January, 1929, suggesting a lasting area of
dense krill in this position. From *D.R.*, vol. XI.

it is only the logical sequence of what has gone before. So far we have
been considering the effects on the distribution of these vertically
migrating animals of changes in the paths or speeds of the moving
water masses; now let us consider what might happen if the animals
were to vary their migrational behaviour: for example, under some
conditions going down deeper than under others, or staying down for
longer or not rising so high in the water at night, and so on. If the

water at different levels is travelling at different speeds—and we have seen that this is nearly always so—then such changes in behaviour as those just suggested might have very considerable effects upon the animals' distributions. At present we know very little about the extent of such changes in behaviour or of the factors that govern them; we do know, however, that the range of vertical migration in a species— or for an individual—is by no means constant: on some days most representatives may be higher in the water than on others and on some nights not so many may come near the surface as on others. Let us also look at this in diagrammatic form, as that below, which represents a section of the sea. For reasons that will become apparent, the effects of variations in the animals' behaviour upon their distrib- ution will be better understood if we consider the movements of the water, and so of the animals contained in it, in relation to the *surface*

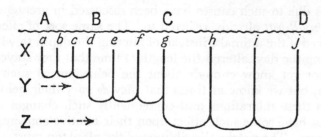

For explanation, see text.

layer rather than to the fixed sea bed. Now let us suppose in the diagram that the lower layers of water Y and Z will be moving *to the right* in relation to the surface layer X at speeds in proportion to the lengths of the arrows. Now let us follow the path of a vertically migrating animal, observing it from the surface layer and let us start by observing it at night when it is up in the surface layer X at a point *a*; at dawn it will begin to sink down to remain during the day time, let us say, at a level approaching that of layer Y, and on the next night it will rise again into the surface layer at a point *b*. The distance of *b* from *a* depends of course on the difference in speed of flow between the two water layers. To the observer in the surface layer it remains stationary during the night at *b* until it sinks again at dawn. It will reappear in the surface layer at *c* and *d* on the next two nights; that is assuming that it went down in the daytime to the same depth each day. Now let us suppose that conditions in the area BC differed in some way from those in the former area AB and that this difference caused the animals to sink more deeply during the day; in relation to the surface layer they would be carried along a greater distance each day than before and on successive nights would occupy positions e, f and g. Suppose further that in area CD they met with conditions which made them migrate still more deeply, then on the following nights they might occupy positions h, i and j. In the figure we have so far followed the path of a single animal; now let us consider what would happen to three separate animals behaving in just the same way as the one just followed, only let us imagine them separated from one another on one night at the points a, b and c. In three nights' time they would respectively be at the points d, e and f, and in another three nights at g, h and i. We see that if the majority of the members of a species behave in the same way under one set of conditions, and then together change their behaviour under some other conditions, we may expect them to be *closer together* in some areas than in others. Further complications in patchiness due to such causes have been discussed in greater detail in the *Discovery Report* already referred to. The same sort of effect would be produced if the animals, instead of altering the depth to which they sank during the day, altered the length of time that they stayed below. We do not yet know enough about the behaviour of such animals in the sea, but we know at times that they *do* vary their behaviour in respect to these migrations and consequently such changes in movement must have some such effect upon their relative concentration in various areas. The patchy distribution of the plankton must, of course, be due to a great variety of causes and this is only one of them.

I want now to return to a question we briefly considered in the last chapter but postponed because it was concerned more with theory than established fact: that of what *causes* the inverse relationship between the distribution of the zoöplankton and the phytoplankton noted in our South Georgia survey. We saw that the krill, and a number of other important plankton animals, were present only in small numbers in the regions of dense phytoplankton production; this must be important in understanding the feeding movements of whales, and so it is worth paying some attention to it.

It has, as a matter of fact, been known for a long time that one not infrequently tends to get such an inverse relationship between the areas of rich plant plankton and those of high animal numbers. When I first became interested in it and looked through the earlier literature for other examples I was quite surprised to find how often it had been recorded and yet what little attention had been given to it by planktologists in general. I have cited most of the earlier examples in our *Discovery Report*.

Several possible explanations, which are not mutually exclusive, have been put forward and may each be true on different occasions. In nature it is never safe to assume that one particular effect must always be brought about by the same set of circumstances. A particular species, for example, might become abundant or rare for any one of a number of reasons, which might include factors such as food supply, predators, or disease; inter-relationships in nature are rarely simple. It is the tracing of these links which gives ecology its fascination; and it is because of their complexity that speedy answers cannot be expected from researches into natural populations.

Let us now consider some of these explanations; there are at least five, and I will take what may be called a false one first. It has been held by some that the effect is not a real one and due to nothing more than a technical fault in collecting; they point out that if the little plants are present in enormous numbers they will quickly clog up the fine meshes of the net and so greatly reduce the water passing through it that very few animals will be caught. No doubt this may well be true *if* the methods of collecting were so badly conceived. In our South Georgia survey, however, for the capture of the larger plankton animals we used nets of much larger mesh than those for the smaller animals and the phytoplankton; here the inverse relationship between the phytoplankton and these larger animals must be a real one because the larger-meshed nets were never clogged with the tiny plants.

Now let us turn to explanations other than error. The first we can call that of grazing. If abundant, the herbivorous animals will graze down the planktonic plants, so many animals will mean few plants; conversely where the animals are scarcer than usual they will allow the plants to multiply and produce an exceptionally dense crop. This simple and reasonable explanation seems to have been first put forward by Conte Castracane who is quoted by the authors of the *Narrative of the Cruises of H.M.S. 'Challenger'* (vol. 1, second part, p. 931, 1885) as having written to them concerning the expedition's plankton samples as follows: 'Another observation, made during the examination of these surface gatherings, is that when the net yielded an abundance of different forms of microscopic animals, Diatoms were extremely rare; for this I have been unable to suggest any explanation other than that the Diatoms serve as food to the animals, so that where the latter were abundant the former are few in number.'

Much has been done in the last two decades to show the reality and importance of this grazing relationship, particularly by H. W. Harvey[1] and his workers at Plymouth and in America by R. H. Fleming[2], and

[1] *J. Mar. biol. Ass. U.K.*, 20, 407-41, 1935. [2] *J. Cons. int. Explor. Mer.*, 14, 3-20, 1939.

G. H. Riley and D. F. Bumpus[1]. There can be no doubt that this explanation is a true and important one; but is it the only and the most important one?

In the same year in which Castracane's explanation was published, 1885, came also a different view put forward independently by F. G. Pearcey[2] who was also associated with the *Challenger*, having been an assistant on the voyage. He later made a voyage in one of the herring sailing luggers from Leith round Shetland, taking a tow-net with him. He came across many areas of dense phytoplankton (mainly the diatoms *Rhizosolenia* and *Thalassiosira*) and in these hardly any herring were caught; in the clear regions, on the other hand, the catches were high. At Lowestoft, where I was appointed Assistant Naturalist at the Fishery Laboratory in 1921, I began to study the feeding habits of the herring and its relations to the plankton in general. It was a poor autumn fishing that year. Going out on a drifter with a tow-net, I had just the same experience as Pearcey: the water was thick with phytoplankton, also *Rhizosolenia*, so that the meshes of my net were clogged with it. The skipper called this water 'weedy water' or 'Dutchman's baccy juice,' because the nets came up slimy and brown, and he said they were unlikely to catch fish in it. Later experiments, which I made with a little plankton sampling device used on herring drifters, gave more evidence of the herring avoiding areas of dense phytoplankton[3]. The herring might avoid the patches of phytoplankton because by experience they would not expect to find their food, the small crustacea and other plankton animals there; and this might be just another instance of a lack of grazing allowing a dense phytoplankton growth. Pearcey, however, considered the phytoplankton when very abundant to have some noxious effect which was avoided by both herring and zoöplankton. He recorded that not only were there few herring in such regions but also few plankton animals and he spoke of the 'exclusive effect' of the diatoms. Now because the herring appeared to avoid the dense phytoplankton at the time of the autumn Yarmouth and Lowestoft fishery when they were *not feeding*, but collecting for spawning, I thought it likely that Pearcey was right; it seemed unlikely that the herring would avoid such areas for the former reason if they were not then concerned with finding food.

It was after this experience that I joined the *Discovery* and then met with this inverse relationship in the distribution of animal and plant plankton at South Georgia. I considered the grazing explanation but became more attracted by the possibility of Pearcey's principle

[1] *J. Mar. Res.*, 6, 33-47, 1946.   [2] *Proc. R. phys. Soc. Edinb.*, 8, 389-415, 1885.
[3] I have discussed this matter at fuller length in my book *The Open Sea* (pp. 293-4).

being correct for several reasons. Firstly the areas of dense phytoplankton appeared to be formed just in relation to certain hydrological conditions, i.e., in the regions of the mixing of waters of different origins discussed in the last chapter (p. 323) and not in a haphazard fashion that might be due to just lack of grazing. Secondly, as we also saw in the last chapter, many different species of animals appeared to be distributed away from the dense plant concentrations, and some of these were much less numerous than other species which must have been far more effective as grazers; it seemed very curious that all these animals *together* should have a similar distribution away from the rich phytoplankton regions. It seemed against the grazing hypothesis, too, that there were also very few animals where the phytoplankton was very scarce (p. 335). Again, although we have as yet little knowledge of the actual species of diatoms usually eaten by the different animals, we should perhaps not expect the animals to be equally effective in grazing down quite different plant communities; yet we do see the same animals having the same inverse distributional relationship with quite different plant plankton 'communities' as shown in the full *Report*.

I now began to consider Pearcey's view very seriously. But how, if it were true, could the drifting plankton animals, with only weak powers of locomotion, migrate away from the dense phytoplankton areas? The ideas I had been forming, and which I have already explained, regarding what I have called the dynamics of distribution, gave a possible clue. Did these two bits of the puzzle fit together? The more I looked at them, the more they seemed to, or was I letting my imagination run away with me? I was certainly excited at what I saw. I cannot here give all the evidence I considered, for it takes up 66 pages in our *Report* (pp. 276-342); I must just pick out the salient features. Because Pearcey had first talked of the 'exclusive effect' of the phytoplankton, I called the idea I now put forward, *the hypothesis of animal exclusion.*

It seemed to me that the inverse distributional relationship between the animals and plants could be brought about by the vertical migrational behaviour of the former being modified by heavy concentrations of the latter. If the plants, when very abundant, produced some effect on the water (a chemical antibiotic effect most likely) which was uncongenial to the animals, then the behaviour of the latter might be modified so that either they did not come up into the dense phytoplankton zone at all or came up for a shorter period than usual[1]; this

[1] A herbivorous animal coming up into dense concentration of plants could get the same amount of food as in a more normal phytoplankton, in a much shorter time.

would automatically have the effect, seen on p. 363, of reducing the numbers of the animals in these areas. It seemed a possible hypothesis; I now looked for evidence to support it.

I had been so impressed by the whale-phosphate correlations which I discussed in the last chapter (p. 336), and with the inverted similarity in the distribution charts of phosphate values and phytoplankton (pp. 324-5), that it occurred to me that for two reasons a range of phosphate values might be a better index of plant production than one of actual phytoplankton measurements. Firstly a scale of phosphate values would indicate relative plant production over a *little time in the past* which might be better for correlation than *contemporaneous* values, since it would allow more time for the animals to show any adjusted distribution; secondly it might give a better indication of the true relative plant production because our denser samples would not be as large as they really should be on account of the clogging of the meshes of the fine net, giving greatly reduced filtration, which we have already discussed[1].

In view of these considerations I now correlated the numbers of all the different zöoplankton species (which occurred with sufficient frequency) with a scale of phosphate values. The detailed correlation tables are too bulky to give here; they will be found in our *Report*. I made separate tables for the animals taken in the different kind of nets: the 1-metre diameter nets, the towed 70 cm. diameter nets, and the 70 cm. vertical nets; I also divided them into separate series of stations taken in daylight and those taken in darkness. Here again we saw that the majority of species on an average were not taken in larger numbers in the regions of lowest phosphate values (i.e., representing higher plant numbers), but in the intermediate phosphate ranges,

[1]Perhaps at this point we should ask ourselves if we are really certain that areas of higher and lower phosphate values are due to there being lower or higher phytoplankton respectively at these places. Could not the higher phosphate values be simply higher because in these places there were more animals, i.e., whales, krill, etc., to add more phosphates to the wate by their excretion? This was a point raised by my old friend, the late Mr. Alan Gardiner, who was, I believe, the first to show how quickly phosphates might be returned to the water by plankton animals. (*J. Cons. int. Explor. Mer.* 12, pp. 144-6, 1937.) When I first showed him our phosphate and whale charts this is just what he asked. This may in part be true, but in addition to phosphate values we also had alkalinity (pH) readings. We should expect those pH values to be higher in the regions of dense phytoplankton on account of their carbon assimilation in the process of photosynthesis; when we compare these pH values with the phosphate values (as in Fig. 160 on p. 295 of our *Discovery Report*) we see that the higher pH figures correspond with the lower phosphate figures which is what we should expect if the phosphate values are indeed a good index of phytoplankton production. A correlation of actual phytoplankton quantities with phosphate values is also shown in our *Report* (in the graph on p. 285).

with fewer again in the very high phosphate regions. It was, however, the copepods which appeared to give the most surprising evidence. Whilst most species, which I will call group A, behaved as just indicated, there were three species, which I will call group B, which seemed to show no correlation at all with phosphate values, and then there were two species, group C, which occurred in *higher* numbers in regions of lowest phosphate values. Now the remarkable thing is that these three groups are just the same three that I had already distinguished in relation to vertical migration! Those in group A were those having a more or less normal migration coming up into the surface layers a little before midnight; those in group B, were *Rhincalanus gigas, Calanus acutus*, and *Oithona similis* which showed no vertical migration at all and lived *below* the phytoplankton zone; and the two species in group C were *Calanus simillimus* and *Drepanopus pectinatus* which, as stated on p. 346, came up into the surface phytoplankton zone much earlier than any others and stayed up for longer in the morning. These differences in behaviour *appeared* to give just the support my hypothesis required.

This was indeed exciting, but if it were really true we should be able to see a difference in the behaviour of animals in regions of dense phytoplankton and of those in regions of poor phytoplankton. I tried to demonstrate this by treating the data in various ways as will be seen in our *Report* (pp. 322-42), but, to tell the truth, looking at it now, I must admit that the evidence is not as strong as I had at one time thought it to be. One gets carried away in one's enthusiasm for a new idea; it seemed to give a possible explanation to a great variety of ocean phenomena.

The whole idea of 'animal exclusion' had been a tantalising one with little bits of evidence here and there to suggest support for it. Dr. C. E. Lucas, when with me in my department at Hull, did some experiments[1] which gave some support to it, and more recently[2] has stressed the importance of the ecological effects of what he calls 'external metabolites,' i.e., substances given off from organisms into the water. Then Dr. J. H. Ryther[3], of Harvard University, made a most interesting study of the effects of phytoplankton on the feeding and survival of the freshwater water-flea *Daphnia*, showing that some product of *ageing* phytoplankton causes the animals to stop feeding and die. Some microscopic plants, such as the small flagellates which cause the so-called 'red-bloom' in the sea, are known to poison the water when they are very abundant and cause the death of fish and other animals. Other experiments I tried myself, and ones which Dr. Richard Bain-

[1] *J. Cons. int. Explor. Mer.* vol. 11, pp. 343-362, 1936.
[2] *Biol. Rev.* vol. 22, pp. 270-95, 1947.   [3] *Ecology*, vol. 35, pp. 522-33, 1954.

bridge did, failed to give the evidence in support of my hypothesis that I had hoped for. It may yet come; there is some interesting work going on at this moment, at the Plymouth Laboratory, on chemical substances given off into the water by diatoms and other planktonic plants. It may well be shown that there is a grain of truth in the idea, but I now have much less confidence in it as a major overriding cause governing ecological events in the pelagic world. It is good for one to realise that one can be wrong! But how then are we to explain the condition we found in our survey?

I now think that one or other of the two remaining explanations of the phyto- and zoöplankton inverse relationship, both suggested after the publication of our *Report*, may give us the reason for the conditions we found there. Dr. Steeman-Nielsen, the Danish marine biologst, while studying the plankton off the south-west of Iceland, found a patch of rich phytoplankton with very little zoöplankton in it, but with abundant zoöplankton all around its edge. He showed that this was an area of upwelling caused by a current striking the edge of the continental shelf, and so bringing water from the lower layers up to the surface. What happens when this occurs? I summarise the eminently reasonable account that he suggests[1]. First a body of water from below comes up to the surface and so pushes aside the normal surface water together with the typical animals it contains; the animals in the water from below are naturally not used to the surface light conditions and so remain below leaving a large patch of water at the surface with very little animal life in it. Now this water from below, rich in phosphates and nitrates, may be carrying many spores and resting stages of diatoms which on coming up into the sunlit surface layers will begin to multiply and so present a dense patch of phytoplankton with few animals to graze it down. The surrounding animals will now begin to graze at it from the edges. This might well give us an explanation of the conditions found at South Georgia: water upwelling over the shelf round the island, both from the Bellingshausen Sea and Weddell Sea sides, would push away the more surface living forms, the krill and associated fauna from some large areas, and then, freed for the time being from grazing animals, would develop into the great phytoplankton patches that we saw. Whilst I believe Dr. Steeman-Nielsen may have given us the key to what happens at South Georgia, there remains yet another explanation of such an inverse phyto-zoöplankton relationship which may be even more important in other parts of the Antarctic.

This last explanation—I am giving them in historical order—was put forward by the Russian oceanographer Dr. B. G. Bogorov in 1939

[1] *Journal du Conseil,* vol. XII, pp. 137-54, 1937.

following his observations on the plankton of the Arctic ocean[1]. Here he gives a most convincing picture of the sequence of events which follow the melting of the pack ice. In spring and early summer we have the sea still covered with ice which cuts off the light and prevents the growth of a plant plankton. As soon as the ice melts the plants will begin to multiply in the light of the long days of the polar summer; they will produce a great outburst of diatoms, as they do in the early spring with us, before the animals have multiplied sufficiently to keep them in check and graze them down. Then the animals increase in numbers and gradually the phytoplankton is grazed away. This is easy to understand and at once assumes greater significance in relation to what we have seen in the Antarctic seas when we remember that all the pack ice does not melt away at the same time. There are vast areas of the pack drifting about under the influences of currents and often driven by the wind. The ice gets broken up into smaller patches before it finally melts away; the patches of water which have been most recently covered by ice will give us the large phytoplankton areas which as yet have only a small population of animals within them. These will soon become rich feeding grounds for the krill which will graze them down, and so whaling grounds also, all following on the melting of the ice. It is possible of course that the phytoplankton patches against South Georgia might represent the surface of the sea which was a short time before covered with drifting ice, but I think there the upwelling theory of Steeman-Nielsen is more likely to apply because pack ice does not usually come so near to the island. Or they may simply be due to the effect of the mixing of the waters as I have suggested on p. 323.

I expect the principles suggested by Steeman-Nielsen and Bogorov are both important in different parts of the Antarctic. We must now leave our theoretical discussions for we are off to see more of the phytoplankton, krill and whales much farther to the south; and in chapters 20 and 21 we shall see something of what our successors on the R.R.S. *Discovery II* have found out about these three great elements in the life of the Southern Ocean right round the pole.

[1]*Comptes Rendus de l'Acad. des Sci. de l'U.S.S.R.* vol XIX, p. 641, 1938.

CHAPTER 16

TO THE SOUTH ORKNEYS AND THE
SOUTH SHETLANDS

Tuesday, 8th February (Back again on the *Discovery*). We sailed on the
4th bound for the South Orkneys and were given a most heartening
send off by all at Grytviken. We took our course round the northern
end of the island rather than the south and were glad we did so, for
when we came to Bird Island the S.W. wind which had been freshening
for some time reached full gale force; it would have been unpleasant
if we had been to the south-west with the rocky south coast on our lee.
The seas were very big—some of the most impressive that I have yet
seen—and we were driven for a time to the north. By Sunday evening
it had blown itself out and yesterday, being between the Shag Rocks
and Bird Island, we decided to make a station, for we wanted to check
if there was, as we expected, a ridge connecting South Georgia with
these isolated rocks; and there was, for we took soundings in only
177 metres.

After a full station, we let down a heavy 4 foot dredge and dragged
it along the bottom for just five minutes with a truly surprising result.
The wealth of animal life on the Antarctic sea bed is indeed amazing;
it is, of course, a consequence of the exceptionally rich plankton above.
The dredge's bag came up laden with beautiful coral-like alcyonarians
of many different kinds; some like bottle-brushes were made up of
innumerable fine branches each bearing rows of tiny flower-like
polyps, or some had their 'flowers' clustered in whorls at intervals
around their single delicate stems; others were branched like true corals
and others yet again were massive and fleshy like pin-cushions studded
with polyps like ornamental pins. There was a great range of colour
with shades of apricot and orange to the fore, but one was of the palest
rose pink and another of the purest white like some small flowering
tree laden with blossom and yet another (a species of *Thouarella*) was
remarkable for an animal in being green. With them were true corals
of several varieties, including one of a vivid flame colour. Then there

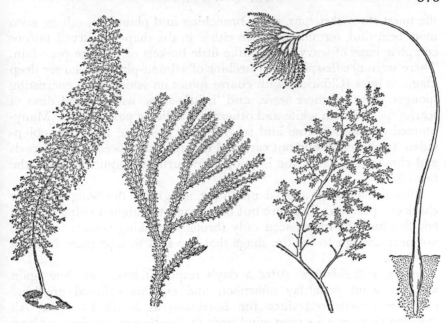

Some plant-like 'soft-corals' of the Antarctic: from left to right, the alcyonarians *Thouarella variabilis* and *Calligorgia* sp., the antipatharian *Antipathella contorta*, and the pennatulid *Umbellula* which is anchored in a soft muddy bottom.

were the white calcareous tubes of serpulid worms: tangled stems from the open ends of which, when undisturbed in a bath of water, project spreading plumes of tentacles. Some of these plant-like animals are shown in my sketches above.

The alcyonarians, particularly the pink and orange varieties, bore a fauna of their own. In and out of the branches, entwined like dragons in some oriental embroidery, were many segmented worms: some banded white and red, and others with tufts of iridescent bristles down their sides. Then those strange worm-like molluscs (Neomeniae) curled themselves round the branches here and there. And in the rose-pink 'foliage', clinging by their sucker-feet were rose-pink holothurians (sea-cucumbers) exactly like their background and spreading out their many-branched tentacles in search of food; while mustard-coloured feather-stars (Crinoids) with still more branching arms clung like big rosettes, for the most part, whether by coincidence or not, to the orange-yellow branches.

There were hydroids and polyzoans; many of the latter possessed the finest stony skeletons, some branching and plant-like, others, even more beautiful, forming a lattice either in the shape of curved fans or complete cups of wavy outline like little baskets of delicate porcelain. There were needle-spined sea urchins of salmon-pink and larger deep magenta ones (Cidarids) with coarse spines on which grew encrusting sponges. Starfish there were, and 'brittle-stars' with central discs of scarlet spotted with white and others of a delicate pale mauve. Many-plumed sea-slugs of rose and scarlet were browsing upon the polyp-laden 'trees' and in and out careered the small crustaceans, amphipods and cumaceans, whilst the isopod, Anarcturus, sat squirrel-like in the branches.

After dredging we moved up to get a sight of the Shag Rocks to check our position. They are but bare crags, the highest rising to some 200 feet and the lowest seen only through breaking waves; we were not near enough to see the shags that are said to nest there in large numbers.

Thursday, 10th February. After a day's respite it began to blow again and the wind yesterday afternoon and evening eclipsed anything we have experienced since the hurricane at South Georgia. All morning there was a strong wind from the north-west helping us along in great style; our fore and main topsails, and foresail, as well as jib and spankers, were swollen out, strained as though to bursting. It was a morning to be remembered; we were flying along at 8½ knots—a rare speed for the old *Discovery*—and a bright sun lit the sails and gave the spume from the curling wave tops a dazzling brilliance. With all her faults from an oceanographer's point of view, I cannot help loving the old ship. There is glory in her sails, massive spars and masts; while every now and again one of the towering blue monsters will break over her wooden walls in a cascade of foaming water.

In the afternoon we saw the stuff our seamen were made of. It is difficult to-day to get a good square-rig sailing crew together, but we have got them; it was a magnificent display. The sky darkened and the wind increased with startling suddenness to full gale. 'All hands take in sail!' ordered the captain from the bridge—and it was echoed below for'ard. At once the whole crew were on deck. The wind was abaft the starboard beam so that the ship, apart from rolling as much as the spread of canvas would allow, was heeling well to port. In a moment or two the huge sheet of the foresail was loosened by some, while others hauled on the ropes that clewed it up; how it tugged on the ropes as it lost its firm contour. Then the topsails followed, fore and main, and now the supreme work of the sailor begins. As soon as the canvas was reduced, the ship, of course, had full scope for her rolling; and the height of the waves appeared to be mounting at every moment. Up aloft go the sailors, as calmly as if the ship had been in port, and out upon the swaying yards which are describing great arcs through the roaring air (see Plate 28, p. 305). Each time a wave breaks against the ship the bridge is blotted out with spray. Filled with admiration, who cannot wish that he had the nerve to stand on the chains which run below the yards, with nothing else for support, and the strength to pull with all one's might at the wet and heavy sail? First the topsail, then the foresail, are methodically tucked away: a smaller party of four are simultaneously at work on the main topsail. All is done in little more time than it takes to write it down. The yards are next trimmed, the ship swung round head to sea and we are hove to; so we remained all night. For an hour and a half from 5 o'clock the wind kept up a steady blow of force eleven: one point off hurricane force. It then eased a little during the night, but the waves were still enormous; sometimes we shipped a green sea over the weather side, but more usually, as we rolled so far over, we took in a massive fall of water over the lee rail.

Yesterday we had a wireless message from the *Scoresby* stating that the pelagic whaling ship *Lancing*, which had sent a catcher[1] into Grytviken with a sick man, had reported an ice island as big as South Georgia—a huge piece of the Barrier broken away—in longitude 40°W., north of the South Orkneys, not far to the eastward of our course.

Tuesday, 15th February. We are at last approaching the South Orkneys, but for the thick weather and quantity of icebergs we should have made it this evening. The weather remained rough all Friday and Saturday; we were in fact driven back to the north on Friday by a strong gale from the south. It moderated on Sunday, when we were visited by a school of a score or so of bottlenose whales, and yesterday, when for the first time in a week we could use a net, we worked a complete station in 3,459 metres of water. Very heavy catches of diatoms were taken in the surface nets[2]. [In view of what was said earlier about the possible effect of the mixing of two different water masses in promoting planktonic production it is interesting to note that this station lies approximately on the boundary between the water from the Bellingshausen Sea and that from the Weddell Sea.] All around us there were large icebergs; on Saturday and Sunday we passed some

---

[1]She herself was not allowed within the three-mile limit since she fishes without a licence.

[2]*Rhizosolenia styliformis* predominated, but *Coscinodiscus*, *Fragellaria*, *Corethron* and several species of *Chaetoceros* were well represented.

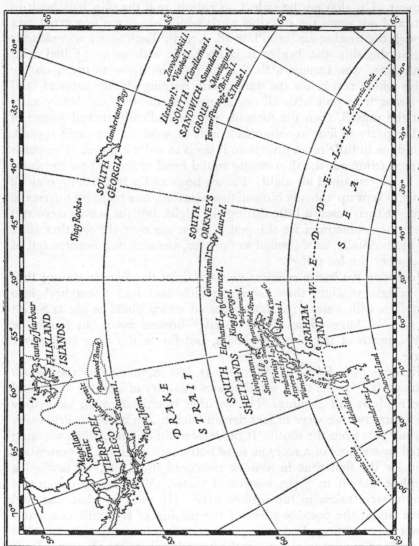

General map of the Falkland Islands and Dependencies from the author's paper in *The Geographical Journal*, 1928.

great pieces of the barrier—floating ice islands—one of which was at least five miles in length.

Since yesterday afternoon we have had a spanking breeze from the north so that we made good progress until the weather became thick and we had to take in sail. Twice this morning we found ourselves bearing down upon great walls of ice which loomed out of the fog ahead; not a very comfortable position with a strong wind behind us! All hands were called to trim yards as we quickly changed tack and stood off from a grim grey 'coast' with huge waves dashing up its perpendicular cliffs.

Monday, 20th February. We had expected to reach Coronation Island, (South Orkneys) on Wednesday but were hemmed in by thick fog; by dead reckoning we had passed to the westward and should now be south of it where two floating whaling factories were working: the *Sevilla* and the *Orwell*. I awoke next morning to feel a bump and a tremor, and the unmistakable sound of striking ice; it was soon followed by the scraping, slithering, sound of ice passing along the ship. Reaching the deck I found we had entered a field of loose hummocky pack with many fine icebergs in it (Plate 29, p. 320). Visibility was still poor but by the afternoon the lower slopes of a line of snow-covered hills became just visible on our port beam and in a short time we were steaming up to the *Sevilla*, anchored in Paul Harbour. Two motor boats, one from her and the other from the *Orwell* which was lying round the corner in Borge Bay, brought their two captains to greet us.

The South Orkneys are more Antarctic than South Georgia, being some five hundred miles farther south. Here the only vegetation consists of the mosses and lichens encrusting the rocks which project through the snow to give a landscape a blotched appearance; whilst the general effect at a distance is black and white, at close quarters the rocks in places are coloured a bright orange by a lichen. Grey clouds nearly always veil the tops of the mountains and only on one occasion did we catch a fleeting glimpse of the peaks; they are not so high as those of South Georgia, the three highest on Coronation Island being 5,397, 4,331 and 1,696 feet according to the Admiralty Chart. The group consists of two main islands, Coronation about 40 miles long and Laurie Island about 15, with a much smaller Powell Island between them and numerous rocky islets scattered along their coasts.

We saw the peaks as we went trawling with a small beam trawl from *Orwell's* motor boat. Borge Bay is wide with two large and several smaller glaciers jutting into it, and there was much floating ice of all shapes and sizes; in and out we threaded our way whilst the sun every now and again broke through to turn the pearly grey water to a deep

blue and the icebergs to blocks of dazzling brilliance. It was a scene
for ever changing with our motion; at every instant the icebergs
seemed rearranged and their grotesque outlines altered as we turned
this way and that. Nor was the change of shape entirely due to *our*
movement, for as we watched, a largish iceberg suddenly canted over
and then completely turned turtle; its jagged outline was exchanged
for the smooth water-worn surface of its formerly-submerged base
which now rocked slowly to and fro before coming to rest. Upon
several flat ice floes were crab-eater seals which allowed us to come
close alongside without showing any concern.

Our trawl brought up a rich and varied haul which included one of
those giant isopods *Glyptonotus*, at least five inches long. Those other
curious very flat isopods *Serolis*, characteristic of the Antarctic fauna,
were here in numbers and I made the mistake of putting the two kinds
together in the same large jar; *Glyptonotus* calmly picked up one of the
Serolis and took great bites out of it as if it had been a slice of cake. I
have added a further note and sketch on p. 411.

Amongst the rocks above the shore just opposite where we were tied
up alongside the *Orwell* were a number of giant petrels with their
enormous chicks, great masses of down, which seemed too heavy for
their legs, for we never saw them stand. Their mothers, shrieking loud
protests, left them as we approached and then the youngsters took up
the cry. When you come near they will shoot out their necks and
snap their beaks at you in the most savage fashion. Beware! Do not
get too close and do not provoke them too much; they have a horrible
method of defence. I was just about to prod the fluffy creature gently
with my camera tripod to see if it could really stand when it thrust
out its head as it had done several times before, but instead of uttering
a cry, it shot me with a blast of vomit. I knew that adult petrels had
this measure of protection, but I somehow did not expect it from the
chick; it fired its stomach contents with a velocity and precision of a
small cannon. I was covered with horrible stinking red bile. It must
certainly be a most effective means of protection when reserved for
the critical moment and directed into the eyes of the attacker. I
certainly did not want a second dose and, having taken the photographs
shown in Plate 30 (p. 321), left them severely alone in the future.

Running about over the stones by the shore were many of those most
comic little birds, the pure white sheathbills (*Chionis alba*) which are also
included in Plate 30. At first sight they might be taken for some
kind of pigeon, but actually they are related to the waders although
they hate the water; they are, I believe, the only Antarctic birds
which have not webbed feet. They were carrying out a very pretty

The South Orkneys, with 'cape-pigeons', redrawn from a watercolour.

little courtship display. A pair would meet, stand close together facing one another and bob up and down five or six times in rapid succession, each going up and down exactly together and making a chattering noise while doing it. Then off they will go, running to and fro over the rocks to meet again in a few minutes' time to repeat the performance. They seem as anxious as you are to make friends. As you land on the rocks they will come running up to welcome you and, if you do not move too quickly, or better still, if you sit down quietly, they will come right up and chatter to you. It is always best to get down as low as possible if you want to make friends with the birds, for apart from your unusual movements it is your height, I think, which is likely most to frighten them. Sitting down and chattering back to one of them, imitating him as nearly as I could, I got him to come and bow to me several times. When I got up and walked along the beach I found I was being followed by some half a dozen of these quaint little birds, like a party of children, only a few yards behind me.

The number of Cape pigeons here reminded me of the great many we saw at Grytviken, South Georgia, last season; vast hordes of them were congregated round the *Orwell* and the air rang with their cries as they gobbled up and fought over the refuse from the flensed carcasses. Just outside they could be seen in thousands resting upon ice floes or on rocks, or flying in swarms like starlings from one part of the bay to another.

At numerous points along the rocky coast are large rookeries of Antarctic or ringed penguins which are made conspicuous not so much by the birds themselves, but by the pink guano, due to their diet of krill. We visited one of them on Saturday, landing from the *Orwell*'s motor-boat. When we first arrived most of the birds were away 'fishing' for the day, although quite a number were left.

Particularly attractive were the young birds, charming downy brown children with white breasts; they were now quite big and some were beginning to get the adult plumage. Many of them were gathered into parties each with one adult bird, like a nurse, in charge. The ringed penguins are easily distinguished from others by the fine black ring round their necks just below the beak—like a chin-strap; also I think they have a larger tail than other species and make more use of it in getting about. They too were very friendly and inquisitive.

We had an opportunity here of seeing their remarkable powers of swimming under water. The rookery was at the end of a little inlet from the sea, deep and sheltered, with perpendicular rocky sides from which you could look down and see anything in the clear water below. Towards 4 o'clock the parents began to return from their fishing expeditions: one after another they came, and you could see them coming up the creek for quite a long way. I have already described how, in their swimming, they use their wings with the movements of flight; here we could see it to perfection. Although relatively slow, the thrust of the wings in water, as compared with air, is so great that they swim exceedingly fast—and with what grace. How fast? It is difficult to judge at close quarters but seeing them out at sea, when they leap clear of the water like porpoises, I should say they must be doing at least twenty knots. They swim straight for the face of rock ahead of them accelerating as they approach, and then, just when it seems they must dash themselves to pieces, they suddenly 'elevate' and shoot vertically upwards, skimming the cliff face to land on its edge some four feet above the water surface.

I have already described a floating factory at South Georgia; the *Orwell* was much the same. The captain and his officers showed us the greatest hospitality; some of us dined on board and had a most pleasant evening (with very good wine). Fresh food in these parts consists mainly of whale meat, shags and fish. The fish, which they catch in large cage-like traps baited with whale meat, are chiefly the *Notothenia rossi*, so popular at South Georgia; and very good they are too. The whales were flensed in the water from a raft floating just astern of us; the strips of blubber, and then parts of the carcass, being pulled up to the deck of the ship by hooks and cables from the great derricks at the masts. It is a grotesque sight to see a huge piece, dripping blood, sometimes with a whole flipper complete, go swinging up through space on to the lofty deck of the factory. Whilst I have seen it often enough at South Georgia, I never fail to be impressed by the cutting open of a whale stomach—a sight not to be forgotten: a good cart-load or more of half digested krill comes gushing out with a stench that is truly dreadful.

We sailed yesterday at nine o'clock, and a beautiful pearly-grey morning it was as we set out through the iceberg-strewn bay. The sun, partly obscured by the hazy clouds immediately above us, produced a soft opalescence on the snowy coastline, while beyond, out over the sea, there was a clear but pale, greenish-blue sky. As we got outside two mincke whales, small rorquals, moved lazily on the surface a little distance from the ship, and later some killer whales were seen, the first we have met. I have never seen so many penguins leaping from the

An iceberg arch, off the South Orkneys, drawn from a photograph.

water together; they kept breaking the surface in showers like shoals of flying fish, perhaps chased by killers. Very soon we met the loose pack again, but, it being clearer, we were able to skirt round it. There were now very many icebergs, and we counted 192 in sight at once; some were carved into the form of natural arches and one presented a whole series in line like a viaduct.

Thursday, 24th February. If some of us were inclined to be sceptical over the *Lancing*'s report of an 'ice-island' the size of South Georgia, our doubts were surely dispelled to-day. We have passed along just one side of a great iceberg for a distance of thirty miles; how far it extended in other directions we could not say, but we saw two other sides of it receding far away to the horizon and perhaps we only passed its narrower end. Using our masts as a measure, its height above the surface was quite 110 feet; so there must have been another 800 feet or so below water. How long does it take such a mass of ice to break up and melt? Half-way along its side we stopped and took a full station, and as we worked we occasionally heard roars coming from it like distant thunder, as part of its huge mass cracked. Later in the day the

sun came out shining full upon its glistening side and making it a cliff
of dazzling blue and white. There were smaller tabular icebergs to
the other side of us, and in the evening the sun went down in a flaming
red sky which made a sharp contrast to the deep blue of the icebergs
in the foreground; I am always surprised to find how intensely blue
some of these icebergs can look when in fact all the light from the sky
appears to be crimson and gold.

Following the station, at which we sounded in 2,512 metres depth
of water, we let out a Petterssen young-fish trawl mounted on a 2-metre
diameter tow-net ring. We let it out on 1,800 metres of wire cable and,
since we towed it at a speed of some two knots, it could not have gone
deeper than 1,200 metres at the most; yet when it came up we knew,
by the kinked up wire, and the closing gear covered in thick mud, that
it had hit the bottom. There was no mistake about the amount of wire
let out for we had used all there was on the small drum of the main
winch: exactly 1,800 metres. As soon as the net was up we sounded
again; this time getting 1,852 metres. In the space of little over a
mile the bottom had risen from 2,512 metres to something like 1,200
and dropped again to 1,852; as a rule the sea bed is only gently
undulating, but here, in the vicinity of volcanic islands, we have an
exceptionally uneven bottom. We would have liked to have taken
many more soundings but we are pressed for time and must hurry on.

At the first sounding we used our new special modification of the
Bayley sounding tube whereby a long core of the ooze from the ocean
floor is brought up in a glass tube (inside a steel protecting casing)
driven into it by heavy weights which are then left at the bottom as the
tube is withdrawn and hauled up. It obtained a 16-inch core of solid
diatom ooze. We have come across samples before (p. 156) but never
in such quantity; here are the remains of diatoms which have lived
at the surface thousands and thousands of years ago—and deeper
down, if our core had been longer, would be those from millions of
years past. A fine smear of this green-brown mud under the microscope
becomes a rich assortment of those beautiful and delicately sculptured
shells of diatoms—the same species as those taken in our plankton nets;
here are the circular caskets of *Coscinodiscus*, the more basket-like shells
of *Biddulphia*, the long pencil-like cylinders of *Rhizosolenia styliformis*,
and, actually complete with its delicate spines, our old friend *Corethron
valdiviae*, which we took in such numbers around South Georgia. What
an inexhaustible supply of diatom ooze there is here. Has it no commercial value? Diatomacious earth (sometimes called infusorial earth),
which, like chalk, is just a fossil sea bed, is valuable for a number of
industrial purposes such as thermal insulation and for filtering and

clarifying in chemical manufacture. From idle curiosity we tried a little of it as a metal polish with excellent results; a few gentle rubs—as the advertisements might say—turned tarnished old brass and copper to shining brilliance. Perhaps one day these vast deposits may be tapped as ships let down special dredging devices to fill their holds with the precious ooze.

Yesterday morning we sighted Clarence Island and by midday were abreast of it. It is a lofty snow-covered mass of mountain and glacier reaching a height of some 7,000 feet. The day was a bad one, raw and bitterly cold, with low, grey, wind-torn clouds which only allowed the higher parts of the island to be seen for brief moments. Its steep slopes reach the water in cliffs, breaking out black between the snow, or in walls of glacier ice. A more forbidding island I have never seen; I did the sketch shown in Plate 33. What would it be like to be shipwrecked here? One can imagine the horror of it. And here it was— or rather on the next island, Elephant Island, which is similar to it— where the party of Shackleton's *Endurance* Expedition were marooned after their ship had been crushed in the ice of the Weddell Sea. After they had dragged their boats over the ice before launching them, they at last reached this 'refuge' with their only hope of rescue being centred on the perilous open boat journey which Shackleton took to South Georgia. [My old friend, the late Dr. Robert Clark, who became Director of the Scottish Fisheries Department's Marine Laboratory at Aberdeen, was zoologist to Shackleton's expedition and one of that party on Elephant Island. He paid me a great compliment many years later, by standing almost spellbound in front of my sketch; Clarence Island was their first sight of land after their struggle through the ice following their disaster. He said their view of it was precisely the view I had taken and that the weather was exactly the same; he was clearly deeply moved by it, so I gave it him and it came back to me at his death.] A little time back (p. 301) we saw the other end of Shackleton's epic journey and we have since crossed the waters over which he went; we have crossed them, not in the little canvas covered boat he used, but in our large stout ship, and we have seen them to be the wildest waters we have yet met. It is a good thing to have visited the scene of so great an achievement.

Our view of Elephant Island (seen to the left in my sketch) was not a good one on account of the poor visibility; we saw enough, however, of its unutterable bleakness to realise, if only dimly, something of what it must have been like for that brave party who, through the polar winter, under Frank Wild's splendid leadership, never lost heart and packed their things and carried them down to the beach every day to be ready for the rescue they hoped for. Earlier, when at the place where Shackleton's journey and his crossing of the mountains of South Georgia ended, I quoted from his book *South*; I will now quote another passage which tells of the end of the party's sojourn on Elephant Island:

August 30, 1916, is described in their diaries as a 'day of wonders.' Food was very short, only two days' seal and penguin meat being left, and no prospect of any more arriving. The whole party had been collecting limpets and seaweed to eat with the stewed seal bones. . . . From a fortnight after I had left, Wild would roll up his sleeping-bag each day with the remark, 'Get your things ready, boys, the Boss may come to-day.' And sure enough, one day the mist opened and revealed the ship for which they had been waiting and longing and hoping for over four months. . . .

(He now quotes from the Elephant Island diaries).

We tried to cheer, but excitement had gripped our vocal chords. . . . Wild put a pick through our last remaining tin of petrol, and soaking coats, mitts, and socks with it, carried them to the top of Penguin Hill at the end of our spit, and soon they were ablaze.

Meanwhile most of us had gathered on the foreshore watching with anxious eyes for any signs that the ship had seen us, or for any answering signals. As we stood and gazed she seemed to turn away as if she had not seen us. Again and again we cheered, though our feeble cries could certainly not have carried so far. Suddenly she stopped, a boat was lowered, and we could recognise Sir Ernest's figure as he climbed down the ladder. Simultaneously we burst into a cheer, and then one said to the other, 'Thank God, the Boss is safe.' For I think that his safety was of more concern to us than was our own.

Soon the boat approached near enough for the Boss, who was standing up in the bows, to shout to Wild, 'Are you all well?' To which he replied, 'All safe, all well,' and we could see a smile light up the Boss's face as he said, 'Thank God!'

To the south of Clarence Island, away on our port beam, was another floating piece of the barrier. We made up to the lee of Clarence, for the weather, none too good, was freshening, and here we took a cast with the dredge in 343 metres depth. The life below appears to get richer and richer; I am only recording a few of the hauls we made. On this occasion our dredge was again on the bottom for just five minutes; yet such was the varied collection of animals it brought up that, with all of us working hard, we have only to-night, twenty-four hours later, got all the material sorted, labelled and put away. Continually to give

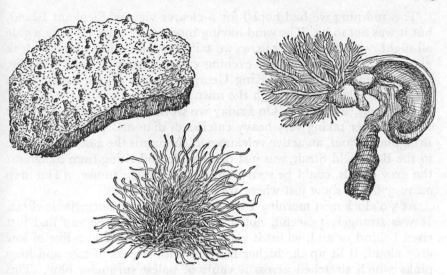

Cephalodiscus: two new species dredged up by the *Discovery* are drawn natural size on the left: part of a colony of *C. fumosus* (above) and a small colony of *C. kempi* (form A) (below); while on the right a single zooid of the former species is shown much enlarged and redrawn from C.C. John, *D.R.*, vol. III.

long lists of animals is tedious. I will mention only a fine and unusually sponge-like *Cephalodiscus*, making the fourth species of these exciting animals that we have obtained since leaving South Georgia. The reader may be surprised, perhaps, that we should be excited by animals looking so much like sponges, yet this is just their point of interest to the zoologist; these strange creatures, which come only from the Antarctic, have some characteristics that show they are actually related to the vertebrate stock and so may give us hints as to the possible evolutionary origin of this great animal group to which we ourselves belong. The little individual animals making up these massive colonies look almost like exotic orchid blooms; I show one above.

[This particular sponge-like colony, of which I show a sketch together with a more typical form, turned out to be the only example we got of an entirely new species. It was named *Cephalodiscus fumosus* by Dr. C. C. John who later wrote the *Discovery Report* on our collection of these animals (vol. III, pp. 223-60, 1931). Altogether on this voyage we obtained five different species including another new one *C. kempi*, which was first dredged up at South Georgia by the *Discovery* whilst I was on the *William Scoresby*. The other three species were *C. hodgsoni*, *C. nigrescens* and *C. densus*.]

N

This morning we had hoped for a clearer view of Elephant Island, but it was not to be. The wind having moderated, after blowing a gale all night, was now helping us, so we sailed on past a line of small bleak glaciated islands and by this evening came abreast of Cape Melville, the most easterly point of King George Island. All we can see is a vague shape looming through the mist.

Wednesday, 2nd March. On Friday we worked a full station off Cape Melville after taking very heavy catches of diatoms. For a short time Bridgman Island, an active volcano, which guards the eastern entrance to the Bransfield Strait, was just discernible and rising from it, against the grey clouds, could be seen a smudge of brown smoke. [The map on p. 376 will show just where we were at this point.]

At 5 o'clock next morning I was called to see an unforgettable effect. It was strangely peaceful, not a breath of wind. The sun had just risen behind us and, whilst it was itself screened behind a line of low grey cloud, it lit up the higher heavens with streaks of rose and fiery pinks which stretched across a vault of palest turquoise blue. This formed the backcloth to a truly stupendous panorama of the greater part of the South Shetland group; here they were, a line of magnificent snow-white mountain islands: Livingstone, Greenwich, Table, Nelson and King George stretching from the horizon ahead of us, past our starboard beam and on into the distance astern. It had snowed heavily in the early part of the night so that there was hardly a dark patch of rock to blot their virgin purity of white. Thin wisps of pale grey cloud lay in bands across many of their lofty peaks, and the highest, that of Mount Barnard (3,860 feet) on Livingstone Island, rising above a thicker belt of cloud, was caught by the morning sun—a dazzling cone against the multi-tinted sky. The little waves, hardly more than ripples, on a surprisingly calm sea, caught and reflected the opal colours in snaky wavy lines across its surface.

By breakfast time Deception Island was in sight ahead of us, and far over on the horizon to the south we could see for the first time, above a bank of haze, the white peaks of Graham Land, that curved finger of the true Antarctic continent, with its outlying islands. The highest point we could see was no doubt Tower Hill on Trinity Island. This first impression of the Bransfield Strait will be one we shall never forget.

Deception Island is well named; it would be a good candidate in a competition for the most extraordinary island in the world. A glance at the chart opposite will show, I think, that the claim is not exaggerated. It is like an atoll, but instead of a low coral reef enclosing its lagoon there is a circular mountain range; note the heights of some of the peaks

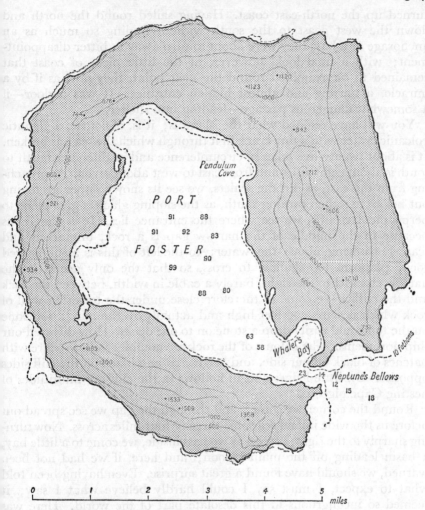

Deception Island: a map redrawn, with some details omitted, from an Admiralty Chart. The heights and contours of the land are shown in feet and the depths of water in fathoms.

n the chart, going round the circle in a clockwise direction from the outh: 1,368, 1,533, 1,000, 744, 1,123 and 1,805 feet. It was named Deception by the early sealers, who coming down from the north in heir little schooners and brigs, were badly in need of a harbour for helter in these most tempestuous latitudes. The story goes that they first came upon the island from the east, looking for a refuge and then turned up the north-east coast. Having sailed round the north and down the west coast to the south without finding so much as an anchorage or a bay, they were about to turn away in bitter disappointment; with a final look, however, at the little piece of coast that remained to be examined round the next point, they saw, as if by a miracle, a narrow and almost hidden entrance. It was a door—if a somewhat dangerous passage—leading into shelter.

You will have realised what the island is; it is, of course, a gigantic volcanic crater with a tiny crack in it through which the sea has broken. It is about twenty-five miles in circumference and its diameter north to south is about eight miles and from east to west about seven. Approaching from the east, as did the sealers, we see its snowy slopes stretching out before us; then turning south, as the sloping glaciers give place to perpendicular cliffs, we see where the entrance lies. It is dangerous because in the middle of the narrow gap is a rock, unmarked and scarcely showing above the water; to the left of this is a submerged rocky platform too shallow to cross, so that the only access is the narrow channel to the right, barely a cable in width, between the rock and the cliffs. We come in therefore close under the towering wall of rock which is some 500 feet high and actually overhanging; someone on the top could easily drop a stone on to our decks. How dwarfed our ship now seems. The colours of the rock are notable: yellow-ochre with patches of black on our side, and bright red and black on the cliff sides opposite. On little ledges and in hollows in the cliff are multitudes of nesting Cape pigeons.

Round the corner we come; and through the gap we see spread out before us the wide inland sea some three or four miles across. Now turning sharply to the right, as soon as we pass inside, we come to a little bay, a basin leading off the main lagoon; and here, if we had not been warned, we should have found a great surprise. Even having been told what to expect, I must say I could hardly believe what I saw; it seemed so incongruous in this desolate part of the world. Here was a fleet of no less than eight really big ships, former ocean liners—crack ships of their day—bought up and converted into factory ships; one had been a famous P. & O. boat and another was the old *Albany Castle* which was the pride of the Union Castle line at the time of the Boer War. Saved from the breakers and fitted out with blubber boilers, oil storage tanks, meal and fertiliser plant and all the rest of the factory equipment, they have been given a new lease of life. In addition to two stout anchor chains for'ard, each ship is secured by stout cables running to huge rings let into concrete blocks on the shore astern. Each is attended by its own little group of catchers which hunt the whales up and down the Bransfield Strait and from time to time bring them in to be flensed through Hell's Gates as the narrow entrance is called[1]. On the Admiralty chart the entrance has a different but almost equally descriptive name of Neptune's Bellows; and how at times the wind whistles, nay shrieks, through the narrow gap.

It was not long before the Bellows worked and we knew why the ships were secured by cables to the shore as well as by double anchors at the bows. We moved up to anchor between two of the factory ships about three in the afternoon. A wind from the north-east had been freshening as we came in, it was getting up to gale force by the time we anchored and by 5 o'clock it was blowing almost a hurricane. Arrangements had been made to secure us to cables ashore; so strong was the wind, however, and so much resistance did our heavy rigging give, that six of the ships' motor-boats, all coming to our assistance, could not bring us up to the cables against it. Two whale-catchers, one on either side of us, finally did the job. This bitterly cold wind only lasted an hour or so and dropped as quickly as it had begun. I show photographs of Deception Island on Plate 31 (p. 352).

That evening we were welcomed and entertained by representatives of all the ships at a party given on the factory ship *Falk*. It was indeed a generous Norwegian welcome and they entertained us royally. The last word is particularly appropriate for they plied us with a most potent beverage which they called by the innocent name of King Oscar's shandy: it is a drink for only very special occasions, being a mixture of brandy and the best champagne! The next day, Sunday, we were kept aboard by a blizzard with blinding snow driven horizontally in a high wind.

Calm and sunshine followed and as soon as we could we visited the 'steaming beach' as the black shore immediately astern of us is called. It is strange in so cold a place, against a background of snow and ice, to find the 'sand' quite warm and to see thin wisps of steam rising all along the water's edge. Digging into this black cinder 'sand' we came at about 8 inches down to water that was as hot as we could bear to put our hands in and at a foot or so it registered 131°F. We realise that the great flooded volcano is still to some extent active; over on the other side of the lagoon is a place, they tell us, where smoke and hot sulphurous fumes emerge through cracks in the ground. Three

---

[1] I see from Captain John Davis's log of the voyage of the *Huron*, quoted in an appendix to Edouard A. Stackpole's *The Voyage of the* Huron *and the* Hundress, that it was also called the 'Dragon's Mouth.' Under the date of 30th December, 1821 he writes 'At 4 a.m. Entered the Dragon's mouth and entered into the spacious Bay of Deception.' He goes on to give perhaps the first and one of the best accounts of the island.

years ago, in 1924, there was an earthquake and an underwater eruption which must have been most alarming while it lasted. One of the whaling captains gave us a graphic account of it at the party. It began, he said, by their seeing the whole of the beach in a state of turmoil as if hundreds of men were violently digging it; then a great piece of the crater collapsed in a deafening roar, falling into the sea to the outside and leaving a gap seen in the background in the photograph of the steaming beach shown on Plate 31. All the great factory ships were tied up for the season with their fires out so that they could not have got steam up for many hours if they had wanted to; a rapid escape from the crater in an emergency was impossible. It was therefore a most unpleasant experience for them to just sit there and realise that the water of the harbour, of the whole lagoon, was getting hotter and hotter till it finally boiled. There they were, powerless to move, anchored in a cauldron of boiling water.

Life on board must have been almost unbearable, but fortunately it lasted only a short time and the whole thing sank back to normal. Little damage was done, except that all the paint came off the ships. There must have been an outburst of molten lava at the bottom of the crater. Could there be a sufficiently violent eruption to blow the whole fleet of ships sky high? I suppose not, for there is far too large a volume of water acting as a stopper. The lagoon has a depth of nearly a hundred fathoms in the centre. What I should be more afraid of would be a great fall of cliff, such as took place in this eruption, but at the narrow entrance; it only needs some of the lofty cliffs above the channel to fall outwards and these large ships would be sealed within.

Jimmy Fraser and I climbed to the top of these high cliffs last evening. It was none too safe, as we soon realised, for the climb was precipitous in places and parts of the rock, having every appearance of solidity, were apt to break away under our weight, being little more than dried volcanic mud. A few mosses and lichens, which we collected, encrusted the surface here and there; they form the sole vegetation of the island. On reaching the top and looking over the brink we were horrified to find that we were on an overhanging edge, projecting right over the waves which were beating at the foot of the cliff far below us. The air was full of the cries of Cape pigeons nesting on ledges below us, but, considering the fragile nature of the rock, we thought it wiser not to hang over to get a better view of them and rapidly retreated a few paces. Farther along, however, at the edge of the gap in the crater just described, we could get a good view of the nests but not reach them. The parents were feeding their young. Wilson petrels and silver grey fulmars, which are said to breed here, were flying round, but we did not find their nests, which, being small holes in the ground or in crevices, are difficult to locate. The beautiful silver greys, or Antarctic fulmars as they are sometimes called, have been constant companions of the ship since passing Clarence Island.

[It was from this cliff top that Benjamin Pendleton in command of a fleet of five American sealing vessels, which were using Deception Island as their base, looked out one clear day and first saw distant mountains to the south. He sent Nathaniel Palmer, captain of the cutter *Hero*, to prospect and so he discovered the line of mountainous islands that are now called the Palmer Archipelago; he thought he had discovered a great Antarctic continent and on the old maps it is shown as Palmer Land.[1] Coming north from making this discovery Palmer, in his little cutter, ran into thick fog and anchored for the night; it was then that he had a remarkable experience. I will give the story as I first heard it and as it is often retold. Palmer who had left his fellow sealers up in Deception Island thought himself to be quite alone in the waters near the new land he had discovered; imagine his surprise—and fear, as if he was surrounded by the supernatural—when he heard close at hand through the dark wall of fog the ringing of a ship's bell, first to starboard, and then a moment later to hear it answered by a similar bell, equally close at hand, in the darkness to port. They were not the bells he was used to on American ships.

I will now continue the story from the account given by Edmund Fanning in his *Voyages Round the World, with selected sketches of voyages to the South Seas* . . . (London, 1834). Alas, there is no mention of the romantic bells which may be an apocryphal embroidery, although I like to think them true; he does not give the source of his account and there may well be another printed version I am not aware of. He writes on pp. 435-8 as follows:

On the *Hero*'s return passage to Yankee Harbour[2] she got becalmed in a thick fog between the South Shetlands and the newly discovered continent, but nearest the former. When this began to clear away Captain Palmer was surprised to find his little barque between a frigate and a sloop of war, and instantly ran up the United States flag; the frigate and sloop of war then set the Russian colors. Soon afterwards a boat was seen pulling from the commodore's ship for the *Hero* and when alongside the lieutenant presented an invitation from his commodore for Captain P. to go on board; this of course was accepted. These ships he then found

[1] He may actually have discovered the coast of Graham Land the true continent but opinion is divided on the point.

[2] The old name of the Deception Island lagoon.

were the two discovery ships sent out by the Emperor Alexander of Russia, on a voyage round the world.

The Russian ships were, of course, those under the command of that great Antarctic explorer, Captain Bellingshausen.

More recently Dr. Frank Debenham, who was then Director of the Scott Polar Institute, has given us, through the Hakluyt Society (London, 1945) a splendid translation of *The Voyages of Captain Bellingshausen in the Antarctic Sea, 1819-21*, which was originally published in two volumes and an atlas (in Russian) at St. Petersburg in 1831. I will quote from it his account of the meeting with Palmer as follows:

In front of this low-lying shore (southwest coast of Livingstone Island) we saw 8 British and American sealing vessels at anchor near the northeast shore of the strait. Proceeding farther along the southern shore to the east-southeast, I soon saw to starboard of our course a high island, with steep cliffs and covered with clouds (Deception Island), 62° 58′ south latitude and 60° 55′ west longitude . . . circumference of 20 miles, separated from the high rocky headlands opposite by a strait, 11 miles wide.

At 10 o'clock, we entered the strait and encountered a small American sealing boat. . . . Soon after Mr. Palmer arrived in our boat and informed us that he had been here for four months, sealing in partnership with three American ships. They were engaged in killing and skinning seals, whose numbers were perceptibly diminishing. There were as many as eighteen vessels about at various points, and not infrequently differences arose amongst the sealers, but so far it had not yet come to a fight. Mr. Palmer told me . . . Capt. Smith, the discoverer of the South Shetlands was on the brig *William*, that he had succeeded in killing as many as 60,000 seals. . . .

I must now digress a little to describe the discovery of these South Shetland islands and the tragedy of the thoughtless butchery of their entire fur seal populations. It is in fact related to our theme for it is another example of the wanton exploitation of natural stocks—similar to those which took place in the northern whale fisheries—which will surely occur again in the south if a wise control is not imposed. I am now, quite shamelessly, going to quote at considerable length from Robert Hugh Mill's masterpiece of Antarctic history *The Siege of the South Pole* (1905); by doing so I hope I may introduce this classic to those of a younger generation who may not have come across it, for it has long been out of print. He writes as follows:

The first absolutely clear episode in the history of Antarctic discovery since Cook was due to a British seaman, William Smith,

33. *Above*, a typical Antarctic mountain at sunset: Mount Parry (6,260 feet), Brabant Island, in the Palmer Archipelago (off Graham Land). The shadow of the earth's rim rises as the sun sinks below the horizon behind the observer. *Below*, Clarence Island in the South Shetlands. Dimly showing in the background is Elephant Island where Shackleton's party were marooned and eventually rescued after their ship, the 'Endurance', was crushed in the ice

captain of the brig *Williams*, of Blyth, one of the north country craft so highly rated by Cook. Trading between Montevideo and Valparaiso he brought his ship round Cape Horn with a bold southward sweep in February, 1819, believing that by keeping far off the land he would find better weather for making what is always an anxious passage under sail. On the 19th, in latitude 62° 40′ S. and longitude 60° W. he thought he saw land. Night fell before he could make quite sure and he prudently hauled off to the north for the few hours of darkness of the southern summer night and stood south again next day when the land appeared to him to be unmistakable.

He happened to have a valuable cargo on board and being himself part owner of the ship he was afraid to run the risk of a storm descending upon him when off an unknown coast; being afraid too that the underwriters might make trouble about his insurances if he were to convert a coasting trip into a voyage of discovery, he resumed his course and reached Valparaiso in due time. Smith spoke of his discovery to the English residents at the Chilean port, but was only laughed at for his pains, and it would appear that some of his ship's company thought that no land had been seen but merely icebergs. It was about mid-winter (June, 1819) before Smith obtained a return cargo, and although he ran south to 62° 12′ he saw nothing of the land and nearly got caught in the sea-ice from which he was glad to escape even without confirmation of his discovery. At Montevideo as at Valparaiso incredulity and ridicule were all he received from his countrymen. . . .

Several months elapsed before he could get a cargo together for another trip to Chile. At last he succeeded and on October 15th, 1819, came up with the land in the position where he had seen it before, got soundings in 40 fathoms and next day sent a boat ashore with the first mate to plant the Union Jack and take possession for Great Britain. He called the new land New South Britain but afterwards changed the name to New South Shetland because it was situated in the same latitude as the Shetland Isles of the northern hemisphere. . . .

Smith spent some days in cruising along the coast, standing out to sea at night and returning in the morning toward the land, picking out now a cape and now a mountain in the fog and naming them more or less appropriately, occasionally losing sight of the coast, and apparently making no other landing. The scenery reminded him strongly of Norway, so strongly that he even

N2

imagined he could see pine trees waving on the distant slopes, and he satisfied himself that the rocks and off-lying islands swarmed with fur-seals, blubber-seals and birds in great variety. Whales too abounded including what he declared to be 'the true spermaceti whale.'

Altogether Smith saw the land more or less continuously along a course of 250 miles, and on reaching Valparaiso at the end of November he was able to give such particulars as convinced the British residents of the reality of the discovery. Apart from the enormous value for the seal and whale fishery the prospect of having some British possession, however desolate, within ten days' sail was very welcome to Smith's compatriots who did not feel too secure under the government of a new republic still at war with its mother country. They resented the recent abandonment of the Falkland Islands and were intensely anxious to have some outpost of the empire nearer than Cape Town on the one side and Sydney on the other. These feelings were fully shared by the British naval commander on the Pacific Station, Captain W. H. Shirreff, who on hearing Smith's story resolved to take immediate action. . . . (He chartered *Williams* and) . . . Edward Bransfield, Master R.N., was put in charge, and three midshipmen of H.M.S. *Andromache* accompanied him to aid in surveying. . . .

Bransfield reached the new land on January 16th, 1820, and remained off its coasts until March 21st, following it for 9° or 10° to the eastward and about 3° from north to south. He sailed amongst the islands and charted them, going as far south as 64° 30′, but did not apparently determine whether the land was entirely insular or in part continental. He landed at one point at least and found the only vegetation to consist of stunted grass. Trees were entirely absent. . . .

Stonington, Connecticut, a small town of seafaring folk, now comes into prominence as a centre of the southern sealing enterprise of the United States. Fleets of small vessels were fitted out there year after year, and the pluck of their skippers and crews led them often far into the Antarctic regions. . . . In July, 1819, the *Hersilia* sailed from Stonington under the command of James P. Sheffield with W. A. Fanning as supercargo. They visited the Aurora islands, or some land which was taken for them, and sailing south to 63° discovered what they took to be the land of Dirk Gerritsz, naming several islands and landing on one at a place named Hersilia Cove in February, 1820. If the latitude is correct these islands must have been members of the South Shetland group, and the *Williams* and *Hersilia* must for a time have been very near neighbours though they did not sight each other. The *Hersilia* came home without delay bringing a quantity of sealskins, including those of the valuable southern fur-seal. There was a flutter of excitement at Stonington, and energetic steps were taken to follow up this successful voyage.

The southern summer of 1820-21 was a dark one for the fur-seals whose ancestors had basked upon the shore of the South Shetlands for untold centuries, following their quaint semi-civilised life and pursuing their patriarchal customs of war and love undisturbed by any being capable of contending with them. The sentry bulls saw, with the stolid unconcern of ignorance, the approach of a fleet of five sail; certainly it was without fear or suspicion, for the intruders found they could butcher the unresisting beasts without any preliminary trouble of hunting or stalking. Nor were the Americans alone, British enterprise was equally ready to profit by the new discovery, and there is little doubt that at least as many ships flew the red ensign as the stars and stripes that summer amongst the southern isles. The killing of seals, perhaps from the pathos of their innocent eyes, seems nearer murder than any other form of butchery or sport, and the first assault upon such a tribe of creatures is really painful to think about.

I can now add a happier postscript to this chapter, just before sending it to press. While the fur seals had been exterminated in these southern regions, a small colony was conserved on the Falkland Islands. Harrison Matthews in his book on South Georgia (1931) records that in 1927 two were seen on the Willis Islands (a former haunt off its northern tip) and then in 1933 the *Discovery II* found a small group on Bird Island (off the north-east coast) but kept it secret. Recently the good news has been published (*New Scientist*, vol. 20, pp. 374-6) that there are now flourishing rookeries at both Bird and Willis Islands with an estimated population of some 20,000 at the former site. From the 1940's increasing numbers have been reported from the South Orkneys; in 1959 it was found to be breeding on Livingstone Island in the South Shetlands and in 1961 a colony of 300 was discovered in the South Sandwich Islands. The species is spreading again and coming back to its old haunts.]

CHAPTER 17

ANTARCTIC SCENE

Wednesday, 2nd March contd. We sailed from Deception this afternoon for our cruise down the Graham Land[1] coast of the Antarctic continent. As we approached the harbour's narrow exit I climbed to the mast head to get some exciting views, through the ropes, yards and stays, as we almost brushed the cliffs; for a change it was surprisingly clear and from this vantage-point I saw what Palmer must have seen: the distant snow peaks far to the south.

Earlier in the season the captain of a whale-catcher, who had made a prospecting cruise as far as Peter I. into the Bellingshausen Sea, reported that it was exceptionally clear of ice, but found few whales. The ice this season came north very much earlier than usual, as well as in greater quantity. We shall not, however, be able to get very far for the nights are lengthening rapidly and by the end of the month the sea begins to freeze; also about now heavy pack from the Weddell Sea is apt to creep round the end of Graham Land and may quickly fill up the Bransfield Strait.

We are first trying to find the Kendad Rocks to fix their position on the chart and then to do the same for the Austins which are said to lie to the south-westward. Sailing in these regions gives you something of the feeling that the old navigators must have experienced; on our Admiralty Chart (New Edition: Sept. 1925) the whole coast of Graham Land bears the legend 'Reported to lie further southward' and many islands, including the rocks we are looking for, are marked P.D. (position doubtful). [There was indeed need for the Falkland Islands Dependency Survey which has done such splendid work in this sector during the last twenty-fiye years.]

Sunday, 6th March. After two days of gale and one of fog, we reached the reported position of the Kendads on Wednesday but found no sign of them and got a sounding of 200 metres depth; after dredging, with darkness coming on and icebergs around us, we hove to for the night

[1]Named after Sir James Graham, First Lord of the Admiralty at the time of its discovery by John Biscoe.

Through the night the wind freshened again to a roaring gale by the morning and kept it up all day; it was an uncomfortable position to be in as visibility was poor and we were drifting off course all the while to leeward. The disturbance was a cyclonic one, for the wind dropped quickly to a dead calm about seven in the evening and then an hour or two later began to blow just as hard in the opposite direction! Early on Friday we once again narrowly escaped being driven on to an iceberg. I was awakened by the sound of the crew running on the deck overhead. Clearly something exciting was afoot, so I threw on a heavy coat and hurried on deck. There, close to leeward of us, was a large iceberg with angry waves breaking on it; it was just perceptibly rocking like the pitching of a big ship. Slowly, terribly slowly, we drew ahead of it and the danger passed.

We have now given up our hunt for the Kendad Rocks, which may well not exist, to go in search of the Austins, but very soon the fog closed around us again so we could only move slowly. Taking a series of tow-net hauls as we went, we arrived in the evening at what should by dead reckoning be the position of the rocks; we made a sounding and found 1,030 metres of water! Whenever we were frustrated a haul with the dredge had now become an almost automatic action; I think perhaps Kemp thought it prevented loss of morale, and certainly on this occasion it brought us many good specimens by way of compensation. There were some primitive, worm-like, molluscs which, having five long ridges down their bodies, fooled us at first into thinking they were Holothuria (sea-cucumbers).

The bottom must be exceedingly uneven for when the fog cleared to-day we soon sighted the Austin Rocks: sharp pinnacles like fantastic pantomime scenery. Passing between Low and Hoseason Islands we came abreast of Brabant Island, with its lofty Mount Parry (6,260 feet) just as the sun was going down. There was Anvers Island beyond, equally high and thick in snow; and in between them were distant views of the long range of the Graham Land mountains. The highlights of the snow were gold and rose, and the shadows a soft violet. Fiery clouds stretched in streaks above, while lower down, out of the sun, they formed purple bands across the mountains; it was all set against a luminous green sky.

Monday, 14th March. After further fog and gales we dropped anchor at Melchior Harbour, between Brabant and Anvers Islands, last Wednesday evening. It is a curious formation, no doubt the remains of a crater like Deception Island, but much smaller and quite low. Two semi-circular reefs face one another in the middle of the strait and so enclose a basin of calm water with narrow entrances opposite

one another. The reefs themselves have little coves which provide
subsidiary harbours; and in one of them we found the most southerly
whaling factory ship: the *Saragossa*. Whilst at anchor at Melchior,
on a perfectly calm day, a small iceberg of curious shape drifted into
us, but with long poles we kept ourselves from suffering damage. It
was very high on one side and low on the other enclosing a lagoon in
and out of which swam a sea-leopard as if in play. The ice in shadow

A calm Antarctic summer day with a seal playing in an iceberg pool; Mount Parry,
on Brabant Island, is in the distance. The sky, sea and the shadows on the ice and
snow are all an intense blue.   Redrawn from a watercolour made from the ship at
anchor.

was an intense blue, as was the sea, and in the distance was Mount
Parry rising to over 6,000 feet on Brabant Island; I did a watercolour
sketch which is here converted into black and white.

Here although we are not actually across the Antarctic Circle, being
in latitude about 64° 25′ south, we have true Antarctic conditions.
Every bit of land is covered by a great snow cap which breaks off
at the water's edge in a pure white cliff some eighty to a hundred feet
in height, and here and there cut by vertical crevasses. You can only
distinguish the smaller islands from icebergs by the thin line of rock

along the water's edge where the waves have undercut the snow cliff.

[The late Dr. William S. Bruce, leader of the Scottish National Antarctic (*Scotia*) Expedition discussed the true Antarctic conditions in his book *Polar Exploration*[1] as follows: 'I have defined the Antarctic Regions as lying within the Antarctic Circle, that is, south of 66½° S. latitude, but in 1892, on board the Scottish whaler *Balaena*, I found that this definition broke down, for we fell in with polar conditions before we reached latitude 60° S., some 500 miles south-eastward of Cape Horn, in the neighbourhood of the South Shetland Islands. . . .' After describing ice conditions such as we have been seeing, he continues: 'We were truly in the Antarctic Regions, although more than 300 miles north of the Antarctic Circle. . . . I prefer to define the Antarctic Regions as being bounded by the average limits of floating ice.' I would agree with him.[2]

Although the weather has been thick all day, both last evening and this, it cleared to give us some remarkable effects which, I think, demonstrate a feature of special interest. Mount Parry stood out in bright flame or rose colours against a turquoise or purple sky whilst across it was a straight sharp line of violet shadow; I begin to realise that these effects are characteristic and perhaps peculiar to the Antarctic scene, or at any rate to the polar regions. As the sun goes down *behind* us we are seeing, of course, the shadow of the rim of the earth rising up the landscape, up the mountains and the clouds, *opposite* the sun. The mountain peaks and higher clouds may be brilliantly lit with roseate light while the lower ground, and lower clouds, will be in shadow. I have seen something of it in Iceland but not with such striking contrasts of colour, and in an entirely softer way you can often see the purple shadow rising in the sky opposite a desert sunset; in the Antarctic, however, I believe there must be some peculiar atmospheric condition which heightens this effect. [It is beautifully shown in two colour photographs illustrating Sir Vivian Fuchs's *The Crossing of the Antarctic*, London, 1958, those between his pages 228 and 229; compare these with my sketch on Plate 33, p. 393.]

Whilst fog and blizzards have delayed our progress we have taken many dredge, trawl and tow-net hauls; the latter gave us some heavy catches of krill, and from the former I expect we shall gain many species new to science. I will mention just one or two animals which we have not seen before. First is the beautiful *Umbellula*, looking like a delicate lily with its group of polyps, each with eight long feathery tentacles,

[1]In William and Norgate's Home University Library, London, 1911.
[2]The lines of the Arctic and Antarctic Circles are, of course, drawn at latitude 66½° to note the areas beyond which north and south the midnight sun is seen in summerde.

Cirroteuthis glacialis, a new species of octopus, drawn from a living specimen. *Left*, an outline sketch of the upper surface; *right*, the lower surface redrawn from a water-colour, showing an outer region (shaded in horizontal lines) which was a deep bluish purple and an inner region (vertical shading) of a vivid crimson purple. Across the lines of suckers, marking the arms, are oval light, almost white, but slightly mottled patches, giving a remarkable appearance. The upper surface of the animal was of a uniform lilac tint.

forming a crown at the top of a slender stem; it seems that these animals, related to our sea-pens, stand with their stems supported in the ooze of the sea bed in positions where a good current of water is flowing; bending over in the stream they spread a net of tentacles to catch the plankton drifting by[1]. Then there were the most curious transparent sea-cucumbers (Holothuria) which appeared to be partly pelagic for their tentacles had oar-like ends; they kept curling themselves in a semi-circle this way and that as if going through a primitive form of swimming. The most exciting animal of all, however, came from to-day's trawl: a brilliant purple octopus with powerful swimming fins. I can find nothing like it in any of our works of reference, so, hoping it may be new, I have done a colour sketch (redrawn here in black and white above). What *can* be the significance of the eight round white patches placed across the arms which give it such an arresting appearance? I painted it while it was still alive in a flat bath on the deck. I had hardly begun when it came on to snow, and not having an umbrella handy (indeed the wind was too strong for one) I covered myself with a round canvas bath I had and so caused some amuse-ment—looking like a large oyster, said the crew. My fingers got so cold

I could hardly hold the brush, but I had to do it out of doors for the light was too poor in the laboratory and artificial illumination is hopeless for correct colouring. [I was well rewarded, for not only did it turn out to be a new species, named by G. C. Robson *Cirroteuthis glacialis*, but so unusual was it that an entirely new suborder—Cirromorpha—had to be set up to receive it[1].] Whilst talking of portraying the specimens we caught I must here record the tireless efforts of our doctor, Hillis Marshall, who was very fully occupied after our dredge or trawl hauls in taking photographs of our more interesting animals when still alive: he had infinite patience, for it was not an easy task getting them to pose in suitable positions in a dish of water on a rolling ship!

Wednesday, 16th March—Saturday, 26th March. [Here I am selecting only a few passages from under three dates, for so much is recorded of views, ice and light effects, that to include them all would become tedious.]

Leaving Melchior we passed what we took to be the so-called Leith Harbour and rounded the easterly corner of Anvers Island; as we did so the mist melted away to give us, under a blue sky, our first views of the fabulous Gerlache Strait. Opposite us, although their highest peaks remained hidden, stretched the Antarctic mountains along the Danco Coast of Graham Land; much of Anvers was now clear and away to the south was the line of little peaks of Wiencke Island. . . . We now turned back to find a secure anchorage in Leith Harbour which was a fairyland of ice. There were many sea leopards on the floes and several seemed to take a special delight in trying to leap on to a particularly high piece; they seemed to regard it as a game, sometimes succeeding after making five or six attempts in which they would get just half their body over the edge only to slip backwards again.

On going farther up the bay we were surprised to find that it opened into the large Fournier Fjord, immediately to the north, and that the piece of land on our starboard, which we had taken to be part of Anvers, was in fact a separate island not recorded on the chart. Leith Harbour is not just an indentation; behind the island we got excellent shelter and anchored in 20 fathoms. Next morning, after Chaplin and his survey party had fixed the position of the island—now Discovery Island on the charts—we steamed into the middle of the Gerlache Strait to take a full vertical station followed by the usual towed nets. Here we took one of the richest hauls of diatoms[2] that

[1] See *Discovery Reports*, vol. II, pp. 375-8.
[2] There was a mixture of many species including *Thalassiosira, Coscinodiscus, Rhizosolemia, Chetocerosa* and *Corethron*.

we have yet made. The zoöplankton was scarce except for numbers of a
small salp *Salpa megellanica* which we had not taken before. In fact
the animal side of the plankton has been poor ever since leaving South
Georgia except for the rich hauls of krill between Anvers and Brabant
Islands that we got recently. There may indeed be a scarcity of
it in these parts this year for the whales are both few in number
and, according to the whalers, in poor condition—starved they
say—in contrast to those at South Georgia.

To-day (17th March) we have passed through what must be some
of the finest scenery in the world. We set off early to reach Port
Lockroy, in the Neumayer Channel inside Wiencke Island. It was
here that Charcot wintered on his 1909 *Pourquoi-pas?* expedition. As
we came again into the Gerlache Straight the clouds lifted so that we
entered the Neumayer Channel with brilliant patches of sunlight
chasing blue shadows over the sides of the mountains which rise
abruptly on either side. Projecting through the snow are rock faces of
red-brown and ochre yellow, whilst one, standing sentinel over the
opening of the channel on the Anvers side, is a vivid green; specimens
of ore from this mountain are said to yield 40 per cent pure copper.
Cliffs of ice meet the water, whose surface is strewn with fantastically
shaped fragments; after a few miles the channel takes an 'S' bend and
tucked away to the left is the little bay, Lockroy, close at the entrance
of a narrow passage which separates a smaller island, called Doumer,
from the larger Wiencke Island. Out beyond is the Bismarck Strait
and the open ocean. After running a little way out for a station we
turned to take up our anchorage for the night. Wiencke Island is shown
on Latitude 65° in the map on p. 376.

The little bay is let into cliffs of solid ice which in places are under-
mined with dark blue caverns having long glistening icicles or complete
pillars of ice to guard their mouths. Small rocky islands lie around the
basin and a low headland, projecting from the ice, provides rookery
space for both gentoo and ringed penguins. Giant petrels and skuas
are also here, there being many young of the former which can hardly
fly. It is a peaceful evening with fleecy pink clouds in a pale blue sky.
Mountains surround us and the *Discovery* is anchored against a high
cliff of ice with miniature icebergs floating beside her (Plate 35, p.
416). It is indeed Antarctica. . . .

On Friday (18th March) we took a full station in the Neumayer
Channel while Chaplin and his surveying party worked ashore fixing
positions. . . . The next day we went out into the Bismarck Strait where
we were anxious to take a station and to follow it by using large deep-
water nets which had never before been used in these southern waters;

in threading our course through a maze of small islands we had to feel our way by constantly sounding for there were no previous records to guide us. Running south-west along the edge of the Biscoe Islands we crossed 65° S. in beautifully clear weather; here on the verge of the Antarctic Circle we could see the mountains of the mainland stretching far into the southern distance. We sounded again at 1 o'clock but still only got 435 metres depth. Continuing we decided to sound again at 4 o'clock, but now the wind was freshening from the N.E.; soon it was mounting to a gale and without taking soundings it was just possible to complete the series of horizontally towed nets before it became too rough, but deep-water nets were now out of the question.

Steaming back to Lockroy (on Monday, the 21st) we came upon a playground of small whales—or was it a battle ground? To port and starboard appeared school after school of small rorquals (mincke whales) from six to a dozen strong going this way and that, sometimes blowing in line, one immediately behind the other. Amongst these schools were several killer whales with their tall curved fins and their black bodies slashed with white; at times when breaking surface they almost cleared the water altogether. It was disappointing that they were never very near the ship so we could not see whether they were attacking the small rorquals or not; perhaps they were after seal for there were many about. . . .

It was lucky we made Port Lockroy for all Monday night and Tuesday it blew a gale from the north-east with heavy blizzards at times. During this time we iced ship, collecting ice from the shore, or from small icebergs that had fallen from the glacier, to fill the special ice-melting tanks which stand along the deck on either side of the engine-room casing. These have steam pipes along their bottom and the ice is fed into them through large square lids at the top; many tons of water can be obtained in a relatively short time (Plate 37, p. 448). Whilst this was going on we made a closer acquaintance with the penguins, both gentoo and ringed. The gentoos are the more nervous and if you wish to get close to them you must crouch low and creep up slowly; the ringed will almost come to greet you. However, there are the charms of music; if you crouch near the gentoos, and softly whistle some little tune, they become fascinated, turning their heads this way and that, first looking at each other and then at you, and then cocking their heads on one side as if rapt in admiration.

On Thursday (the 24th) we steamed through the Peltier Channel to take a station off the mainland at the southern end of the Gerlache Strait. Leaving Lockroy we turned sharply to the left, as if up a narrow side street between the little island of Doumer and Wiencke; it looks like a cul-de-sac but when you come to what appears to be its end you turn sharply to the right into a long narrow lane of water. This is flanked on the left by a line of sharp peaks forming a range which descends steeply to end at the water in a blue cliff of ice; on the right is the irregular ice cap of Doumer. In one place, as we passed, the ice cliff 'carved' and a large part fell with a thunderous roar into a froth of foam and shattered the glass-like surface of the water. These thunder peals of falling ice have now become one of the familiar sounds; hardly an hour passes without one being heard near or far away, and sometimes one follows another in quick succession.

Once out of the channel we saw the long range of the mountains of Graham Land clear cut against a blue sky with little fluffs of cloud above some of the peaks. Immediately in front of us stands Cape Renard, a vast monolith, 2,624 feet in height, with three sides of almost perpendicular rock, crowned with ice and snow; and just beyond was mountainous Booth Wandle Island separated from the mainland by the narrowest of channels. Following a full station we put down a dredge and obtained another magnificent collection of animals including three different species of *Cephalodiscus*[1].

In the afternoon the sun, getting low in the sky, was shining through a very fine film of high altitude cloud and for the first time we saw the famous parahelion effect, that of the mock suns. In its complete form it is a wide halo round the sun with images of the sun, the mock suns, repeated at four points on its circumference: above, below, and left and right; in this instance, however, the upper and the lower ones did not appear for there was clear blue sky above, and below was the sea. The effect is produced by reflections from very small ice crystals of a particular shape high up in the atmosphere. I made the rapid colour sketch seen in Plate 34, p. 408.

I will record only *one more* Antarctic effect and this will really be the last; although in truth it defies description. As we returned to Port Lockroy everywhere we looked in the narrow channel was lit with coloured light, broad sweeps of pure colour passed either by gentle gradations, or sometimes by sharp contrasts, into different hues. In the sun the snow on the steep ranges high above us was a vivid rose pink with the rocks warmed to a rich apricot shade; the sky behind was violet-blue merging lower down to that rich translucent turquoise now so familiar to us, and the shadows in the snow were of the same pure violet-blue so that high up it almost appeared as if you were looking right through the mountain side to the sky beyond. The

[1] *C. nigrescens, hodgsoni* and *C. densus*.

water in the channel ahead was as glass perfectly reflecting every detail of colour above, but then, as we approached, the mirror became alive; it was fascinating to watch the inverted ice and mountain scene being drawn first into distortion as the surface curved and lifted, and then violently stirred into frantic rippling coloured light. It was as if we were steaming in a giant kaleidoscope. It is remarkable that colours in nature, however violent the contrast, never seem to clash; there must, I think, be some subtle natural law of optics that perhaps we do not fully understand.

I have perhaps taken up over much space on this one day, but it stands out, for me at least, as one of the high-lights of the voyage, and it was also our last in this magic region. Yesterday (the 25th) we left Port Lockroy, returning north, and passed through the Neumayer Channel in brilliant sunshine, being accompanied by a school of mincke whale which frequently came up to blow close beside us. We made a station as soon as we got into the Gerlache Strait, but again there was little krill; then finding Fournier Fjord blocked with ice we went on to our old anchorage at Melchior. . . .

Friday, 1st April. Leaving Melchior on Sunday we passed into that part of the Gerlache Strait we had not yet entered and steamed between the mountainous and icebound coasts of Brabant Island and the mainland. At the northerly end we took a station near Two Hummock Island and another the following morning between Low Island and Hoseason, back in the Bransfield Strait. Passing close to Deception Island, we picked up mail and provisions which were most kindly sent out to us in two motor-boats; we then took another station near the island just as it was getting dark and arrived at Admiralty Bay in King George Island on Tuesday afternoon.

At the station near Deception we were lucky to collect a large number of very young krill in various stages of development in the upper vertical nets and in the surface towed nets. This was just what we badly needed to give us a more complete picture of the life history of our key organism. Each one had only a single light-organ developed but there were enough of them to make the end of the tow-net glow brilliantly with blue-green light as it came up to the surface; as we undid the bucket at its end and looked in, the little creatures were milling round, turning this way and that, and flashing in every direction, so that it appeared as if we had uncorked some magic mixture effervescent with fire. The water round the ship was also alive with sparks. This was indeed exciting, for whilst the adult krill were at present so scarce in the area (except for the patch we struck between Brabant and Anvers Islands) we seem to have struck a nursery region where perhaps most of the old generation may have died off earlier in the year.

Although so late in the season we at once planned an intensive survey to chart these nursery grounds: two lines of five stations each at ten-mile intervals across the Bransfield Strait, with an intermediate station between the lines. Would the weather permit it? We knew how sudden and violent were the storms, how dangerous the coasts and how badly charted were the lesser rocky islands about the Strait. We were held up, except for dredging and trawling, for three days by gales.

Whilst dredging here we took a fine specimen of that remarkable animal *Priapulus caudatus*[1]. A curious feature of the distribution of this animal is that they are only known from the north and the south,

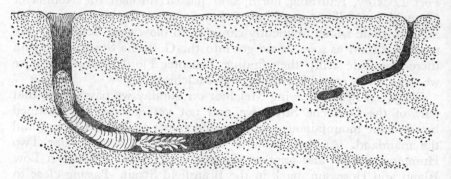

The worm *Priapulus* drawn from a living specimen which has made its burrow against the glass side of an aquarium; for a description of its action see text.

particularly in the polar regions, with no specimens in between. They live at the bottom of 'U'-shaped burrows in thick mud. With rhythmic waves of muscular expansion and contraction passing back-wards down the body—the former fitting its burrow like a piston in a cylinder—*Priapulus* pumps a stream of water past itself; as each new 'section' of water reaches the hind end, the plume-like tail organ enormously expands as it fills with body fluid and so, with its thin elastic walls, acts as a gill to take up dissolved oxygen from the water. If kept in mud in an aquarium they will often make their burrow against one of the glass sides as shown in my sketch and display this respiratory behaviour.

[1]At Oxford, when still an undergraduate, I had made a special study of this creature having obtained specimens in the Essex mud at Brightlingsea. Its position in the animal kingdom is most obscure as there is much concerning both its anatomy and development still to be made clear.

There are mosses and lichens among the lower rocks here as well as two flowering plants—a grass and what appears to be a small cruciferous plant—perhaps introduced with potato peelings thrown out from one of the whaling ships which sometimes anchor here. This reminds me that I failed to remark upon the mosses we collected in Port Lockroy, our most southerly landing; from these we soaked out some of those remarkable little animals, tardigrades, or water-bears as they used to be called by the old naturalists: creatures no bigger than some protozoa (single-celled animalculae) yet having little legs with which they walk about in their microscopic world. They are found in almost all parts of the world and can withstand the most severe conditions; they can remain dried up or frozen for long periods and will then come to life again with moisture or warmth.

Saturday, 8th April. We have had a splendid spell of weather just when we most needed it. Leaving Admiralty Bay early on Sunday morning, and working on through day and night, with short delays through encountering ice in the dark, we completed the whole survey programme by Thursday morning. The first line ran due south across the Strait from Admiralty Bay with a station at a point five miles from the coast and each of the others at ten-mile intervals till the fifth brought us to just about five miles from the ice cliffs of Graham Land. Each was a full station followed by the usual double series of towed nets at the three standard levels.

It was fine but cold; for two days and nights we worked in temperatures of 12—15° F so that the water sampling bottles and nets froze a moment or two after coming up. Handling the nets under these conditions was not the easiest of tasks, especially if accompanied, as often, by showers of driving snow; nevertheless everyone worked eagerly and each station was carried through without a hitch. All the metre wheels and blocks had to be brought into the warmth between stations or they would have been completely frozen up; as it was towards the end of a station, they would be hung with icicles, and often had to be freed by the use of a blow-lamp; the vertical plankton nets, whilst the collected bucket was being changed, took on the appearance of a hoar-frost hedge and the ship's rigging, festooned with snow and ice, was indeed a pretty sight. The second line, parallel to the first, ran from Livingstone Island, just north of Deception, across to Graham Land just north of Tower Island. Close against Livingstone Island, near where a magnificent glacier curved down a serpentine valley to the sea, we saw our first Adélie penguins; they were leaping out of the water and swimming quite close to the ship, unmistakable with their black heads and narrow, hardly visible, white ring round the eye. Near Tower Island we found at last what must be the Kendad Rocks which we had failed to find before; they were miles from their supposed position on the charts.

On this line we passed through very rich patches of still younger stages of krill which were most valuable to us. Consequently on Wednesday night, on our way back to Deception, we took the line of consecutive 70 cm. diameter surface nets, each haul being of ten minutes' duration towed at 2 knots. Thirty-two such samples were taken in five hours, from 3 a.m. to 8 a.m. across the area in which we had found the most young krill. This series has given us a splendid collection of these young stages and another good record of patchiness for several other animals for comparison with our observations at South Georgia; we also got fair numbers of adult krill as will be seen on p. 409 where the results are shown graphically. It is clear that the krill may be just as patchy in its young stages as when full grown. Do they remain all their lives in a close swarm? It would appear so. There were also many of the ubiquitous salps *Salpa fusiformis*. So abundant can these salps be at times as to be almost a curse to the planktologist. At our last station nearest Graham Land there were so many that they burst our 1-metre surface net and still the torn net yielded 33 bucketsful of them. There were many of the white dying forms and we actually saw some disintegrating in the water beside the ship.

The end of our consecutive series found us close against Deception Island. Whales were blowing all round us and the catchers from the island were busy; the sound of their guns was frequent. All night their lights had been visible around us; we might have been among a fishing fleet in the North Sea instead of in the Antarctic. The whaling which had been very bad here this season, as we have already noted, has suddenly improved. During this last week large numbers of fin whales have entered the Strait and are reported to be fat and in excellent condition; they have come from the north-west and are passing up the Strait to the north-east.

We had finished our survey only just in time for a storm was gathering; we made our way through the Neptune's Bellows as it broke —and indeed they are well named. We are now coaling for our attempt to run a line of stations across the Drake Strait to Cape Horn; if we succeed, it will be the first time such a set of plankton and hydrological observations will have been made in the waters connecting the the great Oceans—the Pacific and the Atlantic. I may say at once that we were successful, for it enables me in the next paragraph to relate the results from that line to those of the survey just completed to provide a general picture of the outstanding conditions in this area.

34. *Above*, the par-helion effect (due to fine ice crystals at a high altitude) seen off Graham Land, March, 1927. *Below*, evening at Fournier Fjord, Anvers Island, Palmer Archipelago

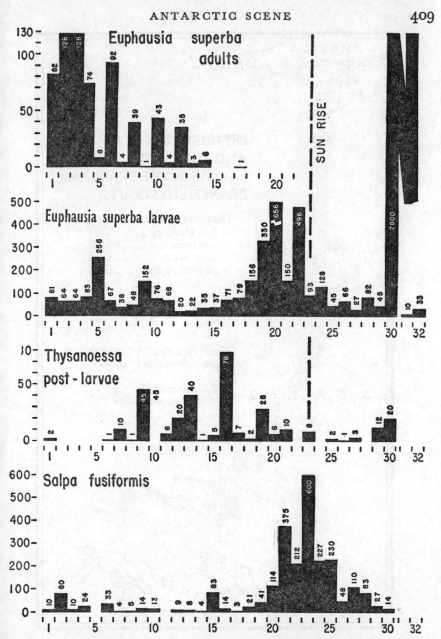

Histograms showing the varying numbers of some plankton animals in thirty-two consecutive net hauls taken just below the surface in the Bransfield Strait off Graham Land. Each haul was of ten minutes' duration and covered a distance of one-third of a mile. The series began at 3.0 o'clock in the morning and ended soon after 8.

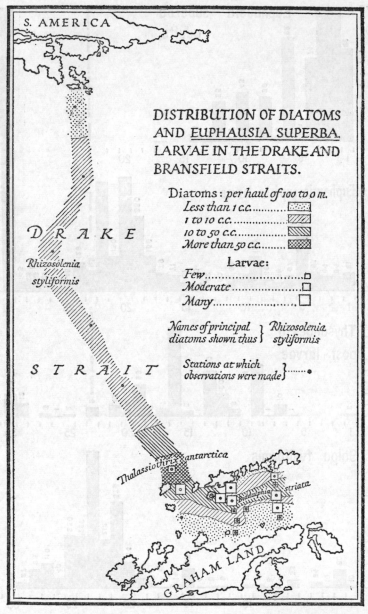

The distribution of the diatoms (phytoplankton) in contours of density, with the names of the dominating species between the Antarctic and Cape Horn, with the abundance of the young krill shown by size of squares. From *The Geographical Journal*, 1928.

[The chart opposite gives the distribution of the phytoplankton and the young krill in the Drake and Bransfield Straits. The area of the young krill is just where the water from the Weddell Sea is curling round the end of Graham Land into the Bransfield Strait to meet the water coming up from the Bellingshausen Sea on the outside of the South Shetlands. It is here, once again in an area of mixture between two water systems, that we see the heavy production of plankton.

I have already mentioned (p. 378) the remarkably flat crustaceans of the genus *Serolis* which were so characteristic of our dredge hauls in the Antarctic. One of them is shown in the drawing below. I will now add that from this one voyage we brought back in our collections specimens of nineteen different species of which six were new to science. They are described by Miss Edith Sheppard in vol. VII of the *Discovery Reports*, pp. 253-362. They remind one of those fossil trilobites that lived in the seas of five hundred million years ago.]

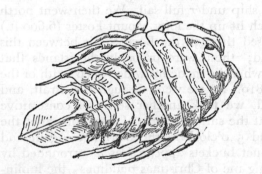

Characteristic crustacea of the Antarctic sea bed: the isopods *Glyptonotus antarctica* (left) of massive build, and *Serolis Cornuta*, extremely flat like a thin wafer, each shown half-size

CHAPTER 18

FROM THE SOUTH TO CAPE HORN

Friday, 15th April. We are now heading for Cape Horn after a busy week at Deception, examining the plankton from our survey of the Bransfield Strait. We have an excellent series of young stages of the krill from the very earliest, the nauplius, upwards; although we were unable to find any eggs, it is still possible that some may be found when the samples come to be examined in greater detail. The whaling fraternity, who have been working overtime throughout the week, gave us a great send off with blasts on their factory ships' sirens as we steamed out of the harbour; they have been most friendly and hospitable hosts to us during our stay.

Turning to the west we passed Sail Rock, rising sheer from the open sea, for all the world like a ship under full sail. We then went north under a brilliant moon which lit up the lofty Mount Foster (6,600 ft.) on Smith Island as we passed through the Boyd Strait between this and the lower Snow Island; these were probably the islands that William Smith first sighted when he made his wide sweep south of the Horn in his little brig in 1819. As we went through the Strait, and out into the ocean beyond, we took another series of consecutive 70 cm. diameter net hauls at the surface: forty of them, one after the other, between 10 p.m. and 5 o'clock in the morning. Again and again the edges of the tow-net buckets appeared as if surrounded by small blue flames—reminding me of Christmas puddings—the luminosity of innumerable larval krill. Again we got splendid samples.

This morning we completed the first of the six full vertical stations, which we propose to take, with intermediate sets of towed nets, between the South Shetlands and the Horn. We regard this as one of our major objectives. Apart from filling a gap between the two great oceans, this line has special significance for our work because it is from here that the westerly drift brings part of the water to the whales' feeding grounds to the east; and our finding such quantities of young krill emphasises its importance. We are fitting in another link in the whale story, for here may well be one of the great nursery grounds for the development both of their food and their young to supply the South

Georgia area by next season. Its importance is equalled by the difficulties of working in such waters with only auxiliary power.

I mentioned (p. 407) the tardigrades we found in the moss at Port Lockroy: with them were also some fly larvae which Fraser kept alive in the laboratory; they pupated and, to our great delight, are now hatching out into those remarkable wingless flies, *Belgica antarctica*, discovered and described by the *Belgica* expedition from this very locality. The evolutionary significance of such wing reduction was, of course, a point made by Darwin, in *The Origin of the Species*: 'Again an organ useful under certain conditions might become injurious under others, as with the wings of beetles living on small and exposed islands; and in this case natural selection would continue slowly to reduce the organ until it was rendered harmless and rudimentary.'

Wednesday, 20th April. Our luck was too good to last; after completing four vertical stations in perfect weather with towed nets in between, it came on to blow yesterday as we started our fifth and the sea rose with surprising suddenness as the glass fell equally steeply. In a very short time the ship was drifting to leeward in a gale with the wires for both nets and bottles straying out to windward. We just managed to complete our vertical nets down to what should have been a thousand metres but some were almost certainly unreliable; the heavy rolling most likely jerked off the closing mechanisms before their proper time, and with the angle of the wire, the nets could not have reached their proper depth. The hydrologists fared worse. Having successfully worked their bottles down to 1,000 metres, they were making a great effort to complete their sampling to 3,500 metres, when the heavy strain, imposed by the tossing ship, snapped the wire close against the winch; they lost three bottles as well as a great length of wire cable. All to-day we have been hove to in an enormous sea just about a hundred miles south of the Horn; occasionally the sun broke through to produce brilliant gleams of blue and green amongst the tumbling foam. To-night we have clear moonlight and the wind has dropped; we hope by morning to be able to wind a new wire on to the hydrographic reel.

Friday, 22nd April. We have now completed the line and sailed under lower topsails right up to this most venerable headland, Cape Horn, in a spanking breeze from the south.

Yesterday whilst there was still a big swell and a stiffish breeze we were able to get back to our old position and repeat the whole station, but not without difficulty. One of the vertical nets, at a depth of over 200 metres, was fouled by the water-bottles, being hauled up for'ard, and torn in two. This is the third time a net has been damaged in this way on this one line of stations, and it had never happened before on the whole of the voyage; there must be some strong deep current carrying the net into the path of the bottle. We have now given up the simultaneous use of the two winches. Since early in the morning a new coil of 6,500 metres of wire had slowly, with great care, been wound on to the hydrographic winch in place of that lost. It was all in vain. No sooner had we begun hauling from 3,500 metres when— snap—the new wire parted as before against the ship and three more Ekmann reversing bottles went to the bottom. This makes seven bottles lost in the last three stations; again these were the first to be lost on the whole voyage. I suppose when working south of the Horn we must expect to pay some tribute to the Deep. We finished the long series of bottle hauls by using them on the wire from the plankton winch.

Last night we towed our last series of 1 metre and 70 cm. diameter nets on the line and this morning worked our last vertical station, just 5 miles off the Cape, in only 112 metres of water. In the towed nets we took again the euphausian, *Euphausia spinifera*, which we had met with south of Cape Town. Since leaving the coastal region of the South Shetlands we have not met with any krill, either young or adult, which is interesting in that they seem to be in the areas of mixture between the Weddell Sea and Bellingshausen Sea waters—the line of mixture which leads on and up to South Georgia. Small pteropods of the genus *Limacina* have been a feature of the towed nets for a good deal of the way, but towards the end they gave way to numbers of *Clio* with their pointed shells. Hydrologically we obtained a splendid section of the ocean traverse showing the varying temperature and saltness of the different water masses we encountered; it illustrates most clearly the system of Antarctic currents which we have already discussed (pp. 316 to 320). Here we see the cold surface layer of poor salinity, due to melting ice, streaming away from the pole, the other cold layer (not diluted with fresh water from the ice) creeping north along the ocean floor, and the warm intermediate layer flowing south between them to take their place.

[It is now at this point that I shall describe the design and development of my continuous plankton recorder, an account which I have postponed until now because it was on this line, from the south to Cape Horn, that it really came into its own and emerged from the experimental state. It had already given a number of records, totalling up to some thousand miles of plankton, but was frequently going wrong; at last, without a hitch, it had given us a complete continuous record right across the Drake Strait. This I regard as its real birth. I designed the instrument before the voyage as a result of being much struck by the very patchy nature of the plankton in the North Sea where I had begun to study it in relation to the herring as an Assistant Naturalist to the Ministry of Fisheries; how very patchy the plankton can be we have conclusively demonstrated with our various series of consecutive nets. Half-way through the voyage I sent, with Dr. Kemp's account of the first season's work, a description of the instrument to the journal *Nature* where it was published in the issue of 30th October, 1926 (vol. 118, pp. 630-2). I will here quote that description, which was written on board, as if it was part of my journal:

Hitherto our knowledge of the density and distribution of the plankton has been gained from samples taken at a number of stations within the area concerned. When, as on long cruises, the stations have to be twenty, fifty, or even a hundred or more miles apart, it may be doubted whether such samples are giving a true idea of the planktonic content of the water traversed: at one point one may strike a swarm of copepods, or between two others miss an important zone of diatoms. For a long time I have felt the need of an instrument which, by giving a continuous record mile by mile to scale, would enable one to study and compare the uniformity or irregularity of planktonic life in different areas, to measure the size, varying internal density, and frequency of patches, and to indicate more exactly than can be done with comparable tow-nettings whether any correlation exists between different species.

Whilst on the *Discovery* expedition I have been experimenting with such an instrument, which I am calling the Continuous Plankton Recorder. Numerous little defects and difficulties have had to be overcome; but now that, taken together, more than 1300 miles of plankton have been recorded, it may be of interest to publish a brief description of the instrument and a note of some of the results obtained by its use. It is a development of the simple Plankton Indicator which I used in the North Sea (*Min. of Agric. and Fisheries Investigations* II, vol. 8, no. 7, 1926) but in place of the silk netting discs, which had to be reloaded for each sample, I have substituted a long continuously moving roll operated by a propeller turned by the water through which it is towed. Like the Indicator, it is used at full speed without stopping the ship.

The accompanying figure is a diagram of the instrument. It has a hollow cylindrical body tapered at each end, is weighted in front and furnished with planes P and P′, a vertical fin V with adjustable rudder R, and buoyancy chamber Q, so that when it is towed at the point T it 'swims' like a paravane in a horizontal

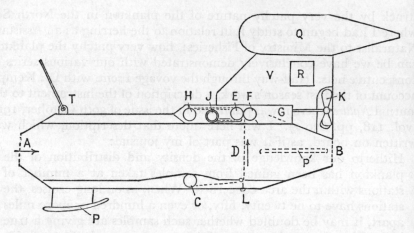

A diagrammatic section of the first continuous plankton recorder; for
explanation see text and compare with Plate 38 (p. 449).

position in the water at the required depth. I am greatly indebted
to H.M.S. *Vernon*, Portsmouth, which carried out stability tests
up to a speed of 16 knots and fitted the present planes and fin in
place of those of my own design which proved unsatisfactory.

As the apparatus is towed, water enters through the circular
opening A, passes through the cylinder and out at B. A length of
silk netting, 9 inches wide and with 60 meshes to the inch, is
arranged to wind off the braked roller C across the stream of water
at D, where, supported behind by a gridwork of fine rollers, it
catches the organisms in the water, then between the driving
rollers E and F, which are of soft rubber but with hard ends gripping
the edges of the silk, and so on to the storage roller H. The
openings A and B, of 4 inches diameter, are smaller than that of D
and approximately equal to the filtration area of the netting; a
steady flow of water is thus assured, which by its pressure causes
the organisms to adhere to the sink. The rollers E and F are driven
through the gear-box G by the propeller K, and the storage roller H
from E by a chain and friction drive, which prevents acceleration
in winding due to its increasing diameter. At J, in a box, is a roll
immersed in 5 per cent formalin; this winds in with the catching
roll between E and F, so preserving and separating the layers of
organisms on the storage roller H. The instrument is hinged at L
and made to open so that the rollers C, J, and H can be quickly
taken out and replaced by others. It will be noted that the opening
A is not masked by any towing bridle and cuts the water cleanly.

35. *Above*, Copper Mountain, Anvers Island, from the Neumayer Channel, so called because the rock is a brilliant green with copper ore. *Below*, the *Discovery* at Port Lockroy, Wiencke I, off Graham Land, so named by Dr. Charcot, when on his 1904 expedition, as a good place to shelter

36. *Above*, colony of gentoo penguins on Wiencke Island. *Below*, the mountains of Graham Land

The detailed machine drawings of the instrument were prepared from my sketches by Mr. M. T. Denne of 310 Regent Street, w., to whom I am indebted for a number of valuable suggestions.

Each silk-catching roll is ruled with transverse numbered lines at 6-inch intervals. Rolls up to 75 sections in length may be used. The blades of the propeller are adjustable so that each section may represent an equal distance of one or more miles as required: the distance actually travelled by the instrument is measured by the ship's log.

At the end of the record the completed roll is unwound across a glass stage with mirror below and examined section by section with a microscope; occasionally an organism may have to be removed from the netting for identification. As detailed an analysis is made as may be desired or time permits, from an exact quantitative record of all the species to only a rough estimation of the general density in different places. The specimens are sometimes damaged in the process of winding, but in nearly all cases they can be identified; in areas where the plankton is well known determination is comparatively easy. The instrument is not intended for collecting purposes, and, having different functions, is a supplement to, rather than a substitute for, the plankton net.

The account then went on to refer to various records which I will not include here, they have all been published in full in *Discovery Reports*, vol. xi, pp. 511-38 (1936). I will only reproduce a graph of the record on this line to Cape Horn (p. 418). We see how both the copepods and the chaetognaths (arrow worms) tend to increase and fall off together and how they are both particularly abundant in a wide zone some 50 miles across lying some 70 miles south of the Horn; we see how patchy too is the small pteropod *Linnacina*.

Here I must express my gratitude to Dr. Herdman, our hydrologist, for his help; he was indeed a doctor of machines, and in those early days of the recorder, when a roller would stick or slip, or the winding clutch might fail, he always seemed to know just what was wrong and how to put it right. Our ship was full of 'gadgets', upon which Henry Herdman was continually performing the most delicate operations with enthusiasm. And I must not forget the help of George Gourlay, our Artificer-Engineer.

Photographs of this old machine are shown in Plate 38. When not in use it stood on deck covered by a closely fitting canvas case made for it by 'Sails'; thus dressed out, with its large buoyancy chamber forming a great hump on its back, it had somewhat the appearance of a camel and very soon came to be known as the Camel's Hump.

O

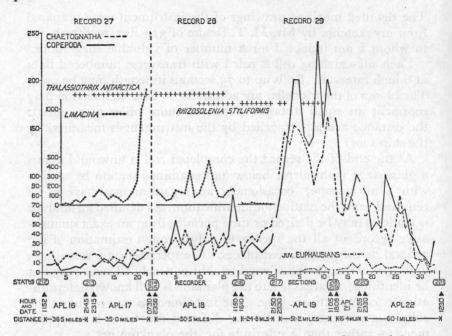

A graphic representation of the variations in the numbers of some of the more important plankton animals as sampled by the continuous plankton recorder on a line across the Drake Strait from the Antarctic (South Shetlands) to Cape Horn. The animals shown are the copepods, the arrow-worms (Chaetognatha), the pteropod *Limacina* and the young euphausians; the presence of diatoms *Thalassiothrix antarctica* and *Rhizosolenia styliformis* are shown by lines of plus signs. From *D.R.*, vol. XI.

Hereby hangs a tale. There were times, when, if sails had to be trimmed in a hurry it got in the way of hauling on some rope; in the stress of one such occasion, the wit in charge of the party, instead of shouting 'mind the camel's hump' called out 'mind the horse's bottom!' At once the name stuck; it became known throughout the ship just by the initials H.B. Now no one ever thought of saying what time is the plankton recorder coming in, it was the H.B.; even my log book for recording the analysis of the rolls I labelled the 'H.B. Book.' Imagine my horror when, at a large and smart cocktail party in Cape Town, some wretched wag took upon himself to induce a party of very distinguished ladies to ask me why my machine was called the H.B.! I was more shy and retiring in those days than I am now and no doubt betrayed my discomfiture. Suddenly I had an inspiration—I said, 'Well, it is rather embarrassing—I've only just got engaged and they will keep calling it Hardy's Baby!'

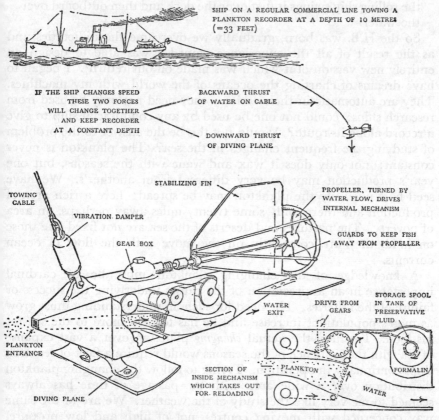

SHIP ON A REGULAR COMMERCIAL LINE TOWING A PLANKTON RECORDER AT A DEPTH OF 10 METRES (=33 FEET)

IF THE SHIP CHANGES SPEED THESE TWO FORCES WILL CHANGE TOGETHER AND KEEP RECORDER AT A CONSTANT DEPTH

BACKWARD THRUST OF WATER ON CABLE

DOWNWARD THRUST OF DIVING PLANE

TOWING CABLE

STABILIZING FIN

PROPELLER, TURNED BY WATER FLOW, DRIVES INTERNAL MECHANISM

VIBRATION DAMPER

GEAR BOX

GUARDS TO KEEP FISH AWAY FROM PROPELLER

PLANKTON ENTRANCE

WATER EXIT

DRIVE FROM GEARS

STORAGE SPOOL IN TANK OF PRESERVATIVE FLUID

SECTION OF INSIDE MECHANISM WHICH TAKES OUT FOR RELOADING

PLANKTON

FORMALIN

WATER

DIVING PLANE

A diagram showing the working of the redesigned plankton recorder, as used in the monthly surveys of the North Sea and Atlantic Ocean, but developed from the original *Discovery* machine. From the author's *The Open Sea*, Part I.

After that the letters 'H.B.' had this new connotation. Here is another extract from Rolfe Gunther's privately printed *Notes and Sketches* which will show how much the instrument and its new name were part of the ship's life. As much as possible it was run between one station and another; here Gunther is describing the typical procedure at a station:

The routine of operation in a station is the following. Lying in one's cabin one hears the order 'In H.B. In H.B.!' That is 'Hardy's Baby', the Continuous Plankton Recorder which has been towing astern ever since the last station. The rumble of the big winch tells that the shipping of the H.B. is under way, and that seamen on the after-grating are grappling with the instrument as the rolling ship swings it first over the deck and then outboard over the water.

So the H.B. was born, gradually we overcame the difficulties and as the result of all the experience gained I was able to design an entirely new version of it which was made on our return[1]. I began to have dreams of charting the oceans of the world with my machines. They are automatic in their action; they need not only be used from research ships; could not one be used by any commercial ship to give a record along its route? Would not this be the answer to the problem of studying the frequent changes in the sea? The plankton is never constant; not only does it wax and wane with the seasons, but one year's production may be very different from another's. We have seen how unevenly the plankton may be spread: here a rich area of production and there, only some twenty miles away perhaps, an area of poverty. The pastures and deserts of the sea are not fixed like those on land, they are constantly on the move with the flow of ocean currents.

A knowledge of the changing plankton must be of cardinal importance in an appreciation of the causes underlying the success or failure of the fisheries. The need for such an understanding must grow as man's populations increase and he has to turn more to the sea for his food. To study the actual *changing* plankton over a vast expanse of sea with the sequence of the seasons would require a fleet of research ships continually in operation. Trying to follow the changing plankton distribution over a wide area with the passage of time has always seemed to me very like the study of the weather. We are in the same way concerned with moving centres, not of high and low pressure, but of high and low plankton production, and plankton production of many different kinds, both plant and animal in nature. In meteorology we could never have a true idea of the course of atmospheric changes if we had only one observatory, even if it moved about; it is, of course, by having observations made at many different places at the same time that we can follow the course of events and begin to forecast the weather conditions ahead of us. In the same way I believe we can only understand the planktonic changes, and attempt to link them with what may happen in the fisheries, if we have observations taken at the same time along a number of different lines and repeated at regular intervals of time.

Fortunately the waters move and change position much more slowly than do the vortices of the wind. By looking at regular monthly charts of plankton spread over the ocean we could begin to compare the

[1] Fully described in *Discovery Reports* vol. XI, pp. 457-510.

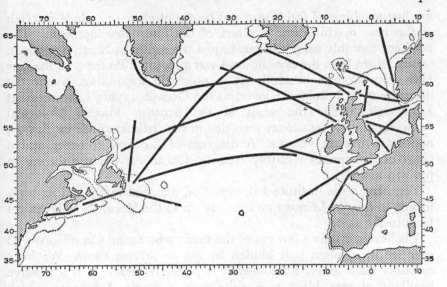

A map of the North Atlantic showing the monthly plankton recorder routes covered by the Edinburgh Oceanographic Laboratory in its survey during 1965.

events of one year with those of another; we could note that this organism came later one year than another, or more to the south or the north, and so on. Then we could further compare these changes with the fluctuations in the fortunes of the fisheries; gradually we should begin, with much study, to link cause and effect, and eventually to predict which will be the most profitable areas to exploit. So in those far-off days, I began to dream of my baby having many grand-children which would plough the oceans from some institute, some international plankton bureau. It was a joke at that time that one day I should have a marble palace, with hundreds of slaves, they said, working at the rolls! A palace perhaps, I replied, but in it will be a band of devoted workers thrilled with the results emerging and so directing the fishing fleets of the world!

It is gratifying in 1966, when some fifty plankton recorders are now in service on many lines, including four linking Europe and America, to look back to these early dreams. We are not yet controlling the fisheries of the world but we are well on the way to being able to give valuable advice. I must not take up more space in this book with matters other than the *Discovery* enterprise; yet, because it grew out of this voyage, and owes so much to Stanley Kemp's encouragement—he persuaded the *Discovery* Committee to provide the funds to make my first machine—I feel it may not be out of place to include a sketch of the new machine and a chart of the latest developments. The northern monthly survey began in just the southern North Sea when, on my return from the expedition, I was appointed Professor at the new University College of Hull. It is now still expanding, under the direction of Mr. Roland Glover, at the Oceanographic Laboratory at Edinburgh, under the aegis of the Scottish Marine Biological Association. The results are recorded in the *Bulletins of Marine Ecology*, now in their sixth volume. A diagram of the new recorder and a chart of the present monthly Atlantic Ocean surveys are shown on pp. 419 and 421.

Yes, here is the institute I dreamed of, one that really had its birth tossing in the old *Discovery* on our way up to the Horn. Now let us get back to the ship.]

I believe it is only a few out of the many who round Cape Horn who ever see it, so often is it hidden by fog or driving snow. We have certainly been lucky, for to-day it is perfectly clear. It is a massive headland of grey, black and white rock, a granite I suppose, which rises in a moderate incline towards the sea, to a height of some 2,000 feet, and then drops in precipitous cliffs to the waves below. And what waves they were! A long rolling swell with crests which the captain estimated at 25 feet in height, broke at its foot in sheets of white spray. I did the accompanying sketch in which I tried to portray the extraordinary regularity of the great waves sweeping towards the Horn; I fear I have given them the appearance of folded linoleum—and yet so even were they that they had almost that quality.

We drew nearer. The Horn stood magnificently before us. To the eastward lay Deceit Island and its cluster of rocks, to the westward Hermite and a number of smaller islands (including Hull Island and Chanteclair), and behind it lay another group, the Wollastons, with, in the far distance, the snow-capped peaks of the mainland of Terra del Fuego. Cape Horn is, of course, itself on an island.

Before making up to the Le Maire Strait between Staten Island and the mainland on our way to the Falklands we decided to anchor in a good harbour, to get shipshape again after the storm and pack away all our plankton and water samples; we made for St. Martin's Cove on the eastern side of Hermite Island. We had heard that there were trees on these islands, and not having seen one, or any vegetation but tussock grass, since leaving South Africa six months ago, we were hungry for the sight of them; little did we expect, however, the sight that greeted our eyes. The island, which appeared so forbidding and barren on its western and seaward prospects, was, on its sheltered

Cape Horn—a sketch redrawn from a watercolour made from the *Discovery* as we approached Hermite Island.

eastern side, and especially in the cove we were entering, clothed in luxuriant forest. The mountain sides were covered thickly in trees with white trunks almost like birches; looking within we could see the richest green, but on the outside some of the leaves, especially higher up, were turning a rich autumnal gold.

We steamed close up to the head of the bay and there dropped anchor just as it was getting dark. We eagerly looked out to see if we could catch sight of any of the Fuegan natives, for this was a favourite haunt of theirs in the old days; that is of the southern race, the Yargons. This St. Martin's Cove is actually the same place visited by Darwin on the *Beagle* but called by him Wigwam Cove on account of the number of native wigwams—rude structures of branches—found along the shores. But to-day this southern race, if not altogether extinct, is reduced to a few hundred and we have seen no signs of them. How these people, wearing but a small loose piece of skin, and living on the sea shores and in caverns, could withstand the rigours of this tempestuous climate, and its driving rain, hail or snow, must always be a source of wonder to the rest of mankind.

Monday, 25th April. These last few days are ones which are likely to remain in our memory as days of great delight: of scrambling through thick forest, up bubbling streams and waterfalls, among moss and ferns, through the upper scrub to the mountain lakes and to the tops of the hills. Our pleasure in these surroundings has no doubt been heightened by our long absence from the rich green of vegetation, although almost anyone could find delight in such a paradise.

As the weather had been blowing up badly outside, we decided to stay in this peaceful spot over Saturday and Sunday to give all hands a change and rest after the strenuous times of the last few weeks; since leaving South Georgia they have been very little ashore and on our last visit to Deception they were kept hard at it coaling ship and preparing for this passage to the Horn.

The trees come right down to the water's edge or nearly so, in places actually overhanging it; they stand on rugged rock which, exposed by the tides, may here and there be hollowed out into dark caverns. In one of these caves lived a family of sea-lions (*Otaria byronia*) father, mother, and seven or eight young; in general appearance they were very like the northern ones but of a ruddy colour. At odd times through the day or night you would hear them give voice, sometimes almost like the roaring of a lion, at others almost approaching the moo of a cow; and often you would hear them splashing in the water like a happy man in his bath. There was much bird life on the water. Large flocks of shag came in close to the ship at the turn of the tide, a different species[1] to that seen in the South Shetlands and Orkneys; and there were several of the remarkable steamer ducks[2] which are unable to fly but by beating their wings 'taxi' across the surface of the water at great speed, almost leaving it but not quite. There were upland geese[3], the female beautifully marked in brown, black and white, and the male almost pure white, and there were gulls in plenty.

At odd points through the trees tumbled mountain streams; the largest drained a small steep valley at the head of the cove and flowed into the sea over a beach of rounded stones. Here we always landed, for it was the only suitable place for a large ship's boat; we are using one of the 'whalers' or lifeboats because a smaller boat would have been dangerous on account of the strong and sudden gusts of wind that frequently sweep down from the mountains. These gusts are quite extraordinary; they are called 'williwars' and may only last for a minute or two, but during that time they can blow at hurricane force, turn the surface of the water into clouds of driving spindrift and cause the ship to heel over under the heavy pressure on its masts and spars. They come when there is a strong wind from the west—and that is the prevailing wind here; sometimes they come at long intervals and at others in quick succession.

[1] *Phalacrocorax carunculatus.*   [2] *Tachyeres cinereus.*   [3] *Chloephaga magellanica.*

To reach the shore we have to pass through a thick belt of kelp (*Macrocystis*) which forms a fringe all round the margin of the cove. At the mouth of the valley stream, against the pebbles and boulders of the narrow beach, and up its banks, the ground was very swampy and free from trees, but very thick in vegetation. Dense clumps of a compositous plant with large white, daisy-like flowers struggled for space with the wild celery; they were joined higher up on the banks of the stream by low thickly-growing plants looking like primulas but bearing little bunches of brilliant red berries. The celery is good to eat and has a distinct flavour of the garden variety; we gathered much of it for it was long since we had tasted fresh vegetables. Small ferns and mosses of many kinds abound, whilst on the stones at the water's edge were very striking salmon-pink lichens.

As soon as you leave the stream you are in the thick forest. It is made up almost entirely of two kinds of tree, a small-leaved beech (*Nothofagus antarcticus*) and an evergreen of the same genus (*N. betuloides*) which predominated over the former species in the higher altitudes. These beeches, with their white peeling bark and small leaves, are so very different from those at home that they might at first sight be mistaken for some kind of birch rather than a beech. Amongst these trees grow many shrubs, one very common one looked like a rhododendron and there were several species of *Berberis*, including higher up the holly-leaved barberry. So thickly do the shrubs and trees grow together that in parts it is only with considerable difficulty that you are able to force your way through; this we found yesterday, when, leaving the stream, we made our way straight up the highest peak—about 1,700 feet.

For a thousand feet you climb steeply through thick forest, at times off the ground altogether, swinging from bough to bough like our simian ancestors. Even where there is a clearing, it is not easy going; so wet and spongy is the mossy ground that in places you may easily sink knee deep into it. A dampness pervades the whole forest. During the three days we have been here it has been raining on and off the whole time so that the branches were always dripping and the trunks streaming with water. This is indeed a temperate rain forest. To make climbing harder so many of the branches, and even the trunks of trees are soft with rot; you may clutch at what you think to be a stout bough to pull yourself up only to find that it comes away as if just lightly resting in position. From higher up the mountains, when you have at last cleared the forest proper and are struggling on through closely woven beech scrub, you may look back and down to see the green valley below: a carpet of tree tops through which

O2

run white lines converging to a somewhat thicker one in the middle; it is like looking at a gigantic green leaf with its veins and midrib picked out in white. These 'veins' are caused by lines of dead and fallen trees with their bare white branches contrasting with the green; they are lines where streams, or just zones of very boggy ground, have killed the trees—lines of drainage running down as tributaries to join the 'midrib', the main stream, in the valley.

From this description it must not be imagined that, because the number of species of trees was few, there was monotony in the scene or that the damp was disagreeable. If stoutly clad in thick boots, leggings and oilskin coat, the dripping forest can be a delight. The air was laden with delicious scents: the mossy, earthy, leafy scents that we have been without for so many months. And as for variety of scene, it was endless. The branches living and dead cross and slope in all directions and are lavishly decorated, in some cases completely covered, with many kinds of mosses, fungi and lichens. A parasitic mistletoe-like plant is common on the branches higher up. The floor of the forest may justly be described as a jungle of moss and fern, for the masses of moss may be as large as great lumps of tussock and sometimes with delicate fern-like fronds. Through this paradise of green and gold— the gold of falling leaves—run little streams in unexpected places; you may hear them gurgling beneath your feet—hidden from view under a covering of fallen, moss-draped branches—or you may push through the thick foliage to come suddenly upon a little waterfall tumbling down the face of a vivid green encrusted rock.

The most joyous feature of the whole, perhaps the one feature that made all the rest seem so enchanting, was a little bird. So far this is the most fascinating little bird I have ever met, I doubt if I shall ever be more captivated by a 'feathered friend.' It is very small, barely bigger than a wren. It is prettily mottled with shades of yellow and brown, and has upon its head a gorgeous cap; from its beak, over the top of its head to the back of its neck run broad stripes of black and orange. It must be the little *Oxyurus tupineri* which Darwin found so numerous in these forests. When we first saw it we did not know its name, but called it 'Happy Larry Bird' because it seemed the embodiment of happiness, and as such I shall always think of it; as 'happy as Larry' is a sailor's expression to denote delight and contentment. With great activity and merry chirping they flit from bough to bough, as they peck here and there for insects, or like tits they can hang upside down upon small branches. Their endearing quality, however, is their friendliness. They delighted in fluttering round and perching on branches close beside you; then fluffing up their feathers, cocking their heads on one side to have a good look at you, they would give a friendly chirp or two. And how pleased they seemed when you chirped back! If you sit still and chirp and whistle softly you can call up these little birds from far around. Here indeed you felt the spirit of Hudson's Rima.

Of other animal life there was little. In the streams we found caddis-fly larvae and freshwater shrimps (gammarid amphipods), under bark and moss were worms, carabid beetles and wood-lice, and in the forest were midges and little moths (Microlepidoptera). Higher up, flying over the scrub, there were many geometrid moths of several species, and here we saw blue-grey finch-like birds. This thick beech scrub above the forest, by the way, is from two to three feet in height and so thickly woven that it sometimes supports your weight, but sometimes lets you through, and so is very tiring to walk over. In the forest there were a few other birds but we only caught momentary glimpses of them: one was a brown thrush-like bird and another black with a patch of white.

Lest it be thought that I have exaggerated the lusciousness of the forest let me quote two descriptions from Darwin's immortal *A Naturalist's Voyage* (his voyage on the *Beagle*):

In both places, and everywhere else, the surface is covered by a thick bed of swampy peat. Even within the forest, the ground is concealed by a mass of slowly putrefying vegetable matter, which, from being soaked with water, yields to the foot.

Finding it nearly hopeless to push my way through the wood, I followed the course of a mountain torrent. At first, from the waterfalls and number of dead trees, I could hardly crawl along; but the bed of the stream soon became a little more open, from the floods having swept the sides. . . . The entangled mass of the thriving and the fallen reminded me of the forests within the tropics—yet there was a difference: for in these still solitudes, Death, instead of Life, seemed the predominant spirit. . . .

In the valleys it was scarcely possible to crawl along, they were so completely barricaded by great mouldering trunks, which had fallen down in every direction. When passing over these natural bridges, one's course was often arrested by sinking knee deep into the rotten wood; at other times, when attempting to lean against a firm tree, one was startled by finding a mass of decayed matter ready to fall at the slightest touch.

Darwin found these forests gloomy—no doubt he was comparing them with the brilliant forests of the Amazons he had come from; to us, coming from the ice, rock and snow of the Antarctic, they were a glory of delicious green.

CHAPTER 19

FROM CAPE HORN TO GOOD HOPE VIA
GOUGH ISLAND

Friday, 29th April. We got away from St. Martin's Cove at sunrise on Wednesday as the mountains, powdered overnight with snow, were caught in a mellow light which turned the yellowing beeches to a glorious gold. Bound for the Falklands, we rounded the Horn only a mile and a half from its point, and yesterday made our way through the famous, and sometimes dreaded, Le Maire Strait separating mountainous Staten Island from the mainland. It is, I suppose, one of the most difficult pieces of water in the world for a sailing ship or an underpowered steamer. It is shallow and running through it is a strong tidal current of at least four knots, but often reaching six or even seven it is said; in addition the frequent gales produce high steep seas in water of such little depth.

With a contrary wind it was a race to get through the channel before two o'clock when the tide would also turn against us. At first, in spite of the head wind, we seemed to make excellent progress with the engines full out and a strong tide to help us; before long, however, the wind increased in violence and, against the tide, produced a most curious and fierce sea. The old ship battled into this clash of elements and pitched as never before, putting down her head and lifting it as if purposely throwing sheets of white spray over her back. Time crept on and with it went the certainty of getting through. Two o'clock came and it now seemed that the turn of the tide must surely carry us back, when suddenly the wind changed from direct ahead to the port bow. There was just room to alter course and bring it abeam with the chance that with all sail we might clear the island. The cry of 'All hands on deck' brought everyone to the ropes and in a very short time, to the chorus of 'Ranzo, boys, Ranzo!', 'Blow the Man Down' and other shanties, upper and lower topsails were set on both the fore and main, and then fore and main sheets, with stay-sails and spankers. The ship heeled over to the wind and never have I seen her look finer;

she was showing off against the magnificent background of the jagged mountains of Staten Island, standing up like a row of savage teeth. With sails filled and engines at full blast we pushed into the heavy sea at some nine or ten knots—and before long we were through.

Friday, 6th May. This evening we anchored in Stanley Harbour after a rough passage in tumbling seas. Six stations have been worked, but only with difficulty; Henry Herdman and Jimmy Fraser on the outboard platforms had to be secured with life-lines, for at times the waves swept up to their waists.

There was quite a variety in the euphausiids; and many of the lobster krill (the pelagic larvae of *Munida*) which we took last year near the Falklands (p. 208). These larvae are strongly attracted towards light and it was a comical sight to see them all backing—for they travel tail first—hard up against the edge of a square glass dish near an electric lamp in the laboratory; unable to get any farther, they remained still swimming, like a row of red-coated soldiers marking time. Their long claws and legs are provided with fringes of closely placed hairs which evidently, in parachute fashion, give them support in the water. Putting them in a tall jar we could watch them climb (backwards again) towards the surface by strong and rapid strokes with their tail-fans, and then see them, with their legs and claws rigidly outstretched, like the ribs of an umbrella, very slowly sink; maintaining their balance whilst parachuting must be very difficult for their centre of gravity is *above* instead of below the umbrella, and occasionally they would tumble head over heels. . . . Anchored in Stanley harbour we found the Swedish ship *Fennia* which had been dismasted while rounding the Horn in the same storm that we had struck; and here was the *William Scoresby* back from an extensive trawling survey between the Falklands and South America.

Our two ships are again going to take different lines of observations across the ocean, this time from the Falklands to the Cape; the *Discovery* will go via Tristan da Cunha and I shall be in charge of the *William Scoresby* once more, going via South Georgia and Gough Island. At South Georgia we shall repeat a line of the plankton survey to compare its more wintry conditions with those we met before. Each ship, on her passage, will take a series of towed nets every night and then a line of full vertical stations on approaching and leaving Tristan or Gough respectively to span the ridge on which they stand. We are anxious to see if they yield good catches of euphausiids, for this ridge, which runs up the Atlantic, might, on account of upwelling, provide a lane of richer plankton to feed the whales migrating from the south towards the coast of Africa in winter. . . .

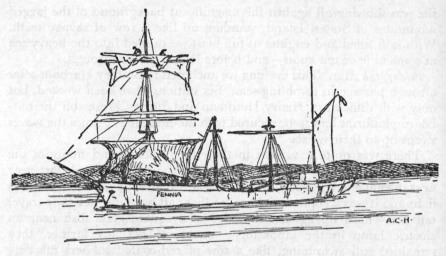

The *Fennia* in Stanley Harbour, a Swedish ship dismasted while rounding the Horn
in the same storm through which we, with heavier rigging, came without damage.

Saturday, 28th May. The days since my last entry have been busy
ones at South Georgia, painting and taking down the engine of the
station motor-boat, stowing away a lot of the expedition's gear for the
winter, etc., but little need be recorded. On our arrival it was cold
enough for pancake ice to be forming on the surface of Cumberland
Bay; this is the beginning of pack-ice formation. The rounds of ice,
which first appear, remind one of the leaves of the giant *Victoria regina*
water-lily which have turned-up margins, for these ice discs also have
an up-turned edge as the ripples round them splash up and freeze in
doing so. The whole bay was a vast lily pond with the clear blue sky
mirrored in the calm water between the white translucent 'leaves';
such calm weather, however, did not last for long.

After waiting through many days of high wind, snow and bitter cold,
we have to-day finished our line of stations across the whaling ground
and run into Prince Olaf Harbour for oil and water before leaving
to-morrow on our voyage to the Cape. The change in the plankton is
interesting; there is little of the large krill, but vast quantities of young
stages at the outside stations. Salps are scarce and there are only a
few of the amphipods *Parathemisto* which had been so common in
March and April of last year.

Tuesday, 7th June. As we sailed from Prince Olaf Harbour on
Monday, the 30th, the mist lifted as we got out to sea to give us a last
glimpse of the mountains and then closed down again—the island's

farewell. Inhospitable as its climate is, there is about its mountains, fjords and glaciers a magic which will often draw us back in memory if not in the flesh.

As we have passed across the Antarctic Convergence and on into warmer waters our nets each evening have shown us progressive changes in planktonic life: different euphausiids, amphipods and copepods among the crustacea, and the pteropods *Clio* and *Cavolinia* (p. 113) taking the place of the usual *Limacina*; then on approaching Gough Island we have met again our old friend *Phronima* (in his barrel) and diphyid siphonophores[1], harbingers of the milder climes to come.

We have passed for the fourth time across the 'roaring forties' and they have not let us through without a dusting. Whilst the seas have been no greater than some experienced on the *Discovery*, being on a ship smaller than a deep-sea trawler, they have been more impressive. At their height, I think I must admit, almost too impressive! She is a small ship on which to cross the Southern Ocean in mid-winter, but no smaller than the craft in which the early sealers ventured south.

On the night of Thursday, the 2nd, being half-way between South Georgia and Gough, I had decided to take a series of consecutive surface hauls, similar to those taken in the Bransfield Strait; no sooner had we started, however, than the wind freshened from the south-west and the glass fell rapidly. By early morning the ship was plunging heavily and as the nets left the water they were whirled about in the air like kites; by 4 o'clock conditions became impossible and we had to heave to. All day we tossed and rolled in very heavy seas, but it was nothing to the night to come. Some of our sailors, hard men, said it was the toughest night they had ever spent at sea. One of the officers said afterwards that the waves, as their curling tops towered above the bridge, seemed to have eyes that glared down at us. The ship began to behave in a curious way which was not a little frightening. As wave after wave broke over her she rolled heavily to port, and then for long times together failed to right herself; she hung over with a sickening list as the seas crashed upon her. What could be the matter with her? 'I think *I* know' said the mate to me with some concern, 'our ballast must have shifted.' It was black as ink, difficult to see much and impossible to get along the deck; to get from the cabin aft to the bridge you had, between the waves, to swing yourself up, make your way, clinging to rails and ropes, along the superstructure past the funnel. The force of the wind was terrific, and as each wave came you had to hang on for dear life. What a blessing oil-skins are.

Dawn was indeed a relief for in its first dim light we could see what

[1] Those similar to *Muggiaea* (p. 74)

our trouble was. The ship, like a trawler, has high iron bulwarks instead of open rails, and these are provided with swinging iron doors, the wash ports, hinged at their tops, to open and let the water run off the deck in heavy seas. Several had in some way become jammed shut and failed to let the water off as fast as it was coming on; the deck on the port side was full up like a bath—no wonder she had a list. Crowbars soon forced them open and the gallant little ship regained her poise.

The damage to the main structures was negligible; some casings to steam-pipes torn away, life-boats lifted from their chocks and so forth, but the laboratory presented a terrible picture of destruction. It is on deck level and a wooden structure built within the steel framing supporting the bridge above; whilst it is generally watertight, the unusual depth of water on the deck outside had caused it, in spite of the lee-boards, to fill up within to an almost equal depth. As the ship rolled, this heavy body of water crashed to and fro inside it. On the floor of the laboratory were several strong wooden cases divided by felt-lined partitions to hold the screw-top jars for our plankton samples; some jars were full, others were not. We thought we had left them safely wedged for the night but had not bargained for their being covered with water; as some of the jars were empty, the boxes were buoyant and before long floated adrift. Throughout the night they had crashed backwards and forwards with the mass of water, and, being so exceptionally strong, with stout iron corner pieces, they had acted as battering rams to smash down the wooden supports of the laboratory tables. The drawers below them now collapsed with all their contents and were smashed to pieces, and the swing table likewise carried away. We lost much apparatus and all the sheets of paper in my drawer, on which I had recorded a preliminary analysis of the plankton from day to day since leaving the Falklands, had been reduced to unrecognisable pulp. However, so strong were our cases and so efficient their felt-lined partitions, that not a single jar inside was broken, not a specimen was lost.

Towards evening the gale moderated so that we were able to proceed on our course taking stations on Sunday night and again last night when there was a remarkably fine lunar rainbow, the best I have ever seen. Showers of rain kept sweeping past us, with bright spells of full moonlight in between. As one shower had just passed, we saw, with the brilliant moon behind us, a complete semi-circle, a ghost of a bow without colour spanning the sky and looking strangely luminous, against the dark cloud of the passing squall.

To-day we sighted the peak of Gough Island and very soon, at

50 miles off, took our first full station on the line in; I had planned four stations on each side of the island: at distances 5, 15, 30 and 50 miles from the coast.

Wednesday, 8th June. Gough Island is so named because it was sighted and reported by Captain Gough, master of the ship *Richmond*, in 1731[1]. It is difficult of access; sheer cliffs appear to rise from the water on all sides except on the east where at their foot is a little beach suitable for landing if a swell does not prevent it. So favourable was the weather— only a slight breeze from the west and a high and steady glass—that I decided to land to do some collecting, and to finish the stations later. During the night we steamed round to the east and dropped anchor about half a mile from the shore beside Penguin Islet. After sighting Gough yesterday we did not get a close view of it before dark, for it became hidden in low clouds; with eagerness, therefore, we came on deck this morning for our first look at this remarkable island. It was indeed unusual.

Like Tristan it is of volcanic origin. It is about 7 miles long by some 3½ miles across and its nearly perpendicular cliffs vary in height from about a hundred to nearly a thousand feet, I should say; above these rise a series of mountainous ridges running up to the highest point[2]. It is not this general prospect of cliffs and mountain, however, which so arrests one's attention, although the proportions are grand enough; it is the detail and decoration added to the structure which give it so unique a character. The cliff tops and ridges above are set with numerous columns, pinnacles and all manner of bizarre shapes of rocks like the works of ultra modern sculptors; no less peculiar is the verdant drapery. The cliffs are hung with green lace, a curtain of a kind of quitch grass which hangs its long trailing runners like a network over the rock face on a truly gigantic scale and sends out, as we found later, little roots into the crevices behind it. Ferns and mosses, also

[1]There is little doubt however that it is the same island as that discovered more than two hundred years earlier by the Portuguese and named by them Gonçalo Alvarez after the captain of Vasco da Gama's flagship; see the account in Martin Holdgate's *Mountains in the Sea*, 1958.

[2]In my journal I have called this highest point Mount Rowett which was so named by the *Quest* Expedition, after their patron Mr. John Quiller Rowett, when they visited the island in 1922 on their way home after Shackleton's death at South Georgia. The members of the recent Gough Island Expedition have, however, found that there is a still higher mountain, 2,986 feet, to the north-west of Rowett and this they have called Edinburgh Peak after H.R.H. Prince Philip, Duke of Edinburgh, who gave their expedition much encouragement and later visited the island during his voyage in the southern ocean in 1957. They found incidentally that Mount Rowett consisted of four separate peaks, West, North, Centre and South, ranging in height from 2,640 to 2,744 feet.

clinging to the cliff, show through the grass net to add to the general greenness. The climate is very damp so that at intervals waterfalls drop precipitously into the sea; and here and there slices of the cliff have slipped seawards to form fantastic islands.

Rolfe Gunther, Dilwyn John and I, after passing through thick kelp, landed opposite Penguin Islet on a narrow strip of boulders, fallen from the cliffs above. Along it lay many elephant seals, reminding us of South Georgia, and here too, at the foot of the cliffs and upon ledges higher up were large tufts of tussock grass, but a different species (*Spartina arundinacea*). Among the tussock at beach level ran birds not unsimilar in size and build to our English moorhens, black with bright red beak and legs and a touch of white upon the head and wing; these are peculiar to the island, and so called the Gough Island rail (*Porphyriornis comeri*). They are particularly interesting, however, in being flightless, for their short wings while assisting them by reducing their weight in a rapid fluttering run, will not take them off the ground. Such a reduction of wings is apparently brought about by natural selection for such reasons as produced the wingless flies we discussed on p. 413, together with the absence of predators on the island. Also running about the beach, over the stranded seaweed and amongst the sea elephants were numbers of beautiful little yellowy-green finch-like birds, and likewise unique, the Gough Island buntings (*Rowettia goughensis*).

From where we had lain at anchor this point had seemed the easiest climb to the interior. We knew from earlier accounts that there was apparently only one easy way up and this had appeared to be it. We were mistaken; the easier way lay to the south as we were later to discover. However, at first sight the cliff in front of us did not appear too difficult for it was lower here (about 120 feet) than at any other point we could see and just above us was a deep ravine coming down with a watercourse and fall. Grass and ferns as elsewhere covered the cliff face. Ridiculous as it may seem, it took us nearly two hours to make this short ascent. The cliff, which had appeared hardly vertical from below, became in places, as we got higher, actually overhanging; the vegetation, to which we clung, and the rock itself, were both most treacherous. It was not a climb that I think any of us would willingly make again. I know I was indeed thankful to make the top. [I find it interesting to compare Rolfe Gunther's account of the same climb in his privately printed *Notes and Sketches* which I have quoted before. He writes as follows:

A small cascade poured from a gully that seemed accessible. But to gain it meant a precipitous climb of over a hundred feet up a rock face loosely overgrown by plants which we found to have as precarious a hold as ourselves. Grass had the texture of cotton wool, ferns were unreliable, while celery plants offered no resistance at all. We felt confident only when on a clump of tussock, and these were usually too big for the ledge upon which they grew. . . .

Time after time the party would be held up for five minutes groping about the cracked and crumbling tufa, determined not to beat retreat. After John had shown us how to negotiate the hardest stretch which had checked us for a quarter of an hour, we found a zone where the island tree *Phylica nitida* formed a bushy forest of the size of a large broom; it allowed the arboreal instinct within us to assert itself and we made rapid advances to the watered gully.]

Once up the cliff we reached the easier sides of the ravine, although these were steep enough. Here the vegetation became thicker and the predominant feature, apart from the tufts of tussock, was a tree heath (the *Phylica nitida* referred to by Gunther) which in places attained a height of fifteen to twenty feet. In among them were ferns, club-mosses and many flowering plants which included, among the more common ones, a wild celery (*Apicum goughensia*) distinct but not unlike that we had seen in Tierra del Fuego[1]. . . Climbing higher and reaching one of the ridges at about 1,200 feet (by our aneroid) we were able to look down into many of the deep ravines that run down from the central ridge of Mount Rowett.

From the sea the pinnacles of rock had appeared fantastic enough, but here it was as if we had come upon some secret playground of the gods. The interior of Gough can certainly be put in the same class of natural oddity as the lunar landscape of Ascension, or the contrasting ice and steaming beaches of the flooded crater of Deception Island. The ground, when not deeply hollowed by ravines, is thrown up into vast buttresses of pinky-purply rock, or into delicate spires, or has resting upon its ridges those curiously shaped blocks that we had seen from the sea; here is the old man's head, the dancing bear, the camel rock or what you will. There are also surprising items of vegetation which, although occurring lower down, are here seen at their best: two species of tree fern, *Lomaria boryana* and higher up *L. alpina*; they are not large, but have stout trunks, two or three feet high, and magnificent crowns of fronds, and give another touch of the unusual to the landscape. It appears that Gough, although some 500 miles

---

[1]These words: 'and a burnet not unlike that at South Georgia' are in my journal but I feared I had mistaken some other plant for a burnet for I could find no species of *Acaena* recorded by other expeditions; however Dr. Holdgate now tells me I was right.

Evening light and shadow on Gough Island, redrawn from a watercolour.

farther south than Tristan, has a more luxuriant plant life; we collected as many specimens as we could. I did a sketch as the afternoon sunlight made the pink rocks glow; this I have redrawn in black and white above. The fauna is not rich. We saw, but were unable to catch, a mouse running through the grass[1]. Our collection of animals consisted almost entirely of snails, wood-lice, beetles, millipedes and free-living nematode worms; most of these came from under the bark of rotten stumps of *Phylica*. We could find no earthworms at all.

Birds there are in plenty. Petrels of many kinds are seen round the island whilst the steep slopes above the cliffs are in places, from 500 feet upwards, riddled with the burrows of the diving petrel (*Pelecanoides georgicus*). It was at first somewhat startling to hear the birds calling and answering one another under the very ground upon which we were standing. Skua gulls flew backwards and forwards over our heads as we climbed. There were many of the little yellowy-green buntings

[1]The *Scotia* expedition found a dead mouse, *Mus musculus*, which must, of course, have been introduced by some former expedition. A party of sealers had lived there in huts from January, 1891 to February, 1892.

we had seen on the shore and also of another kind, greenish but with a speckled breast, flitting about the *Phylica* trees. [These were thought originally to be two distinct species *Neospiza goughensis* and *N. jessive*, as reported by the *Scotia* expedition; they are now, however, regarded as age-plumage differences of the same bird *goughensis* which has been given the special generic name of Rowettia.]

We had hoped to reach the summit of Mount Rowett, but with short daylight and wasting so much time on the early part of the climb, it was impossible. We had, after getting to the top of the cliff, taken the precaution of finding an easier way down so that we were able to stay till it was nearly dark; then sliding down steep banks and jumping from tussock to tussock clump, we reached the shore with just enough light to find our way.

Saturday, 11th June. In the big gale of last week salt water had in some way contaminated our fresh water supply, getting in, it is thought, through turned over ventilation pipes generally considered to be well out of danger from waves. It was thought at first to be only slight, but luckily, before leaving Gough, it was realised that it was actually more serious. On the morning following our landing we loaded the lifeboat with every vessel we could lay our hands on, including all the empty specimen bottles we had in the hold, and with a large funnel, and lengths of screw-connected hose pipes, set off for one of the waterfalls. A slight swell which had arisen made it difficult to get the boat close into the shore so that the long hosepipe had to be supported upon old tree branches which we found along the beach. The funnel fixed at the landward end of the hose was similarly supported by being lashed to a tripod of branches below the fall and, in a very short time, a good supply of excellent drinking water was pouring into the boat. The operation gave an opportunity for some shore collecting but it was disappointing except for some beautiful plum-coloured chitons (primitive molluscs), the largest I have yet seen.

Leaving the anchorage in the late afternoon we dropped a dredge for ten minutes and it brought up among other invertebrates a large number of big crawfish which appeared to be the same species[1] as that taken round the Cape Province. We now took our first station on the eastern side, at 5 miles from the coast, and then proceeded to the west to complete our line on that side. As we had not reached the bottom at a depth of 3,000 metres at this eastern station so near the coast, I decided to make the innermost western one at only 2½ miles from the shore; and even here the depth was 940 metres. This indeed gives

[1]A fishery for these crawfish with a canning factory on Tristan, where they are also caught, was started in 1949; the factory, however, was destroyed by the recent eruption.

Watering ship from a waterfall—falling in a jet like water from a tap—at Gough Island, redrawn from a rough pencil sketch made at the time.

some indication of how very steeply the sea bed falls away from this remarkable island. [How well Martin Holdgate chose the title *Mountains in the Sea* for his book describing his expedition to both Gough Island and Tristan.] It was a source of great regret that, with our Lucas sounding machine out of action, we were unable to make a good series of deep soundings round the island. We completed the eastern line of stations this evening and are now on passage again for the Cape. We did not find the rich euphausiid plankton which, as mentioned on p. 439, we thought might have occurred along this South Atlantic ridge and so provide a path of food for whales migrating to and fro between the south and the warmer breeding grounds.

Saturday, 18th June. Each night since leaving Gough we have continued our series of tow-nets, collecting now many quite warm-water plankton animals. At two points the surface temperature exceeded 17° c. and here we took small specimens of *Physalia* (the Portuguese man-o'-war) and the beautiful blue *Velella*; there was also

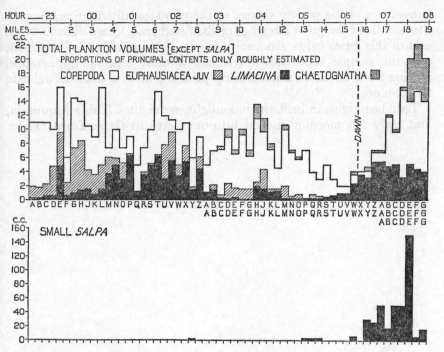

A chart reproduced from the *Discovery Reports*, vol. xi, showing the variations of plankton, expressed in volumes, obtained by the R.S.S. *William Scoresby* in a series of consecutive nets taken in mid-ocean between Gough Island and Cape Town. The relative proportions of the principal constituents of the plankton are shown according to the scale: copepods, young euphausians (krill-like crustacea), pteropods (*Limacina*), arrow-worms (Chaetognatha) and small salps.

a curious little globular floating sea-anemone[1] and an exquisite semi-transparent blue mysid (opossum shrimp) with lavender antennal scales.

Half-way to the Cape, on the night of the 14th, we took another series of consecutive hauls with 70 cm. tow-nets at the surface, each of 10 minutes' duration. Starting at 10.30 p.m. we kept up the series until 8 o'clock next morning, making 57 samples in all. Much variation in the abundance of the plankton was found as will be seen in the diagrammatic representation shown above. Once again it

[1]Some zoological reader might perhaps imagine by this description I was referring to the fabulous pelagic hydroid *Pelagohydra* of which only two specimens have ever been taken, both in New Zealand waters; no, this was a true pelagic anemone; throughout the voyage I had looked in vain for *Pelagohydra*.

is evidence of the patchy nature of the plankton distribution, even in the middle of the great stretches of the Southern Ocean. Towards the end of this series came a dense patch of a remarkable blue copepod, and the sample tubes now presented a most unusual appearance, passing from the more usual shrimp-pink colour to a shade of delicate violet-blue.

Late last night, in brilliant moonlight, we sighted Table Mountain, and early this morning moved into our berth in Cape Town Docks.

CHAPTER 20

MORE ABOUT WHALES

This will be a good place, before leaving the southern waters, to break my narrative to give a brief résumé of the later *Discovery* results concerning the whales, their migrations, their food (the krill) and the plankton in general. It will bring our knowledge up to date and show what has come from the continuation of the work we began. I shall deal largely with the whales in the present chapter and with the krill and plankton in the next.

I have told in the preface how our *Discovery* was replaced at the end of her commission by the new R.R.S. *Discovery II*. It was realised very early that the investigations must extend far beyond the waters of the Dependencies of the Falkland Islands and that the old ship was quite inadequate for such wide-spread surveys. The new vessel, a full-powered oil-burning steamship of 1,036 tons (gross) with a cruising range of 10,000 miles, was specially planned for ocean research by Dr. Kemp with all the experience gained from working in the old ship in these stormy southern seas. It is generally acknowledged that she has been one of the finest research ships ever built.

Not only was an expansion of our work essential for a full understanding of the conditions affecting the whales fished in the Falkland Islands sector; the whole character of whaling was changing and the fishery itself was extending round the Southern Ocean. When we started out on our first expedition, whaling, as we have seen, had to be carried out either from shore stations or from factory ships which flensed their whales alongside and so had to have the shelter of harbours; the fisheries were thus confined to territorial waters and so could be under government control. I have related (p. 197) how, when we were already south, the first of the new pelagic whaling factories began to operate; these great ships are specially built to allow the whales to be drawn up ramps to be cut up on the deck and so they no longer need seek the shelter of the land. Not only did this allow them to fish anywhere in the open ocean but it at once released them from laws limiting their catching power and from the obligation to pay taxes

441

as the price for shelter. No wonder the fishing changed and more and more of these huge ships were built to have rapacious mouths—great steel gates—that opened at the bows or more usually the stern to allow the whales, killed by the serving catchers, to be swallowed whole and drawn up their gullets by grappling irons and cables. 'Surely,' as a journalist remarked, 'this is Jonah avenged.' Whaling spread round the pole and in the 1930-1 season it was estimated that over 40,000 whales were killed in the Antarctic of which only 2,736 came from the traditional grounds of South Georgia.

Just when our work was beginning to provide the data on which to base a scientific regulation of the fisheries it seemed that it might have

The R.R.S. *Discovery II* which replaced the old *Discovery* in 1929 and made five major voyages to the south polar seas before the war and one after it.

been all in vain; the colonial government had lost control. Were we going to see the same destruction of the stock in the south as had been perpetrated in the north? For a time prospects were certainly gloomy. There were two opposing parties in the industry which was now making tremendous profits; one, reckless of the future, favoured making all the money possible while the going was good, the other was conservative and saw the folly of sacrificing what could be a permanent source of wealth for a short period of dazzling prizes. One of the few real benefits to the credit of the old League of Nations was the setting up of a Whaling Committee which agreed to the establishment of international regulations in principle. Luckily the conservative element prevailed and rules governing the shfi'ng were made which were largely based upon our findings in the south; this system of regulation was still further improved by the setting up of the International Whaling

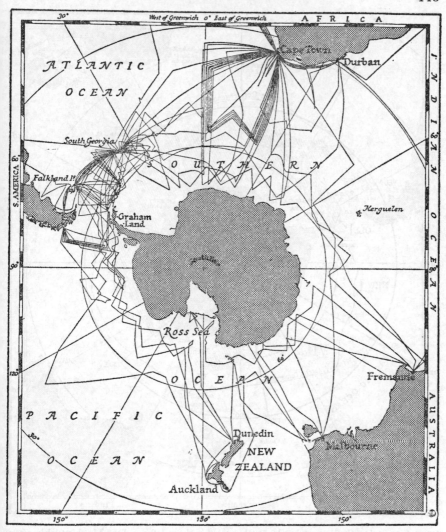

The principal voyages of the *Discovery II*, 1930-9. The tracks are only approximately correct, where they are crowded together they are straightened and separated.

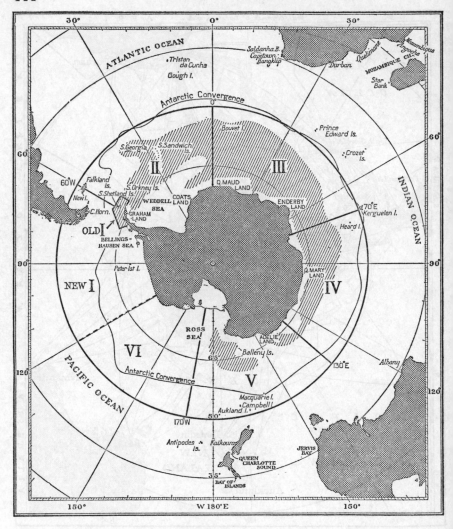

The Antarctic whaling grounds, a chart reproduced from Dr. Mackintosh's 1942 *Discovery Report* with his new Areas I and VI added. The hatched areas show the actual whaling grounds and represent the approximate limits of the regions covered by the whaling ships in the charts available. From *D.R.*, vol. XXII.

Commission in 1946. But could such an international body succeed? There were now more countries involved; would they be able to agree about reasonable restrictions? Alas, there were grave doubts, but to this I shall return at the end of the chapter.

It was fortunate that sufficient money had been accumulated by the far-sighted policy of our Colonial Office which levied the tax on the whalers in the Falkland Island Dependencies to provide the funds for our continued research. In collecting it, as we have seen (p. 36), the Government promised that it should be spent on investigations for the good of the industry; as the hunting had spread round the Antarctic so did the *Discovery* Investigations extend to cover the Southern Ocean as a whole. Here, in a book dealing mainly with the pioneer venture, I can only give the slightest sketch of the great enterprise which followed. The map on p. 443 shows the principal voyages of the *Discovery II* up to the war, i.e., in the period 1930-9, but omits some jo the more intensive work in the Falkland Islands sector; also it does not include the tracks of the *William Scoresby*. I shall say more about the results of these voyages in the next chapter when I am dealing with the environment of the whales and the charting of their food supply; let us first look at the recent work on the whales themselves and what it tells us about their distribution.

As the whaling extended, the blue and fin whales were found in the summer feeding season to be spread in a band around the Southern Ocean as shown by the shaded areas in the chart opposite; the exact location of the zone in terms of latitude would differ from month to month and in different areas and years according to the position of the edge of the pack ice. The chart is divided into areas I to VI; four of these, i.e., II to V are areas which were defined by the Norwegian workers Hjort, Lie and Ruud from an examination of the concentrations of the factory ships in the different years during the '30s. It appeared that the whaling fleets tended to congregate about certain points in the areas II-V. What *they* called area I (shown as OLD I on our chart) was a small region round the South Shetlands to cover the activities of ships working from Ascension and neighbouring islands of the South Shetland group. Dr. Mackintosh in his important study of 'The Southern Stocks of Whalebone Whales'[1] has confirmed the reality of their areas II-V and added a *new* area I between 60° and 120° W. in place of the old one and another new area, VI, to fill the remaining gap between V and the new I; these are shown in our chart. There can be no doubt, as Mackintosh shows, that areas I to V mark definite and separate groupings of humpback whales lying respectively

[1]*Discovery Reports*, vol. XXII, pp. 197-300, 1942.

to the south of the west and east coasts of South America (i.e., I and II), of South Africa (III), of the west coast of Australia (IV) and of New Zealand and the east coast of Australia (v). We shall see in a moment when we come to consider whale movements that these summer humpback concentrations are certainly produced by stocks migrating from the continental coasts lying to the north of each area. The blue and fin whales are clearly more evenly spread than the humpbacks but nevertheless tend to show peaks of abundance in the different areas; it is in relation to these species, particularly the blue whales, that the factory ships make their locations. Let us now turn to the movements of whales.

In my account of our preparations in chapter 2 (p. 52) I briefly described our preliminary trials with the mark we had devised for the study of whale migrations and gave a sketch of it; I have also referred to the whale-marking cruises of the *William Scoresby* but have left any discussion of the results until now. A great many of these marks were fired into whales in the late twenties and all the whaling stations and factory ships of the world were notified to be on the lookout for them and offered £1 for each mark returned with a note of time and place of capture. The tests we had made showed that the barbs on the marks held them firmly in the blubber of a dead whale and also that they should readily be detected by workers on the stations. Yet the years went by and none were returned; clearly some factor had been overlooked. Now Mackintosh and Wheeler, working at the Shore Station at South Georgia, showed how quickly a healthy whale on returning to the Antarctic is able to get rid of certain external parasites (e.g., *Pennella*) which had infected it in warmer latitudes, sending deep roots into the blubber[1]; such parasites, perhaps killed by the colder water, are soon thrown out by suppuration. There could be little doubt that these early marks, penetrating the blubber for only $2\frac{1}{2}$ inches, were being rejected by the whales; it became apparent that any mark which remained in part exposed on the outside would soon be lost.

After several suggested types had proved too costly to produce, a simple 10 inch bullet of stainless steel tube with a weighted head met with success. It buries itself completely in the blubber or flesh and so has to be large enough to be easily found at the factory, yet not so big as to be harmful; it is actually very small compared to the bulk of the whale. It is engraved as shown in the accompanying sketch, with a number and the words 'Reward for return to the Colonial Office, London.'

This mark was first tried in the 1932-3 season from a hired com-

[1] *Discovery Reports*, vol. I, p. 373, 1929 (see also the drawing on p. 204).

mercial catcher working round South Georgia when 207 whales were
marked in three weeks; and some of the marks were returned the same
season. Between then and the outbreak of war seven special whale-
marking expeditions were made, three in commercial catchers and
four in the *William Scoresby*. The results are described in *Discovery
Reports*, vol. XIX, pp. 245-84 (1940) by Mr. George Rayner who led
some of the expeditions; others were led by his colleagues, the late
Mr. Rolfe Gunther, Dr. T. J. Hart, Dr. H. P. F. Herdman and Mr.
A. H. Laurie. It was estimated, on a most conservative basis, that no
fewer than 5,219 whales were marked in this period, a total made
up of 668 blue, 3,915 fin, 28 sei, 548 humpback, 8 right and 52 sperm
whales; perhaps only those who have worked in a small ship in
Antarctic seas will realise what a splendid achievement this was. Up
to the time of Rayner's *Report* 33 blue whale marks had been returned
(4·9 per cent), 118 fin whale marks (3 per cent) and 36 humpback
(6·5 per cent).

The whale mark introduced in 1932.

The results from the marking of the humpbacks are particularly
interesting. It had long been conjectured that this species made
extensive north and south migrations, particularly along the coasts of
Australia and New Zealand: northward in the southern autumn for
breeding and southward to feed in the spring. Striking proof of this is
supplied by these experiments. All the whales were marked in the
Antarctic, yet, out of the 36 of those captured, 22 were taken off the
western coast of Australia, after periods of a half, one and a half, and
two and a half years, and two (marked farther to the west) were caught
off the coast of Madagascar after one and a half and three and a half
years. The remaining twelve were taken in the south: five in the
season in which they were marked, six in the season following marking,
and one in the third year. There is no indication of an east and west
dispersal as was found for the blue and fin whales. These results have
been fully confirmed by marking since the war; a chart of southern
humpback migration paths demonstrated by marking is shown overleaf where ten examples are illustrated. There are many more such
records, but they are similar to those shown.

All the 668 marks shot into blue whales were fired in the Southern
Ocean and all the 33 recovered were taken in the south: 18 in the same

season in which they were marked, 8 in the second season, and 4, 1, and 2 respectively after periods of two, three, and four years. Some had been captured a few days or even hours after marking, but round South Georgia they have never been taken in the same season later than six days after marking, whereas others marked there have been taken much later far to the south. This indicates that the blue whales visiting the South Georgia grounds are on migration; one was taken 500 miles to the south-west of the island, another 300 miles to the

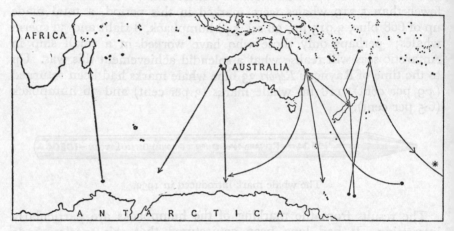

A chart showing the main migration routes of the humpback whale as demonstrated by 'marking'. Each arrow leads from the point where a particular whale was marked to where it was killed and the mark recovered. Many more marks from humpbacks have been recovered, but the lines connecting the points of marking and recovery are all similar to those shown in the chart. The path with an asterisk (*) against it ends at a point on the 95° W. meridian, i.e. some 2,500 miles to the east in the Bellingshausen Sea. Redrawn from S. G. Brown (Discovery Investigations).

south-east. In the wider regions of the Southern Ocean extensive migration is shown in both easterly and westerly directions. One marked near Bouvet Island was captured in the next season at South Georgia, which is 1,180 miles to the westward. Off Enderby Land there appears to be a marked westerly movement in the latter part of the season. The fact that the range of movement recorded after several years is no greater than that found after one year suggests that the dispersal is somewhat limited, and some whales have been shown to return in subsequent seasons to the same region in which they were marked.

I have said 'returned to the same region' because as we have seen

37. *Above*, the *Discovery* icing ship, i.e., getting fresh-water ice to replenish her water supply near Port Lockroy. *Below*, taking the ice on board to be melted in the special tanks (seen in background, right), through which steam pipes pass

38. The continuous plankton recorder in its original form as first used on the expedition. *Above left,* breaking surface on being hauled up at the end of a run. *Right,* opened for loading with its roll of plankton-catching gauze, here shown in position; note the roller-grid which supports the gauze from behind when the breach is closed. *Below,* proud father and child: the author with his invention. The small propeller at the back (below the buoyancy chamber) drives the internal winding rollers as it rotates on being towed through the water

from the circumstantial evidence provided by the work of Mackintosh and Wheeler (p. 201) it is as good as certain that the majority of blue and fin whales migrate in winter to the warmer latitudes for breeding. No marks have yet been recovered from blue whales in these warmer waters but this is not really surprising since they are clearly more dispersed, when they go north, than the humpbacks which tend to hug the coasts and so come to be taken more frequently by the fisheries in these waters. There is also not so much hunting of blue and fin whales in temperate waters as there used to be. From the fin whale marking results up to the war we had only one return showing such a migration; now we have thirteen. No doubt in time there will come direct evidence for such migrations for the blue whale too. At present five times as many fin whales have been marked as blue. The blue whales marked since the war show the same general tendency to return to the area of marking although there have also been some very striking longitudinal migrations recorded, including one from 60° E. to 125° W., almost exactly half-way round the world. Which way round did it go? S. G. Brown who has recently brought up to date the information on 'The Movements of Blue and Fin Whales within the Antarctic Zone'[1] assumes it went westwards through the Drake Straits, although that was actually slightly the longer route between the point of marking and recovery. The total blue whales marked now comes to 889.

Turning now to the fin whales, and again dealing first with the pre-war results reported on by Rayner: of the 118 marks returned, from the 3,915 whales marked, 44 came back in the same season and 34, 21, 13 and 5 respectively in the first, second, third and fourth years after marking. Like the blue whales, the fin whales of the South Georgia region are shown not to be a stationary population but to be moving southward although they appear to 'loiter in the neighbourhood of the island longer than the blue whales.' Also, as with blue whales, in the wider regions of the Southern Ocean there is evidence of a return in following seasons to the locality where they were marked, as well as of a considerable dispersal. Whales have come into the Scotia Sea from regions as far apart as the Bellingshausen Sea and the neighbourhood of Bouvet Island. Striking as the east and west movements are, the experiments actually show that the majority of whales have been found in the *same* region of the Antarctic in which they were marked. While there are connecting links between the fin whales of the Bellingshausen Sea and those off Queen Mary Land at the opposite side of the pole, 'this movement around the Antarctic,' as Mr. Rayner

---

[1]*Discovery Reports*, vol. xxxiii, pp. 1-54, 1962.

writes elsewhere[1], 'may be likened to a relay race in which no individual competitor completes the whole course.' It is suggested that there are large provinces within which considerable movement takes place but between which there is little interchange.

The most striking result of the pre-war fin whale marking was the recovery off Saldanha Bay, South Africa, from a 69 foot female of a mark which had been fired into it $2\frac{1}{2}$ years earlier in nearly 65° S. when it was recorded as a calf accompanying its mother. Brown

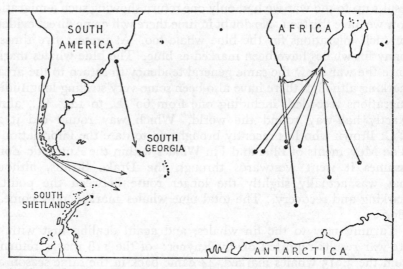

A chart showing the north-south migration routes of fin whales as demonstrated by 'marking'. As in the humpback chart the arrows connect the points where the whales were marked and where they were killed. Redrawn from S. G. Brown (Discovery Investigations).

has recorded[2] eight other recoveries showing such a migration and still more recently reported another five in a personal communication making thirteen: eight from south to north in the South African sector and five in the opposite direction in the South American sector. Of the latter, one was from the east coast and four from the west of the continent, but all were recovered in area II showing that those from the west coast had passed through the Drake Strait; and three of these coming from the west were marked on the same day at points very close together so most likely were members of the same school. The fact

[1] *Nature*, 144 (1939) 999.
[2] *Norsk Hvalfangst-Tidende* 1962, no. 1, pp. 1316 (in English and Norwegian).

that so far all the fin whales proved to be going north are in the South African sector, and those going south are in the South American sector, cannot, of course be regarded as indicating a circular movement because four out of five of those in the latter sector are coming south from the Pacific Ocean and not the Atlantic. It just happens that so far we have not had the opportunity of marking sufficient whales in South African waters to have much chance of getting any returned from the south. The total number of fin whales marked up to 1958 was estimated at 4,566. A chart of all the north-south fin whale migration records to date is shown opposite.

Here I should refer to the valuable evidence of movement obtained from the records of whales observed from the *Discovery II* during a continuous look-out system which was organised by Dr. Mackintosh and reported on by him and Mr. S. G. Brown[1]. The observations were collected at various seasons as the ship steamed on her voyages covering close on 47,000 miles of sea within the Antarctic Zone. They draw a curve of the varying numbers of the larger baleen whales (blue, fin and humpback taken together) sighted in the Antarctic in each month of the year; this clearly shows that most of the population leaves the south in winter. From these figures and an examination of the commercial catches it appears that fin whales spend an average of about four months in the Antarctic zone with the greater part of the population being there from mid-December to mid-April. Elsewhere Mackintosh[2] gives evidence to suggest that the fin whales arriving in the Antarctic grounds in December and early January are mainly males whereas towards the end of the season the females make up the larger proportion. From the series of observations from the *Discovery II* and other ships Mackintosh and Brown make a provisional estimate of the southern populations of whales from which it appears there were then, in 1942, about five fin whales for every blue whale with a total population of fins of about 250,000; and as we shall see, the more valuable blue whales are being killed off at a faster rate than the fin whales. These figures of the extent of the stock of these two species some twenty years ago are of great value in providing evidence as to the extent to which the appalling overfishing has reduced their numbers in spite of the existence of the International Whaling Commission. It has now been calculated on other grounds that by 1964 there 'were

[1] 'Preliminary estimates of the southern populations of the larger baleen whales.' *Norsk Hvalfangsttid.* 45 Årg (9) pp. 469-80 (also included in *Collected Reprints of the National Institute of Oceanography*, vol. 4, No. 161, 1956.

[2] 'The southern stocks of whalebone whales.' *Discovery Reports*, vol. xxii, pp. 197-3000, 1942.

probably no more than 2,000 blue whales and 40,000 fin whales still surviving.'[1]. But we shall return at the end of the chapter to the estimates of stocks and the crisis that now faces the industry.

After discussing marking and migrations, I will now mention some of the very interesting observations made by the late Mr. Rolfe Gunther while engaged in a two months' whale-marking expedition in a catcher in the neighbourhood of South Georgia in the 1936-7 season. The paper under the title 'The Habits of Fin Whales' was published in the *Discovery Reports* (vol. xxv, pp. 113-42, 1949) after his death. So fresh and graphic are his descriptions that it will be better for me to select a few direct quotations from his text rather than give in my own words more of his findings; I hope I shall persuade naturalists and students, who do not already know his *Report*, to go and read it in full. I will begin with his account of whales feeding:

On 11 January, whales in the act of feeding came under direct observation. A heavy concentration estimated to number 100-200 whales was centred over a patch of whale food in an area of about 4-5 square miles.

The krill (*Euphausia superba*) could be seen in a layer no more than 3 m. below the surface, and in places it affected the colour of the sea. An easterly gale the previous day had left a very heavy swell, but the wind had since moderated and waves were no longer breaking. The sky was grey and the bad visibility was reduced from time to time by patches of mist. The sea was grey too, but in places the krill imparted to it a barely noticeable tinge of ochre. In one place where the krill was unusually thick and might have been closer to the surface, a patch of half an acre or so had a brick-tinge. The krill was irregularly spread over the whole region with large gaps between the swarms; some measured a few feet across and had an indefinite contour like that of a gorse bush, and others extended in long wavy bands from one to several feet or even metres in width. The krill did not seem as dense as patches of it often are, and it looked as though it had been broken up by the recent gale and had been depleted by the depredations of the whales.

The whales were banded together in small schools of from two to five or six or more; but the schools were probably mixing. The animals were blowing leisurely, and sounding for short periods. In the early part of the day and late in the afternoon they showed a disposition to run away from the ship; but in the middle of the morning, when they seemed to be feeding most actively,

[1]From the foreword by Dr. Lucas and Dr. Cole to Mackintosh's recent book *The Stocks of Whales* (1965).

they took little heed of us and marking was comparatively easy.

The most conspicuous feature of their feeding was the tendency to swim on one side[1]. From afar, the white ventral surface shone beneath the water so that its blueness was momentarily thrown up. There would appear to be no need to look for any other explanation of this than that it is a method of turning sharply to one side. Whales sometimes turned out of a normal act of blowing on to their side before submerging and sometimes turned while under water; if close to the surface, flipper or fluke broke surface and waved in the air.

A point to be emphasised was the supreme indifference with which the whales accepted the marking and the presence of the marking vessel when actively feeding. They blew leisurely, sometimes swimming towards us, beneath us and by our side, and they seemed to be preoccupied with the question of their meal. . . .

A rather similar state of things was observed north-west of the South Sandwich Islands on 22 January. During the morning the ship had been pursuing whales, but marking with only partial success, for the schools were unapproachable and one after another had led the ship a run of 30-40 miles. In one of these chases at 11.30 hr. the ship came upon an area of about a square mile where ten to thirty whales were blowing leisurely. No krill was to be seen but a concourse of blackfish and dolphins crossed the area during our work. The whales were swimming close under the surface, came within a stone's throw of the ship and allowed themselves to be marked; they seemed to be crossing and recrossing the area. When the ship passed on to another region, the whales there showed the timidity of those we had seen earlier in the day.

Although no krill was visible, the presence of dolphins and blackfish presumes an abundant food supply: and though there is no direct evidence that the whales were feeding, their behaviour bore a resemblance to that of the whales met with on 11 January and contrasts with that of others in the immediate neighbourhood but outside this concentration, which were seen at almost the same time and under the same weather conditions. . . .

Again another example:

On 8 January around the Shag Rocks, in the middle of the day from 10.00 to 16.00 hr., the whales showed an unconcern for the ship which was in marked contrast with their usual behaviour.

[1] I am informed by Mr. G. W. Rayner that Norwegian whalers have the word 'boltering' to describe this habit.

Chasing was begun at dawn in fine calm weather. Whales were plentiful and schools, varying in size from three or four to ten or twenty individuals, were discerned on various quarters of the horizon. Marking efforts were not unsuccessful, for as many as three or four hits in a school of six or seven were sometimes recorded before the school in question split and those whales took to prolonged flight. The whales were not sounding for more than 2-3 min. and, until disturbed, they were blowing leisurely.

Between eight and ten o'clock the attitude of the whales changed: they became scarcer and were more difficult of approach. Marking all but came to an end. The schools seemed to have scattered and apparently regardless of the operations of the ship, the whales seemed to have split up into twos and threes. They were remaining down for long periods (5-7 mins.), and when they came up they were usually up to half a mile from the ship and blowing, if unhurriedly, also a trifle stertorously. . . .

In the evening, between 16.00 and 18.00 hr., whales again tended to coalesce and again allowed themselves to be pursued, and an average of one to two hits in a school of three to five whales was scored. The whales remained below for shorter periods (2-4 min.), and when on the run sounding lasted for still shorter periods (1-2 min.).

Later still, the whales had gathered into even larger schools. At 20.00 hr., a school of some twenty had been formed. They were continually breaking surface and blowing, and appeared to be disporting themselves. At first marking was easy, the whales swimming round without heed. At the sound of the guns they began to make off, but those we chased played around the ship as do dolphins; they leapt high though not completely out of the water, appeared now on the starboard bow, now on the port; then they would streak ahead jumping high, sometimes in pairs, sometimes in threes and sometimes in unison, and then came closer to the ship again. Soon they split again, and the fewer they were the more wary they became and the harder to mark.

This one day was particularly memorable as giving us whales in three distinct moods: in early morning and late afternoon the schools of medium size which allowed pursuit and approach; before and after noon, the very small schools that were indifferent; in the late evening, the sportive whales in a large gathering. . . . The gathering into larger schools towards evening, the high spirits and the attention to the ship, go to indicate that the work of the day was over. We came to regard the evening as a time when

Drawings by the late E. R. Gunther illustrating the posture of fin whales engaged in breaking surface and submerging leisurely. From *D.R.*, vol. xxv.

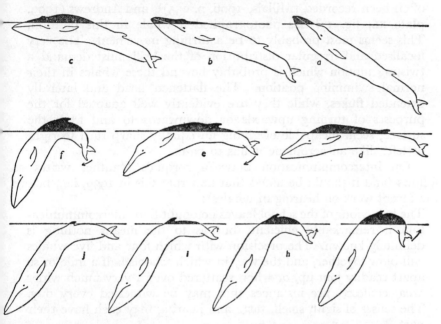

More drawings from Gunther's *Discovery Report* illustrating the posture of fin whales in ten stages while breaking surface and submerging at medium speed. The arrows in e-i indicate the supposed direction of the beat of the tail flukes. From *D.R.* vol. xxv.

whales were likely to be more markable; and in the opinion of the writer the change of attitude affords circumstantial evidence that earlier in the day, good feeding had been found at considerable depths.

From the consideration of a number of sketches and photographs of fin whales breaking surface, when travelling slowly, at medium speed and fast, he infers the posture of the rest of the body below the surface and reconstructs their movements in three series of sketches, two of which I reproduce above. He then has interesting remarks upon the side turning of whales:

As compared to the ease with which rorquals are able to turn sharply upwards or downwards, their movement from side to side appears to be restricted. This is suggested both by the structural arrangement of the fins, flukes and flippers, and also by the behaviour of fin whales when feeding. Their habit of turning on to their sides when moving about among small patches of food has often been recorded (Millais, 1906, p. 255)[1], and Andrews (1909, plate XL, fig. 1)[2] has photographed a whale in this position. This seems most probably to be a turning movement. The very localised and irregular distribution of the krill must demand a twisting motion which is probably beyond these whales in their normal swimming position. The flattened head and laterally extended flukes, while they are evidently well adapted for the purposes of turning upwards or downwards to and from the surface, seem incapable of giving an equally sharp turn to right or left: like an aeroplane it has to bank.

On intercommunication between rorquals Gunther writes as follows (and it should be noted that he wrote this in 1939, i.e., before the recent work on hearing in whales):

The behaviour of the school leaves no doubt that intercommunication is remarkably efficient, but as to the means nothing is definitely known. The precision with which four and five whales will blow together, and the way in which schools half a mile or so apart readily join up, or when scattered over a very much wider area, coalesce, are instances that may be witnessed every day. The senses of sight, smell, taste and hearing may each have their part.

Whales in close formation are doubtless able to see each other, for in deep water and at night they probably leave a trail of luminescence behind them, induced in the planktonic organisms. Such luminescence is known to be produced by dolphins but as an effective recognition signal it can hold for only short distances.

Little is known about the whale's olfactory sense. As regards airborne smell, it is of interest that a whale's breath may be detected at a distance of at least 200 yards to windward, but this may be excluded for purposes of communication because scent is not usually detected on the surface of water. Waterborne smell is a possibility that might affect the whale through some such organ as Jacobsen's organ, or through taste.

The problem of locating food has application here, for if a

[1] *The Mammals of Great Britain and Ireland*, vol. III, London, 1906.
[2] *Bulletin of the American Museum of Natural History*, vol. XXXVI.

sense of smell or the taste buds of the tongue subserve this purpose, they may also enable the whales to trace one another. On the other hand, the presence of food may be detected physically by means of the bristles of the head which have been shown to be highly innervated.

The hearing of whales is remarkably sensitive. The report of a small charge of gunpowder in open ocean against wind and at a distance of several yards, has put whales beneath water to flight. Norwegian whalers believe that whales hear the shout of a man in the crow's nest. A sensitive ear or equivalent sense in the bones of the head, implies use and raises the question of what sounds may be produced by whales.

This naturally brings us to a consideration of the sounds that may be produced by whales and of their sense of hearing. Until Gunther's observations it had often been supposed that whales must have very poor hearing because they have no external ears (pinnae) to collect the sound waves and exceedingly small earholes which seemed likely to be closed under any great pressure of water; we now have both anatomical and physiological evidence that they have excellent auditory organs which are sensitive to a wide range of sound-wave frequencies. Little was known too of the sounds which whales them-selves can make under water until hydrophones began to be used to detect the approach of enemy submarines; these soon showed that the smaller toothed ones, the dolphins and porpoises, could emit a great variety of sounds 'from a low rattling to high pitched whistles'. Indeed experiments carried out with dolphins in the American ocean-aria, by blindfolding them with rubber cups which could be fitted over their eyes, have conclusively shown that they can navigate between all sorts of obstacles by using a method of echo-location not unlike that employed by bats; they are constantly emitting ultra-sonic waves which are reflected back to them from any objects they approach. This use of echoes means the presence of an ear with an extraordinary perception of sound direction. Much less is known about noises produced by the large rorquals; several attempts which have been deliberately made to pick them up on hydrophones have failed, although American patrol boats have reported sounds which they claim were emitted by humpback and other big whales[1]. Nevertheless from what we now know of their ear mechanisms it would seem most unlikely that the rorquals are not communicating by sound.[2] It has been found that they are very sensitive to the waves of Asdic (used for

[1] E. J. Slijper (1962) in his book *Whales*.
[2] Dr. Mackintosh tells me that noises made by baleen whales have recently been recorded.

submarine detection) and can be turned this way and that by their use; in fact Asdic is now being used to control the whale in the chase!

The great advance which has recently been made in our knowledge of the sense of hearing of whales has been given us by the splendid discoveries of Dr. F. C. Fraser, F.R.S., Keeper of Zoology at the British Museum of Natural History, and his colleague Dr. P. E. Purves. This is the same Fraser of our expedition. They began their investigation in 1948 and it culminated, after a number of other publications, in their fine monograph of 1960[1]. I can only briefly summarise their main findings and it will be simplest if I do so by taking in turn the three major problems that the whale has to contend with in its hearing.

The whale, of course, is a mammal derived from a one-time terrestrial stock and so has essentially the same inner mechanism in its auditory equipment as all other mammals: an apparatus evolved for receiving *air-borne* sound waves. For such a mechanism to work satisfactorily in an aquatic animal there must be some means of converting the water-borne vibrations into ones similar to those for which it was fitted when on land. Pressure must be reduced and the amplitude of the vibrations increased. The former is accomplished by a great reduction in the area of the tympanic membrane which is drawn out into a thin ligament instead of being an 'eardrum'; the amplitude of the vibrations is increased by this ligament acting like a piston rod on the cam-like hammer of the middle ear.[2]

The second problem concerns determining the directions from which the sound is coming. The earholes are on each side of the head as in other mammals and being placed so widely apart should, if really efficient, enable the whale to discriminate between differences in the phase or intensity of the sounds received on the two sides and so to judge their direction. It had generally been thought, however, for the reasons I have already given, that the whale's ear-holes must be extremely inefficient, and if this were so, it seemed likely that the sounds from outside would reach the inner ear by vibrations transmitted widely through the surrounding bones of the skull and so make it impossible to distinguish whence they came. This view had been

[1]Fraser and Purves, 'Hearing in Cetaceans.' *Bulletin of the British Museum (Natural History)* vol. 7, no. 1, 1960.

[2]My statement is an over-simplification. In reality it is both more complex and subtle, but to present it adequately would require too long an explanation of the anatomical details for such a general account; the student should refer especially to the paper by Fraser and Purves in the *Proceedings of the Royal Society*, series B, vol. 152, pp. 62-77, 1960.

strengthened by the knowledge that the large rorquals had, in their ear tubes, long plugs which were thought to be of wax and to be serving as stoppers to resist the high water pressure from outside; wax indeed is known to be a very poor sound conductor. The discoveries by Fraser and Purves have completely reversed these views. By many beautiful dissections and reconstructions they have shown that the inner ear is separated from the rest of the skull by a series of spaces filled with an oily foam which forms a most excellent sound-insulating layer preventing all external noises from reaching it except those coming via the outer ear-hole. What then of the plug which was thought so effectively to stop the sounds coming by this channel? They found it not to be of wax at all, except for a thin deceptive covering, but to be of a horny substance; and this they showed, by experiments with fresh material, to be an exceptionally good sound conductor. Whales do, in fact, hear, as other mammals do. As so often in scientific research one thing leads to another quite unexpected result. These so-called wax plugs have turned out to be of even greater interest to us for an entirely different reason, one which is of no *natural* value to the whale yet one that *might* prove to be the salvation of its race; this, however, I shall come to in a moment when I have finished with hearing.

There remains one other difficulty with which the whale's terrestrial type of auditory organs has to contend in going down into the ocean depths: the regulation of pressure in the middle ear. Fraser and Purves have now shown this space to be connected with the foam filled cavities I have just referred to; they have further shown that these form reservoirs of gas for balancing the pressure on the inner side of the ear drum with that outside in the surrounding water. For every five fathoms the whale goes down there is a change of pressure of about 15 lb. per square inch. As the pressure increases the gas in the reservoir becomes compressed into the bony part of the middle ear while its place is taken by the great expansion of blood vessels on the walls of the sacs.

Again Fraser and Purves have shown that the foam also occurs in the bronchi and suggest that, as fat has a nitrogen absorptive capacity six times greater than blood, this fatty foam emulsion is ideal for the absorption of this gas. They think it likely that a fresh fatty emulsion is continually being formed to absorb the nitrogen in the bronchi as the lungs contract and so prevent it going into the blood, thereby saving the whale from caisson sickness (or bends) when the pressure is released. They also believe that some of this emulsion is continually being got rid of by the whale when it blows, and that this in part explains why its breath is visible in the warm air of the tropics (as already mentioned on p. 181, but see also the footnote there).

Now let us return to these remarkable ear plugs. Dr. Purves, who has given us a special *Discovery Report* upon them (vol. XXVII, pp. 293-302, 1955), relates how they were discovered more than fifty years ago by Dr. D. G. Lillie who was chosen in 1909 by the late Sir Sidney Harmer to go and study the whales being brought in to a whaling station set up in 1908 on the island of South Innishkea off the west coast of Ireland. Lillie, who then went south on the *Terra Nova* as a biologist with Scott on his second expedition, wrote in his report in 1910 'In the external auditory meatus [the ear-hole] of all individuals

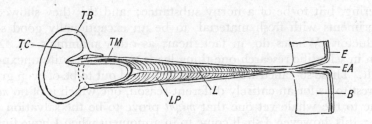

Diagrammatic section through the middle and outer ear of a rorqual to show the relationship of the ear plug to the tympanic cavity. B, blubber; E. epidermis (outer skin); EA, external audiroty meatus (ear hole); L, lumen of auditory meatus; LP, laminal plug; TB, tympanic bulla; TC, tympanic cavity and TM, tympanic membrane. Redrawn in part from Purvis and in part from Lillie.

examined at Innishkea there was a solid plug of wax-like substance of fairly definite size and shape which does not appear to have been hitherto described.' Three of these plugs, two forming a pair and one other, had remained in the British Museum and came to be examined, as we have seen, in the course of this research. Not only were they shown to be horny, rather than waxy and excellent conductors of sound, but to consist of a great many concentric layers. I reproduce here a diagram, taken from Dr. Purves' report, showing the relation of the plug to the tympanic cavity (the middle ear) and the outer ear-hole and now quote from a more general article he wrote in the *New Scientist*:

The origin of this horny substance becomes clear when the structure of the ear is examined in detail. Although the ear passage is completely closed immediately below the blubber layer, it is lined by the same type of epidermis which covers the whole body. Indeed it very frequently contains the black, pigmented layers found on the dorsal surface of most whales. The migratory habit of the larger cetaceans suggests that they may be subject to a bi-annual moult, like that of a great number of terrestrial mammals. In this case, whilst the skin from the body would be shed into the water and lost, that in the inner part of the ear passage would be retained and built up into a series of layers, two of which would represent a period of growth of one year. Over a period of years, the plug would grow in size and the layers would become thinner and more compacted, like those in a tree trunk, but being dead material, could never be resorbed.

I have recorded in chapter 8 (p. 202) how eagerly Dr. Mackintosh and Dr. Wheeler sought for some index of age in the whale such as is found in fish with the annual rings that occur either in their scales or their otoliths (ear stones). No such direct age certificates could then be found but, as we saw, Dr. Wheeler developed a method of estimating age in the female whale from counting the number of *corpora albicantia* in the ovaries. Unfortunately opinion had been divided as to how accurate this index of age really is. Later Professor Ruud in Norway found that a microscopical examination of the surface of the baleen plates (the horny filtering mechanism in the whale's mouth) revealed a number of ridges and that these indicated years of growth; this method, however, which had promised so well, was unfortunately found only to apply to young whales, for in older ones the plates become worn and a number of ridges are lost. The ear-plugs now seemed likely to give the solution. Dr. Purves went to the wnaling station at Stein-shamn in Norway where he was able to examine a number of young whales and so establish that the ear-plug was built up from the moment of birth; and more important, by comparing the ear-plug layers with the ridges on the baleen plates, he confirmed that for young whales at any rate, they were indeed laid down twice in each year. Perhaps at last we now had the key that would tell us what we so urgently want to know: the age composition of the stocks? For a time it certainly looked like it. Now, unfortunately, as I write there has come doubt again. The ear-plugs have just been examined from a whale which also carried a migration mark fired into it some ten years earlier; the laminations in the plug are too few to have been laid down twice a year! In the meantime Dr. Purves had examined some 400 pairs of plugs of fin whales obtained by the *Discovery* Investigations from the south and showed that on a basis of two laminations per year there were a few which were just over 40 years old; or, as he says, if only one layer is laid down each year, then a few were octogenarians! Indeed this latter view now appears to be correct.

It is through a study of the age composition of the population from year to year, telling us of the changes going on in the relative proportion of younger to older members, that we can most certainly judge whether the stock is being too heavily fished or not. But there are other methods. We have already seen that it has been possible to estimate the stock of whales by the observational method of recording whales from ships (p. 451); we can now get an idea of how fast that stock is being reduced by knowing the average number of whales caught by the catching ships in successive seasons. The average catch per day of blue whales has declined from 0·19 in the 1955-6 season (when the stock was already greatly reduced) to 0·05 in 1962-3; and the fin whales over almost the same period were reduced from 3·3 per day in '55-56 to 1·0 per day in the '63-64 season.[1] Let me tell of this terrible decline in the words of Dr. Lucas and Dr. Cole from their Foreword to Dr. Mackintosh's recent and important book: *The Stocks of Whales.* They write as follows:

'The scientific advisers to the International Whaling Commission, like the fisheries scientists, know that the aim should be to maintain the stocks at the level giving the best sustainable yield. Owing to their slow rate of reproduction, whales are very vulnerable to overfishing. As we have seen only too often in successive stocks of whales, they can easily be reduced to near extinction, though whaling operations become commercially impracticable before actual extinction is reached.

'The major Antarctic stocks of blue and fin whales could, if properly managed, produce annually, and in perpetuity, a total of some 25,000 whales. However, they have been reduced far below the level which would provide these maximum sustained yields and at present any catches in excess of about 4,000 fin whales and a few blue whales would further deplete the stocks. Despite this knowledge, in the 1963/4 season 14,000 fin whales were killed— and the cost of taking these 14,000 whales was much in excess of that which would be required to harvest the sustainable catch of 25,000 whales from stocks maintained at their optimum level. Obviously, such irrational fishing is uneconomical and only international agreement and action can restore the situation. Never was a case for international action so obvious, and perhaps never has the response been so inadequate.'

---

[1] Figures given by Dr. J. A. Gulland, one of the scientific advisors to the International Whaling Commission, to the British Association Meeting at Southampton in 1964.

At last when it is almost too late the Commission have agreed to grant complete protection to both the blue and the humpback whales in the south. It will now be a very long time before their stocks can build up to a level when they can be safely fished. Meanwhile in the 1964-65 season the Commission failed to agree with the Scientists' recommendation for a drastic curtailment of the catch of fin whales and in the last season '65-66 the fishery, as forecast by them, was an economic failure. It was international political feelings versus scientific judgment which led to the inevitable result. Will man never learn? I believe the present crisis—only by its bitter lesson—will at last teach man that he must listen to the scientific evidence—and then it will be realised that the *Discovery* scientists have provided the basis for a future properly regulated industry. And may we hope that technology will have provided a more humane method of killing these magnificent animals which we know from observations on their smaller relatives in oceanaria to be creatures of great intelligence and affectionate feelings.

It is a great pity that the method of electrocuting the whales, which was tried and normally gave instantaneous death, should have failed on one occasion and caused the idea to be abandoned; a whale came to life again after it had been pulled up onto the deck of the factory ship and did much damage by a flick of its gigantic tail. The electrical method saves much time and so is more economical; surely the danger of coming to life could be overcome by making sure of death with a shot before the whale was pulled up into the ship.

We must now leave the actual whales and consider what later work has been done on their food—the krill—and on other elements of the plankton; but this will make a chapter in itself. Before closing the present one, however, let me refer the reader, particularly the student, to the series of Buckland Lectures which were given in 1963 by Dr. Mackintosh on the general biology of whales, and now published, as already mentioned, under the title *The Stocks of Whales*. They give so much more information than I have been able to include; and they give it with the authority of the expert.

CHAPTER 21

THE KINGDOM OF THE KRILL

We have seen that the voyage of our old ship, and those of the *Discovery II* which followed her, were essentially concerned with obtaining a better understanding of all the different aspects of the ocean affecting the distribution of the whales. The krill, of course, is the primary key to such an understanding, for the whales come south to feed on it; this *one* species of pelagic 'shrimp,' links them with their environment. In our surveys round South Georgia we saw how the patterns of dispersion of the whales and krill were almost exactly the same. The study of the krill then has been the prime object of our ocean quest; the knowledge we gain of it, and its relation to the rest of the planktonic community and its physical background, must be quite the most important product of our exploration. In this chapter I want to tell something of what these later voyages accomplished and how they extended our work right round the pole. I again hope that the reader will find the account not too technical and worth pursuing, for I believe it gives a more comprehensive picture of the planktonic life of a whole and vast ocean than has ever, anywhere, been achieved before. I believe too, as I shall explain, that it is a major contribution to our knowledge of the world's resources—one which will grow in importance in the future.

The first expedition of *Discovery II* (1929-31), led by Dr. Kemp, made a further and more intensive study of the Atlantic sector, and the second (1931-3) under Dr. Dilwyn John, accomplished the first Antarctic circumpolar cruise in winter months with long V- or W-shaped lines of stations between the southern continents and the ice edge. The third, fourth and fifth commissions (1933-9) were led by Dr. Mackintosh, Dr. Deacon and Dr. Herdman respectively; they included repeated lines of stations on the Greenwich meridian and in 80° W. (in the south-east Pacific), cruises going backwards and forwards across the whale feeding grounds north of the pack ice, and another circumpolar voyage, this time in summer. The map on p. 443 shows most of the tracks. Then since the war the *Discovery II* made her last

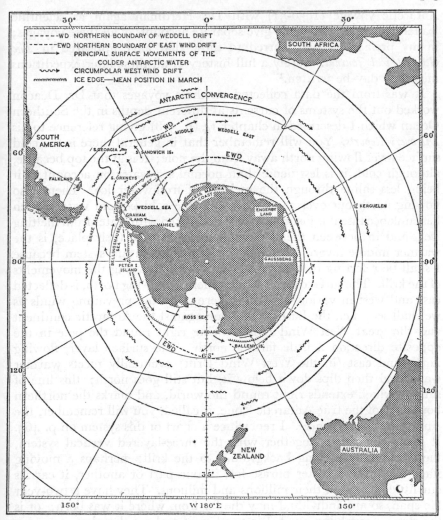

Map of Antarctica and the circumpolar sea showing the Antarctic Convergence, the surface water movements, the northern boundaries of the Weddell and the East Wind drifts and the edge of the ice in March (*i.e.* at the end of the summer). From Marr, *D.R.*, vol. xxxii.

Antarctic voyage (1950-51) with Dr. Herdman again as scientific leader. I cannot, of course, give separate accounts of all these voyages; in my preface I have referred to those that have appeared in *The Geographical Journal*. Surely a full history of all these later expeditions must one day be written.[1]

It was from the data collected on these voyages that Dr. Deacon worked out the systems of currents at different depths in the Southern Ocean which I described in chapter 14 (p. 318) giving reference to his *Discovery Reports*. You will remember that in general there is the cold surface layer flowing north away from the pole; it is at the top because, although cold, it is less dense than normal sea water on account of it being less saline through the melting of freshwater ice. Then, also flowing north but over the sea floor, is the cold bottom water which has sunk because it is just cooled and not mixed with water from melting ice; and in between them, flowing south to take their place, is the warmer middle layer. I remind you of this important system because I shall be referring to it several times when discussing the movements of the krill. The surface layer, while generally flowing north, is deflected east and west in various regions governed by the prevailing winds as we shall see: i.e., the East Wind Zone against the Antarctic continent and the great West Wind Drift flowing right round the pole in the opposite direction a little farther north. The surface layer, flowing north and east (in the West Wind Drift) eventually meets warmer water and then dips down below it, but still goes north; this line of sinking which extends right round the world, and marks the northern boundary of the true Antarctic Zone, is called, you will remember, the Antarctic Convergence[2]. I reproduce a chart of this system on p. 465. It forms, of course, together with the three-layered vertical system, the continually moving background to the krill; perhaps a moving stage would be a better phrase for, in one part or another, it carries our little 'actors' in their millions and millions. They have a two-year life span, so any individual may die far from where it was born; or is the stage a revolving one? We must wait and see the play.

If we call this great domain of ocean a stage we might also say it has a curtain: the screen of pack-ice that covers large areas of it every

---

[1] Since I wrote this Mr. J. Colman-Cooke has published his *Discovery II in the Antarctic* (1963) which is a short account of these voyages for the general reader which aims at recording the endurance and courage of those taking part rather than attempting to cover the scientific achievement.

[2] The student of oceanography should note the *Discovery Report*, vol. XXIII, pp. 177-212, where Dr. Mackintosh gives the position of the Antarctic Convergence and the distribution of surface temperatures in the Antarctic throughout the year.

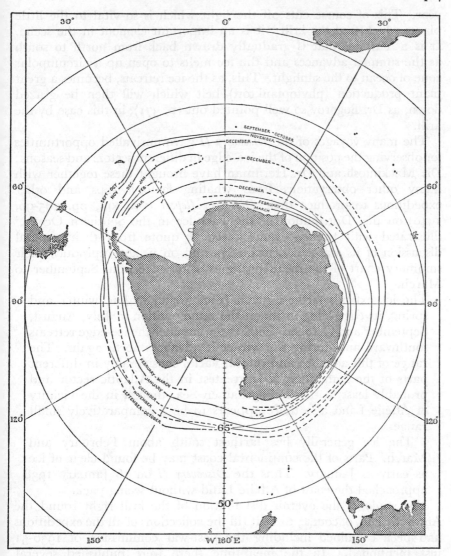

A chart showing the apparent mean positions of the ice-edge round Antarctica in the summer months from September to March. From Mackintosh and Herdman 1940. From *D.R.*, vol. XIX.

year. This of course cuts off the light which is so vital to the little plants which feed the krill; it is an important element in the scene. It is a 'curtain' that is gradually drawn back from north to south as the summer advances and the ice melts to open up a circumpolar zone of ocean to the sunlight. This, as the ice retreats, becomes a great plant production (phytoplankton) belt which will then be grazed down, as Dr. Bogorov so well pointed out (p. 371), in this case by the krill.

The many voyages of the *Discovery II* gave unrivalled opportunities for observing the position of the ice-edge in different sectors and seasons; Dr. Mackintosh and Dr. Herdman have brought these together with many other observations from whaling factory ships and other expeditions to produce their *Discovery Report* (vol. xix, pp. 285-96, 1940) on the 'Distribution of the Pack-ice in the Southern Ocean,' illustrated with twenty-seven charts. I quote from their general discussion of its seasonal distribution and on p. 467 reproduce their summary chart of the mean positions of its edge from September to March.

The ice extends farthest north [they write] in late winter and spring, its edge lying in much the same position in July, August, September and October. During the summer the ice-edge retreats southward and during the winter it advances north again. The range of this advance and retreat varies considerably in different parts of the Antarctic. It is greatest in the Atlantic sector and probably least in the Bellingshausen Sea, though in the vicinity of Adélie Land also there appears to be a comparatively small range.

The ice generally lies farthest south about February and March. Parts of the continental coast may be found clear of ice as early as January. Thus the *Discovery II* on 16 January 1938 approached the coast of Adélie Land without seeing pack.

The study of the overall distribution of the krill right round the Antarctic had, of course, to wait till the collections of all the expeditions had been examined including the post-war commission of 1950-51 just mentioned. In the meantime there were published several important *Discovery Reports* dealing with different aspects of its life; these I shall mention only briefly, because they are more specialised. First there is that 'on the development and distribution of the young stages of krill' (vol. xiv, pp. 1-192, 1936) by Dr. F. C. Fraser—the same old member of our expedition who, as we have just seen in the last chapter, has given us such a splendid insight into the hearing of whales. He has worked out in detail, with beautiful illustrations of all

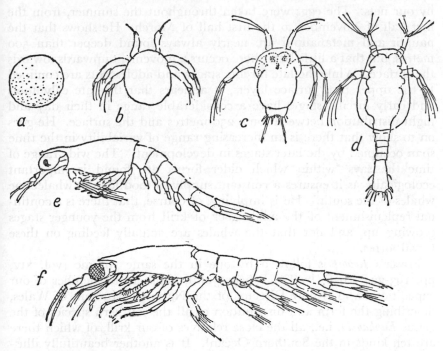

A few of the young stages of the krill (*Euphausia superba*) redrawn from F. C. Fraser: *e*, egg; *b*, first nauplius (× 23); *c*, metanauplius (× 17); *d*, second calyptopis; *a*, first furcilia (× 13); *f*, fifth furcilia (× 9).

their parts, the different young stages passed through by the animal from the egg to adolescence. While a description of their differing structural significance will be too technical to be included here, I give sketches, taken from Fraser's drawings, of some of the principal forms i.e., the egg, the first *nauplius*, the *metanauplius*, the second of the three *calyptopis* stages and the first and fifth of the *furcilia* stages with an indication of their sizes; it will be convenient to remember their names for a moment for I shall mention them again in relation to distribution problems.

He found that the eggs occur in deeper water, the greater numbers (some 70 per cent) being taken from below 250 metres depth. Of the regions examined by him, that of the Bransfield Strait yielded the largest numbers, but eggs were also taken to the north-east as far as South Georgia and to the west as far as 70° W. off the coast of Graham Land; the metanauplii were much more numerous and widespread in the whole of this area, possibly because they were more easily taken by our nets. The eggs were taken throughout the summer, from the first half of November to the first half of March. He shows that the nauplii and metanauplii are nearly always found deeper than 500 metres, but that a little later there occurs a movement upwards towards the surface. While the late furcilia stages and adolescents are confined to the upper near surface layers, it appears that the late calyptopis and early furcilia stages have a considerable range in their day and night distribution between some 250 metres and the surface. He goes on to show that there is an increasing range of variability in the time span occupied by the later stages in development. 'The wide range of time' he says 'within which older forms are found is important ecologically as it ensures a constant supply of food for the whalebone whales of the south.' He is implying, of course, that there is a continual replenishment of the adult stock of krill from the younger stages growing up, and not that the whales are actually feeding on these larval forms.

Fraser's *Report* is followed by one in the same volume (vol. xiv, pp. 193-324, 1936) by Dr. Dilwyn John, another old member of our expedition, who is now Director of the National Museum of Wales, describing the form and distribution of all the southern species of the genus *Euphausia*, i.e., all the close relatives of our krill, of which there are ten kinds in the Southern Ocean[1]. It is another beautifully illustrated work which includes a description of the development of five of the species; it lies, however, outside our immediate story and I will only direct the student to it.

Next we come to two *Reports* dealing directly with the krill by Dr. Helene Bargmann who, from the very early days, has played such an important part in the affairs of the expeditions by being curator, at home, in charge of all the vast collections, filling over 25,000 jars, accumulated as the ships worked in the South; and she has also given much time to providing the material for the many outside specialists reporting on the different animal groups and helping to put their papers into shape for the Press. Her room in the building, known as the *Discovery* Hut, which houses all the collections at the back of the British Museum (Natural History) at South Kensington, has for years been a meeting place for old members of past expeditions; what a pity a recording has not been kept of all the stories that have been told there! Her first *Report* (vol. xiv, pp. 325-50, 1937) is on the reproductive system of the krill and her second (vol. xxiii, pp. 103-76, 1945) continues Fraser's story of its life history as it passes on into the

[1]The ten species of *Euphausia* dealt with are as follows: *crystallorophias, superba, frigida, allentini, lucens, triacantha, longirostris, spinifera, hanseni,* and *similis.*

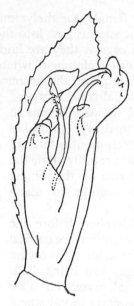

The remarkable hand-like organ, the petasma, of the male *Euphausia superba*, used for attaching the casket of sperm (spermatophore) to the female ($\times$ 15). From Dr. Bargmann's drawing.

adolescent and adult state. In the first, by careful dissections and drawings, she shows us the gradual development of both the male and female organs; this provides other workers with an exact yardstick for estimating the state of maturity of the specimens in their samples, and so enabling them to know how near to reproduction they are, or if they have already paired.

In passing I may say that the process of pairing in these animals is very remarkable and a brief account is worth including for those who do not know of it. In the male the reproductive cells, which are oval[1], pass down from the testis to accumulate in a large sac whose walls secrete a horny cuticle to enclose them within a slender-necked flask-like structure called a spermatophore. This at pairing, when it has been passed out of the genital opening, is transferred and attached to the female by a most elaborate device called the 'petasma' which is developed on the first of the little swimming limbs under the tail (the abdomen) of the male. I show her drawing of it above. It is like a hand with fingers which open out to perform this most delicate of operations—or perhaps more like one of those jack-knives from which a great variety of blades, corkscrews and whatnot can be unfolded. The precious casket, the spermatophore, has to be attached most

[1]It is characteristic of the higher Crustacea that their spermatozoa lack the motile tails which are the rule in those of most animals.

accurately to the opening of a little pouch of the female, the thelycum, just against where the eggs will be extruded; the sperms pass into the pouch where they are kept till they fertilise the eggs as they are laid.

In her second report she takes up the study of development where Fraser's work on the larval stages left off and completes the account of the full two year life-cycle. I quote her principal conclusions:

The spawning season, which extends over $5\frac{1}{2}$ months, begins in November or December. Eggs spawned then are probably adolescent by August, and mature about thirteen months later in September and October. The males grow more rapidly than the females, attaining slightly greater average lengths on the whole, and requiring a probable minimum of 22 months to reach maturity, as against 25 months in the female. . . .

Pairing was first found to take place in October, before the females were fully adult. The spermatophores are therefore carried for some time before fertilisation can occur, the evidence showing that this is effected externally, while the eggs are being laid. Gravid females are present in surprisingly small numbers. This fact, coupled with Fraser's records of eggs and early larval stages in the deeper water layers, seems to indicate that the females go down deep to spawn. More evidence on this point is needed, before this can be definitely established.

We now come to the tremendous task of dealing, in one comprehensive study, with all the data concerning the whale food collected on the many voyages from 1925 to 1939 and the post-war commission of 1950-1. It took years to complete for the material came from no fewer than 12,461 plankton samples. Whilst a little over half of the analysis was done by other members of staff, the bringing together and the consideration of this whole vast collection was accomplished by the late Dr. James Marr and published in a *Discovery Report* (vol. XXXII, pp. 33-464, 1962) of truly monumental proportions; it is entitled 'The Natural History and Geography of the Antarctic Krill (*Euphausia superba*, Dana).' Whilst I shall be dealing with the results and conclusions given by Marr, I know he would have wished me to point out the large part of the initial work that was done by other members of the staff, particularly Mr. W. F. Fry. He describes this earlier work as follows:

At one time or another the majority of the former Discovery Committee's scientific staff took part in the measuring, counting and sexing, etc., of the older krill taken in our stramin nets. Of the many, however, who have contributed to this work, particular mention must be made of our assistant, Mr. W. F. Fry, who, while serving in R.R.S. *Discovery II* worked continuously on krill during the two voyages she undertook between 1935 and 1939, analysing in the course of his task nearly 3000 stramin net samples. It was he too, handling some thousands of specimens, who counted, measured and sexed the vast majority of the krill we gathered, providing much of the basic data from which the development of the older stages of this species has been worked out and contributing much to our understanding of its habit in the sea.

Marr, who first of all went south with Shackleton on the *Quest*, and with Mawson on the old *Discovery* (just after our voyage), before he joined the *Discovery II*, had spent more years afloat in the Antarctic than any other naturalist and was three times awarded the Polar Medal. He, more than anyone else, I think, realised that work on the krill must be the crowning achievement of the whole series of voyages; it was, indeed, as we have seen, their prime objective. He emphasised, as Gunther and I did in our South Georgia *Report*, the importance of the krill to the whole community of the south—for birds, seals and fish in addition to the whales—but collects together many more examples of this from the writings of other naturalists; he sums up his discussion thus:

E. superba then manifestly occupies a key position in the economy and ecology of the Antarctic seas. It supports life on a vast scale, a complex variety of life ranging in size from that of the small organisms of the plankton to that of the immense bulk of the blue whale, the most gigantic animal that has ever existed. It must exist in enormous numbers, in an astronomical abundance far exceeding that of any other pelagic euphausian. . . .

He writes in epic fashion befitting this great theme and the strenuous endeavour of all those who, with him, helped to wrest the story, bit by bit, from the rough and icy waters round the pole. The result is not to be judged entirely as a scientific report; I used the word epic to indicate the vast sweep of the work and that almost poetic quality that marks the writings of those who are naturalists in heart as well as in mind. It is both natural history and science on a grand scale and beautifully written; and it has much of human history as well:

In compiling this report [he writes in his introduction] I have consulted the works of many authors, many of them not, or not strictly, scientific. They include the writings of explorers and sailors, sealers and whalers, historians, geographers and carto-graphers, ship's surgeons, contributors to official departmental publications and compilers of books on whaling, sealing, polar and deep-sea exploration, meteorology, ornithology, oceanography,

marine biology and ecology, as well as sundry other references.
I may sometimes have been critical, but only because in seeking to
unravel a problem of enormous complexity I have had access to a
body of data and material unparalleled in the annals of the
investigation of any single plankton animal, if not indeed of
plankton animals as a whole . . .

Now let us quote from his 'acknowledgements':

To the widely scattered members of the former *Discovery*
Committee's staff, both sailors and scientists, whose sustained
effort in field and laboratory led to the enormous accumulation of
material and data upon which this report is based, the following
pages are dedicated in grateful acknowledgement and appreciation
of their seamanship, comradeship and devotion in the Antarctic
seas.

The many members from the past will indeed be gratified to see
their sustained efforts rewarded with such a splendid addition to the
literature of Antarctic exploration; for the first time it charts what we
might call the kingdom of the krill. This vast and well-defined
circumpolar area of the globe is here securely mapped and its
boundaries related to the flow of ocean currents, to the ice and to the
land. It is a domain which at present is more important to man than
the Antarctic continent itself, and it may remain so in the future if
only he will be reasonable. The work is certainly well called a Natural
History and a Geography; it gives the world important discoveries
in both fields.

The student must go to the original volume; here in a few pages I
can do no more than summarise what I consider to be Marr's main
findings. Here and there I may differ from the conclusions he draws—
but if I do, they are but differences of opinion, and do not detract
from my admiration for the gigantic task he has so successfully carried
through. There are certain inherent difficulties in such a study which
should be mentioned. The voyages were planned to cover all parts of
the Southern Ocean round the Antarctic continent and at different
seasons of the year; on each of them there was an immense area to be
sampled with routine series of nets. The ship had to hurry on from
station to station as quickly as possible to get the programme completed in the limited time available and this was often shortened by
storms. There was little opportunity to examine the collected material
on the spot; it was all preserved for detailed scrutiny at home or later
on the voyage. Only then could the full significance of the samples
be revealed: whether the krill caught were actually in a breeding state
or not, the particular stage of development that the young were in,

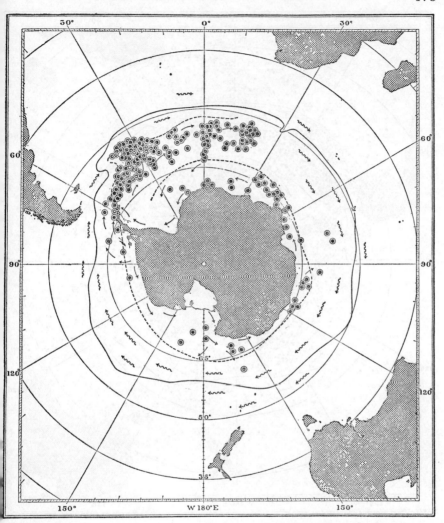

The principal concentrations of krill round the Antarctic continent. From the late Dr. Marr's *Discovery Report*, vol. xxxii. This chart should be compared with that on the next page where all the sampling, both negative and positive, is shown; it will be seen that sampling was much heavier between 60°W and 30°E than elsewhere.

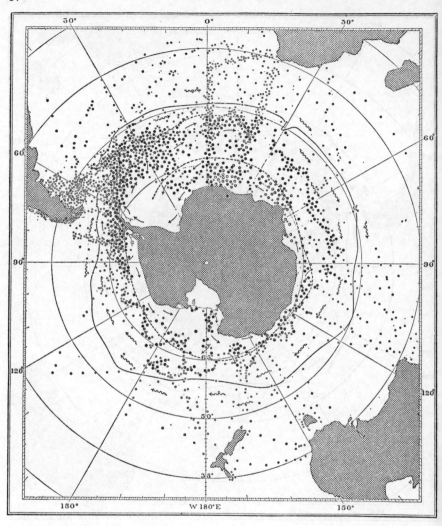

The gross distribution of the Antarctic krill. All the positions at which krill were taken are shown as blacked-in circles; the smaller open circles show the stations at which none were caught. From Marr *D.R.*, vol. xxxii.

and so on. It was then too late to go back and take just a few more samples, perhaps at a different depth, to clear up some point about which the tantalising evidence failed to give a fully convincing conclusion. These were the difficulties with which Marr has had to contend; he could not modify the sampling in the light of the results coming from his work as it went along. The plan of observation was irrevocably fixed.

Now that the whole collection has been worked up it is inevitable that there remain some gaps to be filled and some doubts to be cleared up. This is the price that must be paid for going all out to delimit the whole area, in winter as well as summer. Had the opposite course been adopted, that of altering the method and course of sampling as one went along to suit this or that particular local problem, then some of these points would certainly have been resolved; but with almost equal certainty the complete charting of this great realm would have remained a dream of the future. Time would not give us both. Kemp planned with vision and Marr's *Report* shows just what pieces of the puzzle are still missing and exactly when and where to go and look for them. I hope there may be yet one more *Discovery* voyage south to bring back the answers—and how I should love to go with her!

First and foremost of the results is the main pattern of distribution of the krill around the pole with the marked asymmetry which is shown in the chart on p. 475. To understand this we must look at the surface currents which are shown on the same chart. Close against the coast there is a flow in the East Wind Zone from east to west (i.e., anticlockwise) completely round the continent except where Graham Land juts up to the north opposite South America; it flows round from the Pacific Ocean side, past the Indian Ocean sector, to enter and circulate in the Weddell Sea, that great bight carved out of the continent south of the Atlantic. Out from this Sea in turn flows the strong Weddell Stream up towards South Georgia where it joins into the great West Wind Drift; this forms the outer and completely circumpolar current flowing from west to east, (i.e., clockwise) and in the opposite direction to the inner current of the East Wind Zone. The chart just referred to, that on p. 475, shows only the principal concentrations of the krill, the points where the great swarms were met with; the absolute range of distribution, including occurrences which are small as well as large, is shown opposite with all the points where nets were used but krill were *not* taken. We see that there are two main areas of production: one in the East Wind Zone all round against the coast, and the other where the Weddell Stream flows out to join the West Wind Drift and continues with these waters as far as 30° E. Very few concentrations are found in this drift east of 30° E., and where they do occur (i.e., round about 75° E. and 180°) Marr believes they have most likely been carried thither in tongues of water curling up northwards from the productive East Wind Zone, as indicated by the arrows on the chart. Whilst there are only a few of these large concentrations of krill in the drift east of 30° E. we see that it does occur there in smaller numbers as far as about 100° E. If the sampling has been sufficient then clearly something significant must be happening in the drift round about 30° E., for not only do the main concentrations of adults stop there, but so also do those of the young stages as we shall presently see. If it were not for the disappearance of the young as well, we might perhaps think that the adults, at the end of the season, were just dying off as they came approximately to this meridian.

We must note that many more plankton samples were taken to the west of 30°E than to the east, and this will account for some of the asymmetry in the chart of the krill. Nevertheless it is supported by two other lines of evidence: firstly the similar asymmetry in the overall distribution of the whales (p. 444), and secondly the more marked asymmetry in the production of phytoplankton, the food of the krill, as shown on p. 487 by the work of Dr. Hart. I think it unlikely that these correspondences can be just coincidence.

Now here we come to a problem that is still not completely resolved. All those krill which are produced in the East Wind Zone near the Antarctic coast appear to be transplanted in a continuous stream towards and into the Weddell Sea, except for those in quite minor offshoots which Marr believes may be carried northwards into the West Wind Drift at one or two points. Then from the Weddell Sea the krill is carried to the north and east and appears to meet its journey's end about 30° E. How then is the East Wind Zone restocked? Marr suggests a partial solution. He confirms what Fraser first discovered, that the eggs hatch out in deep water and the very young larval stages have to make a long climb towards the surface layers. For brevity I will quote from his summary:

As they climb towards the surface the larvae, as Second Nauplii, Metanauplii and First Calyptopes, spend some considerable time, perhaps up to 30 days or more, in the warm deep current which in most parts of the Antarctic has a southerly component, and which, therefore, plays an important part in maintaining the population within the normal limits of its geographical range.

This movement, however, except for similar smaller ones *within* the

East Wind Zone, appears only to operate in the limited region south of the Atlantic. Marr clearly recognised this difficulty.

I will only venture my opinion that even the 30 days of young larval existence in the south-going water in the region opposite the Atlantic must be quite inadequate to balance the loss from the Weddell Sea area of the krill population which is continually taking place with its northern and easterly drift for so much of the rest of the animal's two-year life span. There must be some other return journey, but before I discuss it further let us look again at the distribution of the young stages.

Enormous quantities of larvae are produced in the Weddell Sea Zone. Looking, however, at Marr's charts showing where the highest numbers of gravid and spent females were taken you get the impression that South Georgia must also be one of the great breeding grounds of the species; yet he says 'there is, paradoxically, virtually no spawning and certainly *no successful hatching* there.' Here is an important point to be cleared up, and another concerns the depth at which the eggs are laid. The eggs certainly hatch out in deep-water, but are they actually laid at the surface and then sink, as Marr suggests from the evidence of finding spermatophore-carrying males and females as well as spent and gravid females in the surface layers?[1]

There are clearly gaps in the story. Marr, as I have said, has shown where to go and look to fill them; he himself could not go and dip into the depths again as he worked up the material.

He goes on to describe the great production of the young (larval) forms and shows how in the course of the seasons they stream eastwards in the West Wind Drift where it has been fed by the supplies coming up from the Weddell Sea area. But they only stream so far and no farther. I quote from his p. 326.

Throughout April the eastward movement continues until, towards the end of the month, it would appear that the whole Weddell drift from west to east, but most notably Weddell West and Weddell Middle, is carrying these stages in great or very great abundance. There is again, however, evidence of a seemingly abrupt termination of the larval drift somewhere in the neighbourhood of meridian 30° E.

This is well illustrated in his chart (his fig. 89), which I reproduce overleaf, showing the drift of the concentrations from February to June. What happens to them at 30° E? When they reach it they are still only young furcilia stages. There is exactly the same abrupt

[1]Marr must be right. Dr. J. Mauchlin has now found that the northern krill, *Meganyctiphanes* and *Thysanoessa*, both lay eggs in the upper layers which sink to hatch in deeper waters.

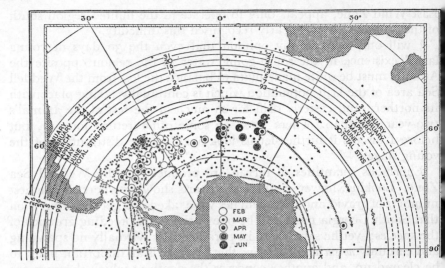

The distribution of the early furcilia stages of the krill during different months from February to June. The large circles indicate catches of more than 10. The ice edges of March and September are shown, and the Antarctic Convergence. The numbers on the circumpolar concentric circles indicate the number of sampling stations in each sector in the different months as labelled. From Marr, *D.R.*, vol. xxxii.

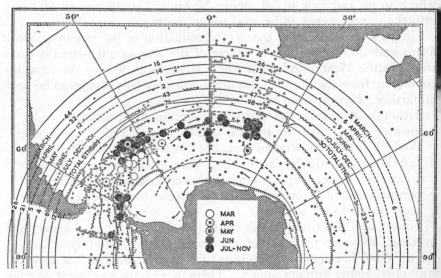

The distribution of the late furcilia stages of the krill in different months; the arrangement of other features as in the previous chart. From Marr, *D.R.*, vol. xxxii.

ending to the drift of a second wave of the later furcilias as shown in his
fig. 96 which I give beside the other for comparison. Here we are
again at this fateful meridian which also seemed a barrier to the
procession of the adults. Something very important must be happening
here. You will note that exactly at 30° E. the otherwise smoothly
running line of the Antarctic Convergence[1] makes a little indentation
southwards; perhaps this gives a hint.

It does indeed look as if there must be a movement of water at this
point returning the krill, young and old, to the south. Marr refers to
the early charts of Meyer who in 1923 postulated such a circulation
and was later followed in his views by Professor Ruud and others.
Both Fraser and Marr, however, point out that the *Discovery* expeditions
have so far gained little evidence of such a system and they quote
from Deacon who in 1937[2] discussed the current system in the Weddell
Sea area. I reproduce what he says but put one specially interesting
sentence into *italics*:

> The movement towards the west, the northward current along
> the east of Graham Land, and the current flowing out of the
> Weddell Sea towards the east, form three parts of a cyclonic move-
> ment which extends across the entire width of the Atlantic Ocean.
> *The surface temperature distribution indicates that the Cyclonic movement*
> *may be completed by a southward movement between* 20° *and* 40° E.;
> there is, however, very little evidence of such a current at the
> surface; the conditions are not very different from those farther
> west and more in keeping with the existence of a small northward
> movement. . . . The curving of the pack-ice boundary towards
> the south has been used by Michaelis (1923, p. 22) as evidence
> of a southward current, but it may be explained alternatively by
> the melting and disappearance of the ice carried eastwards across
> the Atlantic Ocean by the Weddell Sea current.

The surface temperature distribution, of which Deacon writes,
certainly seems to suggest such a circulation. Fraser thinks it likely
that there is such a movement but employing both surface and deeper
currents. He writes (loc. cit., p. 165): 'The present results suggest that
replenishment of the stock of krill is assured by a rotary movement
involving the northward flowing surface water, the southward flowing
deep water and the distribution and migrations of krill within these
currents.'

I have already briefly referred in chapter 14 (p. 348) to Dr.
Mackintosh's demonstration that much of the animal plankton that

[1]Which we discussed on p. 317.   [2]*Discovery Reports*, vol. xv, p. 28, 1937.

gets carried northwards towards the Antarctic convergence in the surface layers in the summer is returned to the south in the warmer deeper layer; this, which I shall discuss more fully on p. 493, may be happening to the krill, but as Marr says, we have no evidence of it. Or there may yet be demonstrated the complete surface circulation, suggested by Deacon's temperature chart; and, indeed, as noted by Marr, the Japanese workers T. Kumagori and S. Yanegawa have quite recently[1] claimed to have discovered such a movement, but farther east in 45° E. Here is an important point that requires further investigation. I think it likely that such a circulation will be confirmed; and it would not surprise me if it were found that there was some flow of water, as Marr also suggests, from the Weddell area via the Bransfield Strait, along the west of Graham Land, to link up with the East Wind Zone and so to feed in the young krill at that end of the coastal circulation which flows right round the continent back to the Weddell Sea. Perhaps my little metaphor of a revolving stage may be a true one; time alone will tell.

Marr discusses many features of the natural history of the krill, but here I can mention only one or two more; the student knows where he can go for the rest. He presents much evidence to show that the adult krill is able to get out of the way of an approaching net in the well-lit upper layers in the daytime; this undoubtedly accounts for much of the smaller catches made near the surface in daylight compared with those made at night. As we shall see in a moment he has much evidence of the krill remaining at the very surface in daylight; nevertheless he agrees that it is likely that at times there is some small vertical migration downwards in the daytime as we had found at South Georgia, but usually going no deeper than perhaps 30 to 50 metres. He gives us many interesting notes on the patchy nature of the krill's distribution, confirming the results we got in our consecutive net series at South Georgia, and quotes numerous examples of patches being seen on or near the surface in broad daylight. I have already (p. 452) recorded how Gunther observed a great school of whales feeding on such patches in 1937; Marr refers as well to other notes made by Gunther in 1931 and gives his sketches of patches which I reproduce opposite. He writes as follows:

During a cruise undertaken by R.R.S. *William Scoresby* into the Weddell Sea in January and February 1931 an area of profuse patchiness was encountered and observed in great detail by Gunther who was on board at the time. The patches were particularly abundant in the neighbourhood of Station WS 540

[1] *Journal of Tokyo University of Fisheries*, vol. I, pp. 231-40, 1958.

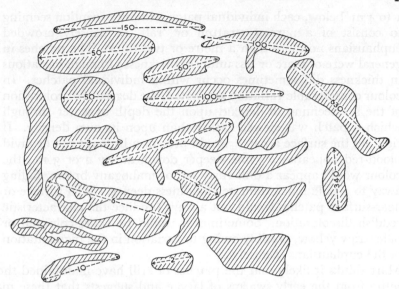

Rough sketches of patches of krill made by the late E. R. Gunther in the Weddell Sea, January to February, 1931. The approximate dimensions of some of them are given in yards. The spacing of the patches has no relation to the natural spacing. From Marr, *D.R.*, vol. xxxII.

in 57° 55′ S., 21° 21′ W. where they were seen continuously over an area estimated to be at least 150 square miles in extent. They were separated from each other by short gaps at most a third or a quarter of a mile wide and although they showed considerable variation in size none was exceptionally large, an average-sized biggish patch covering an area of about 2500 square yards, or say 60 by 40 yards. . . .[1] They varied greatly in shape. Some were irregularly circular, some oval, some irregularly oblong, others occurring as ribbon-like belts which sometimes had narrow tributary out-streamers resembling the pseudopodia of an amoeba. Many were of such irregular outline that they can only be described as amorphous. In a number of instances they were seen to have gaps, resembling vacuoles, of clear water inside them, giving them the appearance of having been hollowed out.

They occurred right on, or very close to, the surface, or from

[1] At this point he says "The biggest seen was a narrow belt 150 yards long by about 20 wide," but he appears to have overlooked two of the patches in Gunther's illustration which are marked as 630 and 340 yards respectively.

1 to 4 m. below, each individual patch without exception seeming
to consist of a narrow stratum or 'raft' of densely crowded
euphausians no more than a metre or two thick. The patches in
general were of more or less uniform thickness although variations
in thickness did sometimes occur within individual patches. In
colour considerable variation was noted, the degree of discoloration
of the sea seeming to depend upon the depth of water through
which a patch was viewed rather than upon its own density. If
right on the surface a patch would present a brilliant red or vivid
blood-red appearance while deeper down, at say 2 or 3 m., the
colour would appear a dull rusty red or mahogany brown, fading
away to a pale indeterminate cloudiness deeper. Even surface or
near-surface patches would not always produce the characteristic
reddish discoloration. Sometimes it would be ochre-coloured or
pale straw yellow, possibly owing to variation in the pigmentation
of the euphausians themselves.

Marr thinks it likely that the patches of krill have maintained their
identity from the early swarms of larvae and suggests that these may
in fact be the products of separate hatchings. Presumably he meant
hatching from the eggs laid by swarms of females laying eggs together,
for these huge swarms of adults, hundreds of yards across, could not
be the result of one female's laying.

He refers to the feeding of the krill:

It is almost exclusively a voracious herbivore, and although at
first sight the regular occurrence of certain small spineless diatoms
in the stomachs seems to point to some measure of selective feeding,
it may be that these forms, being strongly silicified, are not very
easily digested, and that many other less strongly silicified species
are equally important as food.

And he gives lists of the diatoms and other phytoplankton (i.e. plant)
forms that have been found in their stomachs by Dr. T. J. Hart on
the *Discovery* Investigations and by others.

Dr. Hart carries the relation of the whale to its environment one
step farther back; and this, as I have said before, is what is so remarkable, there is only this one further link between the krill and the
physico-chemical background. As he so well says in his first *Discovery
Report* (vol. VIII, pp. 1-268, 1934):

The food of these euphausians consists very largely, if not entirely,
of diatoms and other phytoplankton organisms. Thus we have here
one of the simplest food chains possible, the building up of the
vast body of the whale being only one stage removed from the
organic fixation of the radiant energy of the sun by the diatoms.

From this it will be seen that some knowledge of the phytoplankton is essential to a proper understanding of the economic problems of these regions . . .

In this *Report* he studies the phytoplankton at South Georgia again over several seasons and then extends the work to cover the whole Weddell Sea—Scotia Sea area with special surveys of the Bransfield Strait and an excursion westwards into the Bellingshausen Sea. He finds, as we did in our earlier South Georgia work, that the diatoms make up by far the greater part of the planktonic vegetation, with the dinoflagellates at no time forming any appreciable proportion of it. He shows the differences between the groups of diatom species found in each body of water and distinguishes those coming from the eastern and western parts of the Weddell Sea.

After a more specialised study[1] of one species, which is of great interest to the student, he gives us his second splendid monograph on general distribution (*Discovery Reports*, vol. xxi, pp. 261-356, 1942); it is based on three commissions of the *Discovery II*. Here he presents oceanography with its first knowledge of the broader variations in the plant populations of the plankton over the whole of the Antarctic Zone of the Southern Ocean; he takes us right round the globe and shows us also seasonal differences in various sectors. I have explained, when dealing with our original South Georgia survey (p. 323), the difficulties of getting strictly comparable phytoplankton data from the samples obtained with the ordinary type of fine-mesh net; its meshes very soon become clogged in areas of dense concentration so that the water filtered is greatly cut down and we know that, but for this, our sample would have been very much larger. How much larger? That we could never know. Again there was the second difficulty of estimating the samples we got so that the quantities could be compared; the differences in the sizes and shapes of the different kinds of diatoms made both relative numbers of cells or relative volumes of samples unsatisfactory means of comparison. For this great study Hart introduced the then new Harvey method[2] into the work, one which had not yet been invented when we first went south. He gets over the first difficulty of clogging by having a recording meter in the mouth of the net which, by a propeller, measures the actual volume of water that has passed

---

[1]Here he shows (*Discovery Reports*, vol. xvi, pp. 413-46) how one particular kind of diatom, *Rhizosolenia curvata*, may be used as an indicator of water mixing in the region of the Antarctic Convergence. It is a species, characteristic of the cooler water of the sub-Antarctic zone, which frequently gets carried across the convergence into the Antarctic Zone; when such mixing occurs it enables us to detect these conditions more readily than by other means.

[2]Devised by Dr. H. W. Harvey of the Plymouth Laboratory.

through it; we can now compare sizes of sample per unit volumes of water. The second difficulty of comparing quantities he got over by a system of dissolving out the green pigments and making colourmetric measurements of the different samples in terms of a special scale of 'plant-pigment units.' It is too technical a matter to pursue farther in such a general book as this, but it will be seen at once that it now enables us to compare the relative quantities of plant life that are found in similar volumes of sea water, say per cubic metre, in different areas. The principal constituent species must, of course, also be recorded. This was indeed a step forward towards a better understanding of the link between the krill and its physical environment. Let us see how he deals with this great domain.

The area covered by Antarctic surface waters is very large—at least 12 million square miles. In considering the conditions of existence of phytoplankton organisms in an area of this size, it is obviously essential to adopt some scheme of subdivision, in order to keep both the descriptions of observations, and discussion of their significance, within reasonable proportions. Ideally, such a scheme should be based on the principal changes in the conditions of existence, in practice a degree of arbitrariness will obviously be unavoidable. In nature conditions will always merge more or less gradually, but in practice boundaries must be drawn somewhere. This difficulty is very apparent in the Antarctic zone where the gradient in water temperature, for example, is very slight.

In the areas south of the three great oceans the latitude of the Antarctic Convergence approaches its mean fairly closely. Here a satisfactory division may be made by considering the interaction of two important factors known to exert a profound influence upon phytoplankton production: light, and the distribution of pack-ice. The duration and intensity of the light will vary more or less directly with the distance one proceeds to the south, so long as the latitude of the convergence remains fairly constant, since it is of extra-terrestrial origin. The distribution of the pack-ice, on the other hand, can be extremely erratic as climatic conditions fluctuate. Our knowledge of it is now sufficient, however, to make the following subdivision, based on the gradient of these two factors, reasonably satisfactory in the open oceans. We divide these parts of the Antarctic zone into Northern, Intermediate and Southern Regions.

He defines these three main oceanic regions as follows:

The Northern Region: between the Antarctic Convergence and a

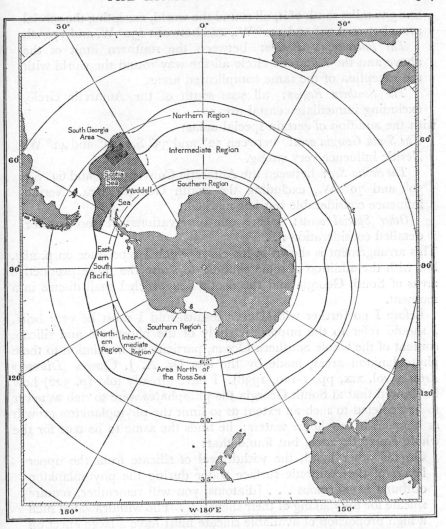

The division of the Antarctic Zone into biogeographical regions and areas according to Dr. Hart (1942), but with added shading in the Scotia Sea and South Georgia areas to indicate the greater phytoplankton production that he has shown to be there. From *D.R.*, vol. XXII.

line 330 miles south of it, all round the world, excepting the special
areas between 30° and 110° W., and between 150° W. and 170° E.

The Intermediate Region: between the southern limit of the
above and the Antarctic circle all the way round the world with
the exception of the same complicated areas.

The Southern Region: all seas south of the Antarctic circle,
excluding immediate coastal areas.
with the addition of certain special areas:

The South Georgia area: between 52° and 55° S.; 33° and 41° W.
Neritic influence very strong.

The Scotia Sea: between the Antarctic Convergence and 62° S.;
30° and 70° W., excluding the South Georgia area. Neritic
influence considerable but less marked.

Other Special areas: where our observations are too few for
detailed consideration . . .

This arrangement is shown in his chart which I reproduce on p. 287.
but with the addition of some shading to show the more productive
areas of South Georgia and the Scotia Sea which I shall discuss in a
moment.

Before I go further with Hart's results, and I must be very brief,
I should refer to the important study of the phosphate and silicate
content of the whole Southern Ocean, particularly in relation to these
phytoplankton areas, made by the late Dr. A. J. Clowes (*Discovery
Reports*, vol. XIX, pp. 1-120, 1938). I have already told (p. 322) how
he showed that at South Georgia the phosphates were so rich as never
to be depleted to such an extent as to limit the phytoplankton growth
as happens in our home waters; he finds the same to be true for the
whole Antarctic zone, but found that:

On the other hand, the withdrawal of silicate from the upper
layers of the Antarctic surface water during the phytoplankton
outburst is enormous . . . [diatoms, you will remember, require
silicate for the making of their shells] . . . The withdrawal of such
a high proportion of available silicate must have a large effect on
the growth of phytoplankton, and silicate paucity is possibly a
limiting factor at one stage of the phytoplankton season . . . As
further evidence of the effect . . . Dr. Hart tells me that the robust,
spiny phase of *Corethron criophilum* (which is a dominant species in
the early part of the phytoplankton season in the Antarctic zone)
tends to change over in late summer to the spineless chain form
with very thin, fragile walls.

Dr. Hart agrees that 'there is now some direct evidence that
temporary shortage of silica may be in part responsible for the post-

maximal summer decrease'; actually he did himself discuss this possibility in his earlier *Report* of 1934. Let us now turn to his other findings. He shows that the amount of the standing phytoplankton crop differs very little in the main northern, intermediate and southern oceanic regions; but that in the Scotia Sea it is twice as much and in the more special area around South Georgia there is *ten times* the quantity. He has said that these boundaries cannot be taken as hard and sharp lines. If we smooth them out and compare his chart with those on pp. 475 and 476 we will see how closely this area of greater plant production corresponds with the similarly greater production of the krill. How gratifying it is to see one after another of the bits of the story supporting each other and telling us that these voyages have indeed discovered some of the vital features in the geography of this great ocean domain—linking together phytoplankton, krill and whales.

The reason for this richer plant growth in these particular regions is not so easy to be certain of. It had been suggested by the Norwegian, the late Professor Gran, one of the leading phytoplankton experts of the world, that the greater production of this life often observed in proximity to land—in what are technically known as *neritic* conditions— may be because of the presence of certain beneficial substances derived from land drainage. Hart calls these two areas of South Georgia and the Scotia Sea *neritic areas* and appears, tentatively, inclined towards such an explanation for their high productivity.

> The greater richness of the neritic areas (he says) remains inexplicable unless we assume that minute quantities of inorganic compounds, as iron or manganese, or of organic compounds derived from the land, exert a strongly favourable influence on diatom growth. We have no direct evidence of this, but the growing body of experimental work by Harvey, Cooper and others favours such an hypothesis.

It is at the moment just a matter of opinion. For myself, however, I feel more inclined towards the hypothesis I advanced on p. 323: that it is an effect produced by the mixing of two main ocean streams— one from the Bellingshausen Sea and the other from the Weddell Sea—each one fertilising the other with some different essential trace substances that they had become respectively short of.

I was very surprised that Hart found that the standing crop of phytoplankton in the main Antarctic regions (i.e., the northern, intermediate and the southern as distinct from his neritic areas) was hardly any higher than that at the time of the spring outburst in our own home waters; indeed he was clearly surprised himself:

> Our ideas of the extreme richness of phytoplankton production

in Antarctic seas were gained when the work was chiefly confined to the Falkland sector. Now that larger numbers of observations from more truly oceanic areas are available it is evident that these ideas stand in need of some modification. The effect of land masses in producing conditions suitable for rapid, rich phytoplankton development appears to be very important, as has long been known in the northern hemisphere. In the far south, however, where all biophysical phenomena appear on the grand scale, the beneficial effects of neritic influence appear at much greater distances from land. Only where these influences are felt do the Antarctic seas retain their claim to be amongst the richest in the world.

Whilst he shows that the standing crop is no larger, I wonder if the actual *production* may not be considerably greater than that at home? With the exceedingly rich zoöplankton of the Antarctic—and I shall be coming to this in a moment—may it not be that the multitudes of animals are grazing down the phytoplankton at a much higher rate than in our home waters? With the very high phosphate content of the Antarctic seas, the plants may well be growing and multiplying at an exceptional rate yet only just keep pace with the grazing. If this were so then the observed crop might be no larger than ours, yet the amount produced per day might be vastly higher[1]. I think this must indeed be so on the evidence of the tremendous wealth of Antarctic animal life, including not only that in the plankton, but also the birds, fish and whales, and the amazing density of life on the sea bed, noted not only by us, but by so many expeditions in the past, all ultimately dependent upon the phytoplankton. The *production* must, I believe, be very high in all areas and yet higher still in the Scotia Sea and round South Georgia. There are still many fascinating problems to be solved by future biological Antarctic expeditions; as Marr's work points the way to new studies of the krill, so Hart shows us how to follow on his phytoplankton lead.

Now I must tell of some of the achievements of the later voyages in increasing our knowledge of the zoöplankton in general—the animals other than the krill—in this great Southern Ocean. Dr. Mackintosh[2] followed our beginnings at South Georgia with a study of the macroplankton, i.e., the larger plankton animals, over the whole of the Falkland Sector, using the material collected by the new system of hauling the 1-metre diameter net obliquely from 100 metres to the surface as the ship steamed slowly forwards. I reproduce his chart

---

[1]This is where the importance of certain new methods of measuring *production* rather than standing crop come in; they were not available at the time of Hart's surveys.

[2]*Discovery Reports*, vol. ix, pp. 65-160, 1934.

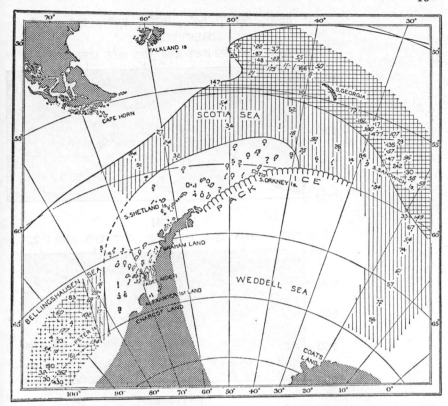

Dr. Mackintosh's chart of the distribution of the macroplankton over the Falkland Sector of the Antarctic in the summer. The figures show the number of hundreds of organisms in each sample, shoaling species being omitted; those in italics are day hauls and the others are night hauls. From *D.R.*, vol. IX.

which here shows the distribution of the quantities of this plankton in the summer; we see an increase as we pass from the South Shetlands through the Scotia Sea to the South Georgia area which agrees well with the distribution of the krill and the increasing phytoplankton crop. He distinguishes groups of warmer water and colder water species, and then shows the southern limits to the distribution of many of the first group and the northern limits to many of the other. By comparing the samples taken at different times through the twenty-four hours, he shows that there is, for most species, a marked variation in the quantities caught, many more being taken at night than in the daytime; this confirms our South Georgia observations on their diurnal

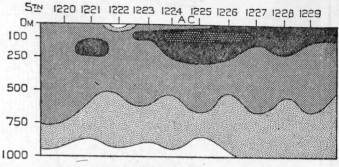

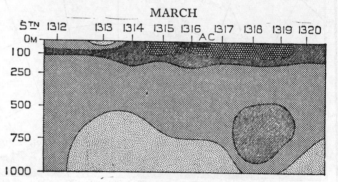

The seasonal vertical migration of the macroplankton demonstrated by Dr. Mackintosh in the Antarctic and Sub-Antarctic Zones. For further explanation see text. From *D.R.*, vol. xvi.

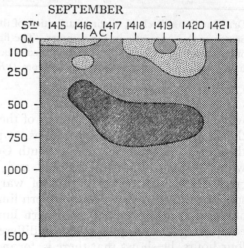

vertical migration, but also, no doubt in part, reflects that avoidance of the net by some species in daytime to which we referred on p. 482.

Now we come to Mackintosh's remarkable demonstration of the seasonal circulation of the macroplankton (*Discovery Reports*, vol. xvi, pp. 365-412, 1937) to which I briefly referred in chapter 14 (p. 348). During her third commission, 1933-4, the *Discovery II* made five lines of stations across the Sub-Antarctic and Antarctic Zones along the meridian of 80° N. at different seasons of the year and at each station 70 cm. diam. closing nets were used in the usual series of vertical hauls from 1,000 metres to the surface. A graphical comparison of the results, which I reproduce from his vertical sections, will show the nature of this circulation better than many words. From December to March we see most of the plankton up in the surface layers which are moving north *away from the pole*; already in March, however, a part of the population has moved down and is now massed between 900 and 500 metres. In September we see that the bulk of the plankton is still between 750 and 500 metres and that is in the warmer south-going water; during the winter then it has been travelling *back towards the pole*. In October and November (which I have not included in my figure) he shows it moving up again towards the surface layer to begin going north once more. This movement is seen in just as striking a fashion if we take some of the more important species separately, as Mackintosh shows in corresponding charts for the copepods *Rhincalanus gigas* and *Calanus acutus*, and the arrow-worm *Eukrohnia hamata*. Here we see a striking example of instinctive behaviour being evolved to bring about this circulation to maintain these stocks in the Antarctic by making unconscious use of the current systems at different depths. He compares this with the energetic extensive daily vertical migrations which similarly enable several other species to maintain their geographical position by travelling north up near the surface during the night and south in the warm return current during the day; examples are the copepod *Pleuromamma robusta*, and the euphausiids *Euphausia frigida* and *E. tricantha* as seen on p. 347. Some other species fail to show how they can maintain themselves in the Antarctic upper layers which are continually carrying them away, but it seems most likely that the return journey is made by eggs or young larval stages with delayed development, which drop below to rise again much later and farther south; we have already considered the possibility of this being the mechanism used by the krill.

I now come to two other important papers on the general plankton which throw much light on the fundamental nature of our realm. The first by Mr. A. de C. Baker (*Discovery Reports*, vol. xxvii, pp. 201-18,

1954) answers the question as to how continuous are the distributions of the commoner plankton species round the pole? Let me quote from his excellent statement of the problem in his introduction:

The Southern Ocean is a continuous circumpolar belt, the greater part of which is drifting eastwards under the influence of the prevailing westerly winds. It is clear from the widespread soundings taken by many ships that there is an uninterrupted belt of deep water, and Deacon (1937), Clowes (1938) and Mackintosh (1946) have shown that there is a circumpolar continuity in the relative positions and movements of the main water masses, in the distribution of nutrient salts and in the surface isotherms. As a general rule the physical features are arranged in zones (with local modifications and distortions) in which uniform conditions persist in east and west directions and changes or gradients occur from north to south. Since the distribution of pelagic species may be expected to extend as far as the environment is uniform, it would be surprising if the distribution of planktonic species were not also circumpolar.

Those who have examined collections of plankton from different parts of the Southern Ocean have observed that the familiar species can indeed be looked for in any longitude at least in the Antarctic zone, and the circumpolar distribution of the plankton is generally taken for granted. This, however, is a far-reaching assumption, and if it is true it may sometimes allow general conclusions based on samples from one sector of the Antarctic to be applied to other sectors. Although much diffuse evidence of circumpolarity may be found in the reports of various expeditions which have collected material during the past sixty years or so, it appears that no evidence has yet been assembled to show that circumpolarity is a general character of the distribution of the plankton of high southern latitudes.

He now sets himself to assemble the evidence from the vast array of *Discovery* samples and does so with great effect. He divides the Southern Ocean's continuous extension through its 360 degrees of longitude round the globe into 20 degree sectors, thus: 0—20° E., 20°—40° E., . . . 160° E.—180°, 180°—160° W., . . . 40°—20° W., 20° W.—0. He then records the *frequency of the occurrence* of each species in each sector; he is not recording relative quantities but the percentage of the samples in any particular sector which contained the species in question. The results are most easily appreciated by looking at one of his diagrammatic charts which I reproduce opposite; this is of the principal species of the Crustacea and is from the samples obtained by the

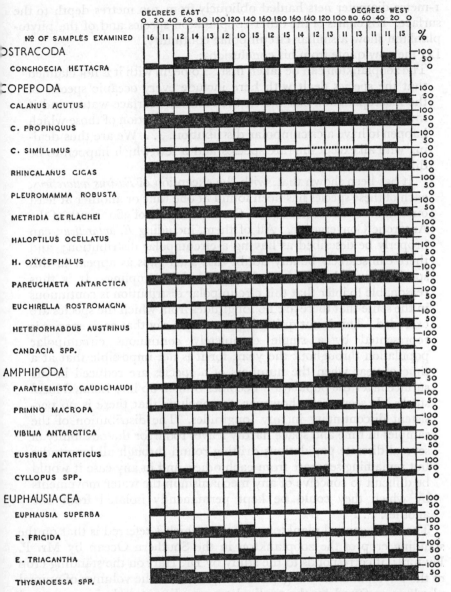

The occurrence of some species of zooplankton in all longitudes around the Antarctic zone of the Southern Ocean showing the percentage frequency of occurrence in samples taken within every 20° of longitude. One of three similar charts, illustrating Mr. A. de C. Baker's *Discovery Report* of 1954, and dealing with all the major species of the zoo and phytoplankton of the Antarctic zone. From *D.R.*, vol. xxvii.

1-metre diameter nets hauled obliquely from 100 metres depth to the surface. His charts of the other zoöplankton species and of the phytoplankton show a similar circumpolar continuity.

Let me now quote from his conclusions:

The zoöplankton can be taken first. To begin with it is not claimed that the species dealt with here include every oceanic species of the macroplankton existing in the Antarctic surface water, and it must be made clear that there has been no selection of those which happen to have a circumpolar distribution. . . . We are thus dealing with all except the rare species and a few which happen to be difficult to identify.

It has been shown that, with the exception of *Eusirus antarcticus*, each of these species has been found at one time or another at least once in every 20° sector round the whole circle of 360° south of the Antarctic Convergence. All of them, including *E. antarcticus*, can properly be described as having a circumpolar distribution; and there can scarcely be any doubt that such gaps as appear in this species would be eliminated with further sampling. It is thus reasonable to infer that this circumpolar distribution is continuous in the sense that there are no longitudes from which the species are excluded. This is not quite the same as to say that each species is represented by a single completely continuous circumpolar population throughout the year, for it is not impossible that at a time of year when the numbers of a species are reduced in the surface layer the population becomes broken up into isolated local stocks. It seems safe, however, to conclude that there is no persistent discontinuity in any longitudes. The distribution of the samples in time and space hardly leaves room for the possibility of several discrete populations drifting round through all longitudes but remaining separate from each other, and in any case it would be difficult to conceive of any mechanism in the water movements by which they could be kept permanently isolated from one another. . . .

The other general plankton report to which I referred is that on the standing crop of the zoöplankton in the Southern Ocean by Mr. P. Foxton[1]; it corresponds to the study by Dr. Hart on the standing crop of the phytoplankton but gives a comparison of the volumes of animal plankton as found by the vertical 70 cm. diameter closing nets used in series from 1,000 metres to the surface at 366 stations. The results show little seasonal variation in the total crop over the whole 1,000 metre column of water, but confirm Mackintosh's findings that the

[1]*Discovery Reports*, vol. xxviii, pp. 191-236, 1956.

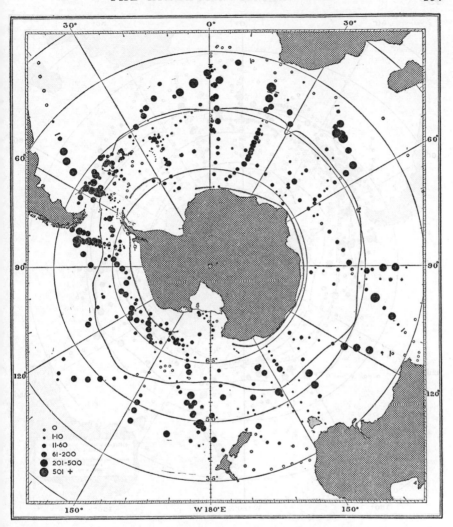

The distribution of the arrow-worm *Sagitta gazellae* in the top 100 metres of water in the Southern Ocean as shown by the 1 metre diameter tow-nets hauled obliquely from 100 metres' depth to the surface. The Antarctic Convergence is shown as a continuous line and closer to the continent a serrated line represents the normal position of the edge of the ice-pack in March. The Sub-Tropical Convergence is shown as a short line at right angles to each line of stations which crossed it, and is the contemporary position found by reference to the continuous thermograph used by the *Discovery II* and not a mean position. From Mr. P. M. David's *Discovery Report* in vol. XXVII. 1955.

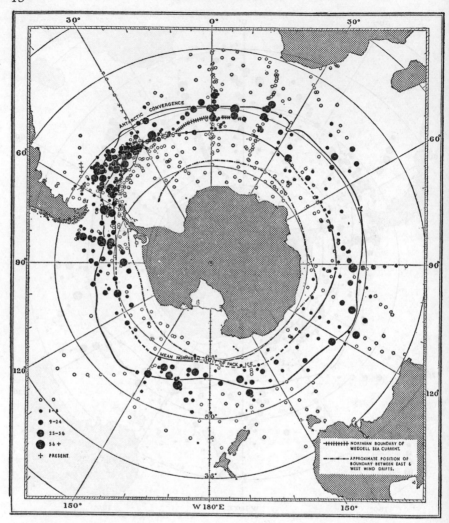

The distribution of the adolescent and adult *Euphausia triacantha* (a distinct species but close relative of the krill *E. superba*) in the top 100 metres of water in the Southern Ocean as shown by the 1 metre diameter tow-nets hauled obliquely from 100 metres to the surface. Labelled lines show the mean position of the Antarctic Convergence and the mean northern limit of the pack-ice, while other lines (see reference in right lower corner of chart) mark the northern boundary of the Weddell Sea current and the boundary between east and west wind drifts. From Mr. A. de C. Baker's *Discovery Report*, vol. XXIX, 1959.

bulk of the plankton in the summer is in the upper layers and lower down in the warm deep current during the winter. There is a gradual increase in the crop from lower to higher latitudes reaching a maximum between 50° and 55° S. with some falling off in the still colder waters farther south; it is pointed out, however, that these nets do not give good catches of the larger macroplankton such as the krill so that the total crop farther south is almost certainly higher than is shown by these nets. We saw that Baker showed there was little variation in the *frequency* of the occurrence of the plankton animals round the pole; here Foxton shows that there is actually very little circumpolar variation in the *quantity* of their standing crop as well; but again the krill must be left out of this—and indeed we saw that Marr showed a marked asymmetry in their circumpolar distribution.

In addition to these general studies which give us a picture of the broad planktonic content of our realm, there have been, and are being, made some splendid researches into the biology and distribution of some of the more important individual zoöplankton species based upon the material in the great *Discovery* collections. We have already discussed at some length that of the krill which has such a direct relation to our work on the whales; space will now only allow me to give brief references to the *Reports* on the others for the benefit of zoological readers who wish to go further into this field. One of the first was that on *Rhincalanus gigas*, one of the most prominent copepods of the macroplankton, by Dr. F. D. Ommanney (*Discovery Reports*, vol. XIII, pp. 277-314, 1936). Then there are the studies by Mr. P. M. David on the distribution of the arrow-worms (Chaetognatha); his first (vol. XXVII, pp. 235-78, 1955) is on the species *Sagitta gazellae* which he shows has two distinct races, one to the north and the other to south of the Antarctic Convergence, and his second (vol. XXIX, pp. 199-228, 1958) on the remaining species. I reproduce his chart of the distribution of *S. gazellae* on p. 497. In his latter *Report* he shows that the form which, in the South, we had hitherto regarded as *Sagitta planktonis*, is really a new species which he names after James Marr: *Sagitta marri*. Mr. A. de C. Baker has made a special *Report* (vol. XXIX, pp. 309-40, 1959) on *Euphausia triacantha*, the close relative of the krill which occurs in a circumpolar band just to the north of the latter's distribution as seen in the chart opposite; it does not occur in anything approaching the high numbers of *superba*, nor does it form dense swarms, but it carries out a most extensive daily vertical migration as we found at South Georgia (p. 346). Then Mr. P. Foxton has given us an account of *Salpa fusiformis* and related species (vol. XXXII, pp. 1-32, 1961) in which he shows us that the various forms hitherto grouped

under the name *fusiformis* are really four distinct species of which two,
S. thompsoni and *S. gerlachei* are new ones[1]. Miss J. E. Kane is now
preparing a *Report* on that common planktonic amphipod *Parathemisto
gaudichaudi* and Mr. K. J. H. Andrews ane on the important copepod
Calanoides acutus.[2] The arrow-worms and this amphipod are important
side links to the whale story in that they are voracious predators which
will prey upon the young stages of the krill.

Now we must leave this great kingdom of the krill which the
Discovery expeditions have explored so effectively for the future of
mankind. As one who was only concerned with the beginnings on the
old ship I can say 'Bravo' to all those who followed on and so successfully extended the work, winter and summer, right round the Antarctic.
In this short space I have only dealt in the most summary fashion with
just part of what has been achieved. As most of it was done by others,
after my time South, I can, I think, without appearing to boast, say
I believe it to be a wonderful achievement—a credit to the British
scientific effort. I feel this wants saying, for hitherto the work has
remained hidden within heavy tomes. Quite recently a well-known
journal (not produced in Britain), with a world-wide sale, issued a
special number devoted to the Antarctic; it is a publication which
endeavours to present the up-to-date findings of science to the
intelligent general reader. In it was a special article entitled 'The
Oceanic Life of the Antarctic' which extended for 16 pages but, would
you believe it, it made no reference whatever to the results of the
Discovery expeditions: seven major expeditions whose main purpose
was to explore the life of this ocean.

I hope my chapter may induce one or two people to take down
some of the 34 volumes of the *Reports* and look inside them. In an
Appendix (p. 523) I am providing a guide to them arranged under
headings such as hydrology, plankton, whale research, etc.; hitherto
it has been impossible for anyone to know, without looking into them
all, in which volumes any particular subject is treated, as no index of
their contents has yet been published. Going through the *Reports* I
find that in our first two years the old *Discovery* and the *Scoresby*
brought back specimens of 432 species of marine animals new to
science, and altogether, including the later expeditions, the total to
date is 763 with many more to be revealed as further specialist reports
come in.

This great Antarctic Zone of the Southern Ocean, so rich in life,

---

[1]Since this was written Mr. Foxton has published another important monograph on the
distribution and life history of *Salpa thompsoni* in *Discovery Reports*, vol. xxxiv, 1966.

[2]Both now published in *Discovery Reports*, vol. xxxiv, 1966.

is bound to play an increasing part in Man's affairs of the future. Even if he is foolish enough to over-exploit the whale to bring about the failure of his fisheries, I believe the organic resources of this great realm must come to provide more direct sources of nourishment to the world's increasing populations. So far it has not proved efficient to harvest the plankton of the temperate seas, but these great swarms of krill are quite another proposition. They are concentrated ready for gathering; nature, by evolving the great whales, has pointed the way to their exploitation. Just as the great shoals of small fish off the coast of Peru are now being swept up from the seas to make fish-meal, so in time, I believe, great steam or diesel—nay perhaps atomic— artificial 'whales' will collect the krill either to make meal for livestock or to feed man more directly with a novel vitamin-rich sea-food. We have seen the extraordinary growth-promoting properties of the krill in nourishing the whale—a mammal like ourselves.

I became convinced of this as soon as I saw the loads of krill drawn from the waters round South Georgia. Before we return to the old ship and our passage home let me quote from the lecture I gave to the Royal Geographical Society, after our return just 38 years ago, as published in *The Geographical Journal* (vol. LXXII, p. 218, 1928). I had already referred in the lecture to the remarkable prophecy about the future of whaling at South Georgia made by Dr. George Forster when he accompanied Captain Cook in the *Resolution* (that which I have quoted in chapter 8, p. 189) and, after discussing the charting of great plankton zones as a contribution to the geography of the world, I went on to say:

These characters are not fixed like the forest and deserts of the land; but within certain limits are moved by the ocean currents and increased or diminished in size and density by the climatic conditions from time to time. This makes their geography not impossible, but more difficult; at first we can only sketch out roughly the possible limits of these zones. Later, when our knowledge of the physical conditions underlying their formation, growth, and decline becomes more complete we can say that we may expect such and such in this and that season and in this and that year. We may be sure that as time goes on these results of oceanography will be welded more and more into the geography of the world as a whole. At present, in general works of geography, little is said about the ocean beyond the movements of water masses and the deposits of dead shells on the bottom. It is the biological, as well as the physical, characters in this and that stretch of water which are important, affecting man through the fisheries;

making cities prosperous and sending men across the world to colonise barren lands. The great regions of summer plankton growth at each Pole, brought about by the long days of sunlight and perhaps the absence of certain bacteria, are almost as striking as the ice-cap itself, and as much stores of solar energy as the plains of wheat and grazing land of lower latitudes. It would not be a bolder prophecy than that of Forster quoted above to say that the time will come in the not too distant future when man will derive food or other power direct from these vast resources.

I would only add one comment: the great Antarctic zone of the Southern Ocean is, of course, so much larger, and so much more important, than its counterpart to the north.

Yes, I feel sure that the krill will be harvested in the future on a very big scale—but I must add a word of warning. It must not be thought, because the Southern Ocean is so vast and large parts of it are naturally protected from exploitation by being covered by pack ice for much of the year, that it would not be necessary to exercise any control over such a fishery. Every effort should be made before it is too late to consider how it would affect the general life of the Antarctic including the remaining stock of whales. If possible such a taking of krill should be limited to certain areas until it is known what effect it may have. An international commission should appoint scientists, organize expeditions to investigate the problems, and then make recommendations. Without such guidance Man is most likely to blunder again.

Knowledge of the Southern Ocean: thirty-three volumes of *Discovery Reports* and more to come; since this was drawn (in 1966) another volume has been published.

CHAPTER 22

HOMEWARD BOUND

[When the *Discovery* arrived at Simonstown Rolfe Gunther and I transferred back to her from the *William Scoresby* which now sailed direct for England with Dilwyn John to get together the equipment for the next season at South Georgia. We on the *Discovery* sailed two days later, on 18th July, to make plankton and hydrological observations off West Africa and visit a number of points where whaling stations or floating factories had worked in recent years; we wanted to find out all we could about the number and kinds of whale going up the coast and if possible to get information about breeding grounds. We are homeward bound, the main work is done and the reader may be getting tired; I will select just sufficient incidents to give a sketch of this tropical voyage which for me, at any rate, had almost the quality of a dream.]

Saturday, 23rd July. We began by repeating last year's line of observations across the whaling grounds off Saldanha Bay. The plankton was less abundant, as was natural since we are now in midwinter; there were only a few of the small blue salps and the brilliant iridescent *Sapphirina* which had been such a feature before.

The phosphorescence has been extraordinary these last few nights. The surface of the water and especially the wash of the ship has been spangled with flashing lights which probably come from euphausiids and copepods; and occasionally, like a torch among the sparks, has passed a brilliant *Pyrosoma*. As a background to these fireworks there has been the milky glow, with a brighter fringe along the edge of the ship, caused by much smaller organisms, most likely dinoflagellates. Two nights ago three or four dolphins kept pace with us and each not only glowed, but, like a rocket, left a trail of flame behind; being alive, they were more exciting than any rockets, and would sweep in graceful curves, crossing one another's tracks, closing in together and bursting apart again, or sometimes turning sharply to dart across our bows.

Dr. Kemp on the way over from the Falklands made an interesting discovery concerning phosphorescence. While passing through large patches of *Pyrosoma* he found that when an electric torch had been shone over the side and then switched off the area which had been covered by the light at once became a circle of brilliant luminescence; where before only a few were giving a display, after passing under the light every colony was stimulated into response.

All to-day we have been bowling along at 8 or 9 knots with all sails set in a good following breeze; we have new sails bent: a brilliant white in the sun against an intense blue sky. To-morrow we pass into the tropic of Capricorn. During the last few evenings our plankton nets, which we are now using every night, have brought in a host of beautiful specimens; conspicuous were some hyperiid amphipods with large and brilliant sapphire eyes, and the delicate, transparent larvae of mantis shrimps with their points picked out in shining metallic green.

Wednesday, 27th July. On Monday night we got into a swarm of large salps, *Salpa maxima*, as well as vast quantities of cymbulid pteropods, those beautiful creatures with large butterfly-like 'wings,' riding in 'carriages' for all the world like glass slippers. Hitherto we have only taken the latter in ones and twos; we had never imagined it possible for them to be so numerous as to fill our large tow-net bucket to overflowing. There were two kinds present: *Cymbulia*, the same or a similar species to the one we have had before, and *Corolla*, a genus new to us, with a cruder form of 'slipper.'

Saturday, 30th July. On Thursday afternoon we dropped anchor in Elephant Bay, a little south of Benguela on the coast of Angola (Portuguese West Africa), where a whaling station was established by the Norwegians as early as 1910. We found, as we had feared from reports, that it had closed at this season. As we landed at a little jetty we were met by Mr. Tyler Thompson, an Englishman who lives at Equamima, the next bay, where he has a bungalow and small plantation; he looks after the whaling station when it is closed and had come to show us round. We found the station, which is a large one, in excellent condition. . . .

Yesterday a number of us, officers and crew, turned out before breakfast to fish with a seine net from the beach to get fresh food for the ship; we were rewarded with a good catch, the commonest fish being a beautiful pink and silver bream of which we got over forty. Along the beach were the holes of ocypodid crabs and occasionally we would see one run across the sand and down its burrow like a rabbit, running on the very tips of its legs. . . . Inside the headland the beach gives way to a rampart of broken rock fragments, fallen from the cliff above, and these, between tide marks, are thickly covered with excellent rock oysters; never have oysters seemed so good as when broken off and eaten on the spot—a delicious early morning appetizer.

After breakfast a party of us set off to look at the country. Passing across the very dry belt against the shore we entered a wide valley through which wound a dried-up river course; here was more vegetation—thick clumps of bush and small trees nearly all of the acacia type except one of great beauty with scarlet honeysuckle-like flowers. Here, too, we saw more butterflies, the more common were two species reminding us of clouded-yellows and Bath-whites at home, and a fine black and white Daneid; while fluttering close over the ground were the smallest blue butterflies I have ever seen. From time to time we put up a number of steinbuck as well as many of the little dik-diks (tiny buck standing only a foot or two in height); they were the only game we saw. Birds were also scarce. . . . Whilst there was nothing extraordinary to relate, it gave us a good impression of dry tropical Africa: the blinding sunlight on the sand and rock, the scattered clumps of bush casting the only shadows to be seen, the occasional flash of a gaudy butterfly, the run of a lizard and over all the oppressive hot silence broken at intervals by the cry of some bird or the drone of a large carpenter bee. . . .

Monday, 1st August. This afternoon we steamed into the harbour of São Paolo de Loanda, entering from the north into a lagoon inside a long spit of sand which joins the mainland to the south. A more tropical scene it would be difficult to imagine: the long bank of sand is lined with coconut palms and groups of native huts. The sun has just set flushing the sky with an afterglow of gold, merging into crimson and again in turn into a line of violet haze along the horizon behind the palms which now stand out in deep purple silhouette. The natives paddle to and fro in their quaint dug-out canoes and some glide along with a small diamond-shaped sail. Loanda itself, the capital of Angola, appears a widely laid-out town with many quite imposing buildings. A new beam wireless station, which has just been opened to give direct communication with Lisbon, dominates the city and offers a striking contrast to the old-fashioned fishing craft with their large lateen sails clustering against the quays. We shall remain here till Thursday, taking in coal from lighters.

I cannot pass over our last two days' voyage without mentioning our oyster feasts. Just before we sailed from Elephant Bay we made a short expedition ashore collecting specimens along the headland and at the same time filling several sacks with the delicious rock-oysters for later consumption, breaking them off with geological hammers. We had an

enormous stock of them and kept them alive by standing them in their
sacks in the shade along the rail and under the hose-pipe taps whose
pumps were kept gently running to provide little cascades of sea water
which continually flowed over them. Before lunch and dinner each
day the oyster party would assemble on the deck with hammers to
break apart the shells which, having grown fused to one another in a
thick encrustation over the rocks, had been broken off in large masses
of a dozen or so at a time. Those pre-luncheon oyster feasts on the deck
below sun-lit sails and the bluest of skies will always remain, I am sure,
among our outstanding gastronomic memories. . . .

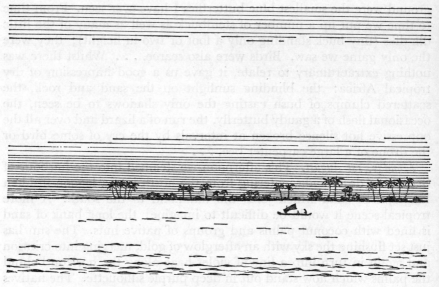

Evening at Loanda, redrawn from a watercolour.

Thursday, 4th August. I must only give the briefest impressions of
Loanda with its scenes of native life, of bullock waggons, shady squares
and little gardens; if somewhat dusty, it is nevertheless clean and with
fine wide streets. The shops are few and there is nothing of peculiar
interest to buy; more interesting are the markets and fish quay. The
main market was a large square courtyard, perhaps an acre in extent,
set about with shady flowering camellias and false-acacia trees, and
surrounded by a colonnade, with an entrance from a street on either
side. Throughout the court, not in ordered rows but anyhow, are the
vendors squatting beside their wares—piles of oranges, melons,
pawpaws, custard-apples and nuts, or cheap and gaudy European

cottons and crude pottery—spread out upon the ground; they are surrounded by groups of gleaming bronze and chocolate natives loosely draped with green and scarlet costumes. Wizened old women smoke pipes of black clay with long carved wooden stems and little naked children play in the sand.

The fish market presents a very different scene, but equally colourful. On a stone flagged floor, in the shade of an extensive roof which is supported on tall iron stanchions, stand the fishmongers in rows with their piles of fish—pink, silver, blue and green—railed off for protection. Here, in contrast to the fruit market, all is noise, crowds surge against the rails bargaining for fish, and up and down walks a native policeman cane in hand. All these figures, being in the shade, stand out in silhouette against the brilliant background of the sunlit quay outside and the glistening blue of the lagoon with the lines of brightly painted fishing craft with furled white sails. . . .

Yesterday, making up a party in three cars, we spent all day motoring through the bush to Calumba on the Cuanza River. The roads near the coast are mere sandy tracks and our cars pitched and rolled like little boats in a choppy sea. At first the way led over rather open country, dry grassland with single or isolated groups of trees at intervals. . . . There were also tall pawpaw trees with their large ripening melon-like fruit, but more characteristic were the baobabs. I know no other trees that I should call ugly, but these baobabs are almost sinister with what appears a grossly 'unnatural' form. They have enormous trunks, great rounded cones, out of all proportion to their slender branches, and appear like the shorn stumps of giant trees just beginning to sprout again; they bear large, sausage-shaped nuts, hanging singly at the very ends of the thin branches which curve over under their weight. Their trunks are nature's water tanks; their soft and spongy tissues store water from the rainy seasons. So numerous can they be that they offered, so we were told, considerable obstruction to the laying of the Loanda railway; their huge trunks, often 30 feet in circumference, could not be felled by ordinary means, but were cut through by a wire made red hot by electricity.

As we went on, the bush became thicker and the baobabs were joined by equal numbers of tall cactus-like euphorbia trees rising to some forty or fifty feet; these, with their small but bright magenta flowers, together with the baobabs presented a most bizarre landscape. Here in the thicker bush we stopped for a time to look at the insect life. . . . Scarlet and black oil beetles were found on most flower heads or seen flying lazily with their heavy bodies hanging vertically below their brilliant outspread wing cases. Ants, of course, there were in plenty and particularly noticeable were the 'weaver ants' which, with silken threads, draw together the leaves of bushes to form a 'nest' the size of two clenched fists. Clustering over their outer walls were large ants which, as we came near, set up an extraordinary rhythmic movement; a quick bending and stretching of the legs made the whole company jerk up and down in perfect unison to form one pulsating mass. . . .

Proceeding farther the bush became still thicker and from time to time we were stopped by branches growing out into the roadway; flocks of grey parakeets flew overhead and troops of monkeys crossed the road ahead of us. Eventually we came out on high ground over-looking a wide valley down the centre of which wound a broad band of gleaming silver, the great Cuanza River lined with palm trees or here and there with wide reed-covered swamps. The valley is the home of crocodile, hippopotamus and buffalo; and where it nears the sea and becomes brackish the manatee is occasionally to be found. From this point the road dipped down and we entered a region of massed euphorbia trees, like a cactus forest; they stretched their stumpy, lumpy, finger-like branches up above our heads. After descending on a winding track we emerged on the valley bed and skirted a swamp where there were tall adjutant birds and graceful cranes; in the little thorn bushes were many nests of weaver birds, delicately-woven spheres with the downward pointing tubes which form their door-ways. . . . [So my journal goes on, but I must refrain from giving any more in a book about the sea; I only intend to give something of the flavour of the voyage home.]

This morning we sailed from the lagoon taking a trawl in shallow water as we went; we got a good haul of the same bream and John Dory-like fish we had caught at Elephant Bay.

Sunday, 7th August. Last night there was an unusual display of phosphorescence. Just before midnight Mr. Sanderson, the officer of the watch, called us up to look at some remarkable patches in the sea—and extraordinary they certainly were. On both sides of the ship were distinct patches of a bright milky phosphorescence each some 20 to 30 yards across. Unfortunately by the time we had got out the tow-nets we had passed them. All night the bow wave and the wake of the ship were brilliantly luminous and this we found on putting over a tow-net was caused by vast numbers of small peridinian-like dino-flagellates. I have little doubt that the patches we saw were caused by the same flagellates being agitated by some larger organisms which were occurring in dense swarms; by their size and nature, I would expect them to have been small salps, of which we took a number in the net, and the form of the patches were like those of salps we saw on the way out when approaching Cape Town.

To-night in the rich plankton samples we have taken a number of small crustacea of the order Cladocera, related to the common water-fleas of our ponds, lakes and rivers. I only know of three truly marine genera of such animals and our specimens certainly do not belong to one of these. We are now not far from the mouth of the Congo so that they may have been carried in the outflow of that great river[1]; the probability that this is so is heightened by our finding in the same sample the larvae of the river prawn *Artia*. The discharge from a large river must carry many freshwater animals to their doom in an uncongenial salty world.

Wednesday, 10th August. We have had another glimpse of tropical Africa: this time at Port Gentil lying just inside—the northern side—of Cape Lopez on the coast of French Equatorial Africa. Here was a whaling station which had been working earlier in the season but was now closed and there was no one who could give us any idea of the number or species of whales taken. Gentil is becoming an important port on the west coast on account of its big trade in oukomme, the so-called Gaboon mahogany, which is a fine wood of mahogany-like appearance but of an entirely different family. There is no city here; a luxuriant forest appears to line the shore which is broken here and there by mangrove swamps, and there are groups of fine coconut palms.

Gentil is a long straggling township with the houses, stores, government buildings, post office, banks and so on set out at intervals amongst the trees in pleasant gardens flaming with bougainvillæa and hibiscus. Wide concrete paths take the place of roads and along the edge of the shore beneath the shady trees runs a pathway of oukomme wood; beside which are the little native stalls where they sell fruit, bread, tobacco pipes, strings of beads and artificial jewellery. Beneath the tall coconut palms the natives are at work upon the oukomme wood, sawing up the great trunks, or splitting up log ends for roadway material by driving in wedges; many others are out upon the floating logs, which have come down the river, and with long bamboos are punting them into the little 'harbours' formed of lines of other logs chained together, or are gathering them into great rafts to be towed out to the waiting ships. . . .

The mangrove swamps, where small streams run into the sea, are of special interest to the naturalist. Most conspicuous are the long-clawed fiddler crabs which cover the flat surface of the mud in

[1]The salinity at this station was subsequently shown to be only 29%o instead of the usual 35%o for oceanic water.

thousands. As you approach they all start running off in the opposite direction holding up the single claw above their heads, but if you sit quite still they will return to normal life and you will see them in the muddy water shovelling organic matter towards the mouth or here and there are males in courtship standing before a female and raising and lowering the long claw (which she does not possess). There are other smaller crabs here as well, but soon your attention is attracted by a number of small animals running over the wet mud, jumping from stone to stone, or swimming in the water. What can they be? They look like some kind of newt, yet who has ever seen a newt as agile as the fastest lizard. They have large eyes like those of a frog but sticking out of the very top of their heads almost on stalks; then you notice that they have no hind limbs and that they are progressing by a quick flicking of their fore limbs. Suddenly you realise that they are fish! They are the famous running and climbing mud skipper, *Periophthalmus*, found on mangrove swamps all over the world. What we took for limbs are fins, by the strokes of which they can leap forward at great speed and are most difficult to catch. However, by driving them round the piles of a wooden pier they could be caught by an accomplice waiting in ambush. Very unfair, but all in the cause of science!

Some of the English timber merchants who came off to dinner with us, invited some of us back with them in one of their large native surf boats. This was paddled by a crew of six, three on each side, controlled by a lusty coxswain standing in the stern; he steered with a large oar and led a curious chant in which the crew joined with a repetitive chorus as they plied their paddles. Owing to the state of the tide we were unable to land on the beach and had to make our way along a line of floating logs, some of which were inclined to roll if you stepped on them without due care; it was not too easy in spite of a good moon. It satisfied all one's ideas of a tropical night: a stroll beneath the palms with an occasional fire-fly flashing by and then a pleasant hour seated with our friends on the veranda of their bungalow talking and looking out over the misty blue night from which came the voices of innumerable frogs. And then the return to the ship by the same boat. By joining in to the chorus of the native chant we apparently gave the crew great encouragement, for they paddled with renewed energy and great delight, sending the spray flying up on either side. The *Discovery* herself seemed enchanted as we approached, riding on a gentle swell with her lights reflecting in the water; her masts, spars and rigging shining in the pale moonlight against a starry sky.

This morning, after leaving, we put down the otter trawl but caught only a few fish; among them, however, was the remarkable porcupine fish *Diodon*, covered all over with spines and able to blow itself up like a football. On the way up it also picked up some of those curious square jelly-fish, so well named Cubomedusae, which have most powerful stinging powers. . . .

Friday, 12th August. The nets on Wednesday night produced a single specimen of a new species of *Sergestes*, a very remarkable planktonic prawn bearing many highly developed light organs each with a large, almost spherical, crystal lens. There were also some of the beautiful spotted and lilac-coloured jelly-fish *Pelagia*. . . .

Yesterday we saw a number of large thresher sharks jumping, but they did not come near the ship.

We are now approaching the island of Annobon, which is the farthest out of a series of four islands in the Gulf of Guinea of which Fernando Po is the first and largest. In all the western hemisphere it is surely most like one's dream of a South Pacific island. Until to-day I had hardly dared to hope that we should reach it, but it now lies in our track to the south-east trades we are making for and we shall certainly call. It is only a small island, about 4 miles long and 2 miles across presenting, as the Encyclopaedia Britannica says, 'a succession of beautiful valleys and steep mountains, covered in rich woods and luxuriant vegetation, and culminating in the Pico de Fogo (about 3,000 feet) an extinct volcano with a crater lake.' It was discovered by the Portuguese on New Year's Day, 1472, hence its name, and its Negro inhabitants are said to be descendants of a cargo of slaves ship-wrecked there in the sixteenth century. It was ceded by the Portuguese to Spain in 1778, but the islanders revolted against their new masters and, so it is said, after a period of anarchy, set up a unique form of government; a body of five natives each of whom in turn held the office of governor for a period measured by the call of ships, a change taking place at every tenth ship to visit the island! In the latter part of last century, however, the authority of Spain was re-established. As I have been writing this, word has come that the island is in sight. It is just midnight, and there, under a full moon, on a silver sea is the grey outline of Annobon on our port bow: it rises to a lofty peak, above which, halo-like, hangs a white cloud.

Before turning in I must record some remarkable patches of dis-coloured water which occurred during part of this afternoon. They were of yellowy rust colour and extended in long parallel bands across the sea in a SW.-NE. direction, about 30 yards across and as seen from the mast head extended some thousand yards in length; many may have been even longer. They occurred at irregular intervals, some a hundred yards apart, others at a greater distance. A tow-net showed that they were caused by vast numbers of colonial radiolarians. Throughout the afternoon the beautiful little floating snails *Ianthina*, with violet-blue shell and little rafts of bubbles to support their mass of eggs, have been very common; at times the surface was speckled with their little white spots of froth almost like a meadow with the 'cuckoo-spittle' (made by the little frog-hopper insects) in summertime at home. *Ianthina* is included in Plate 4 (p. 96).

Both this afternoon and evening we took a number of magnificent siphonophores of two genera *Crystallodes* and *Hippopodius*. The former, *C. vitrea*, are long cylindrical colonies made up of closely fitting swimming bells and bracts, with a small float above and beautiful rose-pink polyps within; they are so fragile, however, as to be impossible to secure intact, for their swimming bells break off at the slightest touch. *Hippopodius* has larger, but fewer, swimming bells, and its polyps are orange and scarlet. *Crystallodes vitrea* is shown in the sketch opposite and another species of *Hippopodius* in Plate 4.

These last few days have been exceedingly hot, steamy relaxing days with calm oily seas. For some time now we have had a sail swimming bath fixed up on the fore deck just abaft the forecastle head. Before dinner to-night, after a sweltering day, I enjoyed a most memorable bathe; the newly risen moon was shining through the rigging, and the water, as if in some magic bath, was alive with sparks of phosphorescence.

Saturday, 13th August. Annobon has more than come up to expectations; it is indeed one of the dream islands of the world.

I had given instructions that I should be called at sunrise so that I could make a sketch as we approached; however, they let me sleep on, as there was a thick mist, and when I came on deck just before breakfast we were already anchored about three-quarters of a mile from the shore and the island was now only just appearing as the vapours melted with the mounting sun. To the left the land rose steeply from the sea and was covered with luxuriant vegetation, but to the right it came up more gradually from a long stretch of silver sand; above the wooded crests of these foothills rose the sugarloaf-like summit of the island just clearing from the clouds. Along the beach were lines of coconut palms and on the more gradual slopes they were mixed with several other kinds; along the shore too were native huts and row upon row of canoes being got ready for launching by a crowd of excited natives. Through glasses we could see them coming down to the beach with baskets laden with fruit. Upon a prominent ridge above the palms was a large white building which I confess, for a moment, took away something of the charm of the scene; but it was no more than the combined Roman Catholic church and house of the Spanish missionaries: the only solid building on the island.

Presently a large dug-out canoe put off flying the Spanish flag at the bows; it proved to be the governor and the doctor, in the state canoe paddled by a crew of natives. As unfortunately none of us understood more than a very little Spanish, and they spoke no other

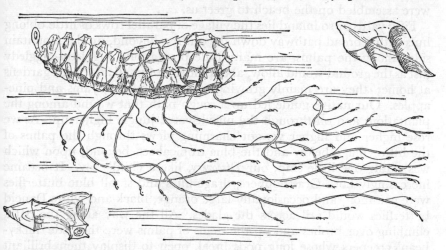

The siphonophore *Crystallodes vitrea* gently swimming in a horizontal position with its stinging tentacles trailing out to form a fishing net. Immediately behind the small float (on the left) are ten swimming-bells, five pointing upwards and five downwards, one of which is shown separately and slightly enlarged (below left); behind these are masses of protective bracts sheltering the reproductive bodies and the feeding polyps which send out the long tentacles. One of the bracts is shown enlarged (top right). Redrawn from Haeckel ($\times \frac{1}{2}$).

language, it was with some effort, humorous at times, that we entertained them. We managed however, with some difficulty, to get some particulars of the whaling factory ships which had visited the island in the past and also to learn of a mountain lake which they said contained a prawn. Dr. Kemp had heard that there was a blind prawn in a similar lake on St. Thomas, the next island, and so was most anxious if possible to obtain specimens from Annobon. We arranged for a guide to take us to the lake, and made all preparations for a day's collecting ashore.

The governor evidently had complete control over the population; not a canoe put to sea until he had returned and given permission. As soon as he had done so, and as we were leaving for the shore in our

R

whaler, they all started for the ship. What a sight it was: a hundred canoes or more approaching the ship at once; large ones paddled by four natives and small ones, only a few feet in length, holding only one, but all laden with bananas, oranges and pineapples. As we went towards the shore we passed through the middle of them, and the governor came out to pilot us to the best landing spot, for there were many rocks and a big surf breaking. A crowd of women and children were assembled on the beach to greet us. . . .

Fifty yards or so inland lies the village of parallel rows of little oblong huts with a broad pathway down the centre. Beyond, up the mountain side among the palms, are many little plantations, higgledy-piggledy just as the ground would allow, about the size of small allotment gardens at home; they are mainly growing maize, mandioca, yams and pineapples. Our native guide led up a rough path that wound among the plantations and on through the uncultivated jungle higher up. As we rose higher and higher we got charming views through the palms of the little village below and the blue tropical sea beyond, upon which was riding one little ship, our *Discovery*, like a child's toy. It became increasingly hot. Grasshoppers, dragonflies and small blue butterflies were common, and occasionally large orange, black and white Daneid butterflies would sail across the glades. All the way along the path, climbing over bushes and up the stems of palms were the little 'lucky-bean' creepers whose long pods break open to display their brilliant scarlet and black beans; they are much favoured by the natives for personal adornment and for making necklaces for their children. . . . Here too were many orange trees and banana palms growing wild together and laden with fruit; the former were the very bitter kind, having almost a quinine flavour, but nevertheless very refreshing in the heat of the day. Also growing together with them were many pineapples wherever there was a little space between the trees; most of them were unripe and very red. There were also rattan cane plants and chillies. After climbing for over 800 feet we dropped down a little through a thick growth of trees, the side of the old crater and came to the lake—an almost circular basin at the bottom of the bowl; along its edge flashed innumerable gaudy dragonflies, some blue and others vivid scarlet. We fished a long time with the net for the prawn we sought, but failed to get it in the flesh. We managed, however, to secure its ghost, in the form of its complete cast skin: a replica in thinnest cuticle which proved its existence and, if carefully preserved, may be sufficient to establish its specific identity. There were many parrots along the edge of the forest and a long-billed crane flew once or twice across the lake but would not alight. . . .

On our way back down the mountain we were surprised, and at first not a little alarmed, to find a great deal of the forest in our path was on fire or had burnt. The blaze must have started far over the other side of the slope and worked across; being very dry the vegetation burned quickly and large stretches that had been so beautiful before were now black and brown. Here and there the fire burnt furiously and swarms of grasshoppers, moths, beetles and other insects flew before it; frightened lizards ran and were evidently so bedazed that they could be caught with the greatest ease—a most unusual thing. Burning palm trees presented a spectacular display: in a moment the trunks became pillars of fire and then, as the crowns caught alight they seemed to burst in all directions, in blazing curving lines, as the flames ran out along the radiating fronds and finally, still flaming, dropped their ends to the ground with a trail of sparks. . . .

It was very hot when we reached the beach and some of us sat in the shade of the palms and watched the breaking surf across the shimmering yellow sand. Swimming was said to be dangerous on account of sharks, and in fact a large one was seen cruising round the ship during the day. . . . Just before sundown we were paddled back to the ship in the governor's canoe and we found her laden with bananas, oranges and pineapples in various states of ripeness to last us along the route; we shall be glad of them, for perhaps our hottest period, working on the equator and across the Gulf of Guinea, is just beginning. . . .

Saturday, 20th August. How right was my last entry; the whole of this week, indeed ever since leaving French Congo, it has been exceedingly hot. We are keeping south of the equator to get the full benefit of the south equatorial (or Benguela) current and the SE. trade-winds; very soon, however, in about meridian 17° W. we shall turn north and run the line of stations across the two currents which here pass one another in opposite directions.

For some days now we have been taking some very extraordinary animals in the plankton which none of us zoologists on board can identify as any known creature and we can find nothing like it in the books. Our guess is that it is some very primitive worm-like mollusc— perhaps one of the Neomeniamorpha which has taken to a pelagic life. As we continue to take them in fair numbers, getting ten together in one of last night's hauls, we cannot believe that such a striking animal has not been noticed before on some former expedition[1]. We have also

---

[1]Only after getting home did we find that a similar form had been described by Semper— and is known as Semper's larva, thought to be a larval form of some yet undiscovered adult form.

taken many small and beautiful pelagic sea anemones that appear to make themselves float with some imprisoned bubble of air. Then the remarkable flat leaf-like pelagic sea-slug *Phyllirhoë* has been quite common; the little spots which speckle it are said to be luminous in the dark, but we never succeeded in seeing one lit up. Among the siphonophores we have had more specimens of the fantastic *Crystallodes vitrea* (p. 513). Perhaps the greatest planktonic surprise, however, of the last few days has been the capture of a number of large pteropods both *Clio* and *Cavolinia*, whose shells are covered all over with a growth of little colonial hydroids reminding one of the similar colonies found growing in home waters upon the shells occupied by bottom-living hermit crabs.

We keep saying that this or the next is the finest show of phosphor-

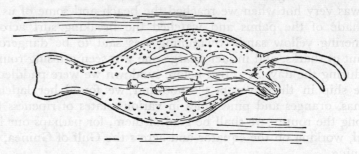

The little, flat, semi-transparent and leaf-like planktonic sea-slug *Phyllirhoe*, × 1½.

escence that we have yet seen, but last night's was certainly the most spectacular of the whole two years' voyage; and it was different from anything we had seen before. All over the surface of the sea, quite apart from the disturbance of the ship, there were countless spontaneous flashes of remarkable brilliance. They lasted but a second or two, then disappeared; but each flash lit up the water for a space of many feet producing great splashes of light like underwater rockets bursting, hundreds of them at a time. By putting out tow-nets we found the performers to be delicate ctenophores (comb-jellies) of the genus *Deiopea*. The display lasted most of the night, but towards midnight it took on a new and even more spectacular appearance in that the animals had in some way become bunched together in long bands stretching across the ocean as far as we could see; the ship passed across band after flashing band, each a hundred yards or so apart. We had not met this ctenophore before, it is one of the lobate forms and according to our books dealing with the group it appears hitherto to have been only known from the Mediterranean. So delicate is its body that all the specimens we secured in our tow-net were smashed to pieces; we then stopped the ship and drew up numerous bucketsful of water and so secured several perfect specimens. Few more exquisite creatures can be imagined than these animals when seen alive swimming in an aquarium; their bodies, of a glass-like transparency with graceful sweeping lines, undergo twisting movements as they glide through the water propelled by their vibrating comb-plates. I have put one into my watercolour plate of tropical ocean life (p. 96).

Monday, 22nd August. We have left the southern hemisphere behind. As a few sailors joining us at Cape Town had not before crossed the Line, a little ceremony was arranged for them. Whilst not so elaborate a performance as on the outward voyage, it followed the same general procedure. Once again, I am sure that all, including the victims, thoroughly enjoyed it. In one way the setting was even better than before for we crossed under full sail—and sail alone, as a good southerly breeze had enabled us to shut off the engines. It was the same colourful pantomime as before but now, performed beneath the sunlit and bellying sails, it took on a new glory. We began the day well by breakfasting off deep-sea prawns and pineapple. Last night our young fish trawl going deeper than usual, brought up a really enormous haul of the large scarlet prawns, *Acanthephyra purpurea*; there were so many that when all the needs of science were satisfied there remained sufficient to make a meal for all who wanted them. And very good they were too. The brightness of their scarlet colouring has to be seen to be believed.

Shutting off the engines has been a great relief to the stokers in the heat. And I was glad of it too for I had kept up my hour's exercise to give, so I said, the stokers a bit more fresh air; in fact, it was because I did not want to be seen to give up when it had become really unpleasant; and stoking in the Gulf of Guinea is certainly hot work— on some days the thermometer registered 150° F in the stoke-hole.

Flying fish have been getting progressively more numerous. They are mostly of the smaller species. To-day shoals of them have been shooting out of the water just ahead of the bows, fanning out, and making long glides of a hundred yards or more to port and starboard; no doubt they take the ship for some monster predator—a whale shark perhaps—and at once make their escape reaction by disappearing from view into the air above. Occasionally one and two of a larger species have been seen.

Thursday, 25th August. This morning we finished the line of six full stations begun on Tuesday night, each fifteen miles apart, across the supposed junction between the Guinea Current flowing from west to east and the Southern Equatorial or Benguela Current flowing in the opposite direction. From our superficial examination of the material as we have gone along, it was impossible to detect any striking change which might be caused by passing from one to the other current; we shall have to wait for a complete analysis before we can know whether our results are of special interest or not.

Tuesday, 30th August. To-night we are passing by the islands of Fogo and São Thiago (St. Jago of the English) of the Cape Verde group on our way to coal at St. Vincent, our last port of call, which we should reach to-morrow night or early on Thursday morning. It has been hazy all day so that the outline of São Thiago, long and rugged, has been only dimly visible to starboard. Fogo, on our port, was quite hidden until sunset when it suddenly emerged as a magnificent silhouette against a vivid afterglow, a crater almost to be classed with Teneriffe and Etna; whilst its base remained screened with mist, its peak stood out in purple against a turquoise-green sky streaked with rose pink wisps of fleecy cloud. Last night we took our last series of routine nets, making station 298.

Friday, 2nd September. Yesterday I saw sunrise behind the rugged and forbidding coast of St. Vincent, whilst over to port, for we were steaming between the two islands, was long and lofty Santo Antão lit by the early sun. St. Vincent, often aptly called a cinder heap, is the most barren island of all the Cape Verde group, being like Ascension Island a mass of extinct volcanoes with very little vegetation; the other islands are also volcanic but more fertile. Santo Antão on its western side grows coffee, sugar and maize, but its eastern face, towards us, is parched by hot winds from the Sahara and presents a patchwork of red, yellow and grey lava and ashes. By breakfast time we had anchored in the wide horseshoe-shaped harbour of Porto Grande, the capital of St. Vincent. Whatever one's opinion about the merits of the town—and we were to find them very few—one cannot deny that, from the water, the scene has a beauty of its own. Like Deception Island the bay is a huge crater into which the sea has broken, but here the best part of one side has gone except for a pinnacle of rock standing up like some man-made monument—an impression heightened by a lighthouse on its summit. Along the centre of the horseshoe stretches the town—a mass of flat-topped houses washed in many colours— all brilliant under the scorching sun. In the foreground, in the blue of the harbour, are many white trading schooners from the neigh- bouring islands; there are also larger steamships here, like ourselves, for coal.

Our anchor had hardly been down a moment before many boats were alongside offering bananas for sale, and others with native boys who dived for pennies. These boys are quite remarkable at swimming down underwater—like little brown frogs—chasing the coins as they flutter into the depths; I never saw one fail to secure one even when it was thrown quite a distance from the boat. . . .

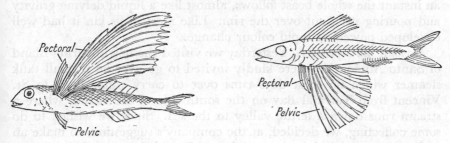

The flying gurnard (*Dactylopterus volitans*) on the left compared with the extinct fossil fish *Chirothrix libanicus*. Each has a similar 'slotted wing', but that of the gurnard is formed by two separate parts of the pectoral fin, whereas that of *Chirothrix* is made by a small pectoral and a greatly enlarged *pelvic* fin placed close together. In the fossil these fins have been pressed down into an unnatural position. The 'slotted wing', like that of an aircraft, prevents stalling when speed is reduced.

There is a great variety of fish to be taken here, some with striking colours, as a black fish like that at Ascension but with a pure white tail, or a bream-like fish covered with bright blue spots upon a scarlet ground. A specimen was also caught of the remarkable flying gurnard *Dactylopterus volitans* which has enormously developed pectoral fins like those of the true flying fish. [They are actually more interesting in that they have a small front section which can be separated from the rest of the fin to give a slit in between the two parts, and this device, aerodynamically, is the same as that of the famous slotted wing invented and applied to aircraft by Handley Page to prevent stalling[1].] . . . To-night

[1]A similar device was evolved quite independently in a pike-like fish *Chirothrix libanicus* which became extinct in the Cretaceous period, only here the effect was produced by the pelvic (or hind paired) fins becoming enormously enlarged wings and the much smaller pectoral fins immediately in front forming the slot, as shown in the sketch of the fossil. This is a good example of parallel or convergent evolution; and there is another in *Thoracopterus*, an extinct fossil fish of the Triassic age which paralleled the normal flying fish *Exococtus*, but belonged to quite a different group (one of the Amioidei). Neither *Thoracopterus* nor *Exococtus* have the slotted wing effect but each have another device, a lengthened lower lobe to the tail to give greater propulsive power when leaving the water; this also probably enables the fish to prolong its flight if it stalls and sinks tail down to the water surface where it can renew its propulsive strokes.

an unusual octopus was caught in a handnet as it was swimming round
the ship; its peculiarity lies in the length, slenderness and rapidity
of movement of its arms. With great speed it explores the confines of
whatever imprisons it (glass bowl, aquarium tank or laboratory sink)
by throwing out its arms as one might throw out a coil of rope; if so
much as the tip of one of these projects over the edge of the vessel, in
an instant the whole beast follows, almost like a liquid defying gravity
and pouring itself out over the rim. Like most of its kin it had well
developed powers of rapid colour change.

Monday, 5th September. Yesterday we visited the neighbouring island
of Santo Antão. We were kindly invited to go over on a small tank
steamer which on most days runs over to carry water back to St.
Vincent from Tarrafal Bay on the south side of the island, where a
stream runs down a fertile valley to the sea. Since we wished to do
some collecting, we decided, at the company's suggestion, to make an
early start at 5 o'clock in the morning. After skirting the barren eastern
side of Antão, we rounded the southerly point and at once saw the
green valley standing out in striking contrast to the neighbouring
slopes of clinker. The stream, as well as supplying the water tanks,
irrigates the valley slopes which are terraced and planted with bananas,
sugar, tobacco and maize in addition to coconut palms and mango
trees. From the shore the water is led by a hose-pipe to our little
steamer which anchors some fifty yards out.

Before going ashore we spent some time collecting examples of
the marine fauna. Dredges were taken off in a rowing boat, dropped
and then pulled across the bottom to the ship by using the capstan,
but the results were disappointing; the plankton, on the other hand,
was superb and included many magnificent comb-jellies (ctenophores)
and siphonophores. The great feature of the day, however, was seeing
many of that most remarkable planktonic animal *Cestus* or, as it is more
poetically called, 'Venus's girdle.' It was the first time that any of us
had come across it in its native haunts although I had seen a living
specimen in the aquarium at Naples. It is a most unusual kind of
ctenophore which is drawn out into a long, flat and transparent band
a foot to two feet in length and an inch or so in width; specimens have
been recorded measuring as much as four and a half feet, but these,
I believe, are very exceptional. Its great beauty lies in its extreme
delicacy, its curving motion in swimming like a letter 'S' slowly coiling
this way and that, and more particularly in the fact that the edges of
the ribbon are lined with little, but brilliantly iridescent, beating plates
which, in the sunlight, sparkle with all the colours of the rainbow, as
they propel the animal slowly upon its sinuous course. (I have included

a drawing of one in Plate 4. p. 96.) They were swimming all round the ship so that we collected many specimens from a rowing boat as well as more of the ctenophore *Dieopea* which had recently given us such a brilliant 'firework display.' We also caught several different siphonophores; apart from our old friend *Crystallodes*, there was a delicate pink and purple species which must be closely related to *Physophora*, and one which appeared to be a species of *Praya* with two very large nectophores and a long trailing chain of smaller units (of bracts, brown polyps and medusoid bodies) of a foot or more in length.

It was the hottest day we have yet experienced and we were certainly glad to get ashore and make our way up the little valley, under the palms and mango trees, to the shady garden of a villa belonging to the water company. From the centre of a lawn rose a massive Indian mohur tree laden with scarlet and orange flowers. Mango trees add to the shade and, together with the flowering oleanders, they frame exquisite views of the glistening sea below, and down one side of the lawn is a flaming bank of crimson bougainvillæa; over it all sweep and glide many swallow-tail butterflies, mostly black and sulphur with occasionally another species flashing an iridescent green.

After exploring and collecting in the ravine higher up, notable for its brilliantly coloured dragonflies, we returned to the boat to find that the crew had caught on their fishing line a considerable rarity: *Panulirus regius*, a large, dark purple crawfish with thin white stripes running down its limbs.

Friday, 9th September. The gale moderated sufficiently on Monday night to allow us to sail early on Tuesday morning. We rounded the south side of Santo Antão, caught a farewell glimpse of our heavenly valley and set our course to the north-west with a strong trade-wind on our starboard beam. The old ship has never looked better, heeling over to port with all the sails drawing full; we are rolling home to dear old England, with Falmouth as our next port of call! We have now stopped all routine stations and are busy finishing copies of the log books, station sheets and so on. To-night we shall pass out of the tropics.

[So ended the last entry in my journal. All that was worth recording of the voyage was over. I might perhaps have dwelt upon our feelings as we approached home after being two years away, but I was too excited, and perhaps too nervous! Sylvia, daughter of (now the late) Professor Walter Garstang, and I had almost got engaged just before I sailed; and then we finally decided by cable, or was it wireless, to announce the event half-way through the voyage. We had expected to sail into Falmouth Bay on the afternoon of 29th September. Mrs. Kemp

R2

and Sylvia had come to meet us, and were watching from the cliffs; a change of wind, however, delayed us and robbed them of the sight of our sails appearing over the horizon—it was dark before we got in. I shall never forget the excitement of dropping anchor, going ashore with Kemp in the ship's boat, and meeting my wife to be for the first time since we were actually engaged—meeting her on the steps of the quay on a dark and windy night. For me it was a fitting end to one voyage and the beginning of another.]

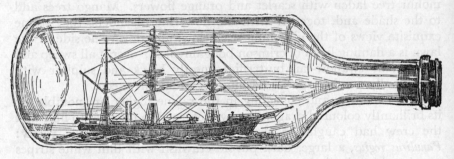

The *Discovery* in a bottle! A sketch of a beautiful model made by the Rev. Basil Turner.

A GUIDE TO THE *DISCOVERY REPORTS*

The following list of all the reports so far issued (up to April 1967), giving volume and page references, and grouped according to subjects, has been prepared to assist those readers who may wish to follow up any of the *Discovery* lines of research in the accounts of the original investigators. It is thought that this may be helpful since no index to the thirty-four volumes has yet been published. In a few instances the same report has been included under more than one heading if it deals with more than one subject.

EQUIPMENT, METHODS AND SHIPS

Discovery Investigations: Objects, Equipment and Methods. By S. KEMP, A. C. HARDY and N. A. MACKINTOSH. Pp. 141-232, vol. I, 1929.

The Royal Research Ship *Discovery II*. By R. A. B. ARDLEY and N. A. MACKINTOSH. Pp. 77-106, vol. XIII, 1936.

The Continuous Plankton Recorder. By A. C. HARDY, with an Appendix: A Test of the Validity of the Continuous Plankton Recorder Method. By A. C. HARDY and NORA ENNIS. Pp. 457-510, vol. XI, 1936.

On the Operation of Large Plankton Nets. By J. W. S. MARR. Pp. 105-20, vol. XVIII, 1938.

STATION LISTS

These lists provide all the basic information about the position, date, hour, depth of any sounding made, type of bottom (if recorded), state of sea and weather, etc., at each station worked on the different voyages of the *Discovery*, the *William Scoresby* and the *Discovery II*. They also record for each station all the hydrological observations made—such as temperature, salinity, density, pH, oxygen, etc., at the different depths sampled—together with details of the various collecting nets, trawls, dredges, etc., that may have been used and the times and depths of their operation. Each list bears the title 'Station List'; the dates and ships concerned are as follows:

R.R.S. *Discovery* (1925-1927) and R.R.S. *William Scoresby* (1926-1927). Pp. 1-140, vol. I, 1929.

R.R.S. *William Scoresby* (1928-1929). Pp. 1-132, vol. III, 1931.

R.R.S. *Discovery II* (1930-1931) and R.R.S. *William Scoresby* (1929-1931). Pp. 1-232, vol. IV, 1932.

R.R.S. *Discovery II* (1931-1933). Pp. 1-226, vol. XXI, 1941.

R.R.S. *Discovery II* (1933-1935). Pp. 1-196, vol. XXII, 1942.

R.R.S. *Discovery II* (1935-1937). Pp. 1-196, vol. XXIV, 1945.

R.R.S. *Discovery II* (1937-1939). Pp. 197-422, vol. XXIV, 1947.

R.R.S. *William Scoresby* (1931-1938). Pp. 143-280, vol. XXV, 1949.

R.R.S. *William Scoresby* (1950). Pp. 211-58, vol. XXVI, 1953.

R.R.S. *Discovery II* (1950-1951). Pp. 299-398, vol. XXVIII, 1957.

HYDROLOGY

A General Account of the Hydrology of the South Atlantic Ocean. By G. E. R. DEACON. Pp. 171-238, vol. VII, 1933.

The Hydrology of the Southern Ocean. By G. E. R. DEACON. Pp. 1-124, vol. XV, 1937.

Notes on the Dynamics of the Southern Ocean. By G. E. R. DEACON. Pp. 125-52, vol. XV, 1937.

On Vertical Circulation in the Ocean due to the Action of the Wind with Application to Conditions within the Antarctic Circumpolar Current. By H. U. SVERDRUP. Pp. 139-70, vol. VII, 1933.

Hydrology of the Bransfield Strait. By A. J. CLOWES. Pp. 1-64, vol. IX, 1934.

A Report on Oceanographical Investigations in the Peru Coastal Current. By E. R. GUNTHER. Pp. 107-276, vol. XIII, 1936.

Phosphate and Silicate in the Southern Ocean. By A. J. CLOWES. Pp. 1-120, vol. XIX, 1938.

Distribution of the Pack-ice in the Southern Ocean. By N. A. MACKINTOSH and H. F. P. HERDMAN. Pp. 285-96, vol. XIX, 1940.

The Antarctic Convergence and the Distribution of Surface Temperatures in Antarctic Waters. By N. A. MACKINTOSH. Pp. 177-212, vol. XXIII, 1946.

The Reliability of Deep-Sea Reversing Thermometers. By H. F. P. HERDMAN and L. H. PEMBERTON. Pp. 229-44, vol. XXIX, 1958.

The Benguela Current. By T. J. HART and R. I. CURRIE. Pp. 123-298, vol. XXXI, 1960.

HYDROGRAPHIC SURVEYS AND SOUNDINGS

Narrative of Hydrographic Survey Operations in South Georgia and the South Shetland Islands, 1926-1930. By J. M. CHAPLIN. Pp. 297-344, vol. III, 1932.

Report on Soundings taken during the *Discovery* Investigations, 1926-1932. By H. F. P. HERDMAN. Pp. 205-36, vol. VI, 1932.

Soundings taken during the *Discovery* Investigations, 1932-1939. By H. F. P. HERDMAN. Pp. 39-106, vol. XXV, 1948.

GEOGRAPHY AND GEOLOGY

The South Sandwich Islands. By S. KEMP and A. L. NELSON, with a Report on Rock Specimens by G. W. TYRRELL. Pp. 133-98, vol. III, 1931.

The South Orkney Islands. By J. W. S. MARR. Pp. 283-382, vol. X, 1935.

Report on Rocks from the South Orkney Islands. By C. E. TILLEY. Pp. 383-90, vol. X, 1935.

Fossil Foraminifera from the Burdwood Bank and their Geological Significance. By W. A. MACFADYEN. Pp. 1-16, vol. VII, 1933.

MacRobertson Land and Kemp Land, 1936. By G. W. RAYNER, with a Report on Rock Specimens, by C. E. TILLEY. Pp. 165-84, vol. XIX, 1940.

Report on Rocks from West Antarctica and the Scotia Arc. By G. W. TYRRELL. Pp. 37-102, vol. XXIII, 1945.

MARINE DEPOSITS

The Marine Deposits of the Patagonian Continental Shelf. By L. HARRISON MATTHEWS. Pp. 175-206, vol. IX, 1934.

The Sea-Floor Deposits: I. General Characters and Distribution. By E. NEAVERSON. Pp. 295-350, vol. IX, 1934.

Faecal Pellets from Marine Deposits. By H. B. MOORE. Pp. 17-26, vol. VII, 1933.

PLANKTON

General Plankton

The Plankton of the South Georgia Whaling Grounds and Adjacent Waters, 1926-1927. By A. C. HARDY and E. R. GUNTHER. Pp. 1-456, vol. XI, 1935.

Observations on the Uneven Distribution of the Oceanic Plankton. By A. C. HARDY. Pp. 511-38, vol. XI, 1936.

The Circumpolar Continuity of Antarctic Plankton Species. By A. DE C. BAKER. Pp. 201-18, vol. XXVII, 1954.

Phytoplankton

On the Phytoplankton of the South-West Atlantic and the Bellingshausen Sea, 1929-1931. By T. J. HART. Pp. 1-268, vol. VIII, 1934.

Rhizosolenia curvata Zacharias, an Indicator Species in the Southern Ocean. By T. J. HART. Pp. 413-46, vol. XVI, 1937.

The Plankton Diatoms of the Southern Seas. By N. I. HENDEY. Pp. 151-364, vol. XVI, 1937.

Phytoplankton Periodicity in Antarctic Surface Waters. By T. J. HART. Pp. 261-356, vol. XXI, 1941.

Zoöplankton, General

Distribution of the Macroplankton in the Atlantic Sector of the Antarctic. By N. A. MACKINTOSH. Pp. 65-160, vol. IX, 1934.

The Seasonal Circulation of the Antarctic Macroplankton. By N. A. MACKINTOSH. Pp. 365-412, vol. XVI, 1937.

The Distribution of the Standing Crop of Zoöplankton in the Southern Ocean. By P. FOXTON. Pp. 191-236, vol. XXVIII, 1956.

Zoöplankton, Special: I. The Antarctic Krill (Euphausia Superba)

The Natural History and Geography of the Antarctic Krill (*Euphausia superba* Dana). By J. W. S. MARR. Pp. 33-464, vol. XXXII, 1962.

The Reproductive System of *Euphausia superba*. By HELENE E. BARGMANN. Pp. 325-50, vol. XIV, 1937.

On the Development and Distribution of the Young Stages of Krill (*Euphausia superba*). By F. C. FRASER. Pp. 1-192, vol. XIV, 1936.

The Development and Life-History of Adolescent and Adult Krill, (*Euphausia superba*). By HELENE E. BARGMANN. Pp. 103-76, vol. XXIII, 1945.

See also HARDY and GUNTHER under 'General Plankton.'

II. Other Species

Lobster-Krill: Anomuran Crustacea that are the Food of Whales. By L. HARRISON MATTHEWS. Pp. 467-84, vol. V, 1932.

The Southern Species of the genus *Euphausia*. By D. DILWYN JOHN. Pp. 193-324, vol. XIV, 1936.

Rhincalanus gigas (Brady), a Copepod of the Southern Macroplankton. By
F. D. OMMANNEY. Pp. 277-384, vol. XIII, 1936.

The Development of *Rhincalanus*. By R. GURNEY. Pp. 207-14, vol. IX,
1934.

The Distribution of *Sagitta gazellae* Ritter-Zahoney. By P. M. DAVID. Pp.
235-78, vol. XXVII, 1955.

The Distribution of the Chaetognatha of the Southern Ocean. By P. M.
DAVID. Pp. 199-228, vol. XXIX, 1958.

Distribution and Life History of *Euphausia triacantha* Holt and Tattersall.
By A. DE C. BAKER. Pp. 309-40, vol. XXIX, 1959.

The Distribution of Pelagic Polychaetes in the South Atlantic Ocean. By
N. TEBBLE. Pp. 161-300, vol. XXX, 1960.

Salpa Fusiformis Cuvier and Related Species. By P. FOXTON. Pp. 1-32, vol.
XXXII, 1961.

The Latitudinal Distribution of *Euphausia* Species in the Surface Waters of
the Indian Ocean. By A. DE C. BAKER. Pp. 309-34, vol. XXXIII, 1965.

The Distribution and Life-History of *Salpa thompsoni* Foxton with observation on a related species *Salpa gerlachei* Foxton. By P. FOXTON. Pp. 1-116,
vol. XXXIV, 1966.

The Distribution and Life-History of *Calanoides Acutus* (Giesbrecht). By
K. J. H. ANDREWS. Pp. 117-62, vol. XXXIV, 1966.

The Distribution of *Parathemisto gaudichandii* (Guer), with observations on
its life-history in the 0° to 20° sector of the Southern Ocean. By J. E. KANE.
Pp. 163-98, vol. XXXIV, 1966.

Plankton of the Benguela Current

The Benguela Current. By T. J. HART and R. I. CURRIE. Pp. 123-298, vol.
XXXI, 1960.

A Preliminary Report on the Ostracoda of the Benguela Current. By E. J.
ILES. Pp. 259-80, vol. XXVI, 1953.

The Pelagic Mollusca of the Benguela Current. Part I First Survey, R.R.S.
William Scoresby, March 1950. With an account of the Reproductive
System and Sexual Succession of *Limacina bullimoides*. By J. E. MORTON.
Pp. 163-200, vol. XXVII, 1954.

The Planktonic Decapod Crustacea and Stomatopoda of the Benguela
Current. Part I First Survey, R.R.S. *William Scoresby*, March 1950. By
MARIE V. LEBOUR. Pp. 219-34, vol. XXVII, 1954.

Cumacea of the Benguela Current. By N. S. JONES. Pp. 279-92, vol. XXVII,
1955.

Euphausiacea of the Benguela Current. First Survey, R.R.S. *William
Scoresby*, March 1950. By B. P. BODEN. Pp. 337-76, vol. XXVII, 1955.

WHALE AND WHALING RESEARCH

Blue, Fin, and Humpback Whales

Southern Blue and Fin Whales. By N. A. MACKINTOSH and J. F. G. WHEELER. Pp. 257-540, vol. I, 1929.

The Age of Fin Whales at Physical Maturity with a note on Multiple Ovulations. By J. F. G. WHEELER. Pp. 403-34, vol. II, 1931.

On the Distribution and Movements of Whales on the South Georgia and South Shetland Whaling Grounds. By S. KEMP and A. G. BENNETT. Pp. 165-90, vol. VI, 1932.

On the Stock of Whales at South Georgia. By J. F. G. WHEELER. Pp. 351-72, vol. IX, 1934.

The Plankton of the South Georgia Whaling Grounds and Adjacent Waters, 1926-1927. By A. C. HARDY and E. R. GUNTHER. Pp. 1-456, vol. XI, 1935.

The Age of Female Blue Whales and the Effect of Whaling on the Stock. By A. H. LAURIE. Pp. 223-84, vol. XV, 1937.

The Humpback Whale, *Megaptera nodosa*. By L. HARRISON MATTHEWS. Pp. 7-92, vol. XVII, 1938.

The Southern Stocks of Whalebone Whales. By N. A. MACKINTOSH. Pp. 197-300, vol. XXII, 1942.

The Habits of Fin Whales. By E. R. GUNTHER. Pp. 113-42, vol. XXV, 1949.

Whale Marking, Progress and Results to December 1939. By G. W. RAYNER. Pp. 245-84, vol. XIX, 1940.

Whale Marking. II. Distribution of Blue, Fin and Humpback Whales marked from 1932 to 1938. By G. W. RAYNER. Pp. 31-8, vol. XXV, 1948.

Dispersal in Blue and Fin Whales. By S. G. BROWN. Pp. 355-84, vol. XXVI, 1954.

The Foetal Growth Rates of Whales with Special Reference to the Fin Whale *Balaenoptera physalus* Linn. By R. M. LAWS. Pp. 281-308, vol. XXIX, 1959.

Reproduction, Growth and Age of Southern Fin Whales. By R. M. LAWS. Pp. 327-486, vol. XXXI, 1961.

The Movements of Fin and Blue Whales within the Antarctic Zone. By S. G. BROWN. Pp. 1-54, vol. XXXIII, 1962.

See also under 'Anatomy and Physiology of Whales' and 'Whale—Miscellaneous.'

Other Species

Notes on the Southern Right Whale, *Eubalaena australis*. By L. HARRISON MATTHEWS. Pp. 169-82, vol. XVII, 1938.

The Sei Whale, *Balaenoptera borealis*. By L. HARRISON MATTHEWS. Pp. 183-290, vol. XVII, 1938.

The Sperm Whale, *Physeter catodon*. By L. HARRISON MATTHEWS. Pp. 93-168, vol. XVII, 1938.

Sperm Whales of the Azores. By R. CLARKE. Pp. 237-98, vol. XXVIII, 1956.

A rare Porpoise of the South Atlantic, *Phocaena dioptrica* (Lahille, 1912). By J. E. HAMILTON. Pp. 227-34, vol. XXI, 1941.

On a Specimen of the Southern Bottlenosed Whale, *Hyperoodon planifrons*. By F. C. FRASER. Pp. 19-36, vol. XXIII, 1945.

Anatomy and Physiology of Whales

The Vascular Network (Retia Mirabilia) of the Fin Whale (*Balaenoptera Physalus*). By F. D. OMMANNEY. Pp. 327-62, vol. V, 1932.

The Urino-Genital System of the Fin Whale (*Balaenoptera Physalus*). By F. D. OMMANNEY. Pp. 363-466, vol. V, 1932.

Some Aspects of Respiration in Blue and Fin Whales. By A. H. LAURIE. Pp. 363-406, vol. VII, 1933.

On the Histological Structure of Cetacean Lungs. By F. HAYNES and A. H. LAURIE. Pp. 1-6, vol. XVII, 1937.

The Wax Plug in the External Auditory Meatus of the Mysticeti. By P. E. PURVES. Pp. 293-302, vol. XXVII, 1955.

See also under 'Blue, Fin and Humpback Whales.'

Whaling

Whaling in the Dominion of New Zealand. By F. D. OMMANNEY. Pp. 239-252, vol. VII, 1933.

Open Boat Whaling in the Azores: The History and Present Methods of a Relic Industry. By R. CLARKE. Pp. 281-354, vol. XXVI, 1954.

Whale, Miscellaneous

A list of Worms Parasitic in Cetacea. By H. A. BAYLIS. Pp. 393-418, vol. VI, 1932.

Cestodes of Whales and Dolphins from the *Discovery* Collections. By S. MARKOWSKI. Pp. 377-95, vol. XXVII, 1955.

On the Diatoms of the Skin Film of Whales, and their possible bearing on Problems of Whale Movements. By T. J. HART. Pp. 247-82, vol. X, 1935.

FISHERY INVESTIGATIONS

Report on Trawling Surveys on the Patagonian Continental Shelf. Compiled mainly from manuscripts left by the late E. R. Gunther. By T. J. HART. Pp. 223-408, vol. XXIII, 1946.

BOTANY

Antarctic Pyrenocarp Lichens. By I. M. LAMB. Pp. 1-30, vol. XXV, 1948.
See also under 'Phytoplankton.'

ANATOMICAL ZOOLOGY

On the Anatomy of a Marine Ostracod, *Cypridina* (*Doloria*) *levis*. By
H. GRAHAM CANNON. Pp. 435-82, vol. II, 1931.

On the Anatomy of *Gigantocypris mülleri*. By H. GRAHAM CANNON. Pp. 185-
244, vol. XIX, 1940.

On the Structure of the Photophores of some Decapod Crustacea. By
R. DENNELL. Pp. 307-82, vol. XX, 1940.

Nebaliopsis typica. By H. GRAHAM CANNON. Pp. 213-22, vol. XXIII, 1946.

The Gut of Nebaliacea. By HELEN G. Q. ROWETT. Pp. 1-18, vol. XXIII,
1943.

On the Reproductive Organs of *Holozoa cylindrica* Lesson. By A. CHRISTIE-
LINDE. Pp. 107-12, vol. XXV, 1949.

The Bathypelagic Angler Fish *Ceratius Holbölli* Kröyor. By R. CLARKE.
Pp. 1-32, vol. XXVI, 1950.

Studies on *Physalia Physalis* (L.): Part I. Natural History and Morphology.
By A. K. TOTTON; Part 2. Behaviour and Histology. By G. O. MACKIE.
Pp. 301-408, vol. XXX, 1960.

Swimbladder Structure of Deep-sea Fishes in Relation to their Systematics
and Biology. By N. B. MARSHALL. Pp. 1-122, vol. XXXI, 1960.

The Appendages of the Halocyprididae. By E. J. ILES. Pp. 299-326, vol.
XXXI, 1960.

Development of the Stolon in *Salpa Fusiformis* Cuvier and *Salpa Aspera*
Chamisso. By R. M. SAWICKI. Pp. 335-84, vol. XXXIII, 1966.

See also under 'Whale anatomy.'

SYSTEMATIC ZOOLOGY

Protozoa and Sponges

Foraminifera. Part I. The Ice-free Area of the Falkland Islands and
Adjacent Seas. By E. HERON-ALLEN and A. EARLAND. Pp. 291-460, vol.
IV, 1932.

Foraminifera, Part II. South Georgia. By A. EARLAND. Pp. 27-138, vol.
VII, 1933.

Foraminifera, Part III. The Falklands Sector of the Antarctic (excluding
South Georgia). By A. EARLAND. Pp. 1-208, vol. X, 1934.

Foraminifera. Part IV. Additional Records from the Weddell Sea Sector from Material obtained by the S.Y. *Scotia*. By A. EARLAND, with a Report on Some Crystalline Components of the Weddell Sea Deposits, by F. A. BANNISTER. Pp. 1-76, vol. XIII, 1936.

Ellobiopsidae. By H. BOSCHMA. Pp. 281-314, vol. XXV, 1949.

Sponges. By M. BURTON. Pp. 237-392, vol. VI, 1932.

Coelenterates

Stylasteridae (Hydrocorals) from Southern Seas. By H. BROCH. Pp. 33-46, vol. XXVI, 1951.

Hydromedusae from the Falkland Islands. By E. T. BROWNE and P. L. KRAMP. Pp. 265-322, vol. XVIII, 1939.

Hydromedusae from the *Discovery* Collections. By P. L. KRAMP. Pp. 1-128, vol. XXIX, 1957.

Siphonophora of the Indian Ocean: together with systematic and biological notes on related specimens from other oceans. By A. K. TOTTON. Pp. 1-162, vol. XXVII, 1954.

Scyphomedusae. By G. STIASNY. Pp. 329-96, vol. VIII, 1934.

New Observations on the Aberrant Medusa *Tetraplatia volitans* Busch. By W. J. REES and E. WHITE. Pp. 129-40, vol. XXIX, 1957.

Octocorals. Part I. Pennatularians. By H. BROCH. Pp. 245-80, vol. XXIX, 1958.

Madreporarian Corals, with an Account of Variation in *Caryophyllia*. By J. STANLEY GARDINER. Pp. 323-38, vol. XVIII, 1939.

Larves de Cérianthaires. By E. LELOUP. Pp. 251-308, vol. XXXIII, 1964.

Worms, etc.

A List of Worms Parasitic in Cetacea. By H. A. BAYLIS. Pp. 393-418, vol. VI, 1932.

Cestodes of Whales and Dolphins from the *Discovery* Collections. By S. MARKOWSKI. Pp. 377-395, vol. XXVII, 1955.

Parasitic Nematoda and Acanthocephala. Collected in 1925-1927. By H. A. BAYLIS. Pp. 541-60, vol. I, 1929.

Nemerteans from the South Atlantic and Southern Oceans. By J. F. G. WHEELER. Pp. 215-94, vol. IX, 1934.

Polychaete Worms. By C. C. A. MONRO. Pp. 1-222, vol. II, 1930.

Polychaete Worms, II. By C. C. A. MONRO. Pp. 59-198, vol. XII, 1936.

Oligochaeta. Part I. Microdrili (mainly Enchytraeidae). By J. STEPHEN-SON. Pp. 233-64, vol. IV, 1932.

Oligochaeta. Part II. Earthworms. By GRACE E. PICKFORD. Pp. 265-90, vol. IV, 1932.

The Echiuridae, Sipunculidae and Priapulidae collected by the Ships of the *Discovery* Committee during the years 1926 to 1937. By A.C. STEPHEN. Pp. 235-60, vol. XXI, 1941.

Crustacea

Thoracic Cirripedes. Collected in 1925-1927. By C. A. NILSSON-CANTELL. Pp. 223-60, vol. II, 1930.

Thoracic Cirripedes collected in 1925-1936. By C. A. NILSSON-CANTELL. Pp. 223-38, vol. XVIII, 1939.

Rhizocephala. By H. BOSCHMA. Pp. 55-92, vol. XXXIII, 1962.

Nebaliacea. By H. GRAHAM CANNON. Pp. 199-222, vol. III, 1931.

Mysidacea. By OLIVE S. TATTERSALL. Pp. 1-190, vol. XXVIII, 1955.

Amphipoda. By K. H. BARNARD. Pp. 1-326, vol. V, 1932.

Isopod Crustacea. Part I. The Family Serolidae. By EDITH M. SHEPPARD. Pp. 253-362, vol. VII, 1933.

Isopod Crustacea. Part II. The sub-order Valifera. Families: Idoteidae, Pseudidotheidae and Xenarcturidae. Fam. N. With a Supplement to Isopod Crustacea Part I. The Family Serolidae. By EDITH M. SHEPPARD. Pp. 141-98, vol. XXIX, 1957.

The Falkland Species of the Crustacean Genus Munida. By G. W. RAYNER. Pp. 209-46, vol. X, 1935.

Larvae of Decapod Crustacea. Part I. Stenopidea. Part II. Amphionidae. Part III. Phyllosoma. By R. GURNEY. Pp. 377-440, vol. XII, 1936.

Larvae of Decapod Crustacea. Part IV. Hippolytidae. By R. GURNEY. Pp. 351-404, vol. XIV, 1937.

Larvae of Decapod Crustacea. Part V. Nephropsidea and Thalassinidea. By R. GURNEY. Pp. 291-344, vol. XVII, 1938.

Larvae of Decapod Crustacea. Part VI. The Genus *Sergestes*. By R. GURNEY and M. V. LEBOUR. Pp. 1-68, vol. XX, 1940.

Arachnids

Spiders Collected by the *Discovery* Expedition, with a Description of a New Species from South Georgia. By W. S. BRISTOWE. Pp. 261-266, vol. III, 1931.

On a new species of Mite of the Family Halarachnidae from the Southern Sea Lion. By SUSAN FINNEGAN. Pp. 319-328, vol. VIII, 1934.

Pycnogonida. By ISABELLA GORDON. Pp. 1-138, vol. VI, 1932.

Molluscs

Mollusca: Gastropoda Thecosomata and Gymnosomata. By ANNE L. MASSY. Pp. 267-296, vol. III, 1932.

Antarctic and Subantarctic Mollusca: Pelecypoda and Gastropoda. By
A. W. B. POWELL. Pp. 47-196, vol. XXVI, 1951.

Antarctic and Sub-Antarctic Mollusca: Amphineura, Scaphopoda and
Bivalvia. By R. K. DELL. Pp. 93-250, vol. XXXIII, 1964.

New Species of Marine Mollusca from New Zealand. By A. W. B. POWELL.
Pp. 153-222, vol. XV, 1937.

Cephalopoda, I. Octopoda. By G. C. ROBSON. Pp. 371-402, vol. II, 1930.

The Vampyromorpha of the *Discovery* Expeditions. By GRACE E. PICKFORD.
Pp. 197-210, vol. XXVI, 1952.

Polyzoa

Polyzoa (Bryozoa). I. Scrupocellariidae, Epistomiidae, Farciminariidae,
Bicellariellidae, Aeteidae, Scrupariidae. By ANNA B. HASTINGS. Pp. 301-
510, vol. XXII, 1943.

Echinoderms

Crinoidea. By D. DILWYN JOHN. Pp. 121-222, vol. XVIII, 1938.

Echinoidea and Ophiuroidea. By T. H. MORTENSEN. Pp. 199-348, vol. XII,
1936.

Asteroidea. By W. K. FISHER. Pp. 69-306, vol. XX, 1940.

Hemi- and Protochordates

Cephalodiscus. By C. C. JOHN. Pp. 223-60, vol. III, 1931.

On the Development of Cephalodiscus. By C. C. JOHN. Pp. 191-204, vol.
VI, 1932.

Ascidiacea. By R. H. MILLER. Pp. 1-60, vol. XXX, 1960.

Fishes

Oceanic Fishes and Flatfishes. Collected in 1925-1927. By J. R. NORMAN.
Pp. 261-370, vol. II, 1930.

Coast Fishes. Part I. The South Atlantic. By J. R. NORMAN. Pp. 1-58,
vol. XII, 1935.

Coast Fishes. Part II. The Patagonian Region. By J. R. NORMAN. Pp.
1-150, vol. XVI, 1937.

Coast Fishes. Part III. The Antarctic Zone. By J. R. NORMAN. Pp. 1-104,
vol. XVIII, 1938.

Alepisauroid Fishes. By N. B. MARSHALL. Pp. 303-336, vol. XXVII, 1955.

Birds

The Birds of South Georgia. By L. HARRISON MATTHEWS. Pp. 561-92,
vol. I, 1929.

The Birds of the South Orkney Islands. By R. A. B. ARDLEY. Pp. 349-76, vol. XII, 1936.

The Sub-Antarctic forms of the Great Skua (*Catharacta skua skua*). By J. E. HAMILTON. Pp. 161-74, vol. IX, 1934.

Report on Penguin Embryos collected during the *Discovery* Investigations. By C. W. PARSONS. Pp. 139-64, vol. VI, 1932.

Seals

The Natural History of the Elephant Seal. By L. HARRISON MATTHEWS. Pp. 233-56, vol. I, 1929.

The Southern Sea Lion, *Otaria byronia* (De Blainville). By J. E. HAMILTON. Pp. 269-318, vol. VIII, 1934.

A Second Report on the Southern Sea Lion, *Otaria byronia* (De Blainville). By J. E. HAMILTON. Pp. 121-64, vol. XIX, 1939.

The Leopard Seal *Hydrurga leptonyx* (De Blainville). By J. E. HAMILTON. Pp. 239-64, vol. XVIII, 1939.

INDEX

Only the more important organisms discussed in the narrative are included in the index and, with a few special exceptions, they are referred to only by their generic names, although their specific names may be mentioned in the text. Subjects which occur frequently throughout the book, such as plankton, whales, ocean currents, etc., are only mentioned in the index when there is more special comment or discussion. Numbers in heavy type refer to pages opposite which photographic or coloured illustrations will be found, or in two cases where such consecutive numbers are hyphenated together they indicate that photographs will be found between such pages.

535